HYMNS
ANCIENT *and* MODERN

FOR USE IN THE SERVICES OF THE CHURCH

With Accompanying Tunes

STANDARD EDITION

PRINTED FOR THE PROPRIETORS BY
WILLIAM CLOWES AND SONS LIMITED
:: PUBLISHING OFFICE ::
LITTLE NEW STREET, LONDON, E.C.4
1924

BIBLIOGRAPHICAL NOTE

FIRST EDITION issued 1861
Appendix added 1868

SECOND EDITION. Edited by W. H. Monk,
Mus.Doc. 1875

SUPPLEMENTAL HYMNS added. Edited by C.
Steggall, Mus.Doc. 1889

The OLD EDITION of 1889 reprinted many times
down to the issue of the NEW EDITION in 1904.
Reprinted with altered Preface, 1906, etc.

SECOND SUPPLEMENT added. Edited by S. H.
Nicholson, M.A., Mus.Bac. 1916

STANDARD EDITION, being the Second Edition
with the two Supplements 1916

THE EDITION OF 1889 reset with Second
Supplement 1924

THE SHORTENED MUSIC EDITION. Edited
by Sir Sydney Nicholson, M.V.O., M.A., D.Mus. . 1939
A MELODY BOOK 1940

MADE AND PRINTED IN GREAT BRITAIN
by WILLIAM CLOWES AND SONS LIMITED
LONDON AND BECCLES

PREFACE

WHEN the Second Supplement was added to *Hymns Ancient and Modern* it was found necessary to alter the size of the large Musical Edition. The type was reset, and a new book in large octavo was issued in 1922 to take the place of the two previously existing quartos.

Similarly it has now been found desirable to reset the smaller Musical Edition in a slightly larger format.

The size is new, but not the contents. This volume is simply the current edition, with its two Supplements, recast. In resetting the type, however, the opportunity has been taken (here, as in the large Musical Edition) of introducing, in the method of printing the hymns, certain rearrangements and minor changes, which will, it is believed, be found convenient.

(1) Where alternative tunes for any hymn had been provided at different stages and therefore in different parts of the collection, they are now all collected together and given once for all with the hymn.

(2) Where a tune is printed more than once, it is often given, not only at the original pitch, but also in a lower key ; and cross-references from one occurrence of the tune to another are provided.

(3) Cross-references are also frequently added in order to suggest another tune to a given hymn as a suitable alternative.

(4) The lists of hymns appropriate to particular occasions or seasons are now printed in a fuller and unified form.

(5) The names of the authors and composers are printed now on the page with each hymn, and not only, as heretofore, in the index.

(6) In several cases an additional form of a Plainsong has been added, which may be found more suitable to present needs than the previous one.

Nothing in the current edition has been omitted, but all has been recast in a more convenient form.

Midsummer, 1924.

COPYRIGHTS

All questions concerning the copyright of these Hymns should be addressed to the CHAIRMAN OF THE PROPRIETORS OF HYMNS A. & M., at the office of the Publishers, WILLIAM CLOWES & SONS, LTD., LITTLE NEW STREET, LONDON, E.C.4.

Permission to reprint any copyright Hymn or Tune for Choral Festivals, or otherwise, must also be sought from them.

GRANTS

Grants-in-aid are offered by the Proprietors of Hymns Ancient & Modern to facilitate the introduction of their books or to assist in the renewal of existing supplies. Applications for such Grants should be made on the printed form to be obtained from the Publishers.

INDEX.

*The Hymns and Hymn-tunes marked * are the copyright of the Compilers; so also are the settings of many other Melodies.*

The Translations marked † have been altered by the Compilers, and in this form are copyright.

a 2

First Line of Hymn.	No.	Author of Hymn.	Name of Tune and Measure.	Composer or Source of Tune.
FATHER, whate'er of earthly bliss	515	Anne Steele, 1760	St. Columba. C.M.	J. A. MacMeikan.
*FATHER, Who dost Thy children feed	721	G. Body	Stella. 8 8 8 8. 8 8	{ Easy Hymns for Catholic Schools, 1851 }
FATHER, Who hast gather'd	750	E. E. Dugmore	Eudoxia. 6 5 6 5	Rev. S. Baring-Gould.
*FATHER, Whose love we have wrong'd by transgression	762	V. S. S. Coles	*Litany. 11 10 11 7	H. A. Branscombe.
Fierce raged the tempest o'er the deep	285	G. Thring	St. Aëlred. 8 8 8 3	Rev. J. B. Dykes.
Fight the good fight with all thy might	540	J. S. B. Monsell	{ 1. Pentecost. L.M.	{ 1. Rev. W. Boyd.
			2. Duke Street. L.M.	2. J. Hatton, 1793.
Fill Thou my life, O LORD my GOD	705	H. Bonar	{ 1. Richmond. C.M.	{ 1. Rev. T. Haweis, 1792.
			2. Angmering. C.M.	2. Sir H. Parry.
First of Martyrs, thou whose name	65	{ I. Williams and Compilers: from the Latin of J. B. de Santeuil }	Gott sei Dank (Lübeck). 7 7 7 7	Freylinghausen, Gesangbuch, 1704.
For all the Saints who from their labours rest	437	Bishop W. Walsham How	{ 1. Troyte's Chant, No. 2. Irreg.	{ 1. A. H. Dyke Troyte.
			2. For all the Saints. 10 10 10 4	2. E. Hutton.
			3. For all the Saints. 10 10 10 4	3. Sir J. Barnby.
For all Thy Saints, a noble throng	418	Mrs. Alexander	4. Engelberg. 10 10 10 4	4. Sir C. V. Stanford.
For ever we would gaze on Thee	461	A. W. Chadfield	St. James. C.M.	R. Courteville, 1697.
For ever with the LORD	231	J. Montgomery, 1835	Semper aspectemus. C.M.	J. H. Casson.
			Nearer Home. D.S.M.	{ J. Woodbury (arr. by Sir A. Sullivan).
For man the Saviour shed	443	{ Compilers (based on Tr. by I. Williams) from the Latin of J. B. de Santeuil }	Aberystwyth. S.M.	Rev. Sir F. A. G. Ouseley.
For the beauty of the earth	663	F. S. Pierpoint	Warden. 7 7 7.7 7	J. Turle.
*For the dear ones parted from us	741	Ada R. Greenaway.	Calvary. 8 7 8 7.4 7	S. Stanley, 1767-1822.
For thee, O dear, dear country	227	{ J. M. Neale: from the Latin of Bernard of Murles }	{ 1. Jenner. 7 6 7 6 D.	{ 1. Bishop Jenner.
			2. Tours. 7 6 7 6 D.	2. B. Tours.
For Thy dear Saint, O LORD	448	Bishop Mant, 1837	St. Helena. S.M.	{ From B. Milgrove (Mount Ephraim), 1769.
For Thy mercy and Thy grace	73	H. Downton	{ Ach, wann kommt (Culbach). 7 7 7 7 }	Scheffler, Heilige Seelenlust, 1657.
Forgive them, O My FATHER	115	Mrs. Alexander	1. St. Margaret. 7 6 7 6	1. Rev. W. Statham.
Forsaken once, and thrice denied	416	Mrs. Alexander	2. Forgiveness. 7 6 7 6	2. B. Gesius, 1605.
Forth in Thy Name, O LORD, I go	8	C. Wesley, 1749	Derry. 7 6 7 6	Rev. J. B. Dykes.
Forty days and forty nights	92	G. H. Smyttan and F. Pott	Song 34 (Angels). L.M.	O. Gibbons, 1623.
Forty days Thy seer of old	503	J. Mason	Aus der Tiefe (Heinlein). 7 7 7 7	Nürnbergisches Gesangbuch, 1676.
Forward! be our watchword	392	H. Alford	Confidence. 7 7 7 7	Rev. Sir F. A. G. Ouseley.
			{ 1. St. Boniface. 6 5 6 5 ter.	1. H. Gadsby.
			2. Esther. 6 5 6 5 ter.	2. A. H. Brewer.
From east to west, from shore to shore	483	{ J. Ellerton and Compilers: from Sedulius }	{ 1. A Patre unigenitus. L.M. (two Versions) }	{ 1. Proper Sarum Melody.
				2. Rev. J. B. Dykes.
			2. Trinity College. L.M.	3. Nürnbergisches Gesangbuch, 1676.
			3. Sedulius. L.M.	
From glory unto glory	485	Frances R. Havergal	*St. Columb. 7 6 7 6.7 6 8 6	W. S. Hoyte.

First Line of Hymn.	No.	Author of Hymn.	Name of Tune and Measure.	Composer or Source of Tune.
From Greenland's icy mountains	358	Bishop Heber, 1819	1. Aurelia. 7 6 7 6 D. 2. Greenland. 7 6 7 6 D.	1. S. S. Wesley, 1864. 2. T. Clark, 1828.
From highest Heav'n the Eternal Son	171	Sir H. W. Baker	St. Petrox. L.M.	*Kirchenampt* (Strasburg, 1525).
From out the cloud of amber light	410	Mrs. Alexander	St. Petrox. L.M.	Rev. R. F. Dale.
*From the depths of sin and failure	688	T. Rees	St. Ambrose. 8 7 8 7 D.	Rev. R. Cecil, 1740–1810.
Give light, O Lord, that we may learn	700	L. Tuttiett	Rothley. 8 6 8 4	Sir J. Goss.
Give us the wings of faith to rise	623	I. Watts, 1709	*Crucis Victoria. C.M.	M. B. Foster.
Glorious is Thy Name, O Lord	511	H. Twells	St. Audrey. 8 7 8 7 87.	C. Bucknall.
Glorious things of thee are spoken	545	J. Newton, 1779	Austria. 8 7 8 7 D.	J. Haydn, 1797.
Glory be to Jesus	107	E. Caswall: from the Italian	Wem in Leidenstagen (Caswall). 6 5 6 5	F. Filitz, 1847.
Glory to God! the morn appointed breaks	651	J. Brownlie	1. Gibeon. 10 10 10 10. 2. Song 22. 10 10 10 10.	1. S. Wesley, 1835. 2. O. Gibbons, 1623.
Glory to the First-begotten	744	Aug. G. Donaldson	St. Audrey. 8 7 8 7 87.	B. Harwood.
Glory to Thee, my God, this night	23	Bishop Ken, 1692	Canon. L.M.	T. Tallis, 1567.
Glory to Thee, O Lord	69	Mrs. Toke	St. Helena. S.M.	B. Milgrove (Mount Ephraim), 1769.
Glory to Thee Who safe hast kept PART 2	3	Bishop Ken, 1692	Canon. L.M.	T. Tallis, 1567.
Go to dark Gethsemane	110	J. Montgomery, 1820	Gethsemane. 7 7 7 7 77.	W. H. Monk: from C. Tye, 1553.
God be in my head	695	*Sarum Primer*, 1514	Poplar. Irreg.	The Right Rev. T. B. Strong.
God be with you till we meet again.	740	J. E. Rankin	Dominus vobiscum. 9 8 8 9	A. Somervell.
God Eternal, Mighty King	343	J. E. Millard	Innocents. 7 7 7 7	*The Parish Choir*, 1850.
God from on high hath heard	58	Bishop Woodford and Compilers: from the Latin of C. Coffin	St. George. S.M	H. J. Gauntlett.
God is a stronghold and a tower	678	Elizabeth Wordsworth: from the German of M. Luther	A stronghold sure. 8 7 8 7.6 6 6 6 7	M. Luther, 1529.
God is working His purpose out as year succeeds to year	735	A. C. Ainger	1. Benson. Irreg. 2. Stoke-on-Tern. Irreg.	1. Miss M. D. Kingham. 2. Sir Walford Davies.
God made me for Himself to serve Him here	627	Sir H. W. Baker.	London New. C.M.	Sir J. F. Bridge.
God moves in a mysterious way	373	W. Cowper, 1779	Harlem. 7 7 7 5	*Psalms* (Edinburgh, 1635).
God of grace, O let Thy light.	364	E. Churton	Heathlands. 7 7 7 7 77	B. Tours.
God of mercy, God of grace	218	H. F. Lyte, 1834	*Trafalgar. 8 8 8 8 8 8 8 8	H. Smart.
God of our fathers, unto Thee	708	A. C. Ainger	*St. Bartholomew. L.M.	S. H. Nicholson.
God of our life, to Thee we call	374	W. Cowper, 1779	*God of the living. 8 8 8 8 8 8.	E. H. Thorne.
God of the living, in Whose eyes	608	J. Ellerton	National Anthem. 6 6 4.6 6 6 4	E. Hulton.
God save our gracious Queen	707	*Anon.*, c. 1743		*Thesaurus Musicus*, c. 1743.
God that madest earth and heaven	26	Bishop Heber and Archbishop Whateley	Nutfield. 8 4 8 4.8 8 8 4	W. H. Monk.
God the All-terrible! King, Who ordainest	742	H. F. Chorley, 1842.	Russian Anthem. 11 10 11 10	A. Lvov, 1833.
God the Father's only Son	519	S. J. Stone	Nutbourne. 7 7 7 7 7	T. E. Aylward.
God the Father! Whose creation	385	J. M. Neale	1. Neale. 8 7.8 7.5 7 2. First Fruits. 8 7.8 7.8 7	1. W. H. Monk. 2. Rev. J. B. Dykes.
Good it is to keep the fast	89	Sir H. W. Baker: from St. Gregory	1. Jejunia. 7 7 7 7 2. Nun Komm. 7 7 7 7	1. Sir J. Stainer. 2. Medieval Melody.

First Line of Hymn.	No.	Author of Hymn.	Name of Tune and Measure.	Composer or Source of Tune.
O heavenly Word, Eternal Light	46	Compilers: from the Latin	Herr Jesu Christ (Breslau). L.M.	Geistliche Gesänge (Leipzig, 1625).
O help us, LORD; each hour of need	279	H. H. Milman, 1827	Bedford. C.M.	W. Wheale, c. 1715.
O HOLY GHOST, Thy people bless	211	Sir H. W. Baker	St. Timothy. C.M.	Rev. Sir H. W. Baker (arr. by W. H. Monk).
O HOLY SPIRIT, LORD of grace	208	J. Chandler and Compilers: from the Latin of C. Coffin	Tallis. C.M.	T. Tallis, 1567.
O Jerusalem the blissful	602	J. Ellerton: from the Latin	Blagdon. 8.7.8.7.87	C. E. Stephens.
*O JESU, Blessed LORD, to Thee	558	A. J. Mason: from the Danish of T. Kingo	1. Wells. L.M. / 2. O Jesu Christ. L.M.	1. W. H. Monk. / 2. P. Reinigius, 1587.
O JESU CHRIST, if aught there be	253	E. Caswall	Burford. C.M.	Chetham, Psalms, 1718.
O JESU, crucified for man	480	Bishop W. Walsham How	Intercession. L.M.	Easy Music for Church Choirs, 1853.
O JESU, King most wonderful PART 2	178	E. Caswall: from the Latin	1. St. Agnes. C.M. / 2. Metzler's Redhead. C.M.	1. Rev. J. B. Dykes. / 2. R. Redhead.
O JESU, LORD of light and grace	2	J. Chandler and Compilers: from St. Ambrose	1. Lauds. L.M. (two Versions) / 2. St. Bernard. L.M.	1. Proper Sarum Melody. / 2. W. H. Monk.
O JESU, Thou art standing	198	Bishop W. Walsham How	St. Catherine. 7 3 7 6 D.	Rev. R. F. Dale.
O JESU, Thou the Beauty art PART 3	178	E. Caswall: from the Latin	1. St. Agnes. C.M. / 2. Metzler's Redhead. C.M.	1. Rev. J. B. Dykes. / 2. R. Redhead.
O JESUS, I have promised	271	J. E. Bode	1. Day of rest. 7 6 7 6 D. / 2. Llanberis. 7 6 7 6 D.	1. J. W. Elliott. / 2. S. Wesley, 1839.
*O LAMB of GOD, Whose love Divine	456	V. S. S. Coles	Intercession. L.M.	Easy Music for Church Choirs, 1853.
O let him, whose sorrow	286	Frances E. Cox: from the German of H. S. Oswald	Clewer. 6 5 6 5	F. Filitz, 1847.
O Light, Whose beams illumine all	345	E. H. Plumptre	1. Bickley. 8 8 8 3.88 / 2. Eaton. 8 8 8 8.88	1. W. H. Monk. / 2. Z. Wyvill, 1802.
O little town of Bethlehem	642	Bishop P. Brooks	Worgen. D.C.M.	Sir Walford Davies.
O LORD, be with us when we sail	592	E. A. Dayman	Dundee. C.M.	Psalms (Edinburgh, 1615).
O LORD, how happy should we be	276	J. Anstice, 1836	1. Innsbruck. 8 8 6 D. / 2. Bridehead. 8 8 6 D. / 3. Anstice. 8 8 6 D.	1. Old Volkslied. H. Isaak (?). / 2. A. H. Dyke Troyte. / 3. G. P. Weimar, 1734–1800.
O LORD, how joyful 'tis to see	273	J. Chandler: from the Latin of C. Coffin	1. Melcombe. L.M. / 2. Almsgiving. L.M.	1. S. Webbe, 1782. / 2. S. S. Wesley.
O LORD most High, Eternal King	144	J. M. Neale: from the Latin	St. Ambrose. L.M.	La Feillée, Méthode, 1808.
O LORD of Heav'n, and earth, and sea	365	Bishop C. Wordsworth	1. *Eastwick. L.M. / 2. Almsgiving. 8 8 8 4	1. T. T. Noble. / 2. Rev. J. B. Dykes.
O LORD of hosts, Whose glory fills	394	J. M. Neale	Melcombe. L.M.	S. Webbe, 1782.
O LORD, our strength in weakness	605	Bishop C. Wordsworth	Stoke. 7 6 7 6 D.	Mrs. G. E. Cole.
O LORD, to Whom the spirits live	748	R. F. Littledale	Barragh (Psalm cxli). 8 8 8 8.88	Chetham, Psalms, 1718.
O LORD, turn not Thy Face from me	93	J. Marckant, 1562	St. Mary. C.M.	Prys, Psalms, 1621.
*O Love Divine, how sweet Thou art	195	C. Wesley, 1746	1. *Purleigh. 8 8 6 D. / 2. Cornwall. 8 8 6 D.	1. A. H. Brown. / 2. S. S. Wesley.
O love, how deep! how broad! how high	173	B. Webb: from Thomas à Kempis	Leipsic (Eisenach). L.M.	J. H. Schein, 1628.
O Love that wilt not let me go	699	G. Matheson	1. *Wyke. 8 8 8 8 6 / 2. Hampstead. 8 8 8 8 6	1. L. L. H. Heward. / 2. Sir Walford Davies.

LITANIES.

METRICAL INDEX OF TUNES.

*The Tunes marked * are copyright of the Compilers; as well as many of the Harmonies of other Tunes.*

TUNES OF FOUR LINES—*continued.*

Aylesbury. 671.
Bella. 673.
Birmingham. 766.
Carlisle. 30, 393, 706.
Coventry. 649.
Dedication. 395.
Dominica. 37, 532.
Doncaster. 692.
Franconia. 48, 261, 488.
Galway. 702.
Halstead. 673.
Hammersmith. 534.
Holy Mount. 759.
Holyrood. 339.
Lyte. 284.
Narenza. 268, 504.
Peterborough. 393.
St. Bride. 101, 249.
St. Ethelwald. 270.
St. George (Gauntlett). 58, 180, 351.
St. Helena. 69, 344, 395, 448.
St. Michael. 70, 152, 380, 446.
St. Omer. 491.
St. Paul's. 185.
Sellinge. 181.
Southwell. 120, 205.
Swabia. 453.
Utrecht. 458.
Venice. 755.
Walmisley. 649.
*We give Thee but Thine own. 366.

6 4 6 6.

St. Columba (Irons). 17.

6 5 6 5.

Caswall. 107.
Clewer. 286.
Eucharisticus. 324.
Eudoxia. 346, 750.
German. 569.
Newland. 569.
North Coates. 773.
Pastor pastorum. 730.
St. Constantine. 194.

6 6 6 6 (Iambic).

*Eccles. 716.
Eden. 701.
Ibstone. 265.
Moseley. 564.
Quam dilecta. 242.
St. Cecilia (Hayne). 217.

6 6 6 6 (Trochaic).

Ravenshaw. 243.
St. Martin. 188.

6 6 8 4.

*Totteridge. 697.
Verbum pacis. 589.

7 5 7 5.

*St. Nicolas. 462.

7 6 7 6.

Forgiveness. 115.
Hic breve vivitur. 225.
Kocher. 224.
Matrimony, 350.
St. Alphege. 225, 350, 429.
St. Margaret. 115.
Vulpius. 405.

TUNES OF FOUR LINES—*continued.*

7 6 7 6 (with Refrain).

All things bright and beautiful. 573.

7 7 7 3.

Vigilate. 269.

7 7 7 5.

Abba. 524.
Capetown. 163.
Charity. 210.
Haarlem. 364.
Vesper. 22.

7 7 7 7 (Iambic).

Ades Pater supreme. 493.

7 7 7 7 (Trochaic).

All Saints (Redhead). 432.
Bewdley. 547.
Buckland. 334.
Calvary (Monk). 113.
Canterbury. 151, 182.
Confidence. 503.
*Crucis milites. 153, 588.
Culbach. 73, 297.
Evermore. 280.
German Hymn. 372.
Glebe Field. 153.
Heinlein. 92, 400.
Innocents. 33, 175, 343.
Jejunia. 89.
*Lancashire. 672.
Lübeck. 34, 65.
Monkland. 381.
Newington. 280.
Nun komm. 89, 113.
Orientis partibus. 447.
Palms of glory. 445.
Richmond (Stephens). 527.
St. Bees. 260.
St. Mary at Hill. 645.
St. Prisca. 105, 399.
Tunbridge. 645.
University College. 291, 432.
Vienna. 38, 412, 568.
Warnborough. 538.
Xavier. 421.

7 7 7 7 (with Alleluia).

Ascension. 147.
Easter Hymn (Carey). 134.
Easter Hymn (Monk). 134.

7 8 7 8 (with Alleluia).

Grosvenor. 717.
Lindisfarne. 140.
St. Albinus. 140.

8 5 8 3.

Cairnbrook. 595.
Christus Consolator. 254.
Stephanos. 254.

8 6 8 4.

Rothley. 700.
St. Cuthbert. 207.

8 7 8 3.

Hornsey. 499.
Mansfield. 499.

b 2

TUNES OF TEN LINES

6 5 10.6 5 10.6 5 6 4.

Jesu Jehovah.   **764.**
Rescue.   **764.**

7 7 4 4 7.7 7 4 4 7.

Dying Stephen.   **674.**
*Hosanna in excelsis.   **724.**

7 7 7 7.7 7 7 7.7 7.

Mendelssohn.   **60.**

8 6 8 6.8 6 8 6.8 8.

*Stonypath.   **680.**

8 8 8 8.8 8 8 8.8 8.

Nomen tersanctum.   **521.**
*Trafalgar.   **708.**

TUNE OF ELEVEN LINES.

8 9 8.8 9 8.6 6 4 8 8.

Sleepers, wake.   **656.**

TUNES OF TWELVE LINES.

6 5 6 5.6 5 6 5.6 5 6 5.

Esther.   **392.**
Hermas.   **683.**
Onward, Christian soldiers.   **391.**
St. Boniface.   **392.**
St. Gertrude.   **391.**
Vexillum.   **390.**

TUNES OF TWELVE LINES—*continued.*

6 6 7 (12 lines).

Old 122nd.   **303.**

7 6 7 6.7 6 7 6.6 6 8 4.

Wir pflügen.   **383, 731.**

7 6 7 6.7 6 7 6.7 6 7 6.

I love to hear the story.   **330.**
*St. Beatrice.   **386.**

8 7 8 7.7 5 7 5.8 7 8 7.

*Fitzroy.   **138.**
Resurrexit.   **138.**

8 7 8 7.8 7 8 7.8 7 8 7.

*Herga.   **711.**

8 8 8.8 8 8 D.

Old 113th.   **171.**

IRREGULAR.

Adeste fideles.   **59.**
Auctor humani generis.   **498.**
Benson.   **735.**
*Berkeley.   **684.**
Cantemus cuncti.   **295.**
Dies Iræ.   **398.**
Ecce Panis.   **310.**
Freshwater.   **694.**
Margaret.   **776.**
Poplar.   **695.**
*Rangoon.   **734.**
St. Patrick's Breastplate.   **655.**
Sebaste.   **18.**
Stoke-on-Tern.   **735.**
The Foe.   **498.**

ALPHABETICAL INDEX OF TUNES.

*Tunes marked * are copyright of the Compilers.*

ALPHABETICAL INDEX OF AUTHORS
AND TRANSLATORS.

*The Hymns marked (*) are for the most part the copyright of the Compilers;
the mark (c) denotes that there may still be copyright remaining in
the author's hands, or in possession of his publishers, executors,
or representatives.*

ALPHABETICAL INDEX OF COMPOSERS.

CLASSIFIED TABLE OF HYMNS.

MORNING, 1–8, 474.
THIRD, SIXTH, AND NINTH HOURS, 9–11.
NOONDAY, 475, 639.
EVENING, 12–32, 476, 477.
SUNDAY, 33–38, 478, 479, 731.
MONDAY, TUESDAY, WEDNESDAY, THURSDAY, 39–42.
FRIDAY, 43, 480. *See also* THE PASSION.
SATURDAY, 44, 481. *See also* 123, 124.
ADVENT, 45–54, 640, 641. *See also* 203–206, 217, 225–236, 268, 288, 289, 362, 398, 520, 535, 536 565, 608, 694, 777, and 463 (Litany of the Four Last Things).
CHRISTMAS, 55–63, 329, 482–484, 642. *See also* 464 (Litany of the Incarnate Word).
ST. STEPHEN'S DAY, 64, 65. *See also* 439, 674.
ST. JOHN THE EVANGELIST, 66, 67.
HOLY INNOCENTS, 68, 69.
THE CIRCUMCISION, 70, 71. *See also* NAME OF JESUS.
NEW YEAR'S DAY, 72–74, 485. *See also* 165, 288, 289, 534, 535, 777.
EPIPHANY, 75–81, 486–488, 643. *See also* OUR LORD, HIS KINGDOM, and MISSIONS.
BEFORE SEPTUAGESIMA, 82.
SEPTUAGESIMA, 83, 489. *See also* THE CREATOR.
SEXAGESIMA. *See* 100, 172, 533, 660.
QUINQUAGESIMA. *See* CHARITY.
LENT, 84–95, 490–492, 644–646, 762 (Litany for Lent). *See also* PENITENCE, and FLEEING TO CHRIST, and OUR LORD, HIS TEMPTATION.
FIFTH SUNDAY IN LENT, 96, 97, 493.
SUNDAY NEXT BEFORE EASTER, 98, 99, 241, 738.
THE PASSION, 100–122, 332, 494–496, 647–649. *See also* 171–173, 180, 182–184, 187–189, 192, 193, 200, 251, 254, 259, 260, 263, 237, 272, 523, 626, 631, 633, 667, 668, 771, 773, 775, and Litanies 467, 625.
EASTER EVEN, 123, 124, 561. *See also* 575, 608.
EASTER, 125–141, 497–504, 650, 651. *See also* 171, 173, 174, 197, 199, 232, 299, 302, 656, 706, 731.
ROGATION DAYS, 142, 143, 505, 468 (Litany for the Rogation Days). *See also* FOR KING AND COUNTRY.
THE ASCENSION, 144–150, 506, 652, 469 (Litany of Jesus Glorified). *See also* 171, 173, 174, 201, 202, 219, 220, 292, 297, 299–302, 304, 306, 315, 316, 329, 439, 522, 548, 556, 565, 656, 674, 704, 711, 744.
WHITSUNTIDE, 151–157, 347, 507, 508, 653, 470, (Litany of the Holy Ghost). *See also* 207–213, 524, 525, 670–673, 766.
TRINITY SUNDAY, 158, 159, 509, 654. *See also* 160–164, 581, 655.

HOLY DAYS—
ST. ANDREW, 403.
ST. THOMAS, 404, 612. *See also* 174.
CONVERSION OF ST. PAUL, 405, 406.
PRESENTATION OF CHRIST IN THE TEMPLE, 407, 611. *See also* FESTIVALS OF B.V.M.
ST. MATTHIAS, 408, 613.
ANNUNCIATION OF B.V.M., 400. *See also* FESTIVALS OF B.V.M.
ST. MARK, 410.
ST. PHILIP AND ST. JAMES, 411. *See also* 199.
ST. BARNABAS, 412, 413.

HOLY DAYS—*continued.*
NATIVITY OF ST. JOHN THE BAPTIST, 414, 415
ST. PETER, 416, 417.
ST. JAMES, 418, 751.
THE TRANSFIGURATION, 460, 461, 759, 760.
ST. BARTHOLOMEW, 419.
ST. MATTHEW, 420, 614, 615.
ST. MICHAEL AND ALL ANGELS, 335, 421, 424, 616, 617, 752, 753.
ST. LUKE, 425.
ST. SIMON AND ST. JUDE, 426.
ALL SAINTS, 427–429, 618, 619.

FESTIVALS—
OF B.V.M., 449, 450, 622.
OF APOSTLES, 430–432, 620, 754.
OF EVANGELISTS, 433, 434, 621, 755.
OF MARTYRS AND OTHER SAINTS, 435–448, 451–457, 623, 756, 757.
OF ST. GEORGE, 758.
OF ST. JOHN BEFORE THE LATIN GATE, 458.
OF ST. MARY MAGDALENE, 459.
OF BEHEADING OF ST. JOHN THE BAPTIST, 462.
DEDICATION FESTIVAL, 395, 396, 747. *See also* 215, 229–242, 273, 393, 526, 529, 545, 600, 746, and 741 (Litany of the Church).
HOLY COMMUNION, 309–324, 552–560, 711–724, 472 (Litany of the Blessed Sacrament). *See also* 107, 177, 178, 187, 190, 191, 197, 203, 291, 294, 302, 529, 545, 656, 668, 675, 706.

GENERAL HYMNS—
THE HOLY TRINITY, 160–164, 281, 654, 655.
THE FATHER, 510.
THE CREATOR, 167, 168, 292, 295, 383, 573, 660–664.
THE DIVINE ATTRIBUTES, 32, 169, 511, 516, 526, 658, 661.
PRAISES OF GOD, 166, 218, 292, 293, 294, 296, 297, 298, 308, 516, 526, 544, 546, 548, 550, 657, 665, 706.
HIS LOVE TOWARD MAN, 171, 192, 195, 260, 298, 634, 660, 779.
HIS FAITHFULNESS, 165, 166, 266, 276, 293, 517, 539, 657, 659, 678.
OUR LORD, HIS GODHEAD, 170, 510.
HIS INCARNATE LIFE, 171–174, 192, 201, 281, 306, 519, 523, 660, 776.
HIS TEMPTATION, 20, 92, 173.
HIS EXAMPLE, 267, 568, 727.
HIS REDEEMING WORK, 171, 172, 173, 180, 187, 188, 189, 192, 200, 251, 259, 260, 298, 299, 302, 332, 521, 660, 776.
PRAISES OF CHRIST, 171, 176, 179, 180, 187, 199, 200, 202, 219, 220, 241, 299, 300, 301, 302, 303, 304, 305, 306, 307, 522, 549, 633, 656, 665, 674, 704, 736.
HIS COMING AGAIN, *see* ADVENT.
HIS KINGDOM, 202, 217–220, 300–302, 304, 513, 656, 675, 689, 704.
NAME OF JESUS, 175–179, 521, 522, 775.
THE HOLY SPIRIT, *see* WHITSUNTIDE.
THE HOLY CHURCH, THE COMMUNION OF SAINTS, 215, 221, 275, 352, 391, 477, 538, 545, 603, 675, 684, 746, 471 (Litany of the Church).
ITS WARFARE, 214, 216, 583, 603, 674, 678.
THE WORD OF GOD, 33, 199, 242, 243, 530, 531, 532, 599, 690, 701.

GENERAL HYMNS—*continued*.

THE HOUSE OF GOD, 166, 237, 239, 240, 241,242, 273, 392, 393, 395, 396, 516, 526, 529, 675, 690, 747.

THE CHRISTIAN LIFE—

THANKSGIVING, 171, 173, 191, 212, 290, 294, 298, 305, 365, 378, 379, 516, 517, 545, 632, 657, 663, 665, 666, 705, 706, 709.

PRAYER, 244, 246, 247, 248, 279, 527, 690, 693, 698, 774.

ALMSGIVING, 365–367.

PENITENCE, 164, 244, 245, 249, 250, 252, 253, 255, 518, 528, 627, 629, 630, 631, 635, 637, 638, 765, 767, 768, and Litanies of Penitence, 465, 466.

SELF-QUESTIONING, 259, 513, 514, 696.

FLEEING TO CHRIST, 182–184, 187, 188, 193, 245, 251, 254, 255, 527, 626, 629, 633, 768, 769, 775.

CHRIST'S INVITATION, 112, 198, 254, 256, 257, 628, 634, 637, 765.

PEACE FOUND IN CHRIST, 257, 258, 530, 537, 632, 667, 770.

PROTECTION AND GUIDANCE IN CHRIST, 181, 182, 185, 186, 188, 193, 196, 200, 209, 271, 280, 281, 282, 287, 305, 655, 669, 674, 700, 769, 772, 777, 778.

LOVE OF CHRIST AND OF GOD, 176, 177, 178, 190, 191, 192, 195, 238, 259, 260, 520, 630, 668, 670, 698, 699, 773, 776.

TRUST IN GOD AND IN CHRIST, 42, 165, 197, 199, 214, 243, 263, 264, 265, 266, 276, 277, 278, 279, 286, 290, 291, 293, 294, 373, 512, 515, 539, 540, 657, 659, 678, 682, 691, 692, 693, 694, 695, 778.

THE LIFE OF PILGRIMAGE, 223, 224, 231, 274, 512, 547, 601, 676.

ASPIRATION, 195, 213, 222, 229, 233, 234, 236, 262, 284.

PRAYER FOR SANCTIFICATION, 194, 209, 211, 261, 272, 349, 513, 518, 520, 525, 549, 600, 605, 631, 635, 636, 655, 658, 671, 672, 673, 695, 698.

PURITY OF HEART AND TEMPERANCE, 261, 513, 549, 605, 671.

CHARITY, 40, 208, 210, 262, 267, 670, 703.

UNITY AND FELLOWSHIP, 208, 216, 273, 274, 275, 380, 391, 541, 551, 604, 677, 679, 680.

WATCHFULNESS, 205, 226, 268, 269, 282, 681.

THE SPIRITUAL COMBAT, 214, 225, 270, 291, 534, 540, 541, 542, 543, 676, 678, 683, 685, 733, 778.

WORK FOR GOD AND THE WELFARE OF MANKIND, 204, 216, 217, 218, 219, 220, 224, 354, 356, 357, 366, 367, 368, 380, 492, 513, 580, 583, 588, 606, 607, 677, 680, 681, 683, 686, 687, 688, 689, 696, 697, 702, 737, 738, 739, 764, 766, 779.

THE CHRISTIAN LIFE—*continued*.

IN AFFLICTION, 188, 200, 204, 217, 224, 248, 254, 263, 264, 277, 283, 284, 285, 286, 373, 374, 537, 623, 682.

PREPARATION FOR DEATH, 251, 283, 287, 288, 289, 535, 694, 775, 777.

THE HEAVENLY REST AND JOY, 222, 223, 225–228, 230–236, 296, 427–429, 435–438, 445–447, 479, 536, 601, 618, 619.

SPECIAL OCCASIONS—

HOLY BAPTISM, 325–328, 561–563, 666, 725.

FOR THE YOUNG, 329–346, 564–575, 726, 732.

FOR SCHOOL AND COLLEGE USE, 576, 577.

CONFIRMATION, 347–349, 733. *See also* WHITSUNDAY.

HOLY MATRIMONY, 350, 351, 578, 579.

BURIAL OF THE DEAD, 398–402, 608–610, 748–750.

EMBER DAYS, 352–355.

FOR THEOLOGICAL COLLEGES, 581, 582.

FOR A TEACHERS' MEETING, 580.

FOR A BIBLE CLASS, 599.

FOR A RETREAT, 600, 761.

FOR A SERVICE FOR WORKING MEN, 584.

FOR TEMPERANCE MEETINGS, 605–607.

FOR FRIENDLY SOCIETIES, 380.

HOSPITALS, 368, 369.

LAY HELPERS AND CHURCH WORKERS, 356, 357, 583, 680, 739, 740.

FOR CHURCH DEFENCE, 603, 604.

LAYING THE FOUNDATION STONE OF A CHURCH, 394.

RESTORATION OF A CHURCH, 397, 602.

MISSIONS, HOME AND FOREIGN, 358–364, 585–588, 734, 735, 736, 737.

MISSIONS TO THE JEWS, 590, 591.

SERVICE OF FAREWELL, 589, 740.

FOR ABSENT FRIENDS, 595, 741.

FOR THOSE AT SEA, 370–372, 592–594, 596, 597, 624.

IN TIMES OF WAR AND PERIL, 373–377, 742, 743. *See also* AFFLICTION.

FOR KING AND COUNTRY, 707–710. *See also* 72, 142, 216, 370, 507, 588, 677, 686, 689, 763 (Litany of Intercession).

FOR A FLOWER SERVICE, 598.

THE HARVEST, 381–389. *See also* THANKSGIVING.

PROCESSIONAL, 305, 390–393, 601, 650, 652, 653, 711, 744, 745, 747.

LITANIES, 463–473, 624, 625, 762, 763. *See also* 142, 251.

FOR MISSION SERVICES AND INSTRUCTIONS, 626–632, 764–779.

Acknowledgments

THANKS ARE DUE to those who have given permission for the use of their copyright hymns or for the inclusion of copyright tunes in this collection. The present owners, so far as can be ascertained, are:

WORDS

The Abbot of Mount St. Bernards 188, 191

Miss E. Alexander's executors 115, 119, 410, 411, 416, 418, 420, 565, 655

The Rev. J. Kyrle Chatfield 185, 461, 661

Mr. S. R. Draper 767

The Rev. W. H. Walsham How 142, 417, 480, 560, 614, 727, 773

The Warden and Council of Keble College, Oxford 322, 348, 404, 591, 615

Longmans, Green & Co. Ltd. 371, 537, 761

Sir Eric Maclagan 116, 122, 425, 428, 719

Macmillan & Co. Ltd. (and Lord Tennyson) 694

Marshall Morgan & Scott, Ltd. 631, 651, 737, 770

Miss M. F. Maude 280

A. R. Mowbray & Co. Ltd. 697

Lt.-Col. A. J. Muirhead 675

Novello & Co. Ltd. 372, 699, 708

The Oxford University Press 12, 30, 118, 153, 217, 397, 401, 406, 413, 419, 426, 475, 477, 483, 497, 533, 562, 578, 579, 580, 595, 602, 604, 608, 611, 613, 618, 633, 709, 731, 753 (and Mrs. Bridges, from *The Yattendon Hymnal*)

Miss M. F. Pott 135, 405, 550

Reid Bros. Ltd. 337, 766

The representatives of the authors 123, 340, 361, 481, 502, 506, 511, 514, 519, 528, 530, 555, 559, 582, 587, 590, 597, 598, 603, 606, 607, 629, 660, 668, 677, 678, 680, 686, 696, 700, 711, 713, 726, 729, 732, 736, 743, 744, 749, 750, 758, 759

A. W. Ridley & Co. 274, 346, 391, 499, 679, 733

Archdeacon F. G. Scott 722

Seeley Service & Co. Ltd. 567, 610

The S.P.C.K. 735

The Vicar of St. Alban's, Birmingham 464, 465, 469, 471, 494, 495, 518, 541, 619, 624, 625, 730

Mr. L. Thring 368

The following belong to the Proprietors of *Hymns Ancient and Modern* 321, 333, 386, 421, 452, 453, 456, 474, 486, 489, 490, 492, 493, 496, 501, 509, 532, 539, 552, 553, 557, 558, 616, 638, 641, 647, 648, 649, 650, 652, 653, 657, 666, 685, 688, 712, 717, 721, 734, 741, 745, 746, 747, 754, 760, 762, 768

TUNES

The Congregational Union 595

Sir Walford Davies 319a, 642, 689, 690, 699b, 735b

Dr. B. Harwood 548b, 604b, 712, 744

Miss Morley Horder 299a, 478a

Hughes & Sons, Wrexham 251b

Dr. B. Johnson 738

The London Church Choir Association 621

Longmans, Green & Co. Ltd. 537a

Sir Eric Maclagan 280b, 318a, 445, 554a, 599, 629a

Novello & Co. Ltd. 9c, 10c, 11c, 35, 60, 106, 129, 137, 138a, 142b, 227b, 231, 240, 241a, 271a, 274b, 305a, 308b, 313b, 325, 350b, 355, 384, 391b, 392b, 406, 428, 436b, 466b, 470a, 494a, 520a, 523, 531b, 540a, 565, 584, 600, 601b, 607, 620, 632, 638, 640b, 694, 761, 773, 776

Mr. E. M. Oakeley 24a, 37, 190, 532, 576, 618b

The Oxford University Press 21b, 433a, 465b, 469a, 470b, 471a, 477, 499a, 695

The Rev. C. Powell 760

The representatives of the composers 6a, 30a, 66, 77, 115a, 119, 122, 132, 164b, 198, 212, 265, 364, 367b, 392a, 396c, 404, 410, 411, 421, 426, 437b, 457, 458, 461, 466a, 484b, 489, 491, 493a, 497, 498a, 500a, 501a, 502, 505, 510, 514, 515, 519, 521, 524, 526, 527, 529a, 534, 536, 538, 542a, 556a, 561, 562, 563, 566, 567, 569b, 571, 577, 579, 583, 585, 594, 602, 609, 612, 617, 618a, 624, 634, 635, 654, 664, 670, 701, 705b, 755, 764b

A. W. Ridley & Co. 346, 750

Rivingtons 611

Mr. W. H. Scott 246b, 759

Lady Somervell 740

The S.P.C.K. 735a

Mrs. Stainer 18, 22, 89a, 145a, 174, 185, 186, 229a, 230b, 252b, 319a, 324, 333, 337, 465a

Stainer and Bell 296c, 401b, 437d, 655, 722

Mr. A. E. Thorne 123

A. Weekes & Co. Ltd. 336

The following belong to the Proprietors of *Hymns Ancient and Modern* 55, 74b, 96b, 102a, 133, 138b, 144b, 153b, 195a, 220, 229b, 241b, 244, 250, 283, 313a, 316b, 323, 326, 335, 340b, 342, 361a, 366, 374, 386, 403, 409, 422, 435b, 449b, 462, 464b, 469b, 473b, 474, 475a, 485, 490, 496, 506b, 507, 511, 513, 520b, 522a, 525, 537b, 539, 553, 555, 559, 570, 586, 587, 588, 590, 603, 608, 610, 619, 623, 627, 636, 637, 641, 646, 648, 650, 652, 653, 659, 661, 668, 669b, 669c, 672, 680, 684, 685, 686, 696b, 697, 699a, 703, 708, 711, 716, 724, 728, 734, 736, 745, 747, 762, 768, 779

November, 1939

Young men and
maidens,
Old men and
children,
Praise the name
of the Lord

Morning.

A - men.

A - men.

" Early in the morning will I direct my prayer unto Thee."

mf NOW that the daylight fills the sky,
We lift our héarts to GOD on high,
That He, in all we dó or say,
Would keep us frée from harm to-day.

May He restrain our tóngues from strife,
And shield from ánger's din our life,
And guard with watchful cáre our eyes
From earth's absórbing vanities.

O may our inmost héarts be pure,
From thoughts of fólly kept secúre,
And pride of sinful flésh subdued
Through sparing úse of daily food.

So we, when this day's wórk is o'er,
And shades of night return once more,
Our path of trial sáfely trod,
Shall give the glóry to our GOD.

f All praise to GOD the FÁTHER be,
All praise, Etérnal SON, to Thee,
Whom with the SPIRIT wé adore
For ever ánd for evermore.

J. M. NEALE: from the Latin.

(1)

ε

Morning.

Hymn 2. LAUDS.—L.M. (*First Tune.*) (*First Version.*)

Proper Sarum Melody.

To be sung in Unison.

A — men. . . .

Hymn 2. LAUDS.—L.M. (*First Tune.*) (*Alternative Version.*)

Proper Sarum Melody.

To be sung in Unison.

A — men.

Hymn 2. ST. BERNARD.—L.M. (*Second Tune.*)

W. H. MONK.

A-men.

Morning.

f O JESU, LORD of light and grace,
 Thou Brightness of the FATHER'S Face,
Thou Fountain of eternal light,
True Day dispersing shades of night ;

Come, Very Sun of heavenly love,
Come in Thy radiance from above,
And shed the HOLY SPIRIT'S ray
On every thought and sense to-day.

mf So we the FATHER'S help will claim,
And sing the FATHER'S glorious Name,
And His Almighty grace implore
That we may stand, to fall no more.

May He our actions deign to bless,
And quench the darts of wickedness ;
In life's rough ways our feet defend,
And grant us patience to the end

May faith, deep rooted in the soul,
Subdue our flesh, our minds control ;
May guile depart, and discord cease,
And all within be truth and peace.

So let us gladly pass the day,
Our thoughts as pure as morning ray,
Our faith as noontide glowing bright,
Our minds undimm'd by shades of night.

f All praise to GOD the FATHER be,
All praise, Eternal SON, to Thee,
Whom with the SPIRIT we adore
For ever and for evermore.

J. CHANDLER and Compilers : from St. Ambrose.

Hymn 3. *(First Part.)* COMMANDMENTS.—L.M. *(First Tune.)*

L. BOURGEOIS, 1547.

A - men.

A higher setting of this Tune is given at Hymn 201.

f A WAKE, my soul, and with the sun
 Thy daily stage of duty run ;
Shake off dull sloth, and joyful rise
To pay thy morning sacrifice.

mf Redeem thy mis-spent time that's past,
And live this day as if thy last ;
Improve thy talent with due care ;
For the great day thyself prepare.

Let all thy converse be sincere,
Thy conscience as the noon-day clear ;
Think how all-seeing GOD thy ways
And all thy secret thoughts surveys.

Wake, and lift up thyself, my heart,
And with the Angels bear thy part,
Who all night long unwearied sing
High praise to the Eternal King.

f Praise GOD, from Whom all blessings flow,
Praise Him, all creatures here below,
Praise Him above, Angelic host,
Praise FATHER, SON, and HOLY GHOST.

Bishop KEN, 1692.

Morning.

Hymn 3. *(First Part.)* MORNING HYMN.—L.M. *(Second Tune.)*

F. H. BARTHELEMON, 1785.

" I myself will awake right early."

f   AWAKE, my soul, and with the sun
    Thy daily stage of duty run ;
Shake off dull sloth, and joyful rise
To pay thy morning sacrifice.

mf   Redeem thy mis-spent time that's past,
And live this day as if thy last ;
Improve thy talent with due care ;
For the great day thyself prepare.

Let all thy converse be sincere,
Thy conscience as the noon-day clear ;

Think how all-seeing GOD thy ways
And all thy secret thoughts surveys.

Wake, and lift up thyself, my heart,
And with the Angels bear thy part,
Who all night long unwearied sing
High praise to the Eternal King.

f   Praise GOD, from Whom all blessings flow,
Praise Him, all creatures here below,
Praise Him above, Angelic host,
Praise FATHER, SON, and HOLY GHOST.

Bishop KEN, 1692.

Hymn 3. *(Second Part.)* CANON.—L.M.

T. TALLIS, 1567.

" I myself will awake right early."

PART 2.

mf   Glory to Thee Who safe hast kept,
And hast refresh'd me whilst I slept ;
Grant, LORD, when I from death shall wake,
I may of endless light partake.

LORD, I my vows to Thee renew ;
Scatter my sins as morning dew ;
Guard my first springs of thought and will,
And with Thyself my spirit fill.

Direct, control, suggest, this day,
All I design, or do, or say ;
That all my powers, with all their might,
In Thy sole glory may unite.

f   Praise GOD, from Whom all blessings flow,
Praise Him, all creatures here below,
Praise Him above, Angelic host,
Praise FATHER, SON, and HOLY GHOST.

Bishop KEN, 1692.

Morning.

Hymn 4. MELCOMBE.—L.M.

S. WEBBE, 1782.

A higher setting of this Tune is given at Hymns **155, 394.**

" His compassions fail not : they are new every morning."

mf NEW every morning is the love
  Our wakening and uprising prove ;
Through sleep and darkness safely brought,
Restored to life, and power, and thought.

New mercies, each returning day,
Hover around us while we pray ;
New perils past, new sins forgiven,
New thoughts of GOD, new hopes of Heav'n.

If on our daily course our mind
Be set to hallow all we find,

New treasures still, of countless price,
GOD will provide for sacrifice.

The trivial round, the common task,
Will furnish all we need to ask,
Room to deny ourselves, a road
To bring us daily nearer GOD.

p Only, O LORD, in Thy dear love
  Fit us for perfect rest above ;
cr And help us, this and every day,
mf To live more nearly as we pray.

J. KEBLE.

Hymn 5. ST. TIMOTHY.—C.M.

Rev. Sir H. W. BAKER.

A higher setting of this Tune is given at Hymn **211.**

" Whatsoever ye do, do all to the glory of God."
" Do all in the name of the Lord Jesus."

mf MY FATHER, for another night
p   Of quiet sleep and rest,
cr For all the joy of morning light,
  Thy Holy Name be blest.

mf Now with the new-born day I give
  Myself anew to Thee,
That as Thou willest I may live,
  And what Thou willest be.

Whate'er I do, things great or small,
  Whate'er I speak or frame,
Thy glory may I seek in all,
p   Do all in JESUS' Name.

mf My FATHER, for His sake, I pray,
  Thy child accept and bless ;
And lead me by Thy grace to-day
  In paths of righteousness.

Sir H. W. BAKER.

Morning.

Hymn 6. BARMOUTH.—7 7. 7 7. 7 7. *(First Tune.)* W. MACFARREN.

(No Org. Ped.)   (Ped.)

A-men.

Hymn 6. SUNRISE.—7 7. 7 7. 7 7. *(Second Tune.)* *Trier Gesangbuch*, 1695.

A-men.

" Hold Thou me up, and I shall be safe: yea, my delight shall be ever in Thy statutes."

mf AT Thy feet, O CHRIST, we lay
    Thine own gift of this new day ;
Doubt of what it holds in store
Makes us crave Thine aid the more ;
Lest it prove a time of loss,
Mark it, Saviour, with Thy Cross.

If it flow on calm and bright,
Be Thyself our chief delight ;
p If it bring unknown distress,
Good is all that Thou canst bless ;
cr Only, while its hours begin,
Pray we, keep them clear of sin.

mf We in part our weakness know,
And in part discern our foe ;
Well for us, before Thine Eyes

All our danger open lies ;
p Turn not from us, while we plead
Thy compassions and our need.

mf Fain would we Thy Word embrace,
Live each moment on Thy grace,
All our selves to Thee consign,
Fold up all our wills in Thine,
Think, and speak, and do, and be
Simply that which pleases Thee.

Hear us, LORD, and that right soon ;
Hear, and grant the choicest boon
That Thy love can e'er impart,
Loyal singleness of heart ;
f So shall this and all our days,
CHRIST our GOD, show forth Thy praise.

W. BRIGHT.

(6)

Morning.

Hymn 7. RATISBON.—7 7.7 7.7 7.   WERNER, *Choralbuch*, 1815.

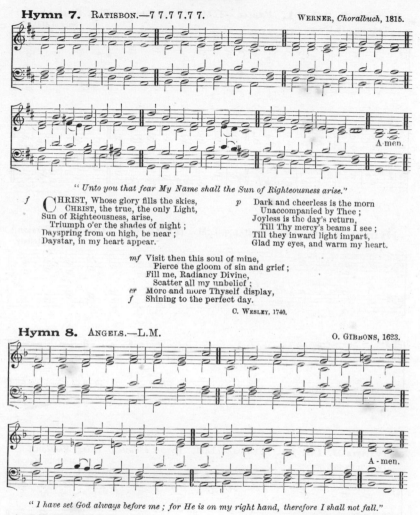

A-men.

" Unto you that fear My Name shall the Sun of Righteousness arise."

f CHRIST, Whose glory fills the skies,
  CHRIST, the true, the only Light,
Sun of Righteousness, arise,
  Triumph o'er the shades of night ;
Dayspring from on high, be near ;
Daystar, in my heart appear.

p Dark and cheerless is the morn
  Unaccompanied by Thee ;
Joyless is the day's return,
  Till Thy mercy's beams I see ;
Till they inward light impart,
Glad my eyes, and warm my heart.

mf Visit then this soul of mine,
  Pierce the gloom of sin and grief ;
Fill me, Radiancy Divine,
  Scatter all my unbelief ;
cr More and more Thyself display,
f Shining to the perfect day.

C. WESLEY, 1740.

Hymn 8. ANGELS.—L.M.   O. GIBBONS, 1623.

A-men.

" I have set God always before me ; for He is on my right hand, therefore I shall not fall."

mf FORTH in Thy Name, O LORD, I go,
  My daily labour to pursue ;
Thee, only Thee, resolved to know,
In all I think, or speak, or do.

The task Thy wisdom hath assign'd
O let me cheerfully fulfil ;
In all my works Thy presence had,
And prove Thy good and perfect Will.

Thee may I set at my right hand,
Whose eyes my inmost substance see,

And labour on at Thy command,
And offer all my works to Thee.

p Give me to bear Thy easy yoke,
  And every moment watch and pray,
And still to things eternal look,
cr And hasten to Thy glorious day ;

mf For Thee delightfully employ
Whate'er Thy bounteous grace hath given,
And run my course with even joy,
And closely walk with Thee to Heav'n.

C. WESLEY, 1749.

ALTERNATIVE TUNE, HYMN 723.

See also Hymn **474.** Awaked from sleep we fall.

Morning.

Hymns 9, 10, 11. Ferial.—L.M. *(First Tune.)* *(First Version.)*

Sarum Melody.

To be sung in Unison.

A - men.

Hymns 9, 10, 11. Ferial.—L.M. *(First Tune.)* *(Alternative Version.)*

Sarum Melody.

To be sung in Unison.

A - men.

Hymns 9, 10, 11. Festal.—L.M. *(Second Tune.)* *(First Version.)*

Mechlin Melody.

To be sung in Unison.

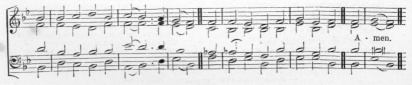

A - men.

Hymns 9, 10, 11. Festal.—L.M. *(Second Tune.)* *(Alternative Version.)*

To be sung in Unison.

Mechlin Melody.

A - men.

Hymns 9, 10, 11. Ludborough.—L.M. *(Third Tune.)* Rev. T. R. Matthews.

A-men.

9. The Third Hour.

"They were all filled with the Holy Ghost."

mf COME, HOLY GHOST, Who ever ONE
Art with the FATHER and the SON,
Come, HOLY GHOST, our souls possess
With Thy full flood of holiness.

In will and deed, by heart and tongue,
With all our powers, Thy praise be sung ;
And love light up our mortal frame,
Till others catch the living flame.

p Almighty FATHER, hear our cry
Through JESUS CHRIST our LORD most High,
or Who with the HOLY GHOST and Thee
f Doth live and reign eternally.

Cardinal J. H. NEWMAN : from St. Ambrose.

10. The Sixth Hour.

" At noonday will I pray."

mf O GOD of truth, O LORD of might,
Who ord'rest time and change aright,
Bright'ning the morn with golden gleams,
Kindling the noonday's fiery beams ;

Quench Thou in us the flames of strife,
From passion's heat preserve our life,
Our bodies keep from perils free,
And give our souls true peace in Thee.

p Almighty FATHER, hear our cry
Through JESUS CHRIST our LORD most High,
cr Who with the HOLY GHOST and Thee
f Doth live and reign eternally.

J. M. NEALE : from St. Ambrose

11. The Ninth Hour.

" The hour of prayer, being the ninth hour."

mf O GOD, of all the Strength and Power,
Who dost, Thyself unmoved, each hour
Through all its changes guide the day,
From early morn to evening's ray ;

Brighten life's eventide with light
That ne'er shall set in gloom of night,

Till we a holy death attain,
And everlasting glory gain.

p Almighty FATHER, hear our cry
Through JESUS CHRIST our LORD most High,
cr Who with the HOLY GHOST and Thee
f Doth live and reign eternally.

J. M. NEALE and Compilers : from St. Ambrose.

See also (for Noon-day) :

475 Behold us, LORD, a little space.   **639** Up to the throne of GOD is borne.

B 2

Evening.

Hymn 12. STRENGTH AND STAY.—11 10 11 10. Rev. J. B. DYKES.

"The Lord was my stay."

mf O STRENGTH and Stay upholding all creation,
    Who ever dost Thyself unmoved abide,
Yet day by day the light in due gradation
    From hour to hour through all its changes guide ;

p Grant to life's day a calm unclouded ending,
    An eve untouch'd by shadows of decay,
The brightness of a holy death-bed blending
cr   With dawning glories of the eternal day.

mf Hear us, O FATHER, gracious and forgiving,
    Through JESUS CHRIST Thy co-eternal WORD,
Who, with the HOLY GHOST, by all things living
    Now and to endless ages art adored.

        J. ELLERTON and F. J. A. HORT : from St. Ambrose.

ALTERNATIVE TUNE, HYMN **494** (THIRD TUNE).

Hymn 13. ST. PETER.—C.M. (*First Tune.*) A. REINAGLE, 1799–1877.

A lower setting of this Tune is given at Hymn **596.**

Evening.

Hymn 13. ST. COLUMBA.—C.M. *(Second Tune.)* Traditional Irish Melody

A · men.

"O look Thou upon me, and be merciful unto me."

mf   AS now the sun's declining rays
   At eventide descend,
p   So life's brief day is sinking down
   To its appointed end.

  LORD, on the Cross Thine Arms were stretch'd
   To draw Thy people nigh ;

   O grant us then that Cross to love,
pp   And in those Arms to die.

f   All glory to the FATHER be,
   All glory to the SON,
   All glory, HOLY GHOST, to Thee,
   While endless ages run.

    J. CHANDLER and Compilers : from the Latin of C. Coffin.

Hymn 14. O LUX BEATA.—L.M. *(First Tune.)* *(First Version.)*
To be sung in Unison.   Proper Sarum Melody.

A · men.

For Alternative Version of this Tune, see page 12.

"Now unto the King eternal, immortal, invisible, the only wise God, be honour and glory
for ever and ever."

mf   O TRINITY, most Blessed Light,
   O UNITY of primal Might,
   As now the fiery sun departs,
   Shed Thou Thy beams within our hearts.

   To Thee our morning song of praise,
   To Thee our evening prayer we raise ;

cr   Thee may our heart and voice adore
   For ever and for evermore.

p   Almighty FATHER, hear our cry
   Through JESUS CHRIST our LORD most High,
cr   Who with the HOLY GHOST and Thee
f   Doth live and reign eternally.

    J. M. NEALE : from the Latin.

(11)

Evening.

Hymn 14. O LUX BEATA.—L.M. *(First Tune.)* *(Alternative Version.)*

*" Now unto the King eternal, immortal, invisible, the only wise God, be honour and glory
for ever and ever."*

Proper Sarum Melody.

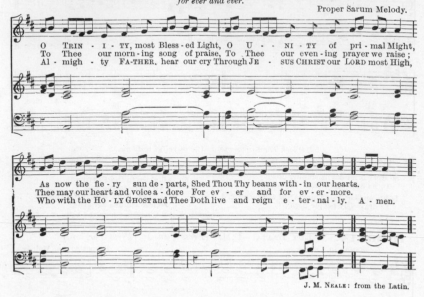

O TRIN - I - TY, most Bless - ed Light, O U - NI - TY of pri - mal Might,
To Thee our morn - ing song of praise, To Thee our even - ing prayer we raise ;
Al - migh - ty FA-THER, hear our cry Through JE - SUS CHRIST our LORD most High,

As now the fie - ry sun de - parts, Shed Thou Thy beams with - in our hearts.
Thee may our heart and voice a - dore For ev - er and for ev - er - more.
Who with the HO - LY GHOST and Thee Doth live and reign e - ter - nal - ly. A - men.

J. M. NEALE : from the Latin.

Hymn 14. WESTMINSTER.—L.M. *(Second Tune.)*

B. COOKE, 1794.

A - men.

*" Now unto the King eternal, immortal, invisible, the only wise God, be honour and glory
for ever and ever."*

mf O TRINITY, most Blessèd Light,
O UNITY of primal Might,
As now the fiery sun departs,
Shed Thou Thy beams within our hearts.

To Thee our morning song of praise,
To Thee our evening prayer we raise ;
cr Thee may our heart and voice adore
For ever and for evermore.

p Almighty FATHER, hear our cry
Through JESUS CHRIST our LORD most High,
cr Who with the HOLY GHOST and Thee
f Doth live and reign eternally.

J. M. NEALE : from the Latin.

Evening.

Hymn 15. Te lucis.—L.M. *(First Version.)* Proper Sarum Melody.

A-men.

" Thou shalt not be afraid for any terror by night."

mf BEFORE the ending of the day,
Creator of the world, we pray
That Thou with wonted love wouldst keep
Thy watch around us while we sleep.

O let no evil dreams be near,
Nor phantoms of the night appear ;
Our ghostly enemy restrain,
Lest aught of sin our bodies stain.

p Almighty FATHER, hear our cry
Through JESUS CHRIST our LORD most High,
cr Who with the HOLY GHOST and Thee
f Doth live and reign eternally.

Compilers : from the Latin.

Hymn 15. Te lucis.—L.M. *(Alternative Version.)*

" Thou shalt not be afraid for any terror by night.

Proper Sarum Melody.

Be - fore the end - ing of the day, Cre - a - tor of the world, we pray
O let no e - vil dreams be near, Nor phan-toms of the night ap - pear ;
Al - migh - ty FA-THER, hear our cry Thro' JE - SUS CHRIST our LORD most High,

That Thou with wont-ed love wouldst keep Thy watch a - round us while we sleep.
Our ghost-ly en - e - my re - strain, Lest aught of sin our bod - ies stain.
Who with the HO - LY GHOST and Thee Doth live and reign e - ter - nal - ly. A-men.

Compilers : from the Latin

ALTERNATIVE TUNE, HYMN 246 (SECOND TUNE).

(13)

Evening.

Hymn 16. St. Flavian.—C.M.

Psalmes, 1562.

A - men.

" Thou shalt not be afraid for any terror by night.'

mf NOW that the daylight dies away,
By all Thy grace and love,
Thee, Maker of the world, we pray
To watch our bed above.

Let dreams depart and phantoms fly,
The offspring of the night,

p Keep us, like shrines, beneath Thine eye,
mf Pure in our foe's despite.

This grace on Thy redeem'd confer,
FATHER, co-equal SON,
And HOLY GHOST, the Comforter,
Eternal THREE in ONE.

Cardinal J. H. NEWMAN : from the Latin.

Hymn 17. St. Columba.—6 4 6 6.

H. S. IRONS.

Amen.

" Let the lifting up of my hands be an evening sacrifice."

p THE sun is sinking fast,
The daylight dies ;
cr Let love awake, and pay
Her evening sacrifice.

p As CHRIST upon the Cross
His Head inclined,
And to His FATHER'S hands
His parting Soul resign'd ;

mf So now herself my soul
Would wholly give
Into His sacred charge,
In Whom all spirits live ;

So now beneath His eye
Would calmly rest,

Without a wish or thought
Abiding in the breast,

Save that His Will be done,
Whate'er betide,
Dead to herself, and dead
In Him to all beside.

f Thus would I live ; yet now
Not I, but He
In all His power and love
Henceforth alive in me.

ONE Sacred TRINITY !
ONE LORD Divine !
May I be ever His,
And He for ever mine.

E. CASWALL : from the Latin.

Hymn 18. Sebaste.—Irregular.

" The true Light."

Sir J. STAINER.

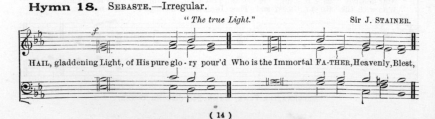

HAIL, gladdening Light, of His pure glo-ry pour'd Who is the Immortal FA-THER, Heavenly, Blest,

Evening.

Ho · li · est of Ho · lies, JE · SUS CHRIST, our LORD.

Now we are come to the sun's hour of rest, The lights of eve · ning round us shine,

We hymn the FA · THER, SON, and HO · LY SPI · RIT Di · vine.

Worthiest art Thou at all times to be sung With un · de · fil · ed tongue,

SON of our GOD, Gi-ver of life, A · lone! There-fore in all the

world Thy glo · ries, LORD, they own. A - - men.

J. KEBLE: from the Greek.

Evening.

Hymn 19. St. Gabriel.—8 8 8 4.
Rev. Sir F. A. G. Ouseley.

A - men.

" The Lord shall be thine everlasting light."

mf THE radiant morn hath pass'd away,
    And spent too soon her golden store ;
The shadows of departing day
    p   Creep on once more.

Our life is but a fading dawn,
    Its glorious noon how quickly past ;
cr Lead us, O Christ, when all is gone,
        Safe home at last.

mf O by Thy soul-inspiring grace
    Uplift our hearts to realms on high ;

Help us to look to that bright place
        Beyond the sky ;—

Where light, and life, and joy, and peace
In undivided empire reign,
And thronging Angels never cease
        Their deathless strain ;—

f Where Saints are clothed in spotless white,
And evening shadows never fall,
Where Thou, Eternal Light of Light,
        Art Lord of all.

G. Thring.

Hymn 20. Angelus.—L.M.
G. Joseph, 1657.

A-men.

" And at even, when the sun did set, they brought unto Him all that were diseased, and them that were possessed with devils. And all the city was gathered together at the door."

mf AT even ere the sun was set,
    The sick, O Lord, around Thee lay ;
p Oh, in what divers pains they met !
f Oh, with what joy they went away !

mf Once more 'tis eventide, and we
    Oppress'd with various ills draw near ;
What if Thy Form we cannot see ?
cr We know and feel that Thou art here.

mf O Saviour Christ, our woes dispel ;
    For some are sick, and some are sad,
And some have never loved Thee well,
And some have lost the love they had ;

And some have found the world is vain,
Yet from the world they break not free ;

And some have friends who give them pain,
Yet have not sought a friend in Thee ;

And none, O Lord, have perfect rest,
For none are wholly free from sin ;
And they, who fain would serve Thee best,
Are conscious most of wrong within.

O Saviour Christ, Thou too art Man ;
Thou hast been troubled, tempted, tried ;
Thy kind but searching glance can scan
The very wounds that shame would hide ;

f Thy touch has still its ancient power ;
No word from Thee can fruitless fall ;
p Hear, in this solemn evening hour,
cr And in Thy mercy heal us all.

H. Twells.

(16)

Evening.

Hymn 21. St. Anatolius.—7 6 7 6.8 8. *(First Tune.)*   Rev. J. B. Dykes.

Hymn 21. St. Anatolius.—7 6 7 6.8 8. *(Second Tune.)*   A. H. Brown.

" It is Thou, Lord, only, that makest me dwell in safety."

THE day is past and over ;
  All thanks, O Lord, to Thee ;
I pray Thee now that sinless
  The hours of dark may be :
O Jesu, keep me in Thy sight,
And guard me through the coming night.

The joys of day are over ;
  I lift my heart to Thee,
And ask Thee that offenceless
  The hours of dark may be :
O Jesu, keep me in Thy sight,
And guard me through the coming night.

The toils of day are over ;
  I raise the hymn to Thee,
And ask that free from peril
  The hours of dark may be :
O Jesu, keep me in Thy sight,
And guard me through the coming night.

Be Thou my soul's preserver,
  For Thou alone dost know
How many are the perils
  Through which I have to go :
O loving Jesu, hear my call,
And guard and save me from them all.

                  J. M. Neale: from the Greek.

Evening.

Hymn 22. VESPER.—7 7 7 5.

Sir J. STAINER.

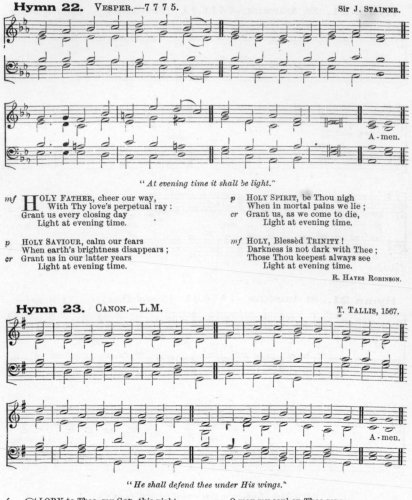

A - men.

" At evening time it shall be light."

mf HOLY FATHER, cheer our way,
    With Thy love's perpetual ray:
Grant us every closing day
    Light at evening time.

p HOLY SAVIOUR, calm our fears
When earth's brightness disappears;
cr Grant us in our latter years
    Light at evening time.

p HOLY SPIRIT, be Thou nigh
When in mortal pains we lie;
cr Grant us, as we come to die,
    Light at evening time.

mf HOLY, Blessèd TRINITY!
Darkness is not dark with Thee;
Those Thou keepest always see
    Light at evening time.

R. HAYES ROBINSON.

Hymn 23. CANON.—L.M.

T. TALLIS, 1567.

A - men.

" He shall defend thee under His wings."

f GLORY to Thee, my GOD, this night
    For all the blessings of the light;
Keep me, O keep me, King of kings,
Beneath Thy own Almighty wings.

mf Forgive me, LORD, for Thy dear SON,
The ill that I this day have done,
That with the world, myself, and Thee,
I, ere I sleep, at peace may be.

Teach me to live, that I may dread
The grave as little as my bed;
p Teach me to die, that so I may
cr Rise glorious at the awful day.

p O may my soul on Thee repose,
And may sweet sleep mine eyelids close,
cr Sleep that shall me more vigorous make
To serve my GOD when I awake.

mf When in the night I sleepless lie,
My soul with heavenly thoughts supply;
Let no ill dreams disturb my rest,
No powers of darkness me molest.

f Praise GOD, from Whom all blessings flow,
Praise Him, all creatures here below,
Praise Him above, Angelic host,
Praise FATHER, SON, and HOLY GHOST.

Bishop KEN, 1692.

Evening.

Hymn 24. ABENDS.—L.M. (*First Tune.*)   Sir H. OAKELEY

A · men.

Hymn 24. KEBLE.—L.M. (*Second Tune.*)   Rev. J. B. DYKES.

A - men

1st line.   end of 2nd line.   3rd line.

3rd verse.   A - bide with me, &c.   live;   A - bide with me, &c.

" Abide with us."

mf SUN of my soul, Thou Saviour dear,
It is not night if Thou be near :
O may no earth-born cloud arise
To hide Thee from Thy servant's eyes.

p When the soft dews of kindly sleep
My wearied eyelids gently steep,
Be my last thought, how sweet to rest
For ever on my Saviour's breast.

mf Abide with me from morn till eve,
For without Thee I cannot live ;
p Abide with me when night is nigh,
For without Thee I dare not die.

mf If some poor wand'ring child of Thine
Have spurn'd to-day the voice Divine,
Now, LORD, the gracious work begin ;
Let him no more lie down in sin.

Watch by the sick ; enrich the poor
With blessings from Thy boundless store ;
Be every mourner's sleep to-night
p Like infant's slumbers, pure and light.

cr Come near and bless us when we wake,
Ere through the world our way we take ;
f Till in the ocean of Thy love
We lose ourselves in Heav'n above.

J. KEBLE.

Evening.

Hymn 24. HURSLEY.—L.M. (Third Tune.) Katholisches Gesangbuch, c. 1775.

A-men.

"Abide with us."

mf SUN of my soul, Thou Saviour dear,
  It is not night if Thou be near :
O may no earth-born cloud arise
To hide Thee from Thy servant's eyes.

p When the soft dews of kindly sleep
  My wearied eyelids gently steep,
  Be my last thought, how sweet to rest
  For ever on my Saviour's breast.

mf Abide with me from morn till eve,
  For without Thee I cannot live ;
p Abide with me when night is nigh,
  For without Thee I dare not die.

mf If some poor wand'ring child of Thine
  Have spurn'd to-day the voice Divine,
  Now, LORD, the gracious work begin ;
  Let him no more lie down in sin.

  Watch by the sick ; enrich the poor
  With blessings from Thy boundless store ;
  Be every mourner's sleep to-night
p Like infant's slumbers, pure and light.

cr Come near and bless us when we wake,
  Ere through the world our way we take ;
f Till in the ocean of Thy love
  We lose ourselves in Heav'n above.

J. KEBLE.

Hymn 25. DRETZEL.—8 7 8 7. 7 7. C. H. DRETZEL, 1731.

A - men.

" I will lay me down in peace, and take my rest."

mf THROUGH the day Thy love has spared us ;
  Now we lay us down to rest ;
Through the silent watches guard us,
  Let no foe our peace molest ;
p JESUS, Thou our Guardian be ;
  Sweet it is to trust in Thee.

mf Pilgrims here on earth, and strangers,
  Dwelling in the midst of foes ;
Us and ours preserve from dangers ;
  In Thine Arms may we repose.
  And, when life's sad day is past,
p Rest with Thee in Heav'n at last.

T. KELLY, 1806.

ALTERNATIVE TUNE, HYMN 102 (SECOND TUNE).

Hymn 26. NUTFIELD.—8 4 8 4. 8 8 8 4. W. H. MONK.

Evening.

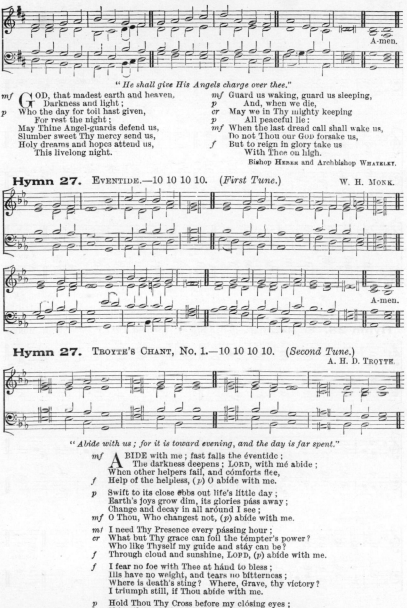

A-men.

"He shall give His Angels charge over thee."

mf GOD, that madest earth and heaven,
    Darkness and light ;
p Who the day for toil hast given,
    For rest the night ;
    May Thine Angel-guards defend us,
    Slumber sweet Thy mercy send us,
    Holy dreams and hopes attend us,
    This livelong night.

mf Guard us waking, guard us sleeping,
p   And, when we die,
cr May we in Thy mighty keeping
p   All peaceful lie :
mf When the last dread call shall wake us,
    Do not Thou our GOD forsake us,
f But to reign in glory take us
    With Thee on high.

Bishop HEBER and Archbishop WHATELEY.

Hymn 27. EVENTIDE.—10 10 10 10. (*First Tune.*)   W. H. MONK.

A-men.

Hymn 27. TROYTE'S CHANT, No. 1.—10 10 10 10. (*Second Tune.*)

A. H. D. TROYTE.

"Abide with us ; for it is toward evening, and the day is far spent."

mf ABIDE with me ; fast falls the éventide :
    The darkness deepens ; LORD, with mé abide ;
    When other helpers fail, and cómforts flee,
f Help of the helpless, (p) O abíde with me.

p Swift to its close ebbs out life's líttle day ;
    Earth's joys grow dim, its glories páss away ;
    Change and decay in all aróund I see ;
mf O Thou, Who changest not, (p) abíde with me.

mf I need Thy Presence every pássing hour ;
cr What but Thy grace can foil the témpter's power ?
    Who like Thyself my guide and stáy can be ?
f Through cloud and sunshine, LORD, (p) abíde with me.

f I fear no foe with Thee at hánd to bless ;
    Ills have no weight, and tears no bítterness ;
    Where is death's sting ? Where, Grave, thy víctory ?
    I triumph still, if Thou abíde with me.

p Hold Thou Thy Cross before my clósing eyes ;
cr Shine through the gloom, and point me tó the skies ;
f Heav'n's morning breaks, and earth's vain shádows flee ;
    In life, (p) in death, O LORD, (cr) abíde with me.

H. F. LYTE.

Evening.

Hymn 28. CHRISTCHURCH.—8 8.8 8 8.8 8. *(First Tune.)*

Rev. Sir F. A. G. OUSELEY.

A-men.

Hymn 28. ST. MATTHIAS. — 8 8.8 8.8 8. *(Second Tune.)*

W. H. MONK.

A-men.

A higher setting of this Tune is given at Hymn 191.

(22)

Evening.

Hymn 28.   IN TENEBRIS LUMEN.   8 8.8 8.8 8.   (*Third Tune.*)

Rev. J. B. DYKES.

A - men.

" The Lord is my light."

mf SWEET Saviour, bless us ere we go ;
     Thy Word into our minds instil,
cr And make our lukewarm hearts to glow
     With lowly love and fervent will.
f Through life's long day and death's dark night,
p O gentle JESUS, (*cr*) be our Light.

p The day is done, its hours have run,
     And Thou hast taken count of all,
The scanty triumphs grace hath won,
     The broken vow, the frequent fall.
f Through life's long day and death's dark night,
p O gentle JESUS, (*cr*) be our Light.

mf Grant us, dear LORD, from evil ways
     True absolution and release ;
And bless us, more than in past days,
     With purity and inward peace.
f Through life's long day and death's dark night,
p O gentle JESUS, (*cr*) be our Light.

f Do more than pardon ; give us joy,
     Sweet fear, and sober liberty,
And simple hearts without alloy
     That only long to be like Thee.
Through life's long day and death's dark night,
p O gentle JESUS, (*cr*) be our Light.

p For all we love, the poor, the sad,
     The sinful, unto Thee we call ;
cr O let Thy mercy make us glad :
f Thou art our JESUS, and our All.
Through life's long day and death's dark night,
p O gentle JESUS, (*cr*) be our Light.

F. W. FABER.

ALTERNATIVE TUNE, HYMN **554** (SECOND TUNE).

(23)

Evening.

Hymn 29. St. Gall.—L.M.

Cantarium S. Galli, 1845.

A - men.

"God, even our own God, shall give us His blessing."

mf O FATHER, Who didst all things make
 That Heav'n and earth might do Thy
Bless us this night for JESU'S sake, [Will,
And for Thy work preserve us still.

O SON, Who didst redeem mankind,
And set the captive sinner free,
Keep us this night with peaceful mind,
That we may safe abide in Thee.

O HOLY GHOST, Who by Thy power
The Church elect dost sanctify,
Seal us this night, and hour by hour
Our hearts and members purify.

f To FATHER, SON, and HOLY GHOST,
The GOD Whom Heav'n and earth adore,
From men and from the Angel-host
Be praise and glory evermore.

W. B. HEATHCOTE.

ALTERNATIVE TUNE, HYMN 712.

Hymn 30. ALLINGTON.—S.M. *(First Tune.)*

J. HOPKINS.

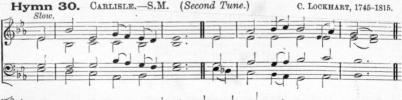

A - men.

Hymn 30. CARLISLE.—S.M. *(Second Tune.)*

C. LOCKHART, 1745–1815.

Slow.

A - men.

A higher setting of this Tune is given at Hymns 393, 706.

(24)

Evening.

"And all the Angels stood round about the throne . . . and worshipped God."

FOR FESTIVALS.

mf OUR day of praise is done ;
p The evening shadows fall ;
cr But pass not from us with the sun,
  True Light that lightenest all.

f Around the Throne on high,
  Where night can never be,
The white-robed harpers of the sky
  Bring ceaseless hymns to Thee.

p Too faint our anthems here ;
  Too soon of praise we tire :
cr But oh, the strains how full and clear
  Of that eternal choir !

mf Yet, LORD, to Thy dear Will
  If Thou attune the heart,
We in Thine Angels' music still
  May bear our lower part.

'Tis Thine each soul to calm,
  Each wayward thought reclaim,
And make our life a daily psalm
  Of glory to Thy Name,

cr A little while, and then
  Shall come the glorious end ;
f And songs of Angels and of men
  In perfect praise shall blend.

J. ELLERTON.

Hymn 31. PAX DEI.—10 10 10 10. *(First Tune.)* Rev. J. B. DYKES.

Amen.

Hymn 31. ELLERS.—10 10 10 10. *(Second Tune.)* E. J. HOPKINS.

A-men.

"The Lord shall give His people the blessing of peace."

AT THE END OF DIVINE SERVICE.

mf SAVIOUR, again to Thy dear Name we raise
  With one accord our parting hymn of praise ;
  We stand to bless Thee ere our worship cease ;
p Then, lowly kneeling, wait Thy word of peace.

  Grant us Thy peace upon our homeward way ;
mf With Thee began, with Thee shall end the day ;
  Guard Thou the lips from sin, the hearts from shame,
  That in this house have call'd upon Thy Name.

p Grant us Thy peace, LORD, through the coming night ;
cr Turn Thou for us its darkness into light ;
f From harm and danger keep Thy children free,
  For dark and light are both alike to Thee.

p Grant us Thy peace throughout our earthly life,
cr Our balm in sorrow, and our stay in strife ;
mf Then, when Thy Voice shall bid our conflict cease,
p Call us, O LORD, to Thine eternal peace.

J. ELLERTON.

(25)

Evening.

Hymn 32. WEYBRIDGE.—C.M. (*First Tune.*)   W. H. SANGSTER.

A - men.

Hymn 32. CREDITON.—C.M. (*Second Tune.*)   T. CLARK, 1807.

A - men.

"O God, Thou art my God."

AT THE END OF DIVINE SERVICE.

mf AND now the wants are told, that brought
Thy children to Thy knee ;
Here lingering still, we ask for nought,
But simply worship Thee.

The hope of Heav'n's eternal days
Absorbs not all the heart
That gives Thee glory, love, and praise,
For being what Thou art.

For Thou art GOD, the One, the Same,
O'er all things high and bright ;
And round us, when we speak Thy Name,
There spreads a heav'n of light.

p O wondrous peace, in thought to dwell
On excellence Divine ;

To know that nought in man can tell
How fair Thy beauties shine !

f O Thou, above all blessing blest,
O'er thanks exalted far,
dim Thy very greatness is a rest
To weaklings as we are ;

mf For when we feel the praise of Thee
A task beyond our powers,
We say, "A perfect GOD is He,
And He is fully ours."

f All glory to the FATHER be,
All glory to the SON,
All glory, HOLY GHOST, to Thee,
While endless ages run.

W. BRIGHT.

See also Hymns :

476 Behold the sun, that seem'd but now.   **477** The day Thou gavest, LORD, is ended.

Sunday.

Hymn 33. INNOCENTS.—7 7 7 7.   *The Parish Choir*, 1850.

Sunday.

A - men.

A higher setting of this Tune is given at Hymns 175, 343.

" In Thy light shall we see light."

MORNING.

f **M**ORN of morns, and day of days !
　　Beauteous were thy new-born rays :
Brighter yet from death's dark prison
CHRIST, the Light of lights, is risen.

He commanded, and His Word
Death and the dread chaos heard :
dim Oh, shall we, more deaf than they,
In the chains of darkness stay ?

p *Nature yet in shadow lies ;
cr Let the sons of light arise,
mf And prevent the morning rays
　　With sweet canticles of praise.

*While the dead world sleeps around,
Let the sacred temples sound

Law, and prophet, and blest psalm
Lit with holy light so calm.

Unto hearts in slumber weak
Let the heavenly trumpet speak ;
And a newer walk express
Their new life to righteousness.

Grant us this, and with us be,
O Thou Fount of charity,
Thou Who dost the SPIRIT give,
Bidding the dead letter live.

f Glory to the FATHER, SON,
And to Thee, O HOLY ONE,
By Whose quickening Breath Divine
Our dull spirits burn and shine.

I. WILLIAMS and Compilers:
from the Latin of C. Coffin.

* These verses should be sung only at a very early Service.

Hymn 34. LÜDECK.—7 7 7 7.

FREYLINGHAUSEN, *Gesangbuch*, 1704.

A - men.

A higher setting of this Tune is given at Hymn 65.

" And God said, Let there be light: and there was light. . . . And the evening and the
morning were the first day."

MORNING.

f **O**N this day, the first of days,
　　GOD the FATHER'S Name we praise ;
Who, creation's LORD and Spring,
Did the world from darkness bring.

On this day the Eternal SON
Over death His triumph won ;
On this day the SPIRIT came
With His gifts of living flame.

O that fervent love to-day
May in every heart have sway,
Teaching us to praise aright
GOD the Source of life and light.

p FATHER, Who didst fashion me
Image of Thyself to be,

Fill me with Thy love Divine,
Let my every thought be Thine.

HOLY JESUS, may I be
Dead and buried here with Thee ;
cr And, by love inflamed, arise
Unto Thee a sacrifice.

mf Thou Who dost all gifts impart,
Shine, Sweet SPIRIT, in my heart ;
Best of gifts Thyself bestow ;
Make me burn Thy love to know.

GOD, the Blessèd THREE in ONE,
Dwell within my heart alone ;
Thou dost give Thyself to me,
p May I give myself to Thee.

Sir H. W. BAKER: from the Latin.

(27)

Sunday.

Hymn 35. CHURCH TRIUMPHANT.—L.M.

J. W. ELLIOTT.

A - men.

A higher setting of this Tune is given at Hymn **129.**

" This is the day which the Lord hath made."

mf AGAIN the LORD'S own day is here,
The day to Christian people dear,
As, week by week, it bids them tell
f How JESUS rose from death and hell.

mf For by His flock their LORD declared
His Resurrection should be shared ;
And we who trust in Him to save
f With Him are risen from the grave.

mf We, one and all, of Him possess'd,
Are with exceeding treasures bless'd ;
For all He did, and all He bare,
He gives us as our own to share.

Eternal glory, rest on high,
A blessèd immortality,
True peace and gladness, and a throne,
Are all His gifts, and all our own.

f And therefore unto Thee we sing,
O LORD of peace, Eternal King ;
Thy love we praise, Thy Name adore,
Both on this day and evermore.

J. M. NEALE and Compilers : from Thomas à Kempis.

ALTERNATIVE TUNE, HYMN 449 (SECOND TUNE).

Hymn 36. WORDSWORTH.—7 6 7 6.7 6 7 6.

W. H. MONK.

A - men.

Sunday.

"The first day of the week."

f O DAY of rest and gladness,
    O day of joy and light,
O balm of care and sadness,
    Most beautiful, most bright ;
On thee the high and lowly,
    Before the Eternal Throne,
Sing Holy, Holy, Holy,
    To the great THREE in ONE.

On thee, at the creation,
    The light first had its birth ;
On thee for our salvation
    CHRIST rose from depths of earth ;
On thee our LORD victorious
    The SPIRIT sent from heaven ;
And thus on thee most glorious
    A triple light was given.

p Thou art a cooling fountain
    In life's dry dreary sand ;
From thee, like Pisgah's mountain,
    We view our promised land ;
A day of sweet refection,
    A day of holy love,
cr A day of resurrection
    From earth to things above.

mf To-day on weary nations
    The heavenly Manna falls,
To holy convocations
    The silver-trumpet calls,
Where Gospel-light is glowing
    With pure and radiant beams,
And living water flowing
    With soul-refreshing streams.

New graces ever gaining
    From this our day of rest,
We reach the Rest remaining
    To spirits of the blest ;
f To HOLY GHOST be praises,
    To FATHER, and to SON ;
The Church her voice upraises
    To Thee, Blest THREE in ONE.

Bishop C. WORDSWORTH.

Hymn 37. DOMINICA.—S.M.

Sir H. OAKELEY.

A - men.

A lower setting of this Tune is given at Hymn 532.

"I was in the Spirit on the Lord's day."

mf THIS is the day of light :
    Let there be light to-day ;
O Day-spring, rise upon our night,
    And chase its gloom away.

p This is the day of rest :
    Our failing strength renew ;
On weary brain and troubled breast
    Shed Thou Thy freshening dew.

This is the day of peace :
    Thy peace our spirits fill ;
cr Bid Thou the blasts of discord cease,
dim The waves of strife be still.

p This is the day of prayer :
    Let earth to Heav'n draw near ;
cr Lift up our hearts to seek Thee there,
    Come down to meet us here.

f This is the first of days :
    Send forth Thy quickening Breath,
And wake dead souls to love and praise,
    O Vanquisher of death.

J. ELLERTON.

Sunday.

Hymn 38.   Vienna.—7 7 7 7.   J. H. Knecht, 1799.

A-men.

A lower setting of this Tune is given at Hymn **568.**

"The day is Thine, and the night is Thine."

Evening.

mf BLEST Creator of the light,
Making day with radiance bright,
Thou didst o'er the forming earth
Give the golden light its birth.

Shade of eve with morning ray
Took from Thee the name of day ;
Darkness now is drawing nigh :
Listen to our humble cry.

p May we ne'er by guilt depress'd
Lose the way to endless rest ;

Nor with idle thoughts and vain
Bind our souls to earth again.

cr Rather may we heavenward rise
Where eternal treasure lies ;
Purified by grace within,
Hating every deed of sin.

p HOLY FATHER, hear our cry,
cr Through Thy SON our LORD most High,
f Whom our thankful hearts adore
With the SPIRIT evermore.

Compilers : from the Latin.

The following Hymns are suitable for Sundays :

478 This is the day the LORD hath made.   **479** Great GOD, Who, hid from mortal sight.

Monday.

Hymn 39.   St. Hugh.—C.M.   E. J. Hopkins.

A-men.

A lower setting of this Tune is given at Hymn **247.**

" And God made the firmament, and divided the waters which were under the firmament from the waters which were above the firmament. . . . And the evening and the morning were the second day."

mf SING we the glory of our GOD,
Who on the second day
Spread out the firmament above,
His wonders to display.

There, floating in the blue expanse,
The watery clouds we view,
Whence fruitful showers at His command
The thirsty soil bedew.

How fair an image of the grace
Which Thou, LORD, dost impart,
Like morning dew or gentle rain,
To gladden every heart.

And when the faithful soul drinks in
Those showers with blessings rife,
cr A well of water springeth up
To everlasting life.

f O happy saints, on whom are pour'd
Such treasures from above !
p LORD, may they ne'er forgetful be,
But render love for love.

f To GOD, Who freely loved us first,
All might, all glory be ;
To FATHER, SON, and HOLY GHOST,
Through all eternity.

J. Chandler and Compilers : from the Latin of C. Coffin.

(30)

Tuesday

Hymn 40. LINCOLN.—C.M.

RAVENSCROFT, *Psalmes*, 1621.

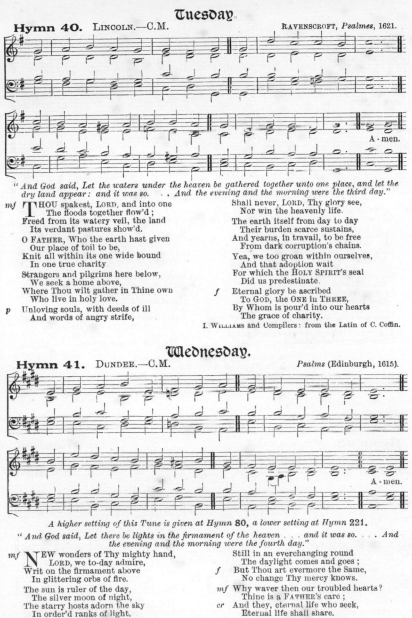

A - men.

"And God said, Let the waters under the heaven be gathered together unto one place, and let the dry land appear: and it was so. . . And the evening and the morning were the third day."

mf THOU spakest, LORD, and into one
 The floods together flow'd ;
Freed from its watery veil, the land
 Its verdant pastures show'd.

O FATHER, Who the earth hast given
 Our place of toil to be,
Knit all within its one wide bound
 In one true charity.

Strangers and pilgrims here below,
 We seek a home above,
Where Thou wilt gather in Thine own
 Who live in holy love.

p Unloving souls, with deeds of ill
 And words of angry strife,

Shall never, LORD, Thy glory see,
 Nor win the heavenly life.

The earth itself from day to day
 Their burden scarce sustains,
And yearns, in travail, to be free
 From dark corruption's chains.

Yea, we too groan within ourselves,
 And that adoption wait
For which the HOLY SPIRIT'S seal
 Did us predestinate.

f Eternal glory be ascribed
 To GOD, the ONE in THREE,
By Whom is pour'd into our hearts
 The grace of charity.

I. WILLIAMS and Compilers : from the Latin of C. Coffin.

Wednesday.

Hymn 41. DUNDEE.—C.M.

Psalms (Edinburgh, 1615).

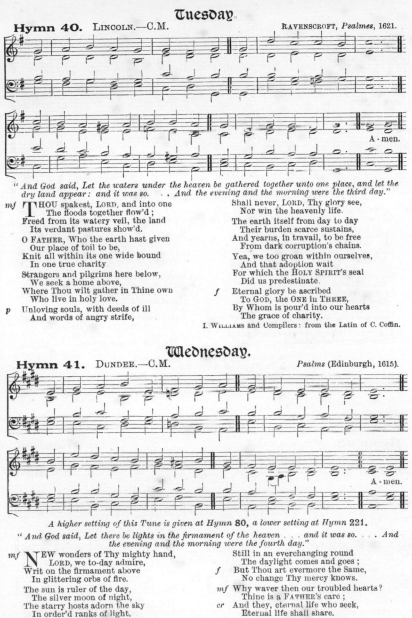

A - men.

A higher setting of this Tune is given at Hymn 80, a lower setting at Hymn 221.

"And God said, Let there be lights in the firmament of the heaven . . . and it was so. . . . And the evening and the morning were the fourth day."

mf NEW wonders of Thy mighty hand,
 LORD, we to-day admire,
Writ on the firmament above
 In glittering orbs of fire.

The sun is ruler of the day,
 The silver moon of night,
The starry hosts adorn the sky
 In order'd ranks of light.

But e'en that glorious sun must set,
 And knows his going down,
That silver moon must wax and wane,
 The stars their courses own.

Still in an everchanging round
 The daylight comes and goes ;
f But Thou art evermore the Same,
 No change Thy mercy knows.

mf Why waver then our troubled hearts ?
 Thine is a FATHER'S care ;
cr And they, eternal life who seek,
 Eternal life shall share.

f All praise, all glory be ascribed
 To GOD the ONE in THREE,
Who bids us cast our care on Him,
 To Him for comfort flee.

J. CHANDLER and Compilers : from the Latin of C. Coffin.

(31)

Thursday.

Hymn 42. St. Flavian.—C.M.

Psalmes, 1562.

A - men.

" And God said, Let the waters bring forth abundantly the moving creature that hath life, and fowl that may fly above the earth. . . . And the evening and the morning were the fifth day."

mf THE fish in wave, the bird on wing,
　　God bade the waters bear ;
Each for our mortal body's food
　　His gracious hands prepare.

But other food, of richer cost,
　　The immortal spirit needs ;
By faith it lives on every word
　　That from His mouth proceeds.

Faith springing from the Blood of Christ
　　Has flow'd o'er every land ;
And sinners through the vanquish'd world
　　Bow down to its command.

Its light the joy of Heav'n reveals
　　To hearts made pure within ;
And bids them seek by worthy deeds
　　Eternal crowns to win.

f By faith the saints of old were strong
　　The lion's wrath to tame ;
By faith they spurn'd the tyrant's threats,
　　And scorn'd the raging flame.

p Lord, grant that we the path may tread
　　Whereon its light doth shine ;
cr And gather, as we onward go,
　　The fruits of love Divine.

f 　O praise the Father ; praise the Son,
　　　On Whose most precious Blood
　　Rests all our faith ; and praise to Him
　　　Who with Them Both is God.

J. Chandler and Compilers : from the Latin of C. Coffin.

Friday.

Hymn 43. Windsor.—C.M.

Damon, Psalmes, 1591.

A - men.

" And God said, Let Us make man in Our image. . . . And the evening and the morning were the sixth day."

mf TO-DAY, O Lord, a holier work
　　Thy secret counsels frame,
A king to rule Thy new-made world,
　　To praise Thy glorious Name.

Thou formest man : Thy Spirit breathes
　　Life into dust of earth :
Man, in Thine own true Image made,
　　From Thee receives his birth.

Friday.

And henceforth he dominion holds
O'er all in earth and sea ;
Yet mindful whence his being came
Must humbly walk with Thee.

p Alas ! his wilful heart rebels
Against Thy gentle sway ;
Proud dust of earth would fain be like
The GOD Whom all obey.

O griefs and sorrows numberless,
Which hence the world o'erspread ;
JESU, Thy mercy succour'd us,
Or hope itself had fled.

f O praise the FATHER, and the SON
Who saved us by His death,
And HOLY GHOST Who quickens us
With His life-giving breath.

J. CHANDLER and Compilers :
from the Latin of C. Coffin.

The following Hymn is suitable for Fridays ·
480 O JESU, crucified for man.

Saturday.

Hymn 44. MALMESBURY ABBEY.—C.M.   J. COMLEY.

A - men.

"*And on the seventh day God ended His work which He had made.*"

mf SIX days of labour now are past ;
Thou restest, HOLY GOD ;
And of Thy finish'd work hast said
That all is very good.

Yet while the seventh day is bless'd,
Hallow'd for rest Divine,
Behold, a new creation needs
That mighty power of Thine.

Ten thousand voices praise Thy Name
In earth and sea and sky ;
One sinner by his sin has marr'd
The blissful harmony.

p O LORD, create man's heart anew,
The heart of stone remove :
cr Then hymns of praise again shall rise,
The fruits of holy love.

mf O for the songs that Thou wilt bless,
Where heart and voice agree ;
O for the prayers that plead aright
With Thy dread Majesty.

f All praise to GOD, the THREE in ONE,
Who high in glory reigns ;
Who by His Word hath all things made,
And by His Word sustains.

J. CHANDLER and Compilers : from the Latin of C. Coffin.

The following Hymn is suitable for Saturdays :
481 Now the busy week is done.

Advent.

Hymn 45. CONDITOR ALME.—L.M. *(First Version.)* Proper Sarum Melody.

A - men.

Hymn 45. CONDITOR ALME.—L.M. *(Alternative Version.)*
To be sung in Unison. Proper Sarum Melody.

A - men.

"Which cometh forth as a bridegroom out of his chamber."

mf CREATOR of the starry height,
     Thy people's everlasting Light,
JESU, Redeemer of us all,
p Hear Thou Thy servants when they call.

Thou, sorrowing at the helpless cry
Of all creation doom'd to die,
cr Didst save our lost and guilty race
By healing gifts of heavenly grace.

mf When earth was near its evening hour,
Thou didst, in love's redeeming power,
Like bridegroom from his chamber, come
Forth from a Virgin-mother's womb.

f At Thy great Name, exalted now,
All knees in lowly homage bow;
All things in Heav'n and earth adore,
And own Thee King for evermore.

p To Thee, O HOLY ONE, we pray,
Our Judge in that tremendous day,
Ward off, while yet we dwell below,
The weapons of our crafty foe.

f To GOD the FATHER, GOD the SON,
And GOD the SPIRIT, THREE in ONE,
Praise, honour, might, and glory be
From age to age eternally.

J. M. NEALE: from the Latin.

ALTERNATIVE TUNE, HYMN 71.

Hymn 46. BRESLAU.—L.M. *Geistliche Gesänge* (Leipzig, 1625).

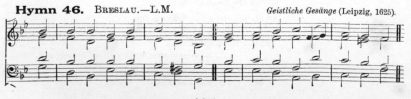

Advent.

Lower settings of this Tune are given at Hymns 200, 246.

" His name is called The Word of God."

mf O HEAVENLY WORD, Eternal Light,
   Begotten of the FATHER'S Might,
Who, in these latter days, art born
For succour to a world forlorn ;

Our hearts enlighten from above,
And kindle with Thine own true love ;
That we, who hear Thy call to-day,
May cast earth's vanities away.

And when as Judge Thou drawest nigh,
The secrets of all hearts to try ;
p When sinners meet their awful doom,
cr And Saints attain their heavenly home ;

p O let us not, for evil past,
Be driven from Thy Face at last ;
cr But with the blessèd evermore
Behold Thee, love Thee, and adore.

f To GOD the FATHER, GOD the SON,
   And GOD the SPIRIT, THREE in ONE,
   Praise, honour, might, and glory be
   From age to age eternally.

                 Compilers : from the Latin.

ALTERNATIVE TUNE, HYMN 415.

Hymn 47. MERTON.—8 7 8 7.   W. H. MONK.

" Now it is high time to awake out of sleep."

f HARK ! a thrilling voice is sounding ;
   " CHRIST is nigh," it seems to say ;
" Cast away the dreams of darkness,
   O ye children of the day ! "

Waken'd by the solemn warning,
   Let the earth-bound soul arise ;
CHRIST, her Sun, all ill dispelling,
   Shines upon the morning skies.

mf Lo ! the LAMB, so long expected,
   Comes with pardon down from Heav'n ;
dim Let us haste, with tears of sorrow,
   One and all to be forgiven ;

mf That when next He comes with glory,
p   And the world is wrapp'd in fear,
cr With His mercy He may shield us,
   And with words of love draw near.

f Honour, glory, might, and blessing
   To the FATHER and the SON,
   With the Everlasting SPIRIT,
   While eternal ages run.

             E. CASWALL : from the Latin

Advent.

Hymn 48. FRANCONIA.—S.M.   *Harmonischer Liederschatz, 1738.*

A - men.

A higher setting of this Tune is given at Hymns 261, 488.

" Tell ye the daughter of Sion, Behold, thy King cometh unto thee."

mf	THE Advent of our King Our prayers must now employ, And we must hymns of welcome sing In strains of holy joy.	*mf*	As Judge, on clouds of light, He soon will come again, And His true members all unite With Him in Heav'n to reign.
p *cr*	The Everlasting SON Incarnate deigns to be ; Himself a servant's form puts on, To set His servants free.		Before the dawning day Let sin's dark deeds be gone ; The old man all be put away, The new man all put on.
mf *p*	Daughter of Sion, rise To meet thy lowly King ; Nor let thy faithless heart despise The peace He comes to bring.	*f*	All glory to the SON Who comes to set us free, With FATHER, SPIRIT, ever ONE, Through all eternity.

J. CHANDLER and Compilers:
from the Latin of C. Coffin.

Hymn 49. VENI EMMANUEL.—8 8. 8 8. 8 8.   (*First Version.*)

To be sung in Unison.   *Hymnal Noted, from a French Missal.*

A-men.

Advent.

" The Redeemer shall come to Zion.'

mf O COME, O come, Emmanuel,
And ransom captive Israel,
p That mourns in lonely exile here,
Until the SON of GOD appear.
ff   Rejoice ! Rejoice ! Emmanuel
Shall come to thee, O Israel.

mf O come, Thou Rod of Jesse, free
Thine own from Satan's tyranny ;
From depths of hell Thy people save,
cr And give them victory o'er the grave.
ff   Rejoice ! Rejoice ! Emmanuel
Shall come to thee, O Israel

mf O come, Thou Day-spring, come and cheer
Our spirits by Thine Advent here ;
Disperse the gloomy clouds of night,
And death's dark shadows put to flight.
ff   Rejoice ! Rejoice ! Emmanuel
Shall come to thee, O Israel.

mf O come, Thou Key of David, come,
And open wide our heavenly home ;
Make safe the way that leads on high,
And close the path to misery.
ff   Rejoice ! Rejoice ! Emmanuel
Shall come to thee, O Israel.

mf O come, O come, Thou LORD of Might,
Who to Thy tribes, on Sinai's height,
In ancient times didst give the law
In cloud, and majesty, and awe.
ff   Rejoice ! Rejoice ! Emmanuel
Shall come to thee, O Israel.

J. M. NEALE and Compilers : from the Latin.

Hymn 49. VENI EMMANUEL.—8 8.8 8 8.8 8. *(Alternative Version.)*

" The Redeemer shall come to Zion.'

Hymnal Noted, from a French Missal.

O come, O come, Em·man·u·el, And ran·som cap·tive Is·ra·el,
O come, Thou Rod of Jes·se, free Thine own from Sa·tan's ty·ran·ny ;
O come, Thou Day-spring, come and cheer Our spi·rits by Thine Ad·vent here ;
O come, Thou Key of Da·vid, come, And o·pen wide our heaven·ly home ;
O come, O come, Thou LORD of Might, Who to Thy tribes, on Si·nai's height,

That mourns in lone·ly ex·ile here, Un·til the SON of GOD ap·pear.
From depths of hell Thy peo·ple save, And give them vic·tory o'er the grave.
Dis·perse the gloo·my clouds of night, And death's dark sha·dows put to flight.
Make safe the way that leads on high, And close the path to mis·e·ry.
In an·cient times didst give the law In cloud, and ma·jes·ty, and awe.

Re·joice ! Re·joice ! Em·man·u·el Shall come to thee, O Is·ra·el. A·men.

(57)

Advent.

Hymn 50. WINCHESTER NEW.—L.M.   *Musikalisch Handbuch* (Hamburg, 1690).

A-men.

A lower setting of this Tune is given at Hymn **327.**

" The voice of one crying in the wilderness, Prepare ye the way of the Lord, make His paths straight.'

f   ON Jordan's bank the Baptist's cry
       Announces that the LORD is nigh ;
Awake, and hearken, for he brings
Glad tidings of the King of kings.

mf Then cleansed be every breast from sin ;
Make straight the way for GOD within ;
Prepare we in our hearts a home,
Where such a mighty Guest may come.

For Thou art our Salvation, LORD,
Our Refuge, and our great Reward ;
dim Without Thy grace we waste away,
Like flowers that wither and decay.

p   To heal the sick stretch out Thine Hand,
And bid the fallen sinner stand ;
cr Shine forth, and let Thy light restore
Earth's own true loveliness once more.

f   All praise, Eternal SON, to Thee
Whose Advent doth Thy people free,
Whom with the FATHER we adore
And HOLY GHOST for evermore.

J. CHANDLER and Compilers : from the Latin of C. Coffin.

Hymn 51. ST. THOMAS.—8 7.8 7.8 7.   *(First Tune.)*   Traditional Melody.

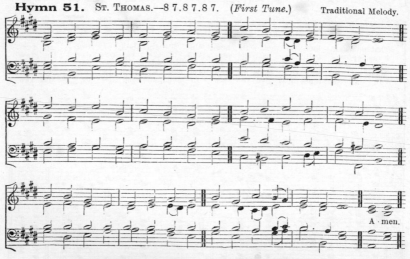

A · men.

A lower setting of this Tune is given at Hymn **309** *(Third Tune).*

Advent.

Hymn 51. HELMSLEY.—8 7. 8 7. 8 7. *(Second Tune.)* T. OLIVERS, 1765.

A - men.

" Behold, He cometh with clouds ; and every eye shall see Him, and they also which pierced Him."

mf LO! He comes with clouds descending,
Once for favour'd sinners slain ;
f Thousand thousand Saints attending
Swell the triumph of His train :
Alleluia !
CHRIST appears on earth again.

mf Every eye shall now behold Him
Robed in dreadful majesty ;
p Those who set at nought and sold Him,
Pierced and nail'd Him to the Tree,
pp Deeply wailing,
p Shall the true Messiah see.

mf Those dear tokens of His Passion
Still His dazzling Body bears,
cr Cause of endless exultation
To His ransom'd worshippers ;
mf With what rapture
Gaze we on those glorious scars !

f Yea, Amen, let all adore Thee,
High on Thine eternal Throne ;
mf Saviour, take the power and glory ;
Claim the kingdom for Thine own :
ff Alleluia !
Thou shalt reign, and Thou alone.

C. WESLEY and J. CENNICK.

(39)

Advent.

Hymn 52. LUTHER.—8 7 8 7.8 8 7.

M. LUTHER, 1529.

A-men.

" The Lord Himself shall descend from heaven with a shout, with the voice of the Archangel, and with the trump of God."

mf GREAT GOD, what do 1 see and hear?
     The end of things created :
The Judge of all men doth appear
     On clouds of glory seated :
ff The trumpet sounds, the graves restore
      The dead which they contain'd before ;
p   Prepare, my soul, to meet Him.

f The dead in CHRIST are first to rise
     At that last trumpet's sounding ;
Caught up to meet Him in the skies,
     With joy their LORD surrounding :
No gloomy fears their souls dismay ;
His Presence sheds eternal day
     On those prepared to meet Him.

p The ungodly, fill'd with guilty fears,
     Behold His wrath prevailing ;
In woe they rise, but all their tears
     And sighs are unavailing :
rp The day of grace is past and gone :
Trembling they stand before His Throne,
     All unprepared to meet Him.

mf Great Judge, to Thee our prayers we pour,
     In deep abasement bending ;
O shield us through that last dread hour,
     Thy wondrous love extending :
cr May we, in this our trial day,
     With faithful hearts Thy word obey,
     And thus prepare to meet Thee.

B. RINGWALDT, W. B. COLLYER, and others.

Advent.

Hymn 53. BRISTOL.—C.M.   RAVENSCROFT, *Psalmes*, 1621.

Hymn 53. BRISTOL.—C.M.   (*Alternative Version.*)
     Harmonised by T. RAVENSCROFT, 1621.

" He hath sent Me to bind up the broken-hearted, to proclaim liberty to the captives."

f HARK the glad sound! the Saviour
    The Saviour promised long :   [comes,
Let every heart prepare a throne,
    And every voice a song.

He comes, the prisoners to release
    In Satan's bondage held ;
The gates of brass before Him burst,
    The iron fetters yield.

p   He comes, the broken heart to bind,
    The bleeding soul to cure,
And with the treasures of His grace
    To bless the humble poor.

f   Our glad hosannas, Prince of peace,
    Thy welcome shall proclaim ;
And Heav'n's eternal arches ring
    With Thy belovèd Name.

P. DODDRIDGE, 1735.

The Alternative Version may be used for verses 2 and 4.

Advent.

Hymn 54. St. Gall.—L.M.

Cantarium S. Galli, 1845.

A-men.

" I sleep, but my heart waketh."

For a Late Evening Service.

p WHEN shades of night around us close,
And weary limbs in sleep repose,
The faithful soul awake may be,
And longing sigh, O Lord, to Thee.

mf Thou true Desire of nations, hear,
Thou Word of God, Thou Saviour dear;
In pity heed our humble cries,
And bid at length the fallen rise.

O come, Redeemer, come and free
Thine own from guilt and misery;
The gates of heav'n again unfold,
Which Adam's sin had closed of old.

f All praise, Eternal Son, to Thee,
Whose Advent sets Thy people free,
Whom with the Father we adore
And Holy Ghost for evermore.

Compilers: from the Latin of C. Coffin.

Alternative Tune (Plainsong), Hymn 15.

The following Hymns are suitable for this season:

Christmas.

Hymn 55. Redemptor mundi.—10 10 10 10.

A. H. Brown.

Christmas.

A · men.

" The Word was made flesh."

mf O COME, Redeemer of mankind, appear,
    Thee with full hearts the Virgin-born we greet ;
Let every age with rapt amazement hear
That wondrous birth which for our GOD is meet.

Not by the will of man, or mortal seed,
But by the SPIRIT'S breathed mysterious grace
p The WORD of GOD became our flesh indeed,
And grew a tender plant of human race.

Lo ! Mary's virgin womb its burthen bears,
Nor less abides her virgin purity ;
cr In the King's glory see our nature shares ;
Here in His temple GOD vouchsafes to be.

mf From His bright chamber, virtue's holy shrine,
The royal Bridegroom cometh to the day ;
Of twofold substance, human and Divine,
As giant swift, rejoicing on His way.

p Forth from His FATHER to the world He goes,
mf Back to the FATHER'S Face His way regains,
p Far down to souls beneath His glory shows,
f Again at GOD'S right hand victorious reigns.

With the Eternal FATHER equal, Thou
Girt with our flesh dost triumph evermore,
Strengthening our feeble bodies here below
With endless grace from Thine own living store.

mf How doth Thy lowly manger radiant shine !
On the sweet breath of night new splendour grows ;
So may our spirits glow with faith Divine,
Where no dark cloud of sin shall interpose.

f All praise and glory to the FATHER be,
All praise and glory to His Only SON,
All praise and glory, HOLY GHOST, to Thee,
Both now, and while eternal ages run.

D. T. MORGAN · from the Latin of St. Ambrose.

Christmas.

Hymn 56. DIVINUM MYSTERIUM (CORDE NATUS).—8 7 8 7.8 7 7.
(First Version.)

NYLAND, *Piœ Cantiones*, 1582.

A · men.

Hymn 56. DIVINUM MYSTERIUM.—8 7 8 7.8 7 7. *(Alternative Version.)*

NYLAND, *Piœ Cantiones*, 1582.

Christmas.

A - men.

" God was manifest in the flesh."

mf OF the FATHER'S Love begotten
　　Ere the worlds began to be,
He is Alpha and Omega,
He the source, the ending He,
Of the things that are, that have been,
　　And that future years shall see,
　　　　Evermore and evermore.

**At His Word the worlds were framèd ;
　　He commanded ; it was done :
Heav'n and earth and depths of ocean
In their threefold order one ;
All that grows beneath the shining
　　Of the moon and burning sun,
　　　　Evermore and evermore*

p **He is found in human fashion,
　　Death and sorrow here to know,
That the race of Adam's children,
Doom'd by Law to endless woe,
May not henceforth die and perish
　　In the dreadful gulf below,
　　　　Evermore and evermore.*

f O that Birth for ever blessèd !
　　When the Virgin, full of grace,
By the HOLY GHOST conceiving,
Bare the Saviour of our race,
And the Babe, the world's Redeemer,
　　First reveal'd His sacred Face,
　　　　Evermore and evermore.

This is He Whom seers in old time
　　Chanted of with one accord ;
Whom the voices of the Prophets
Promised in their faithful word ;
Now He shines, the long-expected ;
　　Let creation praise its LORD,
　　　　Evermore and evermore.

ff O ye heights of Heav'n, adore Him ,
　　Angel-hosts, His praises sing ;
All dominions, bow before Him,
And extol our GOD and King ;
Let no tongue on earth be silent,
　　Every voice in concert ring,
　　　　Evermore and evermore.

p **Righteous Judge of souls departed,
　　Righteous King of them that live,
On the FATHER'S Throne exalted
None in might with Thee may strive ;
Who at last in vengeance coming
　　Sinners from Thy Face shalt drive,
　　　　Evermore and evermore.*

f Thee let old men, Thee let young men,
　　Thee let boys in chorus sing ;
Matrons, virgins, little maidens,
With glad voices answering ;
Let their guileless songs re-echo,
　　And the heart its praises bring,
　　　　Evermore and evermore.

f CHRIST, to Thee, with GOD the FATHER,
　　And, O HOLY GHOST, to Thee,
Hymn, and chant, and high thanksgiving,
And unwearied praises be,
Honour, glory, and dominion,
　　And eternal victory,
　　　　Evermore and evermore.

J. M. NEALE and Sir H. W. BAKER : from Prudentius.

* *These verses may be omitted*

Christmas.

Hymn 57. ERFURT.—L.M.   *Geistliche Lieder* (Leipzig, 1539).

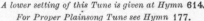

A lower setting of this Tune is given at Hymn **614.**
For Proper Plainsong Tune see Hymn **177.**

"Christ Jesus came into the world to save sinners."

mf O CHRIST, Redeemer of our race,
Thou Brightness of the FATHER'S Face,
Of Him, and with Him ever ONE,
Ere times and seasons had begun ;

Thou that art very Light of Light,
Unfailing Hope in sin's dark night,
Hear Thou the prayers Thy people pray,
The wide world o'er, this blessèd day.

p Remember, LORD of life and grace,
How once, to save a ruin'd race,
Thou didst our very flesh assume
In Mary's undefilèd womb.

mf To-day, as year by year its light
Sheds o'er the world a radiance bright,
One precious truth is echoed on,
f " 'Tis Thou hast saved us, Thou alone."

mf Thou from the FATHER'S Throne didst come
To call His banish'd children home ;
And Heav'n, and earth, and sea, and shore
His love Who sent Thee here adore.

And gladsome too are we to-day,
Whose guilt Thy Blood has wash'd away ;
Redeem'd the new-made song we sing ;
f It is the birthday of our King.

O LORD the Virgin-born, to Thee
Eternal praise and glory be,
Whom with the FATHER we adore
And HOLY GHOST for evermore.

Sir H. W. BAKER : from the Latin.

Hymn 58. ST. GEORGE.—S.M.   H. J. GAUNTLETT.

A lower setting of this Tune is given at Hymn **351.**

" He is our Peace."

mf GOD from on high hath heard ;
Let sighs and sorrows cease ;
Lo ! from the opening Heav'n descends
To man the promised Peace.

Hark ! through the silent night
Angelic voices swell ;
Their joyful songs proclaim that " GOD
Is born on earth to dwell."

See how the shepherd-band
Speed on with eager feet ;
Come to the hallow'd cave with them
The Holy Babe to greet.

But, oh, what sight appear.
Within that lowly door !
p A manger, stall, and swaddling clothes,
A Child, and Mother poor !

Art Thou the CHRIST ? the SON ?
The FATHER'S Image bright ?
And see we Him Whose Arm upholds
Earth and the starry height ?

cr Yea, faith can pierce the cloud
Which veils Thy glory now ;
f We hail Thee GOD, before Whose Throne
dim The Angels prostrate bow.

mf A silent Teacher, LORD,
Thou bidd'st us not refuse
To bear what flesh would have us shun,
To shun what flesh would choose.

Our sinful pride to cure
With that pure love of Thine,
cr O be Thou born within our hearts,
Most Holy Child Divine.

Bishop WOODFORD and Compilers :
from the Latin of C. Coffin.

(46)

Christmas.

Hymn 59. ADESTE FIDELES.—Irregular.

" Let us now go even unto Bethlehem."   Traditional Melody

1. O come, all ye faith - ful, Joy - ful and tri - um - phant, O
2. *f* GOD of . . GOD, . . LIGHT . . of . . LIGHT, . .
3. *f* Sing, choirs of An - gels, Sing in ex - ul - ta - tion,
4. *f* Yea, LORD, we greet Thee, Born this hap - py morn - ing;

come ye, O come ye to Beth - - le - hem;
p Lo! He ab - hors not the Vir - - gin's womb;
Sing, all ye ci - ti - zens of Heav'n . . a - bove;
JE - SU, to Thee be . . glo - - ry given;

Come and be - hold Him Born, the King of An - gels;
f Ve - ry . . GOD, Be - got - ten, not cre - a - ted;
"Glo - ry to GOD . . In . . the . . high - est;"
WORD of the FA - THER, Now in flesh ap - pear - ing;

p   *cres.*   *f*

O come, let us a - dore Him, O come, let us a - dore Him, O

come, let us a - dore Him, CHRIST the LORD. A - men.

F. OAKELEY and Compilers.

(47)

Christmas.

Hymn 60.* MENDELSSOHN.—7 7 7 7. 7 7 7 7. 7 7. F. MENDELSSOHN-BARTHOLDY.

Harmony. Unison. A - men.

"Glory to God in the highest, and on earth peace, good will toward men."

f HARK! the herald-angels sing
　　Glory to the new-born King,
p Peace on earth, and mercy mild,
cr GOD and sinners reconciled.
f Joyful, all ye nations, rise,
　Join the triumph of the skies;
　With the Angelic host proclaim,
　"CHRIST is born in Bethlehem."
ff Hark! the herald-angels sing
　　Glory to the new-born King.

f CHRIST, by highest Heav'n adored,
　CHRIST, the Everlasting LORD,
dim Late in time behold Him come,
　Offspring of a Virgin's womb.
p Veil'd in flesh the GODHEAD see!
　Hail, the Incarnate Deity!
　Pleased as Man with man to dwell
cr JESUS, our Emmanuel.
ff Hark! the herald-angels sing
　　Glory to the new-born King.

f Hail, the heaven-born Prince of peace!
　Hail, the Sun of righteousness!
　Light and life to all He brings,
　Risen with healing in His wings.
mf Mild He lays His glory by,
　Born that man no more may die,
cr Born to raise the sons of earth,
　Born to give them second birth.
ff Hark! the herald-angels sing
　　Glory to the new-born King.

C. WESLEY, 1739.

* To be sung in Unison, except the 9th line.

(48)

Christmas.

A - men.

" Behold I bring you good tidings of great joy."

mf CHRISTIANS, awake, salute the happy morn,
    Whereon the Saviour of the world was born ;
Rise to adore the mystery of love,
Which hosts of Angels chanted from above ;
With them the joyful tidings first begun
Of GOD Incarnate and the Virgin's Son.

Then to the watchful shepherds it was told,
Who heard the Angelic herald's voice, "Behold,
I bring good tidings of a Saviour's birth
To you and all the nations upon earth :
This day hath GOD fulfill'd His promised word,
This day is born a Saviour, CHRIST the LORD."

He spake ; and straightway the celestial choir
In hymns of joy, unknown before, conspire :
The praises of redeeming love they sang,
And Heav'n's whole orb with Alleluias rang :
GOD'S highest glory was their anthem still,
p Peace upon earth, and unto men good will.

mf To Bethlehem straight the enlighten'd shepherds ran,
To see the wonder GOD had wrought for man,
And found, with Joseph and the Blessèd Maid,
Her Son, the Saviour, in a manger laid :
Then to their flocks, still praising GOD, return,
And their glad hearts with holy rapture burn.

p O may we keep and ponder in our mind
GOD'S wondrous love in saving lost mankind ;
Trace we the Babe, Who hath retrieved our loss,
From His poor manger to His bitter Cross :
Tread in His steps, assisted by His grace,
Till man's first heavenly state again takes place.

mf Then may we hope, the Angelic hosts among,
To sing, redeem'd, a glad triumphal song :
He that was born upon this joyful day
Around us all His glory shall display ;
Saved by His love, incessant we shall sing
Eternal praise to Heav'n's Almighty King.

J. BYROM. 1749

(49)

Christmas.

Hymn 62. WINCHESTER OLD.—C.M.

ESTE, *Psalms*, 1592.

Hymn 62. WINCHESTER OLD.—C.M. (*Alternative Version.*)
CONGREGATION.

Harmonised by J. KIRBY in ESTE, *Psalms*, 1592.

CHOIR.

"*Unto you is born this day in the city of David a Saviour, which is Christ the Lord.*"

mf WHILE shepherds watch'd their flocks
All seated on the ground, [by night,
The Angel of the LORD came down,
And glory shone around.

"Fear not," said he; for mighty dread
Had seized their troubled mind;
"Glad tidings of great joy I bring
To you and all mankind.

"To you in David's town this day
Is born of David's line
A Saviour, Who is CHRIST the LORD;
And this shall be the sign:

"The heav'nly Babe you there shall find
To human view display'd,
All meanly wrapp'd in swathing bands,
And in a manger laid."

Thus spake the seraph; and forthwith
Appear'd a shining throng
Of Angels praising GOD, who thus
Address'd their joyful song:

f "All glory be to GOD on high,
p And to the earth be peace;
f Good will henceforth from Heav'n to men
Begin and never cease."

N. TATE, 1700.

The Alternative Version may be used for verses 2, 3, 4.

Hymn 63. WAREHAM.—L.M.

W. KNAPP, 1738.

Christmas.

A-men.

FOR A LATE EVENING SERVICE. *"The Lord is our defence."*

mf   O SAVIOUR, LORD, to Thee we pray,
     Whose love has kept us safe to-day,
    Protect us through the coming night,
    And ever save us by Thy might.

p   Be with us now, in mercy nigh,
    And spare Thy servants when they cry ;
    Our sins blot out, our prayers receive,
cr   Thy light throughout our darkness give.

mf Let not dull sleep the soul oppress,
    Nor secret foe the heart possess ;

    Our flesh keep chaste, that it may be
    A holy temple meet for Thee.

    To Thee, Who dost our hearts renew,
    With fervent prayer we humbly sue,
    That pure in thought and free from stain
    We from our beds may rise again.

f   All praise to GOD the FATHER be,
    All praise, Eternal SON, to Thee,
    Whom with the SPIRIT we adore
    For ever and for evermore.

Compilers and J. COPELAND : from the Latin.

For Proper Plainsong Tune see Hymn 347.
This Hymn may also be sung on Holy Days, except from Ash Wednesday to Whitsunday.

The following Hymns are suitable for this season :

464 Litany of the Incarnate Word.   **483** From east to west, from shore to shore.
482 Angels, from the realms of glory.   **484** Christians, sing out with exultation.
          642 O little town of Bethlehem.

St. Stephen's Day.

Hymn 64.   HERI MUNDUS EXULTAVIT.—8 8 7.8 8 7.   W. MACFARREN.

A-men.

*"He, being full of the Holy Ghost, looked up steadfastly into Heaven, and saw the glory of
God, and Jesus standing on the right hand of God."*

mf YESTERDAY, with exultation,
     Join'd the world in celebration
    Of her promised Saviour's birth ;
    Yesterday the Angel-nation
    Pour'd the strains of jubilation
     O'er the Monarch born on earth ;

    But to-day o'er death victorious,
    By his faith and actions glorious,
     By his miracles renown'd,
    See the Deacon triumph gaining,
    'Midst the faithless faith sustaining,
cr   First of holy Martyrs found.

f   Onward, champion, falter never,
    Sure of sure reward for ever,
     Holy Stephen, persevere ;
    Perjured witnesses confounding,
    Satan's synagogue astounding
     By thy doctrine true and clear

mf Thine own Witness is in Heaven,
    True and faithful, to thee given,
     Witness of thy blamelessness :
    By thy name a crown implying,
    Meet it is thou shouldst be dying
     For the crown of righteousness.

    For the crown that fadeth never
    Bear the torturer's brief endeavour ;
     Victory waits to end the strife :
    Death shall be thy life's beginning,
    And life's losing be the winning
     Of the true and better life.

    Fill'd with GOD's most Holy SPIRIT,
    See the Heav'n thou shalt inherit,
     Stephen, gaze into the skies :
    There GOD's glory steadfast viewing,
    Thence thy victor-strength renewing,
     Pant for thy eternal prize.

    See, as Jewish foes invade thee,
    See how JESUS stands to aid thee,
     Stands at GOD's right hand on high :
    Tell how open'd Heav'n is shown thee,
    Tell how JESUS waits to own thee,
     Tell it with thy latest cry.

p   As the dying Martyr kneeleth,
    For his murderers he appealeth,
     For their madness grieving sore ;
pp Then in CHRIST he sleepeth sweetly,
cr And with CHRIST he reigneth meetly,
ff   Martyr first-fruits, evermore.

ALTERNATIVE TUNE, HYMN 434.   J. M. NEALE and Compilers
                                   from Adam of St. Victor.

(51)

St. Stephen's Day.

Hymn 65. LÜBECK.—7 7 7 7.　　　　FREYLINGHAUSEN, *Gesangbuch*, 1704.

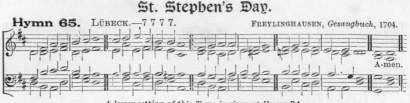

A-men.

A lower setting of this Tune is given at Hymn **34.**

"Be thou faithful unto death, and I will give thee a crown of life."

mf FIRST of Martyrs, thou whose name
　　Doth thy golden crown proclaim,
Not of flowers that fade away
Weave we this thy crown to-day.

Bright the stones which bruise thee gleam,
Sprinkled with thy life-blood's stream ;
Stars around thy sainted head
Never could such radiance shed.

Every wound upon thy brow
Sparkles with unearthly glow ;
Like an Angel's is thy face
Beaming with celestial grace.

Oh, how blessèd first to be
Slain for Him Who bled for thee ;
First like Him in dying hour
Witness to Almighty power ;

First to follow where He trod
Through the deep Red Sea of blood ;
First, but in thy footsteps press
Saints and Martyrs numberless.

f Glory to the FATHER be,
Glory, VIRGIN-BORN, to Thee,
Glory to the HOLY GHOST,
Praised by men and heavenly host.

I. WILLIAMS and Compilers : from
the Latin of J. B. de Santeuil.

St. John the Evangelist's Day.

Hymn 66. WHITWELL.—C.M.　　　　J. HOPKINS.

A - men.

*"That . . . which we have looked upon, and our hands have handled, of the Word of Life, . . .
declare we unto you."*

mf THE life, which GOD'S Incarnate WORD
　　Lived here below with men,
Three blest Evangelists record
With Heav'n-inspirèd pen :

John soars on high, beyond the three,
　To GOD the FATHER'S Throne ;
And shows in what deep mystery
The WORD with GOD is ONE.

p Upon the Saviour's loving Breast
Invited to recline,

'Twas thence he drew, in moments blest,
Rich stores of truth Divine :

mf And thence did that angelic love
His inmost spirit fill,
Which, once enkindled from above,
Breathes in his pages still.

f JESU, the Virgin's Holy SON,
We praise Thee and adore,
Who art with GOD the FATHER ONE
And SPIRIT evermore.

E. CASWALL : from the Latin.

ALTERNATIVE TUNE, HYMN 279.

Hymn 67. ALLELUIA DULCE CARMEN.—8 7. 8 7. 8 7.
　　　　Essay on the Church Plain Chant, 1782.

St. John the Evangelist's Day.

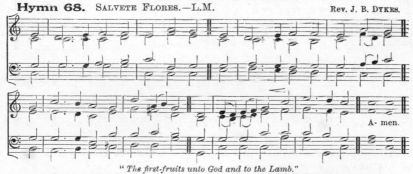

A-men

A lower setting of this Tune is given at Hymn 82.

" The disciple whom Jesus loved."

mf WORD Supreme, before creation
Born of GOD eternally,
Who didst will for our salvation
To be born on earth, and die ;
Well Thy Saints have kept their station,
Watching till Thine hour drew nigh.

Now 'tis come, and faith espies Thee ;
Like an eaglet in the morn,
One in steadfast worship eyes Thee,
Thy beloved, Thy latest born :
In Thy glory he descries Thee
Reigning from the Tree of scorn.

p He upon Thy Bosom lying
Thy true tokens learn'd by heart ;
And Thy dearest pledge in dying,
LORD, Thou didst to him impart ;
Show'dst him how, all grace supplying,
Blood and water from Thee start.

mf He first, hoping and believing,
Did beside the grave adore ;
Latest he, the warfare leaving,
Landed on the eternal shore ;
And his witness we receiving
Own Thee LORD for evermore.

Much he ask'd in loving wonder,
On Thy Bosom leaning, LORD ;
In that secret place of thunder
Answer kind didst Thou accord,
Wisdom for Thy Church to ponder
Till the day of dread award.

Lo ! Heav'n's doors lift up, revealing
How Thy judgments earthward move ;
Scrolls unfolded, trumpets pealing,
Wine cups from the wrath above ;
p Yet o'er all a soft voice stealing—
" Little children, trust and love !"

f Thee, the Almighty King Eternal,
FATHER of the Eternal WORD,
Thee, the FATHER'S WORD Supernal,
Thee, of Both, the BREATH adored,
Heaven, and earth, and realms infernal
Own ONE glorious GOD and LORD.

J. KEBLE.

ALTERNATIVE TUNE (PLAINSONG), HYMN 396.
Hymn 458 is also suitable.

The Innocents' Day.

Hymn 68. SALVETE FLORES.—L.M.

Rev. J. B. DYKES.

A- men.

" The first-fruits unto God and to the Lamb."

mf SWEET flow'rets of the martyr band,
p So early pluck'd by cruel hand ;
Like rosebuds by a tempest torn,
As breaks the light of summer morn ;

First victims offer'd for the LORD,
cr Ye little knew your high reward,
mf As, at the very altar, gay
With palms and crowns ye seem'd to play.

Ah ! what avail'd King Herod's wrath ?
He could not stay your Saviour's path :
cr The Child he sought alone went free ;
f That Child is King eternally.

O LORD, the Virgin-born, to Thee
Praise, honour, might, and glory be,
Whom with the FATHER we adore
And HOLY GHOST for evermore.

Sir H. W. BAKER : from Prudentius.

For Proper Plainsong Melody see Hymn 177.
ALTERNATIVE TUNE, HYMN 449 (SECOND TUNE).

The Innocents' Day.

Hymn 69. St. Helena.—S.M.

B. Milgrove (Mount Ephraim), 1769.

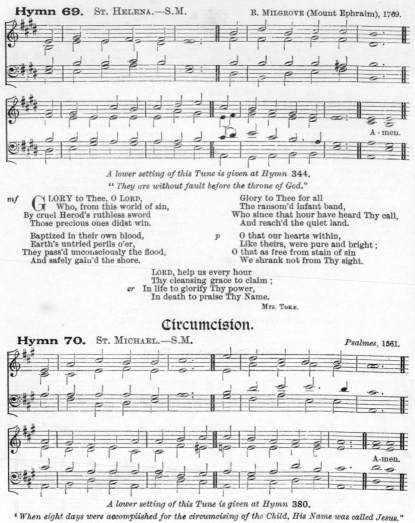

A - men.

A lower setting of this Tune is given at Hymn 344.

" They are without fault before the throne of God."

mf GLORY to Thee, O Lord,
　　Who, from this world of sin,
By cruel Herod's ruthless sword
　　Those precious ones didst win.

　　Baptized in their own blood,
　　Earth's untried perils o'er,
They pass'd unconsciously the flood,
　　And safely gain'd the shore.

Glory to Thee for all
　　The ransom'd infant band,
Who since that hour have heard Thy call,
　　And reach'd the quiet land.

p O that our hearts within,
　　Like theirs, were pure and bright ;
　　O that as free from stain of sin
　　We shrank not from Thy sight.

　　Lord, help us every hour
　　　Thy cleansing grace to claim ;
cr In life to glorify Thy power,
　　　In death to praise Thy Name.

Mrs. Toke.

Circumcision.

Hymn 70. St. Michael.—S.M.

Psalmes, 1561.

A - men.

A lower setting of this Tune is given at Hymn 380.

' When eight days were accomplished for the circumcising of the Child, His Name was called Jesus."

mf THE ancient law departs,
　　And all its terrors cease ;
For Jesus makes with faithful hearts
　　A covenant of peace.

　　The Light of Light Divine,
　　True Brightness undefiled,
He bears for us the shame of sin,
　　A Holy Spotless Child.

p His Infant Body now
　　Begins our pain to feel ;
Those precious drops of Blood that flow
　　For death the victim seal.

mf To-day the Name is Thine
　　At which we bend the knee ;
They call Thee Jesus, Child Divine,
　　Our Jesus deign to be.

f All praise, Eternal Son,
　　For Thy redeeming love,
With Father, Spirit, ever One,
　　In glorious might above.

Compilers : from the Latin of S. Besnault.

(56)

Circumcision.

Hymn 71. ALFRETON.—L.M. *Supplement to the New Version,* 1708.

A - men.

" *God sent forth His Son, made of a woman, made under the law, to redeem them that were under the law.*"

mf O BLESSÈD day, when first was pour'd
　　The Blood of our Redeeming LORD !
　　O blessèd day, when first began
p　His sufferings borne for sinful man !
　　Scarce enter'd on this life of woe,
　　His Infant Blood begins to flow ;
　　A foretaste of His death He feels,
cr　An earnest of His love reveals.

mf From Heav'n descending to fulfil
　　The bidding of His FATHER'S Will,
p　A victim even now He lies
　　Before the day of sacrifice.

mf For love of us His woes begin ;
　　The Sinless suffers for our sin ;

The Law's great Maker for our aid
Obedient to the Law is made.

p　The wound He through the Law endures
cr　Our freedom from that Law secures ;
　　Henceforth a holier law prevails,
　　The law of love which never fails.

mf LORD, circumcise our hearts, we pray,
　　And take what is not Thine away ;
　　Write Thine own Name within our hearts,
　　Thy law upon our inmost parts.

f　O LORD, the Virgin-born, to Thee
　　Eternal praise and glory be.
　　Whom with the FATHER we adore
　　And HOLY GHOST for evermore.

J. CHANDLER and Compilers :
from the Latin of S. Besnault.

ALTERNATIVE TUNE (PLAINSONG), HYMN 9 (FIRST TUNE).
The following Hymns are suitable for this Festival :
175 Conquering kings their titles take.　　**179** To the Name of our Salvation.

New Year's Day.

Hymn 72. TALLIS.—C.M.　　T. TALLIS, 1567.

A - men.

A lower setting of this Tune is given at Hymn **78.**
" *And now, Lord, what is my hope ; truly my hope is even in Thee.*"

mf THE year is gone, beyond recall,
　　With all its hopes and fears,
　　With all its bright and gladdening smiles,
p　With all its mourners' tears :

mf Thy thankful people praise Thee, LORD,
　　For countless gifts received ;
　　And pray for grace to keep the Faith
　　Which Saints of old believed.

　　To Thee we come, O gracious LORD,
　　The new-born year to bless ;
　　Defend our land from pestilence ;
　　Give peace and plenteousness ;

　　Forgive this nation's many sins ;
　　The growth of vice restrain ;

And help us all with sin to strive,
And crowns of life to gain.

From evil deeds that stain the past
　We now desire to flee ;
And pray that future years may all
　Be spent, good LORD, for Thee.

O FATHER, let Thy watchful Eye
　Still look on us in love,
That we may praise Thee, year by year,
　With Angel-hosts above.

f　All glory to the FATHER be,
　　All glory to the SON,
　　All glory, HOLY GHOST, to Thee,
　　While endless ages run.

F PITT and Compilers : from the Latin.

New Year's Day.

Hymn 73. CULBACH.—7 7 7 7. SCHEFFLER, *Heilige Seelenlust*, 1657.

A - men.

A higher setting of this Tune is given at Hymn 297.

" So teach us to number our days, that we may apply our hearts unto wisdom."

mf FOR Thy mercy and Thy grace,
   Faithful through another year,
Hear our song of thankfulness ;
JESU, our Redeemer, hear.

In our weakness and distress,
Rock of strength, be Thou our Stay ;
In the pathless wilderness
Be our true and living Way.

p Who of us death's awful road
In the coming year shall tread,

With Thy rod and staff, O GOD,
Comfort Thou his dying bed.

mf Keep us faithful, keep us pure,
Keep us evermore Thine own,
Help, O help us to endure,
Fit us for Thy promised crown.

f So within Thy palace gate
We shall praise, on golden strings,
Thee the only Potentate,
LORD of lords and King of kings.

H. DOWNTON.

Hymn 74. FATHER, LET ME DEDICATE.—7 5 7 5. 7 5 7 5. (*First Tune.*)

Sir G. A. MACFARREN.

A - men.

Hymn 74. PERRANPORTH.—7 5 7 5. 7 5 7 5. (*Second Tune.*) A. W. WILSON.

New Year's Day.

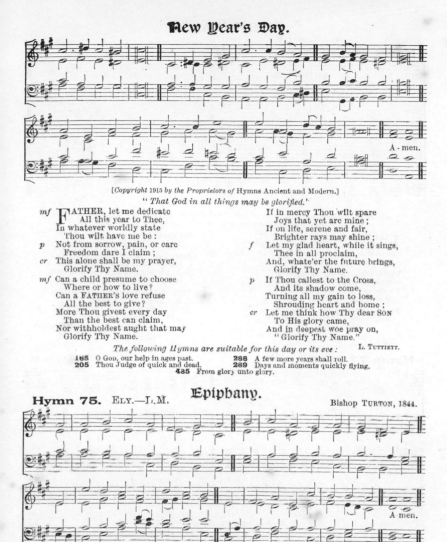

A - men.

" *That God in all things may be glorified.*"

mf FATHER, let me dedicate
    All this year to Thee,
In whatever worldly state
    Thou wilt have me be :
p Not from sorrow, pain, or care
    Freedom dare I claim ;
cr This alone shall be my prayer,
    Glorify Thy Name.

mf Can a child presume to choose
    Where or how to live ?
Can a FATHER'S love refuse
    All the best to give ?
More Thou givest every day
    Than the best can claim,
Nor withholdest aught that may
    Glorify Thy Name.

If in mercy Thou wilt spare
    Joys that yet are mine ;
If on life, serene and fair,
    Brighter rays may shine ;
f Let my glad heart, while it sings,
    Thee in all proclaim,
And, whate'er the future brings,
    Glorify Thy Name.

p If Thou callest to the Cross,
    And its shadow come,
Turning all my gain to loss,
    Shrouding heart and home ;
cr Let me think how Thy dear SON
    To His glory came,
And in deepest woe pray on,
    " Glorify Thy Name."

L. TUTTIETT.

The following Hymns are suitable for this day or its eve :

185 O GOD, our help in ages past.   **288** A few more years shall roll.
205 Thou Judge of quick and dead.   **289** Days and moments quickly flying.
    485 From glory unto glory.

Epiphany.

Hymn 75. ELY.—L.M.

Bishop TURTON, 1844.

A men.

A lower setting of this Tune is given at Hymn 425.

" *The Life was manifested, and we have seen it.*"

mf HOW vain the cruel Herod's fear,
    When told that CHRIST the King is
He takes not earthly realms away,   [near !
Who gives the realms that ne'er decay.

The Eastern sages saw from far
And follow'd on His guiding star ;
By light their way to Light they trod,
And by their gifts confess'd their GOD.

Within the Jordan's sacred flood
The heavenly LAMB in meekness stood,

That He, to Whom no sin was known,
Might cleanse His people from their own.

And oh, what miracle Divine,
When water redden'd into wine !
He spake the word, and forth it flow'd
In streams that nature ne'er bestow'd.

f All glory, JESU, be to Thee
For this Thy glad Epiphany :
Whom with the FATHER we adore
And HOLY GHOST for evermore.

J. M. NEALE and Compilers : from Sedulius.

For Proper Plainsong Tune see Hymn 486.

Epiphany.

Hymn 76. STUTTGART.—8 7 8 7.   C. F. WITT, 1715.

A-men.

"And thou, Bethlehem, in the land of Juda, art not the least among the princes of Juda ; for out of thee shall come a Governor, that shall rule My people Israel."

mf EARTH has many a noble city ;
    Bethlehem, thou dost all excel :
Out of thee the LORD from Heaven
    Came to rule His Israel.

Fairer than the sun at morning
    Was the star that told His birth,
To the world its GOD announcing
    Seen in fleshly form on earth.

Eastern sages at His cradle
    Make oblations rich and rare ;

See them give, in deep devotion,
    Gold, and frankincense, and myrrh.

Sacred gifts of mystic meaning ;
    Incense doth their GOD disclose,
p Gold the King of kings proclaimeth,
    Myrrh His sepulchre foreshows.

f JESU, Whom the Gentiles worshipp'd
    At Thy glad Epiphany,
Unto Thee, with GOD the FATHER
    And the SPIRIT, glory be.

         E. CASWALL and Compilers :
         from Prudentius.

Hymn 77. SYDNEY.—L.M.   J. HOPKINS.

A-men.

"We have seen His star in the east."

f WHAT star is this, with beams so bright,
    More beauteous than the noonday
It shines to herald forth the King,   [light ?
And Gentiles to His cradle bring.

mf See now fulfill'd what GOD decreed,
    "From Jacob shall a star proceed ;"
And Eastern sages with amaze
Upon the wondrous vision gaze.

The guiding star above is bright ;
    Within them shines a clearer light,
Which leads them on with power benign
To seek the Giver of the sign.

True love can brook no dull delay ;
    Nor toil nor dangers stop their way :
Home, kindred, fatherland, and all
They leave at their Creator's call.

p O JESU, while the star of grace
    Allures us now to seek Thy Face,
Let not our slothful hearts refuse
The guidance of that light to use.

f All glory, JESU, be to Thee
    For this Thy glad Epiphany,
Whom with the FATHER we adore
And HOLY GHOST for evermore.

         J. CHANDLER and Compilers :
         from the Latin of C. Coffin.

ALTERNATIVE TUNES, HYMN 9 (PLAINSONG) AND HYMN 723.

Epiphany.

Hymn 78. TALLIS.—C.M.

T. TALLIS, 1567.

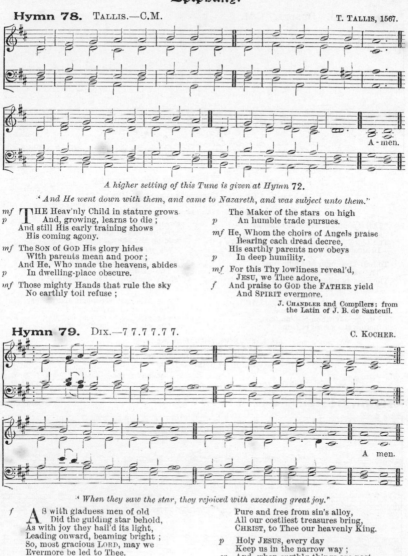

A - men.

A higher setting of this Tune is given at Hymn 72.

'And He went down with them, and came to Nazareth, and was subject unto them.'

mf THE Heav'nly Child in stature grows
p   And, growing, learns to die ;
And still His early training shows
His coming agony.

mf The SON of GOD His glory hides
With parents mean and poor ;
And He, Who made the heavens, abides
p In dwelling-place obscure.

mf Those mighty Hands that rule the sky
No earthly toil refuse ;

The Maker of the stars on high
p   An humble trade pursues.

mf He, Whom the choirs of Angels praise
Bearing each dread decree,
His earthly parents now obeys
p In deep humility.

mf For this Thy lowliness reveal'd,
JESU, we Thee adore,
f And praise to GOD the FATHER yield
And SPIRIT evermore.

J. CHANDLER and Compilers : from
the Latin of J. B. de Santeuil.

Hymn 79. DIX.—7 7.7 7.7 7.

C. KOCHER.

A men.

'When they saw the star, they rejoiced with exceeding great joy.'

f AS with gladness men of old
   Did the guiding star behold,
As with joy they hail'd its light,
Leading onward, beaming bright ;
So, most gracious LORD, may we
Evermore be led to Thee.

mf As with joyful steps they sped,
Saviour, to Thy lowly bed,
There to bend the knee before
Thee Whom Heav'n and earth adore ;
So may we with willing feet
Ever seek Thy mercy-seat.

As they offer'd gifts most rare
At Thy cradle rude and bare ;
So may we with holy joy,

Pure and free from sin's alloy,
All our costliest treasures bring,
CHRIST, to Thee our heavenly King.

p Holy JESUS, every day
Keep us in the narrow way ;
cr And, when earthly things are past,
Bring our ransom'd souls at last
mf Where they need no star to guide,
Where no clouds Thy glory hide.

f In the Heav'nly country bright
Need they no created light ;
Thou its Light, its Joy, its Crown,
Thou its Sun which goes not down ;
ff There for ever may we sing
Alleluias to our King.

W. C. DIX.

Epiphany.

Hymn 80. Dundee.—C.M. Psalms (Edinburgh, 1615).

A - men.

A lower setting of this Tune is given at Hymns 41, 221.

A setting with Alternative Harmonies is given at Hymn 221.

" The people which sat in darkness saw great light."

mf THE people that in darkness sat
　A glorious light have seen ;
The Light has shined on them who long
　In shades of death have been.

f To hail Thee, Sun of Righteousness,
　The gathering nations come ;
They joy as when the reapers bear
　Their harvest treasures home.

For Thou their burden dost remove,
　And break the tyrant's rod,
As in the day when Midian fell
　Before the sword of God.

For unto us a Child is born,
　To us a Son is given,
And on His Shoulder ever rests
　All power in earth and heaven.

His Name shall be the Prince of peace,
　The Everlasting Lord,
The Wonderful, the Counsellor,
　The God by all adored.

His righteous government and power
　Shall over all extend ;
On judgment and on justice based,
　His reign shall have no end.

mf Lord Jesus, reign in us, we pray,
　And make us Thine alone,
f Who with the Father ever art
　And Holy Spirit One.

J. Morrison, 1770.

Hymn 81. St. Edmund.—7 7 7 7. 7 7 7 7. C. Steggall.

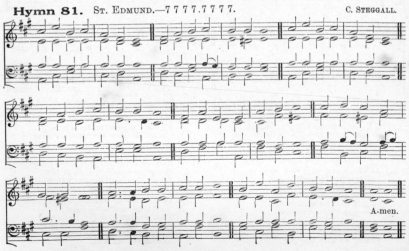

A-men.

Epiphany.

"The Son of God was manifested."

mf SONGS of thankfulness and praise,
  Jesu, Lord, to Thee we raise,
Manifested by the star
To the Sages from afar ;
Branch of royal David's stem
In Thy Birth at Bethlehem ;
f Anthems be to Thee addrest,
God in Man made manifest.

mf Manifest at Jordan's stream,
Prophet, Priest, and King supreme ;
And at Cana wedding-guest
In Thy Godhead manifest ;
Manifest in power Divine,
Changing water into wine ;
f Anthems be to Thee addrest,
God in Man made manifest.

mf Manifest in making whole
Palsied limbs and fainting soul ;
Manifest in valiant fight,
Quelling all the devil's might ;

Manifest in gracious will,
Ever bringing good from ill ;
f Anthems be to Thee addrest,
God in Man made manifest.

p Sun and Moon shall darken'd be,
Stars shall fall, the heavens shall flee ;
cr Christ will then like lightning shine,
mf All will see His glorious Sign ;
All will then the trumpet hear,
All will see the Judge appear ;
f Thou by all wilt be confest,
God in Man made manifest.

mf Grant us grace to see Thee, Lord,
Mirror'd in Thy holy Word ;
May we imitate Thee now,
And be pure, as pure art Thou ;
That we like to Thee may be
At Thy great Epiphany ;
f And may praise Thee, ever Blest,
God in Man made manifest.

Bishop C. Wordsworth.

From the Octave of the Epiphany to Septuagesima General Hymns may be sung ; especially

For the Week before Septuagesima.

Hymn 32. Alleluia dulce carmen.—8 7. 8 7. 8 7.

Essay on the Church Plain Chant, 1782.

A - men.

A higher setting of this Tune is given at Hymn **67.**

"And again they said, Alleluia."

f ALLELUIA, song of sweetness,
  Voice of joy that cannot die ;
Alleluia is the anthem
Ever dear to choirs on high ;
In the house of God abiding
Thus they sing eternally.

Alleluia thou resoundest,
True Jerusalem and free ;
Alleluia, joyful Mother,
All thy children sing with thee ;
p But by Babylon's sad waters
Mourning exiles now are we.

Alleluia cannot always
Be our song while here below ;
Alleluia our transgressions
Make us for awhile forego ;
For the solemn time is coming
When our tears for sin must flow.

mf Therefore in our hymns we pray Thee
Grant us, Blessèd Trinity,
At the last to keep Thine Easter
In our Home beyond the sky,
f There to Thee for ever singing
Alleluia joyfully.

J. M. Neale and Compilers : from the Latin.

Septuagesima.

Hymn 83. St. Gregory.—L.M.

Darmstadt Gesangbuch, 1698.

A - men.

A lower setting of this Tune is given at Hymn 95.

" How shall we sing the Lord's song in a strange land ?"

mf CREATOR of the world, to Thee
    An endless rest of joy belongs ;
And heavenly choirs are ever free
To sing on high their festal songs.

p But we are fallen creatures here,
Where pain and sorrow daily come ;
And how can we in exile drear
Sing out, as they, sweet songs of Home ?

mf O FATHER, Who dost promise still
    That they who mourn shall blessèd be,
p Grant us to weep for deeds of ill
    That banish us so long from Thee :

But, weeping, grant us faith to rest
In hope upon Thy loving care ;
cr Till Thou restore us, with the blest,
mf Their songs of praise in Heav'n to share.

f To FATHER, SON, and HOLY GHOST,
    The GOD Whom Heav'n and earth adore,
From men and from the Angel-host
Be praise and glory evermore.

Compilers· from the Latin.

From Septuagesima Sunday to Lent the Hymns for Sunday and the other days of the week should be sung ; and the following Hymns are also suitable :

For Septuagesima :
162 Have mercy on us, GOD most High.
168 There is a book, who runs may read.
489 O GOD, the joy of Heav'n above.

For Sexagesima :
172 Praise to the Holiest in the height.
For Quinquagesima :
210 Gracious SPIRIT, HOLY GHOST.
262 Great Mover of all hearts.

Lent.

Hymn 84. Hereford.—C.M.

Rev. Sir F. A. G. OUSELEY.

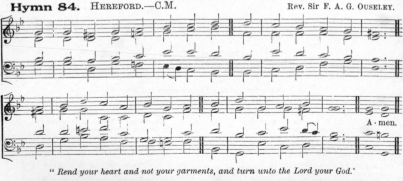

A - men.

" Rend your heart and not your garments, and turn unto the Lord your God."

p ONCE more the solemn season calls
    A holy fast to keep ;
And now within the temple walls
Let priest and people weep.

mf But vain all outward sign of grief,
    And vain the form of prayer,
Unless the heart implore relief,
And penitence be there.

(62)

Lent.

We smite the breast, we weep in vain,
  In vain in ashes mourn,
Unless with penitential pain
  The smitten soul be torn.

p   In sorrow true then let us pray
  To our offended GOD,
From us to turn His wrath away,
  And stay the uplifted rod.

O GOD, our Judge and Father, deign
  To spare the bruisèd reed ;
We pray for time to turn again,
  For grace to turn indeed.

mf Blest THREE in ONE, to Thee we bow :
  Vouchsafe us, in Thy love,
To gather from these fasts below
  Immortal fruit above.

J. CHANDLER and Compilers
from the Latin.

Hymn 85. SAXONY.—L.M.   *Christlichs Gesangbüchlein*, 1568.

A - men.

*" Now, saith the Lord, turn ye even to Me with all your heart, and with fasting, and with
weeping, and with mourning."*

mf BY precepts taught of ages past,
  Now let us keep again the fast
Which, year by year, in order meet
Of forty days is made complete.

The law and seers that were of old
In divers ways this Lent foretold,
Which CHRIST Himself, the LORD and Guide
Of every season, sanctified.

More sparing therefore let us make
The words we speak, the food we take,
Deny ourselves in mirth and sleep,
In stricter watch our senses keep.

In prayer together let us fall,
And cry for mercy, one and all ;
And weep before the Judge, and say,
p O turn from us Thy wrath away.

Thy grace have we offended sore
By sins, O GOD, which we deplore ;
Pour down upon us from above
The riches of Thy pardoning love.

Remember, LORD, though frail we be,
That yet Thine handiwork are we :
Nor let the honour of Thy Name
Be by another put to shame.

Forgive the ill that we have wrought,
Increase the good that we have sought ;
That we at length, our wanderings o'er,
May please Thee now and evermore

mf Blest THREE in ONE, and ONE in THREE,
Almighty GOD, we pray to Thee,
That Thou wouldst now vouchsafe to bless
Our fast with fruits of righteousness.

J. M. NEALE and Compilers from the Latin.

ALTERNATIVE TUNE, HYMN 516 (SECOND TUNE).

Lent.

Hymn 86. INNSBRUCK.—8 8 6. 8 8 6.
Old Volkslied. H. ISAAC (?).

A-men.

A higher setting of this Tune is given at Hymn 276.

" In due season we shall reap, if we faint not."

mf O THOU Who dost to man accord
His highest prize, his best reward,
Thou Hope of all our race ;
JESU, to Thee we now draw near,
Our earnest supplications hear,
Who humbly seek Thy Face.

p With self-accusing voice within
Our conscience tells of many a sin
In thought, and word, and deed :
cr O cleanse that conscience from all stain,
The penitent restore again,
From every burthen freed.

mf If Thou reject us, who shall give
Our fainting spirits strength to live ?
'Tis Thine alone to spare ;
With cleansèd hearts to pray aright,
And find acceptance in Thy sight,
Be this our lowly prayer.

'Tis Thou hast bless'd this solemn fast ;
So may its days by us be pass'd
In self-control severe,
cr That, when our Easter morn we hail,
Its mystic feast we may not fail
To keep with conscience clear.

mf O Blessèd TRINITY, bestow
Thy pardoning grace on us below,
And shield us evermore ;
cr Until, within Thy courts above,
We see Thy Face, and sing Thy love,
And with Thy Saints adore.

J. W. HEWETT : from the Latin.

Hymn 87. FORD.—L.M.
T. FORD, 1614.

A-men.

Lent.

" O deliver us, and be merciful unto our sins, for Thy Name's sake."

p O MERCIFUL CREATOR, hear ;
In tender pity bow Thine ear :
Accept the tearful prayer we raise
In this our fast of forty days.

Each heart is manifest to Thee ;
Thou knowest our infirmity :
Repentant now we seek Thy Face ;
cr Impart to us Thy pardoning grace.

p Our sins are manifold and sore,
But spare Thou them who sin deplore ;

And for Thine own Name's sake make whole
The fainting and the weary soul.

Grant us to mortify each sense
By means of outward abstinence,
That so from every stain of sin
The soul may keep her fast within.

mf Blest THREE in ONE, and ONE in THREE,
Almighty GOD, we pray to Thee,
That Thou wouldst now vouchsafe to bless
Our fast with fruits of righteousness.

J. M. NEALE : from the Latin.

ALTERNATIVE TUNE, HYMN 658 (SECOND TUNE).

Hymn 88. WEIMAR.—L.M. *(First Tune.)* German.

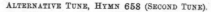

A - men.

Hymn 88. PRESERVE US, LORD.—L.M. *(Second Tune.)* Mediæval Melody.

A - men.

" Behold, now is the accepted time ; behold, now is the day of salvation."

mf LO ! now is our accepted day,
The time for purging sins away,
The sins of thought, and deed, and word,
That we have done against the LORD.

For He the Merciful and True
Hath spared His people hitherto ;
Not willing that the soul should die,
Though great its past iniquity.

p Then let us all with earnest care,
And contrite fast, and tear, and prayer,

And works of mercy and of love,
Entreat for pardon from above ;

mf That He may all our sins efface,
Adorn us with the gifts of grace,
And join us to the Angel band
For ever in the heavenly land.

Blest THREE in ONE and ONE in THREE,
Almighty GOD, we pray to Thee,
That Thou wouldst now vouchsafe to bless
Our fast with fruits of righteousness.

J. M. NEALE and Compilers : from the Latin.

(65)

D

Lent.

Hymn 89. JEJUNIA.—7 7 7 7. *(First Tune.)*   Sir J. STAINER.

Amen.

Hymn 89. NUN KOMM.—7 7 7 7. *(Second Tune.)*   Medieval Melody.

A-men.

" Then shall they fast in those days."

mf GOOD it is to keep the fast
Shadow'd forth in ages past,
Which our own Almighty LORD
Hallow'd by His deed and word.

Moses, while he fasted, saw
GOD Who gave by him the Law ;
To Elijah Angels came,
Steeds of fire and car of flame.

So was Daniel meet to gaze
On the sight of latter days,

And the Baptist to proclaim
Blessings through the Bridegroom's Name.

p Grant us, LORD, like them to be
Oft in prayer and fast with Thee ;

cr Fill us with Thy heavenly might,
Be our joy and true delight.

p FATHER, hear us through Thy SON,
And the SPIRIT, with Thee ONE,

cr Whom our thankful hearts adore
Ever and for evermore.

       Sir H. W. BAKER : from St. Gregory.

Hymn 90. WINDSOR.—C.M.   DAMON, *Psalms*, 1591.

A - men.

Hymn 90. WINDSOR.—C.M. *(Alternative Version.)*

CONGREGATION.   Harmonised by J. ARNOLD, 1741.

CHOIR.

Lent.

"I sat down and wept, and mourned certain days, and fasted, and prayed before the God of heaven."

mf JESU, our Lenten fast of Thee
    We duteous learn to keep,
A healing time, by Thy decree,
    For all Thy wounded sheep;

A time in which towards Paradise,
    Once lost by carnal sense,
The souls redeem'd by Thee may rise
    Through chastening abstinence.

Now with Thy Church be present, LORD,
    In all Thy saving grace,
And hear us as with one accord,
p   Mourning, we seek Thy Face.

Most Merciful, forgive the past.
    The sins which we deplore ;
Thy sheltering arms around us cast,
    That we may sin no more.

mf To Thee our sacrifice we bring
    Of Lenten fast and prayer.
cr Till, cleansed by Thee, our GOD and King,
f   Thy Paschal joy we share.

mf Grant this, O FATHER, through Thy SON,
    And through the SPIRIT Blest,
Who art with Them for ever ONE,
    Eternally confest.

Compilers: from the Latin.

The Alternative Version may be used for verses 2, 4, 6.

Hymn 91. ST. ANDREW OF CRETE.—6 5 6 5.6 5 6 5.

Rev. J. B. DYKES.

Unison in verses 1, 2, 3.   *Harmony.*

A - men.

"Whom resist, steadfast in the faith."

p CHRISTIAN, dost thou see them
    On the holy ground,
cr How the troops of Midian
dim   Prowl and prowl around?
ff Christian, up and smite them,
    Counting gain but loss ;
Smite them by the merit
    Of the holy Cross.

p Christian, dost thou feel them,
    How they work within,
cr Striving, tempting, luring,
    Goading into sin?
f Christian, never tremble ;
    Never be down-cast ;
Smite them by the virtue
    Of the Lenten fast.

p Christian, dost thou hear them,
    How they speak thee fair?
cr "Always fast and vigil ?
    Always watch and prayer?"
ff Christian, answer boldly,
    "While I breathe I pray :"
p Peace shall follow battle,
f   Night shall end in day.

mf "Well I know thy trouble,
    O My servant true ;
Thou art very weary,—
p   I was weary too ;
f But that toil shall make thee
    Some day all Mine own,
And the end of sorrow
ff   Shall be near My Throne."

ALTERNATIVE TUNE, HYMN 749.   J. M. NEALE: from the Greek.

Lent.

Hymn 92. HEINLEIN.—7 7 7 7.

Nürnbergisches Gesangbuch, 1676.

A-men.

" And Jesus . . . was led by the Spirit into the wilderness, being forty days tempted of the devil. And in those days He did eat nothing."

mf FORTY days and forty nights
 Thou wast fasting in the wild ;
Forty days and forty nights
Tempted, and yet undefiled.

Sunbeams scorching all the day ;
Chilly dew-drops nightly shed ;
Prowling beasts about Thy way ;
Stones Thy pillow ; earth Thy bed.

Shall not we Thy sorrow share,
And from earthly joys abstain,
Fasting with unceasing prayer,
Glad with Thee to suffer pain?

And if Satan, vexing sore,
 Flesh or spirit should assail,
cr Thou, His Vanquisher before,
 Grant we may not faint nor fail.

p So shall we have peace Divine ;
cr Holier gladness ours shall be ;
 Round us too shall Angels shine,
dim Such as minister'd to Thee.

mf Keep, O keep us, Saviour dear,
 Ever constant by Thy side ;
f That with Thee we may appear
 At th' eternal Eastertide.

G. H. SMYTTAN and F. POTT.

Hymn 93. ST. MARY.—C.M.

PRYS, Psalms, 1621.

A - men.

" Enter not into judgment with Thy servant ; for in Thy sight shall no man living be justified.'

p O LORD, turn not Thy Face from me,
 Who lie in woeful state,
Lamenting all my sinful life
 Before Thy mercy-gate ;

A gate which opens wide to those
 That do lament their sin ;
Shut not that gate against me, LORD,
 But let me enter in.

And call me not to strict account
 How I have sojourn'd here ;
For then my guilty conscience knows
 How vile I shall appear.

Mercy, Good LORD, mercy I ask ;
 This is my humble prayer ;
For mercy, LORD, is all my suit,
 O let Thy mercy spare.

J. MARCKANT, 1562.

Hymn 94. ST. PHILIP.—7 7 7. *(First Tune.)*

W. H. MONK.

A - men.

Lent.

Hymn 94. CONSOLATION.—7 7 7. (*Second Tune.*)

Vollständige Psalmen (Bremen, 1639).

A - men.

" My soul fleeth unto the Lord."

p LORD, in this Thy mercy's day,
Ere it pass for aye away,
On our knees we fall and pray.

Holy JESU, grant us tears,
Fill us with heart-searching fears,
Ere that awful doom appears.

mf LORD, on us Thy SPIRIT pour
Kneeling lowly at the door,
Ere it close for evermore.

pp By Thy night of agony,
By Thy supplicating cry,
By Thy willingness to die ;

By Thy tears of bitter woe
For Jerusalem below,
Let us not Thy love forego.

p Grant us 'neath Thy wings a place,
cr Lest we lose this day of grace
mf Ere we shall behold Thy Face.

I. WILLIAMS.

Hymn 95. ST. GREGORY.—L.M.

Darmstadt Gesangbuch, 1698.

A-men.

A higher setting of this Tune is given at Hymn **83**.

" I am the Light of the World."

FOR A LATE EVENING SERVICE.

f O CHRIST, Who art the Light and Day,
Thy beams chase night's dark shades away ;
The very Light of Light Thou art,
Who dost Thy blessèd Light impart.

mf All-Holy LORD, to Thee we bend,
Thy servants through this night defend,
And grant us calm repose in Thee,
A quiet night from peril free.

Let not the tempter round us creep
With thoughts of evil while we sleep,
Nor with his wiles the flesh allure
And make us in Thy sight impure.

While wearied eyes light slumber take,
The heart to Thee be still awake,

And Thy right Hand stretch'd forth above
Protect the children of Thy love.

O LORD, our strong Defence, be nigh ;
Bid all the powers of darkness fly ;
Preserve and watch o'er us for good,
Whom Thou hast purchased with Thy Blood.

p Remember us, dear LORD, we pray,
While burden'd in the flesh we stay ;
cr 'Tis Thou alone our souls canst keep ;
Abide with us this night in sleep.

mf Blest THREE in ONE, and ONE in THREE,
Almighty GOD, we pray to Thee,
That Thou wouldst now vouchsafe to bless
Our fast with fruits of righteousness.

W. J. COPELAND and Compilers : from the Latin.

ALTERNATIVE TUNE (PLAINSONG), HYMN 15.

The following Hymns, and some of the Hymns on the Passion, are suitable for this season :

The Fifth Sunday in Lent.

OTHERWISE CALLED PASSION SUNDAY.

Hymn 96. VEXILLA REGIS.—L.M. *(First Tune.)* *(First Version.)*

To be sung in Unison.

Proper Sarum Melody.

For Alternative Version of this Tune, see page 71.

Hymn 96. ST. CECILIA.—L.M. *(Second Tune.)*

REV. J. HAMPTON.

" God forbid that I should glory, save in the Cross of our Lord Jesus Christ."

f THE Royal Banners forward go,
    The Cross shines forth in mystic glow ;
Where He in Flesh, our flesh Who made,
Our sentence bore, our ransom paid.

mf There whilst He hung, His sacred Side
    By soldier's spear was open'd wide,
To cleanse us in the precious flood
Of Water mingled with His Blood.

f Fulfill'd is now what David told
    In true prophetic song of old,
How GOD the heathen's King should be ;
ff For GOD is reigning from the Tree.

mf O Tree of glory, Tree most fair,
    Ordain'd those Holy Limbs to bear,
How bright in purple robe it stood,
p The purple of a Saviour's Blood !

mf Upon its arms, like balance true,
    He weigh'd the price for sinners due,
The price which none but He could pay,
f And spoil'd the spoiler of his prey.

To Thee, Eternal THREE in ONE ;
    Let homage meet by all be done :
As by the Cross Thou dost restore,
So rule and guide us evermore.

ALTERNATIVE TUNE, HYMN 771.

J. M. NEALE and Compilers ·
from Venantius Fortunatus.

This Hymn may be sung daily till Thursday before Easter.

(70)

The Fifth Sunday in Lent.

OTHERWISE CALLED PASSION SUNDAY.

Hymn 96. VEXILLA REGIS.—L.M. *(First Tune.)* *(Alternative Version.)*

"God forbid that I should glory, save in the Cross of our Lord Jesus Christ."

Proper Sarum Melody.

The Roy - al Ban - ners for - ward go, The Cross shines forth in
There whilst He hung, His sa - cred Side By sol - dier's spear was
Ful - fill'd is now what Da - vid told In true pro - phe - tic
O Tree of glo - ry, Tree most fair, Or - dain'd those Ho - ly
Up - on its arms, like bal - ance true, He weigh'd the price for
To Thee, E - ter - nal THREE in ONE, Let hom - age meet by

mys - tic glow; Where He in Flesh, our flesh Who made,
o - pen'd wide, To cleanse us in the pre - cious flood
song of old, How GOD the hea - then's King should be ;
Limbs to bear, How bright in pur - ple robe it stood,
sin - ners due, The price which none but He could pay,
all be done; As by the Cross Thou dost re - store,

Our sen - tence bore, our ran - som paid.
Of Wa - ter min - gled with His Blood.
For GOD is reign - ing from the Tree.
The pur - ple of a Sa - viour's Blood !
And spoil'd the spoil - er of his prey.
So rule and guide us ev - er - more. A - men.

J. M. NEALE and Compilers: from Venantius Fortunatus.

This Hymn may be sung daily till Thursday before Easter.

(71)

The Fifth Sunday in Lent.

OTHERWISE CALLED PASSION SUNDAY.

Hymn 97. PANGE LINGUA.—8 7. 8 7. 8 7.   Proper Sarum Melody.

To be sung in Unison.

A better form of this Melody is given at Hymn 309.
A lower setting of this Tune is given at Hymn 309.

" The Cross of our Lord Jesus Christ."

f SING, my tongue, the glorious battle,
 Sing the last, the dread affray ;
O'er the Cross, the Victor's trophy,
 Sound the high triumphal lay,
p How, the pains of death enduring,
f Earth's Redeemer won the day.

mf He, our Maker, deeply grieving
 That the first-made Adam fell,
When he ate the fruit forbidden
 Whose reward was death and hell,
Mark'd e'en then this Tree the ruin
 Of the first tree to dispel.

Thus the work for our salvation
 He ordainèd to be done ;
To the traitor's art opposing
 Art yet deeper than his own ;
Thence the remedy procuring
 Whence the fatal wound begun.

Therefore, when at length the fulness
 Of the appointed time was come,
He was sent, the world's Creator,
 From the FATHER'S heavenly home,
And was found in human fashion,
 Offspring of the Virgin's womb.

p Lo ! He lies, an Infant weeping,
 Where the narrow manger stands,
While the Mother-Maid His members
 Wraps in mean and lowly bands,
And the swaddling clothes is winding
 Round His helpless Feet and Hands.

  PART 2.

mf Now the thirty years accomplish'd
 Which on earth He will'd to see,
Born for this, He meets His Passion,

Gives Himself an Offering free ;
 On the Cross the LAMB is lifted,
 There the Sacrifice to be.

p There the nails and spear He suffers,
 Vinegar, and gall, and reed ;
From His sacred Body piercèd
 Blood and Water both proceed ;
cr Precious flood, which all creation
 From the stain of sin hath freed.

f Faithful Cross, above all other
 One and only noble Tree,
None in foliage, none in blossom,
 None in fruit thy peer may be ;
Sweetest wood, and sweetest iron ;
 Sweetest weight is hung on thee.

mf Bend, O lofty Tree, thy branches,
 Thy too rigid sinews bend ;
And awhile the stubborn hardness,
 Which thy birth bestow'd, suspend ;
And the Limbs of Heav'n's high Monarch
p Gently on thine arms extend.

mf Thou alone wast counted worthy
 This world's ransom to sustain,
That a shipwreck'd race for ever
 Might a port of refuge gain,
With the sacred Blood anointed
 Of the LAMB for sinners slain.

f Praise and honour to the FATHER,
 Praise and honour to the SON,
Praise and honour to the SPIRIT,
 Ever THREE and ever ONE,
One in might, and One in glory,
 While eternal ages run.

J. M. NEALE and Compilers :
from Venantius Fortunatus.

ALTERNATIVE TUNE, HYMN 309 (FOURTH TUNE).

This Hymn may be sung daily till Good Friday ; and the following Hymns are suitable :
 200 We sing the praise of Him Who died.   **467** Litany of the Passion.

The Sunday next before Easter.

OTHERWISE CALLED PALM SUNDAY.

Hymn 98. St. Theodulph.—7 6 7 6. 7 6 7 6. (*First Tune.*)

M. Teschner, 1615.

All glo-ry, &c.

FINE. A - men.

D.C.

"Out of the mouth of babes and sucklings Thou hast perfected praise."

f ALL glory, laud, and honour
    To Thee, Redeemer, King,
To Whom the lips of children
    Made sweet Hosannas ring.

mf Thou art the King of Israel,
    Thou David's Royal Son,
Who in the LORD'S Name comest,
    The King and Blessèd One.
        f All glory, &c.

mf The company of Angels
    Are praising Thee on high,
And mortal men and all things
    Created make reply.
        f All glory, &c.

mf The people of the Hebrews
    With palms before Thee went ;
Our praise and prayer and anthems
    Before Thee we present.
        f All glory, &c.

mf To Thee before Thy Passion
    They sang their hymns of praise ;
To Thee now high exalted
    Our melody we raise.
        f All glory, &c.

mf Thou didst accept their praises,
    Accept the prayers we bring,
Who in all good delightest,
    Thou good and gracious King.
        f All glory, &c.

J. M. NEALE : from St. Theodulph.

The Sunday next before Easter.

OTHERWISE CALLED PALM SUNDAY.

Hymn 98. GLORIA LAUS.—7 6 7 6.7 6 7 6. (*Second Tune.*) (*First Version.*)

"*Out of the mouth of babes and sucklings Thou hast perfected praise.*"

VERSE 1 BY SEVEN BOYS, REPEATED IN CHORUS.　　　　　　Proper Sarum Melody.

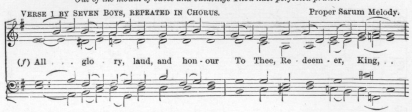

(*f*) All . . . glo - ry, laud, and hon - our To Thee, Re - deem - er, King, . .

To Whom the lips . . . of chil - dren Made sweet Ho - san - nas ring.

SEVEN BOYS.

(*mf*) Thou art the King of Is - rael, Thou Da - vid's Roy - al Son,

SECOND TREBLE.

ALTO.

Repeat Chorus of verse 1.

Who in the LORD's Name com - est, The King and Bless - ed One.

Verses 3, 4, 5, 6, similarly ; always repeating Chorus of verse 1.

mf The company of Angels
　　Are praising Thee on high,
And mortal men and all things
　　Created make reply.
　　　　f All glory, &c.

mf The people of the Hebrews
　　With palms before Thee went ;
Our praise and prayer and anthems
　　Before Thee we present.
　　　　f All glory, &c.

mf To Thee before Thy Passion
　　They sang their hymns of praise ;
To Thee now high exalted
　　Our melody we raise.
　　　　f All glory, &c.

mf Thou didst accept their praises,
　　Accept the prayers we bring,
Who in all good delightest,
　　Thou good and gracious King.
　　　　f All glory, &c.

J. M. NEALE : from St. Theodulph.

(74)

The Sunday next before Easter.

OTHERWISE CALLED PALM SUNDAY.

Hymn 98. GLORIA LAUS.—7 6 7 6.7 6 7 6. *(Second Tune.)* *(Alternative Version.)*

"Out of the mouth of babes and sucklings Thou hast perfected praise."

This Refrain is first sung by Solo Voices, then repeated by Chorus. Proper Sarum Melody.

All glo·ry, laud, and hon·our To Thee, Re·deem·er, King,

FINE.

To Whom the lips of chil·dren Made sweet Ho·san·nas ring.

Solo Voices sing the Verses.

Thou art the King of Is·rael, Thou Da·vid's Roy·al Son,
The com·pa·ny of An·gels Are prais·ing Thee on high,
The peo·ple of the He·brews With palms be·fore Thee went;
To Thee be·fore Thy Pas·sion They sang their hymns of praise;
Thou didst ac·cept their prais·es, Ac·cept the prayers we bring,

Repeat Chorus of verse 1.

Who in the LORD'S Name com·est, The King and Bless·ed One.
And mor·tal men and all things Cre·at·ed make re·ply.
Our praise and prayer and an·thems Be·fore Thee we pre·sent.
To Thee now high ex·alt·ed Our me·lo·dy we raise.
Who in all good de·light·est, Thou good and gra·cious King.

J. M. NEALE: from St. Theodulph

(75)

The Sunday next before Easter.

Otherwise called Palm Sunday.

Hymn 99. St. Drostane.—L.M. (*First Tune.*)   Rev. J. B. Dykes.

A men.

Hymn 99. Winchester New.—L.M. (*Second Tune.*)
Musikalisch Handbuch (Hamburg, 1690).

A-men.

A lower setting of this Tune is given at Hymn 327.

'*And the multitudes that went before, and that followed, cried saying, Hosanna to the Son of David.*'

f   RIDE on ! ride on in majesty !
    Hark ! all the tribes Hosanna cry ;
p   O Saviour meek, pursue Thy road
    With palms and scatter'd garments strow'd.

f   Ride on ! ride on in majesty !
p   In lowly pomp ride on to die ;
cr   O Christ, Thy triumphs now begin
    O'er captive death and conquer'd sin.

f   Ride on ! ride on in majesty !
mf   The Angel armies of the sky

p   Look down with sad and wondering eyes
    To see the approaching Sacrifice

f   Ride on ! ride on in majesty !
mf   The last and fiercest strife is nigh :
    The Father on His sapphire Throne
    Awaits His own Anointed Son.

f   Ride on ! ride on in majesty !
p   In lowly pomp ride on to die ;
    Bow Thy meek Head to mortal pain,
f   Then take, O God, Thy power, and reign.

H. H. Milman, 1827.

Hymns on the Passion.*

Hymn 100. Cassel.—7 7.7 7.7 7.   Christen-schatz (Basle, 1745.)

A-men.

* Some of these Hymns may be sung throughout the year.

Hymns on the Passion.

" And being in an agony He prayed more earnestly."

mf SION'S Daughter, weep no more,
Though thy troubled heart be sore ;
He of Whom the Psalmist sung,
He Who woke the Prophet's tongue,
CHRIST, the Mediator Blest,
Brings thee everlasting rest.

p In a garden man became
Heir of sin, and death, and shame :
cr JESUS in a garden wins
Life, and pardon for our sins ;
dim Through His hour of agony
Praying in Gethsemane,

mf There for us He intercedes ;
There with GOD the FATHER pleads ;
Willing there for us to drain
To the dregs the cup of pain
That in everlasting day
He may wipe our tears away.

f Therefore to His Name be given
Glory both in earth and Heav'n ;
To the FATHER, and the SON,
And the SPIRIT, THREE in ONE,
Honour, praise, and glory be
Now and through eternity.

Sir H. W. BAKER : from the Latin.

ALTERNATIVE TUNE, HYMN 318 (SECOND TUNE).

Hymn 101. ST. BRIDE.—S.M.
S. HOWARD, 1710–1782.

" Looking unto Jesus."

p O'ERWHELM'D in depths of woe,
Upon the Tree of scorn
Hangs the Redeemer of mankind,
With racking anguish torn.
See how the nails those Hands
And Feet so tender rend ;
See down His Face, and Neck, and Breast
His sacred Blood descend.
mf Oh, hear that last, loud cry
Which pierced His Mother's heart,
p As into GOD the FATHER'S hands
He bade His soul depart.
mf Earth hears, and trembling quakes
Around that tree of pain ;

f The rocks are rent ; the graves are burst ;
The veil is rent in twain.
mf Shall man alone be mute ?
Have we no griefs, or fears ?
Come, old and young, come, all mankind,
And bathe those Feet in tears.
p Come, fall before His Cross
Who shed for us His Blood ;
Who died, the Victim of pure love,
To make us sons of GOD.
f JESU, all praise to Thee,
Our Joy and endless Rest ;
Be Thou our Guide while pilgrims here,
Our Crown amid the blest.

E. CASWALL : from the Latin.

Hymn 102. IRA JUSTA.—8 7 8 7. 7 7. (*First Tune.*)
E. H. THORNE.

poco rit.

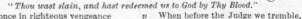

" Thou wast slain, and hast redeemed us to God by Thy Blood."

p HE, Who once in righteous vengeance
Whelm'd the world beneath the flood,
mf Once again in mercy cleansed it
With His own most precious Blood,
p Coming from His Throne on high
On the painful Cross to die.
f O the wisdom of the Eternal !
O the depth of love Divine !
mf O the sweetness of that mercy
Which in JESUS CHRIST did shine !
dim We were sinners doom'd to die ;
JESUS paid the penalty.

p When before the Judge we tremble,
Conscious of His broken laws,
cr May the Blood of His Atonement
Cry aloud, and plead our cause,
Bid our guilty terrors cease,
p Be our pardon and our peace.
f Prince and Author of salvation,
LORD of Majesty supreme,
JESU, praise to Thee be given
By the world Thou didst redeem ;
Glory to the FATHER be
And the SPIRIT ONE with Thee.

E. CASWALL : from the Latin.

Hymns on the Passion.

Hymn 102. COBLENTZ.—8 7 8 7. 7 7. (*Second Tune.*) NEANDER, A und Ω, 1680.

A-men.

"Thou wast slain, and hast redeemed us to God by Thy Blood."

p HE, Who once in righteous vengeance
  Whelm'd the world beneath the flood,
mf Once again in mercy cleansed it
  With His own most precious Blood,
p Coming from His Throne on high
  On the painful Cross to die.

f O the wisdom of the Eternal!
  O the depth of love Divine!
mf O the sweetness of that mercy
  Which in JESUS CHRIST did shine!
dim We were sinners doom'd to die;
  JESUS paid the penalty.

p When before the Judge we tremble,
  Conscious of His broken laws,
cr May the Blood of His Atonement
  Cry aloud, and plead our cause,
  Bid our guilty terrors cease,
p Be our pardon and our peace.

f Prince and Author of salvation,
  LORD of Majesty supreme,
  JESU, praise to Thee be given
  By the world Thou didst redeem;
  Glory to the FATHER be
  And the SPIRIT ONE with Thee.

E. CASWALL: from the Latin.

Hymn 103. ST. DENYS.—8 7. 8 7. 8 7. W. H. MONK.

A-men

"He was wounded for our transgressions."

mf NOW, my soul, thy voice upraising,
  Tell in sweet and mournful strain
How the Crucified, enduring
  Grief, and wounds, and dying pain,
  Freely of His love was offer'd,
  Sinless was for sinners slain.

Scourged with unrelenting fury
  For the sins which we deplore,
By His livid Stripes He heals us,
  Raising us to fall no more;
  All our bruises gently soothing,
  Binding up the bleeding sore.

Hymns on the Passion.

ṡ See ˌ His Hands and Feet are fasten'd ;
cr　So He makes His people free ;
Not a wound whence Blood is flowing
　But a fount of grace shall be ;
Yea the very nails which nail Him
　Nail us also to the Tree.

p Through His Heart the spear is piercing,
　Though His foes have seen Him die ;
Blood and Water thence are streaming
　In a tide of mystery,
cr Water from our guilt to cleanse us,
　Blood to win us crowns on high.

mf JESU, may those precious fountains
　Drink to thirsting souls afford :
Let them be our cup and healing,
　And at length our full reward ;
So a ransom'd world shall ever
　Praise Thee, its redeeming LORD.

Sir H. W. BAKER and J. CHANDLER : from the Latin of C. de Santeuil.

ALTERNATIVE TUNE, HYMN 309 (FOURTH TUNE).

Hymn 104. ATTOLLE PAULUM.—8 7. 8 7. 8 8 7. *Geistliche Lieder*, 1539.

A - men.

" Behold the Man "

mf O SINNER, lift the eye of faith,
　To true repentance turning ;
Bethink thee of the curse of sin,
　Its awful guilt discerning ;
Upon the Crucified One look,
And thou shalt read, as in a book,
　What well is worth thy learning.

p Look on His Head, that bleeding Head,
　With crown of thorns surrounded ;
Look on His sacred Hands and Feet
　Which piercing nails have wounded ;
See every Limb with scourges rent :
On Him, the Just, the Innocent,
　What malice hath abounded !

'Tis not alone those Limbs are rack'd,
　But friends too are forsaking ;
And, more than all, for thankless man
　That tender Heart is aching ;
Oh, fearful was the pain and scorn,
By JESUS, Son of Mary, borne,
　Their peace for sinners making.

None ever knew such pain before,
　Such infinite affliction,
None ever felt a grief like His
　In that dread crucifixion ·
For us He bare those bitter throes,
For us those agonizing woes,
　In oft-renew'd infliction.

mf O sinner, mark, and ponder well
　Sin's awful condemnation ;
Think what a sacrifice it cost
　To purchase thy salvation ;
Had JESUS never bled and died,
Then what could thee and all betide
　But uttermost damnation ?

LORD, give us grace to flee from sin
　And Satan's wiles ensnaring,
And from those everlasting flames
　For evil ones preparing.
f JESU, we thank Thee, and entreat
cr To rest for ever at Thy Feet,
　Thy heavenly glory sharing.

J. M. NEALE : from the Latin.

79)

Ibymns on the Passion.

Hymn 105. ST. PRISCA.—7 7 7 7. R. REDHEAD.

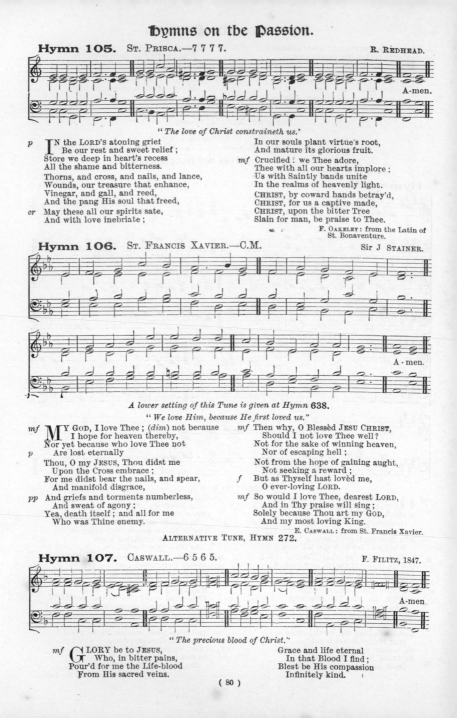

A-men.

"The love of Christ constraineth us."

p IN the LORD'S atoning grief
     Be our rest and sweet relief ;
Store we deep in heart's recess
All the shame and bitterness.

Thorns, and cross, and nails, and lance,
Wounds, our treasure that enhance,
Vinegar, and gall, and reed,
And the pang His soul that freed,

cr May these all our spirits sate,
     And with love inebriate ;

In our souls plant virtue's root,
And mature its glorious fruit.

mf Crucified ! we Thee adore,
Thee with all our hearts implore :
Us with Saintly bands unite
In the realms of heavenly light.

CHRIST, by coward hands betray'd,
CHRIST, for us a captive made,
CHRIST, upon the bitter Tree
Slain for man, be praise to Thee.

F. OAKELEY : from the Latin of
St. Bonaventure.

Hymn 106. ST. FRANCIS XAVIER.—C.M. Sir J STAINER.

A - men.

A lower setting of this Tune is given at Hymn 638.

"We love Him, because He first loved us."

mf MY GOD, I love Thee ; *(dim)* not because
      I hope for heaven thereby,
Nor yet because who love Thee not
p   Are lost eternally

Thou, O my JESUS, Thou didst me
Upon the Cross embrace ;
For me didst bear the nails, and spear,
And manifold disgrace,

pp And griefs and torments numberless,
      And sweat of agony ;
Yea, death itself ; and all for me
Who was Thine enemy.

mf Then why, O Blessèd JESU CHRIST,
      Should I not love Thee well ?
Not for the sake of winning heaven,
Nor of escaping hell ;

Not from the hope of gaining aught,
Not seeking a reward ;
f   But as Thyself hast lovèd me,
      O ever-loving LORD.

mf So would I love Thee, dearest LORD,
      And in Thy praise will sing ;
Solely because Thou art my GOD,
And my most loving King.

E. CASWALL : from St. Francis Xavier.

ALTERNATIVE TUNE, HYMN 272.

Hymn 107. CASWALL.—6 5 6 5. F. FILITZ, 1847.

A-men

"The precious blood of Christ."

mf GLORY be to JESUS,
      Who, in bitter pains,
Pour'd for me the Life-blood
From His sacred veins.

Grace and life eternal
In that Blood I find ;
Blest be His compassion
Infinitely kind.

Hymns on the Passion.

Blest through endless ages
Be the precious stream,
Which from endless torments
Did the world redeem.

Abel's blood for vengeance
Pleaded to the skies ;
cr But the Blood of JESUS
For our pardon cries.

p Oft as it is sprinkled
On our guilty hearts,

mf Satan in confusion
Terror-struck departs :
Oft as earth exulting
Wafts its praise on high,
cr Angel-hosts rejoicing
Make their glad reply.
f Lift ye then your voices;
cr Swell the mighty flood ;
Louder still and louder
Praise the (*dim*) precious Blood.

E. CASWALL: from the Italian.

Hymn 108. ROCKINGHAM.—L.M.   E. MILLER, 1735–1807.

A - men.

A lower setting of this Tune is given at Hymn 371.

" What things were gain to me, those I counted loss for Christ."

mf WHEN I survey the wondrous Cross
On which the Prince of glory died,
My richest gain I count but loss,
And pour contempt on all my pride.

Forbid it, LORD, that I should boast
Save in the Cross of CHRIST my GOD ;
All the vain things that charm me most,
I sacrifice them to His Blood.

p See from His Head, His Hands, His Feet,
Sorrow and love flow mingling down ;

cr Did e'er such love and sorrow meet,
Or thorns compose so rich a crown?
mf Were the whole realm of nature mine,
That were an offering far too small ;
f Love so amazing, so Divine,
Demands my soul, my life, my all.

mf To CHRIST, Who won for sinners grace
p By bitter grief and anguish sore,
f Be praise from all the ransom'd race
For ever and for evermore.

I. WATTS (1707) and Compilers.

Hymn 109. BATTY.—8 7 8 7.   *Christen-schatz* (Basle, 1745).

A - men.

" Unto you therefore which believe He is precious."

mf SWEET the moments, rich in blessing,
Which before the Cross I spend,
Life, and health, and peace possessing
From the sinner's dying Friend.

Here I rest, for ever viewing
Mercy pour'd in streams of Blood ;
Precious drops, my soul bedewing,
Plead and claim my peace with GOD.

p Truly blessèd is the station,
Low before His Cross to lie,
Whilst I see Divine compassion
Beaming in His languid Eye.

mf LORD, in ceaseless contemplation
Fix my thankful heart on Thee,
Till I taste Thy full salvation,
And Thine unveil'd glory see.

J. ALLEN and Hon. W. SHIRLEY.

Hymns on the Passion.

Hymn 110. GETHSEMANE.—7 7.7 7.7 7.   W. H. MONK : from C. Tye, 1553.

A-men.

" Remembering Mine affliction and My misery, the wormwood and the gall.'

p GO to dark Gethsemane,
       Ye that feel the Tempter's power,
Your Redeemer's conflict see,
   Watch with Him one bitter hour ;
   Turn not from His griefs away,
cr Learn of JESUS CHRIST to pray.

p Follow to the judgment-hall,
   View the LORD of life arraign'd ;
   Oh, the wormwood and the gall !

Oh, the pangs His soul sustain'd !
Shun not suffering, shame, or loss ;
cr Learn of Him to bear the cross.
p Calvary's mournful mountain climb ;
cr   There, adoring at His Feet,
   Mark that miracle of time,
   —GOD'S own Sacrifice complete ;
p "It is finish'd," hear Him cry ;
cr Learn of JESUS CHRIST to die.

ALTERNATIVE TUNE, HYMN 691.   J. MONTGOMERY, 1820.

Hymn 111. PASSION CHORALE.—7 6 7 6.7 6 7 6.   H. L. HASSLER, 1601.

A-men.

" Who loved me, and gave Himself for me."

mf O SACRED Head, surrounded
       By crown of piercing thorn !
O bleeding Head, so wounded,
   Reviled, and put to scorn !
p Death's pallid hue comes o'er Thee,
   The glow of life decays,
cr Yet Angel-hosts adore Thee,
dim And tremble as they gaze.

p I see Thy strength and vigour
   All fading in the strife,
   And death with cruel rigour
   Bereaving Thee of life ;

mf O agony and dying !
   O love to sinners free !
p JESU, all grace supplying,
   O turn Thy Face on me.

In this Thy bitter Passion,
   Good Shepherd, think of me
With Thy most sweet compassion,
   Unworthy though I be :
mf Beneath Thy Cross abiding
   For ever would I rest,
In Thy dear love confiding,
   And with Thy Presence blest.

(82)

Sir H. W. BAKER and Compilers :
from the German of P. Gerhardt.

Hymns on the Passion.

Hymn 112. St. Bernard.—C.M.   *Tochter Sion* (Cologne, 1741).

A higher setting of this Tune is given at Hymn 183.

" Come unto Me, all ye that labour and are heavy-laden, and I will give you rest.'

mf   A LL ye who seek for sure relief
       In trouble and distress,
    Whatever sorrow vex the mind,
      Or guilt the soul oppress,

     JESUS, Who gave Himself for you
p   Upon the Cross to die,
cr   Opens to you His sacred Heart ;
      O to that Heart draw nigh.

mf   Ye hear how kindly He invites ;
      Ye hear His words so blest ;

     " All ye that labour come to Me,
p   And I will give you rest."

mf   O JESUS, Joy of Saints on high,
      Thou Hope of sinners here,
    Attracted by those loving words
      To Thee we lift our prayer.

p   Wash Thou our wounds in that dear Blood
      Which from Thy Heart doth flow ;
cr   A new and contrite heart on all
      Who cry to Thee bestow.

E. CASWALL: from Prudentius.

Hymn 113. Calvary.—7 7 7 7. *(First Tune.)*   W. H. MONK.

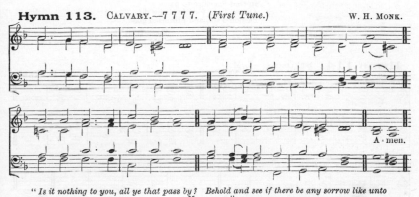

" Is it nothing to you, all ye that pass by ? Behold and see if there be any sorrow like unto My sorrow."

mf   S EE the destined day arise !
      See, a willing Sacrifice,
    JESUS, to redeem our loss,
    Hangs upon the shameful Cross !

p   JESU, who but Thou had borne,
    Lifted on that Tree of scorn,
    Every pang and bitter throe,
    Finishing Thy life of woe ?

    Who but Thou had dared to drain,
    Steep'd in gall, the cup of pain,

    And with tender Body bear
    Thorns, and nails, and piercing spear ?

mf   Thence the cleansing Water flow'd,
    Mingled from Thy Side with Blood ;
    Sign to all attesting eyes
    Of the finish'd Sacrifice.

p   Holy JESU, grant us grace
    In that Sacrifice to place
cr   All our trust for life renew'd,
    Pardon'd sin, and promised good.

Bishop MANT, 1837.

Hymns on the Passion.

Hymn 113. NUN KOMM.—7 7 7 7. (Second Tune.)

Medieval Melody.

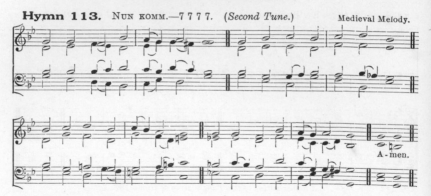

A - men.

"Is it nothing to you, all ye that pass by? Behold and see if there be any sorrow like unto My sorrow."

mf SEE the destined day arise !
  See, a willing Sacrifice,
JESUS, to redeem our loss,
Hangs upon the shameful Cross !

p JESU, who but Thou had borne,
Lifted on that Tree of scorn,
Every pang and bitter throe,
Finishing Thy life of woe ?

Who but Thou had dared to drain,
Steep'd in gall, the cup of pain,
And with tender Body bear
Thorns, and nails, and piercing spear ?

mf Thence the cleansing Water flow'd,
Mingled from Thy Side with Blood ;
Sign to all attesting eyes
Of the finish'd Sacrifice.

p Holy JESU, grant us grace
In that Sacrifice to place
cr All our trust for life renew'd,
Pardon'd sin, and promised good.

Bishop MANT, 1837.

Hymn 114. ST. CROSS.—L.M.

Slow.

Rev. J. B. DYKES.

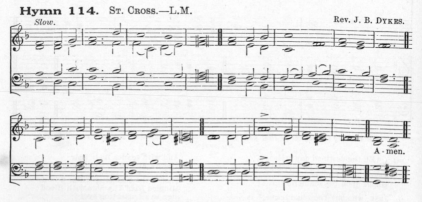

A - men.

"They crucified Him."

mf O COME and mourn with me awhile ;
  O come ye to the Saviour's side ;
O come, together let us mourn ;
pp JESUS, our LORD, is crucified.

mf Have we no tears to shed for Him,
While soldiers scoff and Jews deride ?
Ah ! look how patiently He hangs ;
pp JESUS, our LORD, is crucified.

Hymns on the Passion.

p How fast His Hands and Feet are nail'd ;
His Throat with parching thirst is dried ;
His failing Eyes are dimm'd with Blood :
pp JESUS, our LORD, is crucified.

p Seven times He spake, seven Words of love ;
And all three hours His silence cried
For mercy on the souls of men ;
pp JESUS, our LORD, is crucified.

p Come, let us stand beneath the Cross ;
So may the Blood from out His Side
Fall gently on us drop by drop ;
pp JESUS, our LORD, is crucified.

mf A broken heart, a fount of tears,
Ask, and they will not be denied ;
LORD JESUS, may we love and weep,
Since Thou for us art crucified.

F. W. FABER.

Hymn 115. ST. MARGARET.—7 6 7 6. (*First Tune.*)   Rev. W. STATHAM.

Hymn 115. FORGIVENESS.—7 6 7 6. (*Second Tune.*)   B. GESIUS, 1605.

A - men.

" Father, forgive them, for they know not what they do."

mf "FORGIVE them, O My FATHER,
    They know not what they do : "
p The Saviour spake in anguish,
    As the sharp nails went through.

No pain'd reproaches gave He
    To them that shed His Blood,
But prayer and tenderest pity
cr   Large as the love of GOD.

mf For me was that compassion,
    For me that tender care ;
I need His wide forgiveness
As much as any there.

p It was my pride and hardness
    That hung Him on the Tree ;
pp Those cruel nails, O Saviour,
    Were driven in by me.

p And often I have slighted
    Thy gentle voice that chid ;
cr Forgive me too, LORD JESUS ;
    I knew not what I did.

mf O depth of sweet compassion !
    O Love Divine and true !
Save Thou the souls that slight Thee,
And know not what they do.

MRS. ALEXANDER.

Hymns on the Passion.

Hymn 116. CRY OF FAITH.—10 10 10 10.   H. J. GAUNTLETT.

A - men.

"Verily I say unto thee, To-day shalt thou be with Me in Paradise."

mf " LORD, when Thy Kingdom comes, remember me ;"
p   Thus spake the dying lips to dying Ears ;
cr O faith, which in that darkest hour could see
      The promised glory of the far-off years !

mf No kingly sign declares that glory now,
      No ray of hope lights up that awful hour ;
p A thorny crown surrounds the bleeding Brow,
      The Hands are stretch'd in weakness, not in power.

mf Yet hear the Word the dying Saviour saith,
p rall "Thou too shalt rest in Paradise to-day ;"
tempo cr O Words of love to answer words of faith !
      O Words of hope for those who live to pray !

mf LORD, when with dying lips my prayer is said,
      Grant that in faith Thy kingdom I may see ;
      And, thinking on Thy Cross and bleeding Head,
      May breathe my parting words, (*p*) " Remember me."

cr Remember me, but not my shame or sin ;
f   Thy cleansing Blood hath wash'd them all away ;
mf Thy precious Death for me did pardon win ;
      Thy Blood redeem'd me in that awful day.

p Remember me ; yet how canst Thou forget
      What pain and anguish I have caused to Thee,
      The Cross, the Agony, the Bloody Sweat,
      And all the sorrow Thou didst bear for me ?

cr Remember me ; and, ere I pass away,
      Speak Thou th' assuring Word that sets us free,
      And make Thy promise to my heart, (*p*) " To-day
      Thou too shalt rest in Paradise with Me."

                               Archbishop MACLAGAN.

ALTERNATIVE TUNE, HYMN 715 (FIRST TUNE).

Hymn 117. STABAT MATER. NO. 1.—8 8 7. 8 8 7. (*First Tune.*)

To be sung in Unison.   Proper Mechlin Melody.

Hymn 117. Stabat Mater. No. 2.—8 8 7. 8 8 7. (*Second Tune.*)

Rev. J. B. Dykes.

Hymn 117. Stabat Mater. No. 3.—8 8 7. (*Third Tune.*)

Traditional Melody.

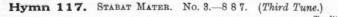

" Woman, behold thy son . . . Behold thy mother."

mf A T the Cross her station keeping
      Stood the mournful Mother weeping,
  Where He hung, the dying LORD ;
For her soul of joy bereavèd,
Bow'd with anguish, deeply grievèd,
  Felt the sharp and piercing sword.

p Oh, how sad and sore distressèd
Now was she, that Mother blessèd
  Of the sole-begotten One ;
Deep the woe of her affliction,
When she saw the Crucifixion
cr Of her ever-glorious Son.

mf Who, on CHRIST'S dear Mother gazing
Pierced by anguish so amazing,
  Born of woman, would not weep?

Who, on CHRIST'S dear Mother thinking
Such a cup of sorrow drinking,
  Would not share her sorrows deep?

p For His people's sins chastisèd,
She beheld her Son despisèd,   [twined :
  Scourged, and crown'd with thorns en-
Saw Him then from judgment taken,
And in death by all forsaken,
  Till His Spirit He resign'd

mf JESU, may her deep devotion
Stir in me the same emotion,
  Fount of love, Redeemer kind,
cr That my heart fresh ardour gaining,
And a purer love attaining,
  May with Thee acceptance find.

E. CASWALL and Compilers : from the
Latin of Jacopone da Todi (?).

Hymns on the Passion.

Hymn 118. GETHSEMANE.—7 7.7 7.7 7.   Rev. Sir F A. G. OUSELEY.

A-men.

"My God, My God, why hast Thou forsaken Me?"

mf THRONED upon the awful Tree,
    King of grief, I watch with Thee;
dim Darkness veils Thine anguish'd Face,
    None its lines of woe can trace,
    None can tell what pangs unknown
pp Hold Thee silent and alone.

p Silent through those three dread hours,
cr Wrestling with the evil powers,
dim Left alone with human sin,
    Gloom around Thee and within,
    Till the appointed time is nigh,
pp Till the LAMB of GOD may die.

mf Hark that cry that peals aloud
    Upward through the whelming cloud!
cr Thou, the FATHER'S only SON,
    Thou, His own Anointed One,
    Thou dost ask Him—(*p*) can it be?—
dim "Why hast Thou forsaken Me?"

p LORD, should fear and anguish roll
    Darkly o'er my sinful soul,
    Thou, Who once wast thus bereft,
cr That Thine own might ne'er be left,
    Teach me by that bitter cry
mf In the gloom to know Thee nigh.

ALTERNATIVE TUNE, HYMN 184.   J. ELLERTON.

Hymn 119. ASSISI.—8 8 8 6.   Sir F. CHAMPNEYS.

A - men.

"I thirst."

mf HIS are the thousand sparkling rills,
    That from a thousand fountains burst,
    And fill with music all the hills;
p And yet He saith, "I thirst."

mf All fiery pangs on battle-fields,
    On fever beds where sick men toss,
    Are in that human cry He yields
p To anguish on the Cross.

mf But more than pains that rack'd Him then
    Was the deep longing thirst Divine,
cr That thirsted for the souls of men:
p Dear LORD! and one was mine.

mf O Love most patient, give me grace;
    Make all my soul athirst for Thee;
p That parch'd dry Lip, that fading Face,
    That Thirst were all for me.

ALTERNATIVE TUNE, HYMN 255.   Mrs. ALEXANDER.

Hymn 120. ABER.—S.M. (*First Tune.*)   W. H. MONK.

A-men.

(*No organ Ped.*)   (*Ped.*)

Hymns on the Passion.

Hymn 120. SOUTHWELL.—S.M. (*Second Tune*.) DAMON, *Psalms*, 1579.

A-men.

A higher setting of this Tune is given at Hymn **205.**

" It is finished."

mf O PERFECT life of love !
　　　All, all is finish'd now ;
All that He left His Throne above
　To do for us below.

　No work is left undone
　Of all the FATHER will'd ;
p His toil, His sorrows, one by one,
cr The Scripture have fulfill'd.

p No pain that we can share
　But He has felt its smart ;
All forms of human grief and care
　Have pierced that tender Heart.

And on His thorn-crown'd Head,
And on His sinless Soul,

Our sins in all their guilt were laid,
cr That He might make us whole.

p In perfect love He dies :
　For me He dies, for me :
cr O all-atoning Sacrifice,
　I cling by faith to Thee.

mf In every time of need,
　Before the judgment-throne,
cr Thy work, O LAMB of GOD, I'll plead,
　Thy merits, (*dim*) not my own.

mf Yet work, O LORD, in me
　As Thou for me hast wrought ;
cr And let my love the answer be
　To grace Thy love has brought.

　　　　　　　　Sir H. W. BAKER.

Hymn 121. COMMENDATIO.—11 10 11 10. REV. J. B. DYKES.

A-men.

" Father, into Thy hands I commend My Spirit."

p AND now, belovèd LORD, Thy Soul resigning
　　Into Thy FATHER'S arms with conscious Will,
Calmly, with reverend grace, Thy Head inclining,
pp The throbbing Brow and labouring Breast grow still.

mf Freely Thy life Thou yieldest, meekly bending
　E'en to the last beneath our sorrows' load,
cr e dim Yet strong in death, in perfect peace commending
　Thy Spirit to Thy FATHER and Thy GOD.

mf Sweet Saviour, in mine hour of mortal anguish,
　dim When earth grows dim, and round me falls the night,
cr e dim O breathe Thy peace, as flesh and spirit languish ;
　cr At that dread eventide let there be light.

p To Thy dear Cross turn Thou my eyes in dying ;
　Lay but my fainting head upon Thy Breast ;
Those outstretch'd Arms receive my latest sighing ;
　cr And then, oh ! then, Thine everlasting Rest.

　　　　　　　　MRS. ALDERSON.

ALTERNATIVE TUNE, HYMN **494** (THIRD TUNE).

Hymns on the Passion.

Hymn 122. AD INFEROS.—8 7 8 7.

W. H. SANGSTER.

A-men.

"In Paradise."

p IT is finish'd! Blessèd JESUS,
   Thou hast breathed Thy latest sigh,
cr Teaching us the sons of Adam
   How the SON of GOD (*dim*) can die.

p Lifeless lies the broken Body,
   Hidden in its rocky bed,
   Laid aside like folded garment:
   Where is now the Spirit fled?

mf In the gloomy realms of darkness
   Shines a light unknown before,
   For the LORD of dead and living
   Enters at the open door.

p See! He comes, a willing Victim,
   Unresisting hither led;
   Passing from the Cross of sorrow
   To the mansions of the dead.

mf Lo! the heavenly light around Him
   As He draws His people near;
cr All amazed they stand rejoicing
   At the gracious Words they hear.

mf For Himself proclaims the story
   Of His own Incarnate life,
   And the death He died to save us,
   Victor in that awful strife.

   Patriarch and Priest and Prophet
   Gather round Him as He stands,
cr In adoring faith and gladness,
dim Hearing of the piercèd Hands.

f Oh, the bliss to which He calls them,
   Ransom'd by His precious Blood,
   From the gloomy realms of darkness
   To the Paradise of GOD!

mf There in lowliest joy and wonder
   Stands the robber at His side,
cr Reaping now the blessèd promise
dim Spoken by the Crucified.

p JESUS, LORD of dead and living,
   Let Thy mercy rest on me;
   Grant me too, when life is finish'd,
   Rest in Paradise with Thee.

ALTERNATIVE TUNE, HYMN 109.

Archbishop MACLAGAN.

Hymn 123. HOLY SEPULCHRE.—8 8 8.

E. H. THORNE.

p   *ppp*   A-men.

"Mary Magdalene and Mary the mother of Joses beheld where He was laid."

p BY JESUS' grave on either hand,
   While night is brooding o'er the land,
   The sad and silent mourners stand.

   At last the weary life is o'er,
   The agony and conflict sore
   Of Him Who all our sufferings bore.

   Deep in the rock's sepulchral shade
   The LORD, by Whom the worlds were made,
   The Saviour of mankind, is laid.

mf O hearts bereaved and sore distress'd,
   Here is for you a place of rest;
p Here leave your griefs on JESUS' Breast.

I. GREGORY SMITH.

Hymn 124. PETRA.—7 7.7 7.7 7.

R. REDHEAD.

Hymns on the Passion.

A-men.

"And when Joseph had taken the Body, he wrapped it in a clean linen cloth, and laid it in his own new tomb, which he had hewn out in the rock . . . . And there was Mary Magdalene, and the other Mary, sitting over against the sepulchre."

mf RESTING from His work to-day
    In the tomb the Saviour lay ;
Still He slept, from Head to Feet
Shrouded in the winding-sheet,
Lying in the rock alone,
Hidden by the sealèd stone.

Late at even there was seen
Watching long the Magdalene ;
Early, ere the break of day,
p Sorrowful she took her way
To the holy garden glade,
Where her buried LORD was laid.

mf So with Thee, till life shall end,
    I would solemn vigil spend :
Let me hew Thee, LORD, a shrine
In this rocky heart of mine,
Where in pure embalmèd cell
None but Thou may ever dwell.

Myrrh and spices will I bring,
True affection's offering ;
p Close the door from sight and sound
Of the busy world around ;
And in patient watch remain
cr Till my LORD appear again.

T. WHYTEHEAD.

The following Hymns are also suitable for this season :—

494 My LORD, my Master, at Thy Feet adoring.
495 Weep not for Him Who onward bears.
496 O scorn'd and outcast LORD.

647 LORD, through this Holy Week of our salvation.
648 O Word of pity, for our pardon pleading.
649 O perfect GOD, Thy love.

Easter.

Hymn 125. ST. FULBERT.—C.M.

H. J. GAUNTLETT.

A lower setting of this Tune is given at Hymn 189.

"O death, where is thy sting ? O grave, where is thy victory ?"

f YE choirs of new Jerusalem,
    Your sweetest notes employ,
The Paschal victory to hymn
    In strains of holy joy.

For Judah's Lion bursts His chains,
    Crushing the serpent's head ;
And cries aloud through death's domains
    To wake the imprison'd dead.

Devouring depths of hell their prey
    At His command restore ;
His ransom'd hosts pursue their way
    Where JESUS goes before.

ff Triumphant in His glory now
    To Him all power is given ;
mf To Him in one communion bow
    All saints in earth and Heav'n.

While we, His soldiers, praise our King,
dim His mercy we implore,
cr Within His palace bright to bring
    And keep us evermore.

f All glory to the FATHER be,
    All glory to the SON,
All glory, HOLY GHOST, to Thee,
    While endless ages run.

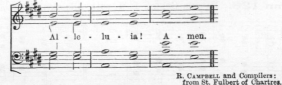

Al - le - lu - ia! A - men.

R. CAMPBELL and Compilers :
from St. Fulbert of Chartres.

Easter.

Hymn 126. TRISTES ERANT.—L.M. (*First Tune.*)

Hymn 126. TRISTES ERANT.—L.M. (*First Tune.*)

W. H. MONK.

A - men.

Hymn 126. EASTER CHANT.—L.M. (*Second Tune.*)

Rev. J. B. DYKES.

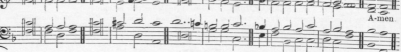

A-men.

" The Lord is King, and hath put on glorious apparel."

f   ***L**IGHT'S glittering morn bedécks the sky ;
    Heav'n thunders forth its victor-cry ;
The glad earth shouts her tríumph high,
And groaning hell makes wild reply ;

*While He, the King, the mighty King,
Despoiling death of áll its sting,
And, trampling down the pówers of night,
Brings forth His ransom'd Saints to light.

mf *His tomb of late the thréefold guard
Of watch and stone and séal had barr'd ;

f   But now, in pomp and tríumph high,
He comes from death to victory.

*The pains of hell are lóosed at last ;
The days of mourning nów are past ;
An Angel robed in light hath said,

ff   "The LORD is risen from the dead."

PART 2.

p   Th' Apostles' hearts were fúll of pain
For their dear LORD so látely slain,
By rebel servants dóomed to die
A death of cruel agony.

mf With gentle voice the Ángel gave
The women tidings át the grave ;
"Fear not, your Master sháll ye see ;
He goes before to Galilee."

cr   Then, hastening on their eáger way
The joyful tidings tó convey,
Their LORD they met, their líving LORD,
dim And falling at His Feet adored.

mf Th' Eleven, when they héar, with speed
To Galilee forthwith proceed,
That there once more they máy behold
The LORD'S dear Face, as He foretold.

PART 3.

f   *That Easter-tide with jóy was bright,
The sun shone out with fáirer light,
When, to their longing éyes restored,
Th' Apostles saw their risen LORD.

mf *He bade them see His Hánds, His Side,
Where yet the glorious Woúnds abide ;
The tokens true which máde it plain
f   Their LORD indeed was risen again.

mf JESU, the King of Géntleness,
Do Thou Thyself our heárts possess,
That we may give Thee áll our days
The tribute of our grateful praise.

*The following may be sung at the end of
each Part:*

mf O LORD of all, with ús abide
In this our joyful Eáster-tide ;
From every weapon deáth can wield
Thine own redeem'd for ever shield.

ff   *All praise be Thine, O risen LORD,
From death to endless life restored :
All praise to GOD the FÁTHER be
And HOLY GHOST eternally.

J. M. NEALE and Compilers: from the Latin.

* *When the whole Hymn is sung to the Chant, these verses may be sung in unison.*

Hymn 126. EASTER SONG.—L.M. with Alleluias. (*Third Tune.*)

Catholische Kirchengesänge (Cologne, 1623).

Easter.

Al - le - lu - ia! Al - le - lu - ia!
Al - le - lu - ia! Al - le -
- lu - ia! Al - le - lu - ia! Al - le - lu - ia! Al - le - lu - ia! A - men.

" The Lord is King, and hath put on glorious apparel."

f LIGHT'S glittering morn bedecks the sky ;
Heav'n thunders forth its victor-cry ;
Alleluia !
The glad earth shouts her triumph high,
And groaning hell makes wild reply ;
Alleluia !

While He, the King, the mighty King,
Despoiling death of all its sting,
Alleluia !
And, trampling down the powers of night,
Brings forth His ransom'd Saints to light.
Alleluia !

mf His tomb of late the threefold guard
Of watch and stone and seal had barr'd ;
Alleluia !
f But now, in pomp and triumph high,
He comes from death to victory.
Alleluia !

The pains of hell are loosed at last ;
The days of mourning now are past ;
Alleluia !
An Angel robed in light hath said,
ff " The LORD is risen from the dead."
Alleluia !

PART 2.

v Th' Apostles' hearts were full of pain
For their dear LORD so lately slain,
Alleluia !
By rebel servants doom'd to die
A death of cruel agony.
Alleluia !

mf With gentle voice the Angel gave
The women tidings at the grave ;
Alleluia !
" Fear not, your Master shall ye see ;
He goes before to Galilee."
Alleluia !

cr Then, hastening on their eager way
The joyful tidings to convey,
Alleluia !

Their LORD they met, their living LORD,
dim And falling at His Feet adored.
Alleluia !
mf Th' Eleven, when they hear, with speed
To Galilee forthwith proceed,
Alleluia !
That there once more they may behold
The LORD'S dear Face, as He foretold.
Alleluia !

PART 3.
f That Easter-tide with joy was bright,
The sun shone out with fairer light,
Alleluia !
When, to their longing eyes restored,
Th' Apostles saw their risen LORD.
Alleluia !
mf He bade them see His Hands, His Side,
Where yet the glorious Wounds abide ;
Alleluia !
The tokens true which made it plain
f Their LORD indeed was risen again.
Alleluia !

mf JESU, the King of Gentleness,
Do Thou Thyself our hearts possess,
Alleluia !
That we may give Thee all our days
The tribute of our grateful praise.
Alleluia !

*The following may be sung separately, or at the
end of each Part :*
mf O LORD of all, with us abide
In this our joyful Easter-tide ;
Alleluia !
From every weapon death can wield
Thine own redeem'd for ever shield.
Alleluia !
ff All praise be Thine, O risen LORD,
From death to endless life restored :
Alleluia !
All praise to GOD the FATHER be
And HOLY GHOST eternally.
Alleluia !

J. M. NEALE and Compilers : from the Latin

(93)

Easter.

Hymn 127. SALZBURG.—7 7 7 7. 7 7 7 7.

J. HINTZE, 1622-1702.

A - men.

" Sing ye to the Lord, for He hath triumphed gloriously."

f   AT the LAMB's high feast we sing
      Praise to our victorious King,
mf Who hath wash'd us in the tide
    Flowing from His piercèd Side ;
f   Praise we Him, Whose love Divine
    Gives His Sacred Blood for wine,
    Gives His Body for the feast,
    CHRIST the Victim, CHRIST the Priest.

mf Where the Paschal blood is pour'd,
    Death's dark Angel sheathes his sword ;
f   Israel's hosts triumphant go
    Through the wave that drowns the foe.
    Praise we CHRIST, Whose Blood was shed,
    Paschal Victim, Paschal Bread ;
mf With sincerity and love
    Eat we Manna from above.

f   Mighty Victim from the sky,
    Hell's fierce powers beneath Thee lie ;
    Thou hast conquer'd in the fight,
    Thou hast brought us life and light ;
    Now no more can death appal,
    Now no more the grave enthral ;
    Thou hast open'd Paradise,
    And in Thee Thy Saints shall rise.

    Easter triumph, Easter joy,
mf Sin alone can this destroy ;
    From sin's power do Thou set free
    Souls new-born, O LORD, in Thee.
f   Hymns of glory and of praise,
    Risen LORD, to Thee we raise ;
    Holy FATHER, praise to Thee,
    With the SPIRIT, ever be.

                R. CAMPBELL : based on the Latin.

Hymn 128. AD CŒNAM AGNI.—L.M. *(First Tune.)* *(First Version.)*

Mechlin Melody.

To be sung in Unison.

A - men.

Easter.

Hymn 128. PLAINSONG.—L.M. (*First Tune.*) (*Alternative Version.*)

To be sung in Unison.

Proper Sarum Melody.

A - men.

Hymn 128. PADDINGTON.—L.M. (*Second Tune.*)

R. REDHEAD, 1853.

A-men.

"Christ our Passover is sacrificed for us; therefore let us keep the feast."

f THE LAMB'S high banquet call'd to share,
Array'd in garments white and fair,
The Red Sea past, we fain would sing
To JESUS our triumphant King.

mf Upon the Altar of the Cross
His Body hath redeem'd our loss;
And, tasting of His precious Blood,
Our life is hid with Him in GOD.

Protected in the Paschal night
From the destroying Angel's might,
In triumph went the ransom'd free
From Pharaoh's cruel tyranny.

Now CHRIST our Passover is slain,
The LAMB of GOD without a stain;
His Flesh, the true unleaven'd Bread,
Is freely offer'd in our stead.

O all-sufficient Sacrifice,
Beneath Thee hell defeated lies;
Thy captive people are set free,
And crowns of life restored by Thee.

f We hymn Thee rising from the grave,
From death returning, strong to save;
Thine own Right Hand the tyrant chains,
And Paradise for man regains.

ff All praise be Thine, O risen LORD,
From death to endless life restored;
All praise to GOD the FATHER be
And HOLY GHOST eternally.

J. M. NEALE and Compilers: from the Latin.

(95)

Easter.

Hymn 129. Church Triumphant.—L.M.

J. W. Elliott.

A-men.

A lower setting of this Tune is given at Hymn 35.

" Buried with Him in baptism, wherein also ye are risen with Him through the faith of the operation of God, Who hath raised Him from the dead."

mf O CHRIST, the heavens' Eternal King,
Creator, unto Thee we sing,
With GOD the FATHER ever ONE,
Co-equal, co-eternal SON.

Thy Hand, when first the world began,
Made in Thine own pure Image man,
And link'd to fleshly form of earth
A living soul of heavenly birth.

And when the envious crafty foe
Had marr'd Thy noblest work below,
Thou didst our ruin'd state repair
By deigning flesh Thyself to wear.

Once of a Virgin born to save,
And now new-born from death's dark grave,
O CHRIST, Thou bidd'st us rise with Thee
From death to immortality.

Eternal Shepherd, Thou art wont
To cleanse Thy sheep within the font,
That mystic bath, that grave of sin,
Where ransom'd souls new life begin.

p Divine Redeemer, Thou didst deign
To bear for us the Cross of pain,
And freely pay the precious price
Of all Thy Blood in sacrifice.

mf JESU; do Thou to every heart
Unceasing Paschal joy impart :
From death of sin and guilty strife
Set free the new-born sons of life

f All praise be Thine, O risen LORD,
From death to endless life restored ;
All praise to GOD the FATHER be
And HOLY GHOST eternally.

Compilers : from the Latin.

ALTERNATIVE TUNE, HYMN 1 (SECOND TUNE).

Hymn 130. O FILII ET FILIÆ.—8 8 8 and Alleluias.

French Melody (17th cent.).

To be sung in Unison.

mf AL-LE-LU-IA! *f* AL-LE-LU-IA! *ff* AL-LE-LU-IA!

f Al-le-lu-ia! A-men.

Easter.

" This is the day which the Lord hath made ; we will rejoice and be glad in it."

f ALLELUIA ! ALLELUIA ! ALLELUIA !
 O sons and daughters, let us sing !
The King of Heav'n, the glorious King,
O'er death to-day rose triumphing.
   Alleluia !

mf That Easter morn, at break of day,
The faithful women went their way
To seek the tomb where JESUS lay.
   Alleluia !

An Angel clad in white they see,
Who sat, and spake unto the three,
" Your LORD doth go to Galilee."
   Alleluia !

p That night th' Apostles met in fear ;
cr Amidst them came their LORD most dear,
And said, (*p*) " My peace be on all here."
   Alleluia !

mf When Thomas first the tidings heard,
How they had seen the risen LORD,
He doubted the disciples' word.
   Alleluia !

p " My piercèd Side, O Thomas, see ;
My Hands, My Feet I show to thee ;
Not faithless, but believing be."
   Alleluia !

mf No longer Thomas then denied ;
He saw the Feet, the Hands, the Side ;
f " Thou art my LORD and GOD," he cried.
   Alleluia !

How blest are they who have not seen,
And yet whose faith hath constant been,
For they eternal life shall win.
   Alleluia !

On this most holy day of days,
To GOD your hearts and voices raise
In laud, and jubilee, and praise.
  ff Alleluia !

J. M. NEALE: from the Latin of J. Tisserand.

Hymn 131. ST. GEORGE.—7 7 7 7. 7 7 7 7.

Sir G. J. ELVEY.

A · men.

" Worthy is the Lamb that was slain to receive power, and riches, and wisdom, and strength, and honour, and glory, and blessing."

f CHRIST the LORD is risen to-day ;
 Christians, haste your vows to pay ;
Offer ye your praises meet
At the Paschal Victim's feet.
mf For the sheep the LAMB hath bled,
Sinless in the sinner's stead ;
ff " CHRIST is risen," to-day we cry ;
Now He lives no more to die.

f CHRIST, the Victim undefiled,
Man to GOD hath reconciled ;
Whilst in strange and awful strife
Met together Death and Life :

Christians, on this happy day
Haste with joy your vows to pay ;
ff " CHRIST is risen," to-day we cry ;
Now He lives no more to die.

mf CHRIST, Who once for sinners bled,
f Now the first-born from the dead,
ff Throned in endless might and power,
Lives and reigns for evermore.
Hail, Eternal Hope on high !
Hail, Thou King of victory !
Hail, Thou Prince of life adored !
mf Help and save us, gracious LORD.

JANE E. LEESON.

(97)

E

Easter.

Hymn 132. ROTTERDAM.—7 6 7 6. 7 6 7 6.　　　　B. TOURS.

A - men.

"Jesus met them, saying, All hail.'

f　THE Day of Resurrection !
　　　Earth, tell it out abroad ;
　The Passover of gladness,
　　The Passover of GOD !
　From death to life eternal,
　　From earth unto the sky,
　Our CHRIST hath brought us over
　　With hymns of victory.

mf　Our hearts be pure from evil,
　　That we may see aright
　The LORD in rays eternal
　　Of resurrection-light ;

　And, listening to His accents,
　　May hear so calm and plain
　His own " All hail," and, hearing,
　　May raise the victor strain.

f　Now let the heav'ns be joyful,
　　And earth her song begin,
　The round world keep high triumph,
　　And all that is therein ;
　Let all things seen and unseen
　　Their notes of gladness blend,
ff　For CHRIST the LORD is risen,
　　Our Joy that hath no end.

J. M. NEALE : from the Greek of
St. John of Damascus.

ALTERNATIVE TUNES, HYMNS 666 AND 765.

Hymn 133. ST. JOHN DAMASCENE.—7 6 7 6. 7 6 7 6.　　　A. H. BROWN.

A - men.

Easter.

" Lo, the winter is past."

f COME, ye faithful, raise the strain
    Of triumphant gladness ;
GOD hath brought His Israel
    Into joy from sadness ;
mf Loosed from Pharaoh's bitter yoke
    Jacob's sons and daughters ;
f Led them with unmoisten'd foot
    Through the Red Sea waters.

'Tis the Spring of souls to-day ;
    CHRIST hath burst His prison,
And from three days' sleep in death
    As a sun hath risen ;
mf All the winter of our sins,
    Long and dark, is flying
f From His Light, to Whom we give
    Laud and praise undying.

Now the Queen of seasons, bright
    With the Day of splendour,
With the royal Feast of feasts,
    Comes its joy to render ;
Comes to glad Jerusalem,
    Who with true affection
Welcomes in unwearied strains
    JESU'S Resurrection.

ff Alleluia now we cry
    To our King Immortal,
Who triumphant burst the bars
    Of the tomb's dark portal ;
Alleluia, with the SON
    GOD the FATHER praising ;
Alleluia yet again
    To the SPIRIT raising.

J. M. NEALE : from the Greek.
Doxology by Compilers

Hymn 134. EASTER HYMN. No. 1.—7 7 7 7 and Alleluias. (*First Tune.*)

W. H. MONK

" The Lord is risen indeed."

f JESUS CHRIST is risen to-day,
    Alleluia !
Our triumphant holy day,
    Alleluia !
mf Who did once, upon the Cross,
    Alleluia !
Suffer to redeem our loss.
    Alleluia !

f Hymns of praise then let us sing
    Alleluia !
Unto CHRIST, our heavenly King,
    Alleluia !
mf Who endured the Cross and grave,
    Alleluia !
Sinners to redeem and save.
    Alleluia !

But the pain which He endured
    Alleluia !
f Our salvation hath procured ;
    Alleluia !
ff Now above the sky He's King,
    Alleluia !
Where the Angels ever sing.
    Alleluia !

From *Lyra Davidica*, 1708.

Easter.

Hymn 134. Easter Hymn. No. 2.—7 7 7 7 and Alleluias. (*Second Tune.*)

Lyra Davidica, 1708.

"The Lord is risen indeed."

f   JESUS CHRIST is risen to-day,
        Alleluia!
  Our triumphant holy day,
        Alleluia!
mf Who did once, upon the Cross,
        Alleluia!
  Suffer to redeem our loss.
        Alleluia!

f   Hymns of praise then let us sing
        Alleluia!
  Unto CHRIST, our heavenly King,
        Alleluia!
mf Who endured the Cross and grave,
        Alleluia!
  Sinners to redeem and save.
        Alleluia!

  But the pain which He endured
        Alleluia!
f   Our salvation hath procured;
        Alleluia!
ff   Now above the sky He's King,
        Alleluia!
  Where the Angels ever sing.
        Alleluia!

From *Lyra Davidica*, 1708.

Hymn 135. VICTORY.—8 8 8 and Alleluias.   From P. DA PALESTRINA, 1591.

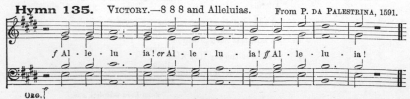

Org.

(100)

Easter.

A - men.

" O sing unto the Lord a new song ; for He hath done marvellous things.'

f ALLELUIA ! ALLELUIA ! ALLELUIA !
   The strife is o'er, the battle done ;
Now is the Victor's triumph won ;
ff O let the song of praise be sung.
             Alleluia !

f Death's mightiest powers have done their
And JESUS hath His foes dispersed ; [worst,
ff Let shouts of praise and joy outburst.
             Alleluia !

f On the third morn He rose again
Glorious in majesty to reign ;
O let us swell the joyful strain.
             Alleluia !

p LORD, by the stripes which wounded Thee
From death's dread sting Thy servants free,
f That we may live, and sing to Thee
      ff Alleluia !

F. POTT: from the Latin.

Hymn 136. WÜRTEMBURG.—7 7 7 7 4.

J. ROSENMÜLLER (?) (1610–1686).

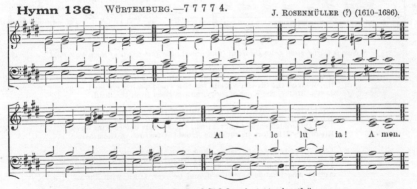

Al - le - lu - ia ! A - men.

" Alleluia ! for the Lord God Omnipotent reigneth."

f CHRIST the LORD is risen again ;
   CHRIST hath broken every chain ;
Hark ! Angelic voices cry,
Singing evermore on high,
             Alleluia !

mf He, Who gave for us His life,
Who for us endured the strife,
Is our Paschal LAMB to-day ;
f We too sing for joy, and say
             Alleluia !

mf He, Who bore all pain and loss
Comfortless upon the Cross,
f Lives in glory now on high,
Pleads for us, and hears our cry ;
             Alleluia !

mf He, Who slumber'd in the grave,
f Is exalted now to save ;
ff Now through Christendom it rings
That the LAMB is King of kings.
             Alleluia !

mf Now He bids us tell abroad
How the lost may be restored,
How the penitent forgiven,
How we too may enter Heav'n.
             Alleluia !

Thou, our Paschal LAMB indeed,
CHRIST, Thy ransom'd people feed :
Take our sins and guilt away,
f Let us sing by night and day
      ff Alleluia !

CATHERINE WINKWORTH : from
the German of M. Weisse.

(101)

Easter.

Hymn 137. Lux Eoi.—8 7 8 7. 8 7 8 7.

Sir A. Sullivan.

A - men.

" Now is Christ risen from the dead, and become the first-fruits of them that slept."

f   ALLELUIA ! Alleluia ! Hearts to Heav'n and voices raise ;
         Sing to GOD a hymn of gladness, sing to GOD a hymn of praise ;
p   He, Who on the Cross a Victim for the world's salvation bled,
f   JESUS CHRIST, the King of glory, now is risen from the dead.

     CHRIST is risen, CHRIST the first-fruits of the holy harvest field,
     Which will all its full abundance at His second coming yield ;
     Then the golden ears of harvest will their heads before Him wave,
     Ripen'd by His glorious sunshine, from the furrows of the grave.

mf   CHRIST is risen, we are risen ; shed upon us heavenly grace.
     Rain, and dew, and gleams of glory from the brightness of Thy Face ;
     That we, with our hearts in Heav'n, here on earth may fruitful be,
     And by Angel-hands be gather'd, and be ever, LORD, with Thee.

ff   Alleluia ! Alleluia ! Glory be to GOD on high ;
     Alleluia to the SAVIOUR, Who has gain'd the victory ;
     Alleluia to the SPIRIT, fount of love and sanctity ;
     Alleluia ! Alleluia ! to the TRIUNE Majesty.

Bishop C. Wordsworth.

Hymn 138. Resurrexit.—8 7 8 7. 7 5 7 5. 8 7 8 7.   (*First Tune.*)

Sir A. Sullivan.

Easter.

" He is risen."

f CHRIST is risen! CHRIST is risen!
  He hath burst His bonds in twain;
 CHRIST is risen! CHRIST is risen!
  Alleluia! swell the strain!
mf For our gain He suffer'd loss
   By Divine decree;
p He hath died upon the Cross,
   But our GOD is He.
ff CHRIST is risen! CHRIST is risen!
  He hath burst His bonds in twain;
 CHRIST is risen! CHRIST is risen!
  Alleluia! swell the strain!

mf See the chains of death are broken;
  Earth below and heav'n above
 Joy in each amazing token
  Of His rising, LORD of love;
f He for evermore shall reign
   By the FATHER'S side,

dim Till He comes to earth again,
  Comes to claim His Bride.
ff CHRIST is risen! CHRIST is risen!
  He hath burst His bonds in twain;
 CHRIST is risen! CHRIST is risen!
  Alleluia! swell the strain!

mf Glorious Angels downward thronging
  Hail the LORD of all the skies;
 Heav'n, with joy and holy longing
  For the WORD Incarnate, cries,
f "CHRIST is risen! Earth, rejoice!
   Gleam, ye starry train!
  All creation, find a voice;
   He o'er all shall reign."
ff CHRIST is risen! CHRIST is risen!
  He hath burst His bonds in twain;
 CHRIST is risen! CHRIST is risen!
  O'er the universe to reign.

A. T. GURNEY.

(103)

Easter.

Hymn 138. Fitzroy.—8 7 8 7. 7 5 7 5. 8 7 8 7. *(Second Tune.)*

"He is risen."

Sir C. V. STANFORD.

UNISON.

ORGAN.

f 1. CHRIST is ris - en! CHRIST is ris - en! He hath
mf 2. See the chains of death are bro - ken; Earth be -
mf 3. Glo - rious An - gels down - ward throng - ing Hail the

burst His bonds in twain; CHRIST is ris - en!
low and heav'n a - bove Joy in each a -
LORD of all the skies; Heav'n, with joy and

CHRIST is ris - en! Al - le - lu - ia! swell the strain!
- maz - ing tok - en Of His ris - ing, LORD of love;
ho - ly long - ing For the WORD In - car - nate, cries,

mf For our gain He suf - fer'd loss By Di - vine de - cree;
f He for ev - er - more shall reign By the FA - THER'S side,
f "CHRIST is ris - en! Earth, re - joice! Gleam, ye star - ry train!

Easter.

p He hath died up-on the Cross, f But our GOD is He.
dim Till he comes to earth a-gain, Comes to claim His Bride.
All cre-a-tion, find a voice; He o'er all shall reign."

ff
CHRIST is ris-en! CHRIST is ris-en! He hath burst His
CHRIST is ris-en! CHRIST is ris-en! He hath burst His
CHRIST is ris-en! CHRIST is ris-en! He hath burst His

bonds in twain; CHRIST is ris-en! CHRIST is ris-en!
bonds in twain; CHRIST is ris-en! CHRIST is ris-en!
bonds in twain; CHRIST is ris-en! CHRIST is ris-en!

Al-le-lu-ia! swell the strain!
Al-le-lu-ia! swell the strain!
O'er the u-ni-verse to reign. A-men.

A. T. GURNEY.

E 2

Easter.

W. HAYES, 1774.

A-men.

" The First-begotten of the dead."

mf COME see the place where JESUS lay,
   And hear Angelic watchers say,
f   " He lives, Who once was slain :
mf Why seek the living 'midst the dead ?
Remember how the Saviour said
f   That He would rise again."

O joyful sound ! O glorious hour,
When by His own Almighty power
   He rose, and left the grave !
ff Now let our songs His triumph tell,
Who burst the bands of death and hell,
   And ever lives to save.

f The First-begotten of the dead,
For us He rose, our glorious Head,
   Immortal life to bring ;
What though the saints like Him shall die,
They share their Leader's victory,
   And triumph with their King.

mf No more they tremble at the grave,
For JESUS will their spirits save,
   And raise their slumbering dust :
f   O risen LORD, in Thee we live,
dim To Thee our ransom'd souls we give,
p   To Thee our bodies trust.

T. KELLY, 1804, and Compilers.

Hymn 140. ST. ALBINUS.—7 8.7 8.4. *(First Tune.)*

H. J. GAUNTLETT.

f Al-le-lu - ia !   A-men.

Hymn 140. LINDISFARNE.—7 8.7 8.4. *(Second Tune.)*

Rev. J. B. DYKES.

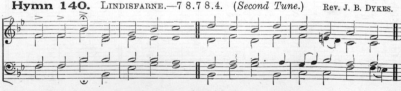

Easter.

Al - le - lu - ia! A-men.

"I am He that liveth, and was dead; and behold, I am alive for evermore, Amen; and have the keys of hell and of death."

f **J**ESUS lives! no longer now
　Can thy terrors, death, appal us;
JESUS lives! by this we know
　Thou, O grave, canst not enthral us.
　　　　Alleluia!

JESUS lives! henceforth is death
　But the gate of life immortal;
p This shall calm our trembling breath,
　When we pass its gloomy portal.
　　　mf Alleluia!

JESUS lives! to Him the Throne
Over all the world is given;
mf May we go where He is gone,
cr 　Rest and reign with Him in Heaven.
　　　　Alleluia!

f JESUS lives! (*p*) for us He died;
mf 　Then, alone to JESUS living,
Pure in heart may we abide,
Glory to our Saviour giving.
　　　　Alleluia!

f JESUS lives! our hearts know well
　Nought from us His love shall sever;
Life, nor death, nor powers of hell
Tear us from His keeping ever.
　　　　Alleluia!

FRANCES E. COX: from the German of C. F. Gellert.

Hymn 141. SHROPSHIRE.—L.M.

E. J. HOPKINS.

A - men.

"When thou liest down, thou shalt not be afraid; yea, thou shalt lie down, and thy sleep shall be sweet."

FOR A LATE EVENING SERVICE.

mf **J**ESU, the world's redeeming LORD,
　The FATHER'S co-eternal WORD,
Of Light invisible true Light,
Thine Israel's Keeper day and night;

Our great Creator and our Guide,
Who times and seasons dost divide,
Refresh at night with quiet rest
Our limbs by daily toil oppress'd:

That while in this frail house of clay
A little longer here we stay,
p Our flesh in Thee may sweetly sleep,
Our souls with Thee their vigils keep.

mf We pray Thee, while we dwell below,
Preserve us from our ghostly foe;
Nor let his wiles victorious be
O'er them that are redeem'd by Thee.

O LORD of all, with us abide
In this our joyful Easter-tide;
From every weapon death can wield
Thine own redeem'd for ever shield.

f All praise be Thine, O risen LORD,
From death to endless life restored;
All praise to GOD the FATHER be,
And HOLY GHOST eternally.

J. W. COPELAND and Compilers:
from the Latin.

ALTERNATIVE PLAINSONG TUNE, HYMN 15.

The following Hymns are suitable for this season:

Rogation Days.

Hymn 142. LATCHFORD.—6 6 6 6.8 8. *(First Tune.)* Rev. W. STATHAM.

A-men.

"Lord, Thou art become gracious unto Thy land."

mf TO Thee our GOD we fly
For mercy and for grace;
O hear our lowly cry,
And hide not Thou Thy Face.
f O LORD, stretch forth Thy mighty hand,
mf And guard and bless our Fatherland.

f Arise, O LORD of hosts!
Be jealous for Thy Name,
And drive from out our coasts
The sins that put to shame.
O LORD, stretch forth Thy mighty hand,
mf And guard and bless our Fatherland.

Thy best gifts from on high
In rich abundance pour,
That we may magnify
And praise Thee more and more.
f O LORD, stretch forth Thy mighty hand,
mf And guard and bless our Fatherland.

The powers ordain'd by Thee
With heavenly wisdom bless;
May they Thy servants be,
And rule in righteousness.
f O LORD, stretch forth Thy mighty hand,
mf And guard and bless our Fatherland.

The Church of Thy dear SON
Inflame with love's pure fire,
Bind her once more in one,
And life and truth inspire.
f O LORD, stretch forth Thy mighty hand,
mf And guard and bless our Fatherland.

The Pastors of Thy fold
With grace and power endue,
That faithful, pure, and bold,
They may be Pastors true.
f O LORD, stretch forth Thy mighty hand,
mf And guard and bless our Fatherland.

O let us love Thy house,
And sanctify Thy day,
Bring unto Thee our vows,
And loyal homage pay.
f O LORD, stretch forth Thy mighty hand,
mf And guard and bless our Fatherland.

p Give peace, LORD, in our time;
O let no foe draw nigh,
Nor lawless deed of crime
Insult Thy Majesty.
f O LORD, stretch forth Thy mighty hand,
mf And guard and bless our Fatherland.

p Though vile and worthless, still
Thy people, LORD, are we;
cr And for our GOD we will
None other have but Thee.
f O LORD, stretch forth Thy mighty hand,
And guard and bless our Fatherland.

Bishop W. WALSHAM HOW.

This Hymn may also be sung at other seasons.

Hymn 142. PRO PATRIA.—6 6 6 6.8 8. *(Second Tune.)*
"Lord, Thou art become gracious unto Thy land."

Verses 1, 2, 4, 5, 7, 9 in Unison.
Slowly.

J. ARMISTEAD.

1. To Thee our GOD we fly   For mer - cy and for grace;   O
2. A - rise, O LORD of hosts!   Be jeal - ous for Thy Name,   And
4. The powers or - dain'd by Thee   With heav'n - ly wis - dom bless;   May
5. The Church of Thy dear SON   In - flame with love's pure fire,   Bind
7. O let us love Thy house,   And sanc - ti - fy Thy day,   Bring
9. Though vile and worth - less, still   Thy peo - ple, LORD, are we;   And

ORGAN. *f*

[For copyright, see p. lv.]

(108)

Rogation Days.

hear our low‑ly cry, And hide not Thou Thy Face.
drive from out our coasts The sins that put to shame.
they Thy ser‑vants be, And rule in right‑eous‑ness.
her once more in one, And life and truth in‑spire.
un‑to Thee our vows, And loy‑al hom‑age pay.
for our GOD we will None o‑ther have but Thee.

O LORD, stretch

forth Thy migh‑ty hand, And guard and bless our Fa‑ther‑land. A‑men.

Verses 3, 6, 8 in Harmony.

3. Thy best gifts from on high . . In rich a‑bun‑dance pour, . . That
6. The Pas‑tors of Thy fold . . With grace and power en‑due, . . That
8. Give peace, LORD, in our time; . . O let no foe draw nigh, . . Nor

we may mag‑ni‑fy And praise Thee more and more.
faith‑ful, pure, and bold, They may be Pas‑tors true.
law‑less deed of crime In‑sult Thy Ma‑jes‑ty.

O LORD, stretch

forth Thy migh‑ty hand, . . And guard and bless our Fa‑ther‑land.

Bishop W. WALSHAM HOW.

Rogation Days.

Hymn 143. LINCOLN.—C.M. RAVENSCROFT, *Psalmes*, 1621.

A - men.

"The eyes of all wait upon Thee, O Lord; and Thou givest them their meat in due season."

mf LORD, in Thy Name Thy servants plead,
    And Thou hast sworn to hear;
Thine is the harvest, Thine the seed,
    The fresh and fading year.

Our hope, when Autumn winds blew wild,
    We trusted, LORD, with Thee:
And still, now Spring has on us smiled,
    We wait on Thy decree.

The former and the latter rain,
    The summer sun and air,

The green ear, and the golden grain,
    All Thine, are ours by prayer.

Thine too by right, and ours by grace,
    The wondrous growth unseen,
The hopes that soothe, the fears that brace,
    The love that shines serene.

So grant the precious things brought forth
    By sun and moon below,
That Thee in Thy new Heav'n and earth
    We never may forego.

J. KEBLE.

The following Hymns are suitable for this season:

468 Litany for the Rogation Days.   **505** O throned, O crown'd with all renown.

Ascensiontide.

Hymn 144. ST. AMBROSE.—L.M. (*First Tune.*) LA FEILLÉE, *Méthode*, 1808.

A - men.

Hymn 144. EASTWICK.—L.M. (*Second Tune.*) T. T. NOBLE.

A - men.

Ascensiontide.

" All power is given unto Me in heaven and in earth."

mf O LORD most High, Eternal King,
 By Thee redeem'd Thy praise we sing ;
The bonds of death are burst by Thee,
And grace has won the victory.

Ascending to the FATHER'S Throne
Thou claim'st the kingdom as Thine own ;
Thy days of mortal weakness o'er,
All power is Thine for evermore.

To Thee the whole creation now
Shall, in its threefold order, bow,
Of things on earth, and things on high,
And things that underneath us lie.

p In awe and wonder Angels see
How changed is man's estate by Thee,
How Flesh makes pure as flesh did stain,
And Thou, True GOD, in Flesh dost reign.

f Be Thou our Joy, O mighty LORD,
As Thou wilt be our great Reward ;
Let all our glory be in Thee
Both now and through eternity.

All praise from every heart and tongue
To Thee, ascended LORD, be sung ;
All praise to GOD the FATHER be
And HOLY GHOST eternally.

J. M. NEALE : from the Latin.

For Plainsong Tune, see Hymn 311.

Hymn 145. ASCENDIT. 8 8 6. 8 8 6. (*First Tune.*)   Sir J. STAINER.

A-men.

Hymn 145. HASLINGDEN.—8 8 6. 8 8 6. (*Second Tune.*)   H. HILES.

A - men.

*" This same Jesus, Which is taken up from you into heaven, shall so come in like manner
as ye have seen Him go into heaven."*

f O CHRIST our Joy, gone up on high
 To fill Thy Throne above the sky,
How glorious dost Thou shine !
Thy Sovereign rule the worlds obey,
And earthly joys all fade away
 In that pure light of Thine.

p To Thee in prayer Thy people bow ;
O may our sins Thy pardon know,
 The cleansing of Thy grace ;
cr Then lift our hearts to Thee above,
On wings of faithfulness and love,
 To seek Thy holy place.

mf So, when the sudden call shall sound,
And with Thy robe of clouds around
 Thou, CHRIST, shalt come once more,
dim Thyself our Judge may'st turn away
 The penalty our sins should pay,
cr And our lost crowns restore.

f Ascended up from mortal sight,
JESU, we praise Thee in the height,
 Our Joy, our great Reward ;
Whom with the FATHER we confess,
And with the HOLY SPIRIT bless,
 ONE ever-glorious LORD.

D. T. MORGAN : from the Latin.

Ascensiontide.

Hymn 146. BISHOP.—L.M.

J. BISHOP, 1665-1737.

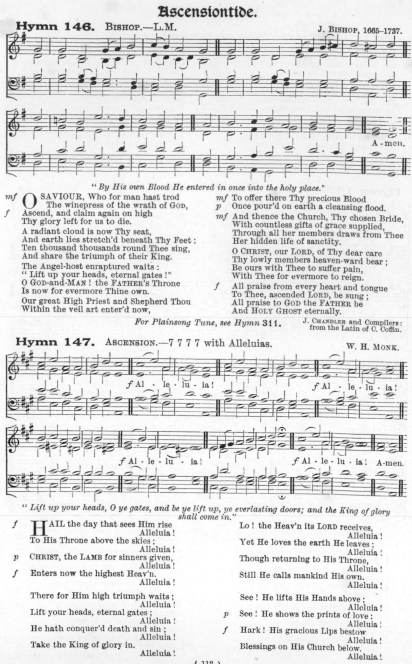

"By His own Blood He entered in once into the holy place."

mf O SAVIOUR, Who for man hast trod
  The winepress of the wrath of GOD,
f Ascend, and claim again on high
Thy glory left for us to die.

A radiant cloud is now Thy seat,
And earth lies stretch'd beneath Thy Feet:
Ten thousand thousands round Thee sing,
And share the triumph of their King.

The Angel-host enraptured waits :
" Lift up your heads, eternal gates !"
O GOD-and-MAN ! the FATHER'S Throne
Is now for evermore Thine own.

Our great High Priest and Shepherd Thou
Within the veil art enter'd now,

mf To offer there Thy precious Blood
p Once pour'd on earth a cleansing flood.

mf And thence the Church, Thy chosen Bride,
With countless gifts of grace supplied,
Through all her members draws from Thee
Her hidden life of sanctity.

O CHRIST, our LORD, of Thy dear care
Thy lowly members heaven-ward bear ;
Be ours with Thee to suffer pain,
With Thee for evermore to reign.

f All praise from every heart and tongue
To Thee, ascended LORD, be sung ;
All praise to GOD the FATHER be
And HOLY GHOST eternally.

For Plainsong Tune, see Hymn 311.

J. CHANDLER and Compilers:
from the Latin of C. Coffin.

Hymn 147. ASCENSION.—7 7 7 7 with Alleluias.

W. H. MONK.

*" Lift up your heads, O ye gates, and be ye lift up, ye everlasting doors; and the King of glory
shall come in."*

f HAIL the day that sees Him rise
      Alleluia !
To His Throne above the skies ;
      Alleluia !
p CHRIST, the LAMB for sinners given,
      Alleluia !
f Enters now the highest Heav'n.
      Alleluia !

There for Him high triumph waits ;
      Alleluia !
Lift your heads, eternal gates ;
      Alleluia !
He hath conquer'd death and sin ;
      Alleluia !
Take the King of glory in.
      Alleluia !

Lo ! the Heav'n its LORD receives,
      Alleluia !
Yet He loves the earth He leaves ;
      Alleluia !
Though returning to His Throne,
      Alleluia !
Still He calls mankind His own.
      Alleluia !

See ! He lifts His Hands above ;
      Alleluia !
p See ! He shows the prints of love ;
      Alleluia !
f Hark ! His gracious Lips bestow
      Alleluia !
Blessings on His Church below.
      Alleluia !

(112)

Ascensiontide.

<table>
<tr><td>p</td><td>Still for us He intercedes,
Alleluia !</td><td>p</td><td>LORD, though parted from our sight
Alleluia !</td></tr>
<tr><td></td><td>His prevailing Death He pleads,
Alleluia !</td><td>cr</td><td>Far above the starry height,
Alleluia !</td></tr>
<tr><td>cr</td><td>Near Himself prepares our place,
Alleluia !</td><td></td><td>Grant our hearts may thither rise,
Alleluia !</td></tr>
<tr><td>f</td><td>He the first-fruits of our race.
Alleluia !</td><td>f</td><td>Seeking Thee above the skies.
Alleluia :</td></tr>
</table>

C. WESLEY and T. COTTERILL

Hymn 148. *(First Part.)* REX GLORIÆ.—8 7 8 7.8 7 8 7. H. SMART.

A · men.

A lower setting of this Tune is given at Hymn 397.

"*Thou art gone up on high, Thou hast led captivity captive, and received gifts for men.*"

f SEE the Conqueror mounts in triumph, see the King in royal state
Riding on the clouds His chariot to His heavenly palace gate ;
Hark ! the choirs of Angel voices joyful Alleluias sing,
And the portals high are lifted to receive their Heavenly King.

mf Who is this that comes in glory, with the trump of jubilee ?
f LORD of battles, GOD of armies, He has gain'd the victory ;
p He Who on the Cross did suffer, (mf) He Who from the grave arose,
f He has vanquish'd sin and Satan, He by death has spoil'd His foes.

mf While He lifts His Hands in blessing, He is parted from His friends ;
While their eager eyes behold Him, He upon the clouds ascends ;
He Who walk'd with GOD, and pleased Him, preaching truth and doom to come.
He, our Enoch, is translated to His everlasting home

p Now our heavenly Aaron enters, with His Blood, within the veil ;
mf Joshua now is come to Canaan, and the kings before Him quail ;
Now He plants the tribes of Israel in their promised resting-place ;
Now our great Elijah offers double portion of His grace.

He has raised our human nature on the clouds to GOD'S right hand ;
There we sit in heavenly places, there with Him in glory stand :
f JESUS reigns, adored by Angels ; MAN with GOD is on the Throne ;
Mighty LORD, in Thine Ascension (p) we by faith behold our own.

The following Doxology may be sung at the end of either Part :

ff Glory be to GOD the FATHER ; glory be to GOD the SON,
Dying, ris'n, ascending for us, Who the heavenly realm has won ;
Glory to the HOLY SPIRIT ; to ONE GOD in Persons THREE
Glory both in earth and Heaven, glory, endless glory be.

Bishop C. WORDSWORTH.

ALTERNATIVE TUNE, HYMN 677.

Ascensiontide.

Hymn 148. *(Second Part.)* ILLUMINATOR.—8 7 8 7.8 7 8 7. C. STEGGALL.

A - men.

" Thou art gone up on high, Thou hast led captivity captive, and received gifts for men."

PART 2.

mf HOLY GHOST, Illuminator, shed Thy beams upon our eyes,
Help us to look up with Stephen, and to see, beyond the skies,
Where the SON of Man in glory standing is at GOD'S right hand,
Beckoning on His Martyr army, succouring His faithful band ;

f See Him, Who is gone before us, heavenly mansions to prepare,
p See Him, Who is ever pleading for us with prevailing prayer,
f See Him, Who with sound of trumpet and with His Angelic train,
Summoning the world to judgment, on the clouds will come again.

mf Lift us up from earth to Heaven, give us wings of faith and love,
Gales of holy aspirations wafting us to realms above ;
That, with hearts and minds uplifted, we with CHRIST our LORD may dwell,
Where He sits enthroned in glory in His heavenly citadel.

So at last, when He appeareth, we from out our graves may spring,
With our youth renew'd like eagles, flocking round our Heavenly King,
cr Caught up on the clouds of Heaven, and may meet Him in the air,
Rise to realms where He is reigning, and may reign for ever there.

The following Doxology may be sung at the end of either Part :

ff Glory be to GOD the FATHER ; glory be to GOD the SON,
Dying, ris'n, ascending for us, Who the heavenly realm has won ;
Glory to the HOLY SPIRIT ; to ONE GOD in Persons THREE
Glory both in earth and Heaven, glory, endless glory be.

Bishop C. WORDSWORTH.

ALTERNATIVE TUNE, HYMN 677.

Ascensiontide.

Hymn 149. OLIVET.—D.S.M. (*First Tune.*)   Rev. J. B. DYKES.

A - men.

Hymn 149. OLD 25TH.—D.S.M. (*Second Tune.*)   Psalmes, 1558.

A - men.

" Who is gone into heaven."

f   THOU art gone up on high,
        To mansions in the skies ;
And round Thy Throne unceasingly
        The songs of praise arise ;
p   But we are lingering here,
        With sin and care oppress'd ;
cr   LORD, send Thy promised Comforter,
        And lead us to Thy rest.

f   Thou art gone up on high ;
p   But Thou didst first come down,
Through earth's most bitter misery
cr   To pass unto Thy Crown ;

p   And girt with griefs and fears
        Our onward course must be ;
cr   But only let this path of tears
        Lead us at last to Thee.

f   Thou art gone up on high ;
        But Thou shalt come again,
With all the bright ones of the sky
        Attendant in Thy train.
mf   LORD, by Thy saving power
        So make us live and die,
cr   That we may stand in that dread hour
f   At Thy right Hand on high.

MRS. TOKE, 1851

(175)

Ascensiontide.

Hymn 150. METZLER'S REDHEAD.—C.M.

R. REDHEAD.

A - men

"Who being the Brightness of His Glory, and the express image of His person, and upholding all
things by the word of His power, when He had by Himself purged our sins, sat down on the
right hand of the Majesty on high."

mf   JESU, our Hope, our heart's Desire,
     Thy work of grace we sing ;
Redeemer of the world art Thou,
     Its Maker and its King.

p   How vast the mercy and the love,
     Which laid our sins on Thee,
And led Thee to a cruel death,
     To set Thy people free !

f   But now the bonds of death are burst ;
     The ransom has been paid ;
And Thou art on Thy FATHER'S Throne,
     In glorious robes array'd.

mf   O may Thy mighty love prevail
     Our sinful souls to spare !
O may we stand around Thy Throne,
     And see Thy glory there !

JESU, our only Joy be Thou,
     As Thou our Prize wilt be ;
In Thee be all our glory now
     And through eternity

f   All praise to Thee Who art gone up
     Triumphantly to Heav'n ,
All praise to GOD the FATHER'S Name
     And HOLY GHOST be given.

J. CHANDLER and Compilers:
from the Latin.

The following Hymns are suitable for this season :

Whitsun=Even.

Hymn 151. CANTERBURY.—7 7 7 7. *(First Version.)*

O. GIBBONS, 1623.

A - men.

Hymn 151. CANTERBURY.—7 7 7 7. *(Alternative Version.)*   O. GIBBONS, 1623.

Whitsun-Even.

A - men.

"If I go not away, the Comforter will not come unto you; but if I depart, I will send Him unto you."

mf RULER of the hosts of light,
  Death hath yielded to Thy might;
And Thy Blood hath mark'd a road
Which will lead us back to GOD.

From Thy dwelling-place above,
From Thy FATHER'S Throne of love,
With Thy look of mercy bless
p Those without Thee comfortless.

Bitter were Thy throes on earth,
Giving to the Church her birth

From the spear-wound opening wide
In Thine own life-giving Side.

f Now in glory Thou dost reign
Won by all Thy toil and pain;
mf Thence the promised SPIRIT send,
While our prayers to Thee ascend.

f JESU, praise to Thee be given
With the FATHER high in heaven;
HOLY SPIRIT, praise to Thee,
Now and through eternity.

J. CHANDLER: from the Latin.

Whitsuntide.

Hymn 152. ST. MICHAEL.—S.M.   *Psalmes*, 1561.

A - men.

A lower setting of this Tune is given at Hymn 380.

"And when the day of Pentecost was fully come, they were all with one accord in one place."

mf ABOVE the starry spheres,
  To where He was before,
CHRIST had gone up, the FATHER'S gift
Upon the Church to pour.

At length had fully come,
On mystic circle borne
Of seven times seven revolving days,
The Pentecostal morn:

When, as the Apostles knelt
At the third hour in prayer,
cr A sudden rushing sound proclaim'd
p That GOD Himself was there.

mf Forthwith a tongue of fire
Is seen on every brow,
Each heart receives the FATHER'S light,
The WORD'S enkindling glow;

The HOLY GHOST on all
Is mightily outpour'd,

Who straight in divers tongues declare
The wonders of the LORD.

While strangers of all climes
Flock round from far and near,
And their own tongue, wherever born,
All with amazement hear.

But Judah, faithless still,
Denies the hand Divine;
And, mocking, jeers the saints of CHRIST
As full of new-made wine.

Till Peter, in the midst,
By Joel's ancient word
Rebukes their unbelief, (*cr*) and wins
Three thousand to the LORD.

f The FATHER and the SON
And SPIRIT we adore;
O may the SPIRIT'S gifts be pour'd
On us for evermore.

E. CASWALL and Compilers:
from the Latin.

ALTERNATIVE TUNE, HYMN 759.

Whitsuntide.

Hymn 153. GLEBE FIELD.—7 7 7 7. (*First Tune.*)   Rev. J. B. DYKES.

A - men.

Hymn 153. CRUCIS MILITES.—7 7 7 7. (*Second Tune.*)   M. B. FOSTER.

A - men.

A higher version of this Tune is given at Hymn **588.**

" I will pour out My Spirit upon all flesh."

f   JOY! because the circling year
     Brings our day of blessings here ;
   Day when first the light Divine
   On the Church began to shine.

mf   Like to quivering tongues of flame
   Unto each the SPIRIT came,
   Tongues, that earth might hear their call,
   Fire, that love might burn in all.

f   So the wondrous works of GOD
   Wondrously were spread abroad ;
   Every tribe's familiar tone
   Made the glorious marvel known.

mf   Harden'd scoffers vainly jeer'd ;
   Listening strangers heard and fear'd,
   Knew the prophet's word fulfill'd,
   Own'd the work which GOD had will'd.

   Still Thy SPIRIT'S fulness, LORD,
   On Thy waiting Church be pour'd ;
p   Grant our burden'd hearts release ;
   Grant us Thine abiding peace.

J. ELLERTON and Compilers : from the Latin.

(118)

Whitsuntide.

Hymn 154. WINCHESTER OLD.—C.M.   ESTE, *Psalms*, 1592.

A-men.

A setting of this Tune with Alternative Harmonies is given at Hymn 62.

" And suddenly there came a sound from heaven, as of a rushing mighty wind."

mf WHEN GOD of old came down from Heav'n,
      In power and wrath He came ;
Before His feet the clouds were riven,
      Half darkness and half flame :

p   But, when He came the second time,
      He came in power and love ;
Softer than gale at morning prime
      Hover'd His holy Dove.

mf The fires, that rush'd on Sinai down
      In sudden torrents dread,
p   Now gently light, (*cr*) a glorious crown,
      On every sainted head.

f   And as on Israel's awe-struck ear
      The voice exceeding loud,

The trump, that Angels quake to hear,
      Thrill'd from the deep, dark cloud ;

So, when the SPIRIT of our GOD
      Came down His flock to find,
A voice from Heav'n was heard abroad,
      A rushing, mighty wind.

mf It fills the Church of GOD ; it fills
      The sinful world around ;
Only in stubborn hearts and wills
      No place for it is found.

p   Come LORD, come Wisdom, Love, and Power,
      Open our ears to hear ;
Let us not miss the accepted hour ;
      Save, LORD, by love or fear.

                              J. KEBLE.

Hymn 155. MELCOMBE.—L.M.   S. WEBBE, 1782.

A-men.

Lower settings of this Tune are given at Hymns 4 and 363.

" And the same day there were added unto them about three thousand souls."

mf SPIRIT of mercy, truth, and love,
      O shed Thine influence from above ;
And still from age to age convey
The wonders of this sacred day.

f   In every clime, by every tongue,
      Be GOD's surpassing glory sung ;

Let all the listening earth be taught
The acts our great Redeemer wrought.

mf Unfailing Comfort, Heavenly Guide,
Still o'er Thy Holy Church preside ;
Still let mankind Thy blessings prove,
SPIRIT of mercy, truth, and love.

      From *Foundling Hospital Collection*, 1774.

ALTERNATIVE TUNE, HYMN 1 (SECOND TUNE).

(119)

Whitsuntide.

Hymn 156. VENI SANCTE SPIRITUS.—7 7 7.7 7 7.   S. WEBBE, 1782.

A - men.

" When Thou lettest Thy breath go forth they shall be made, and Thou shalt renew the face of the earth."

mf COME, Thou HOLY SPIRIT, come ;
    And from Thy celestial home
Shed a ray of light Divine ;
Come, Thou Father of the poor,
Come, Thou source of all our store,
    Come, within our bosoms shine :

Thou of Comforters the best,
Thou the soul's most welcome guest,
p   Sweet refreshment here below ;
In our labour rest most sweet,
Grateful coolness in the heat,
    Solace in the midst of woe.

mf O most Blessèd Light Divine,
Shine within these hearts of Thine,
    And our inmost being fill ;

p Where Thou art not, man hath nought,
Nothing good in deed or thought,
    Nothing free from taint of ill.

mf Heal our wounds ; our strength renew ;
On our dryness pour Thy dew ;
    Wash the stains of guilt away :
Bend the stubborn heart and will ;
Melt the frozen, warm the chill ;
    Guide the steps that go astray.

On the faithful, who adore
And confess Thee, evermore
    In Thy sevenfold gifts descend :
Give them virtue's sure reward,
cr Give them Thy salvation, LORD,
f   Give them joys that never end.

E. CASWALL and Compilers : from the
Latin of Abp. Stephen Langton (?).

This Hymn may also be sung at other seasons.

Hymn 157. VENI CREATOR. No. 1.—L.M. *(First Tune.)*

To be sung in Unison.   Proper Sarum Melody.

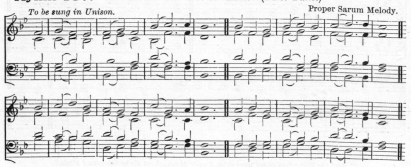

" The Comforter which is the Holy Ghost."

mf COME, HOLY GHOST, our souls inspire,
    And lighten with celestial fire ;
Thou the anointing SPIRIT art,
Who dost Thy sevenfold gifts impart :

Thy blessèd unction from above
Is comfort, life, and fire of love ;
Enable with perpetual light
The dulness of our blinded sight :

Anoint and cheer our soilèd face
With the abundance of Thy grace :
Keep far our foes, give peace at home ;
Where Thou art Guide no ill can come.

Teach us to know the FATHER, SON,
And THEE, of Both, to be but ONE ;
That through the ages all along
This may be our endless song,

(120)

Whitsuntide.

f Praise . . to Thy e - ter - nal me - rit,

FA - THER, SON, and HO - LY SPI - RIT. A - men. . .

Bishop COSIN: from the Latin of Rabanus Maurus.

This Hymn may also be sung at other seasons.

Another form of this Tune is given at Hymn 347.

Hymn 157. VENI CREATOR. No. 2.—L.M. *(Second Tune.)* REV. J. B. DYKES.

(v. 4.) That through the ag - es all a - long . . This may be our end - less song,

"The Comforter which is the Holy Ghost."

mf COME, HOLY GHOST, our souls inspire,
And lighten with celestial fire ;
Thou the anointing SPIRIT art,
Who dost Thy sevenfold gifts impart :

Thy blessèd unction from above
Is comfort, life, and fire of love ;
Enable with perpetual light
The dulness of our blinded sight :

Anoint and cheer our soilèd face
With the abundance of Thy grace :
Keep far our foes, give peace at home ;
Where Thou art Guide no ill can come.

Teach us to know the FATHER, SON,
And THEE, of Both, to be but ONE ;
That through the ages all along
This may be our endless song,

rall.

f Praise to Thy e - ter - nal mer-it, p FA - THER, SON, and HO - LY SPIRIT. A - men.

Bishop COSIN: from the Latin of Rabanus Maurus.

This Hymn may also be sung at other seasons.

The following Hymns are suitable for this season:

207 Our Blest Redeemer, ere He breathed.
208 O HOLY SPIRIT, LORD of grace.
209 Come, gracious SPIRIT, heavenly Dove.
210 Gracious SPIRIT, HOLY GHOST.
211 O HOLY GHOST, Thy people bless.
212 To Thee, O Comforter Divine.
470 Litany of the HOLY GHOST.
507 Bounteous SPIRIT, ever shedding.
508 Come, HOLY GHOST, Eternal GOD.
653 Hail, festal day, of never-dying fame.

Trinity Sunday.

Hymn 158. O Lux Beata.—L.M.

To be sung in Unison.

Sarum Melody of "O Lux Beata."

A - - men.

An Alternative Version of this Tune is given at Hymn 14.

"And one cried unto another, and said, Holy, Holy, Holy, is the Lord of hosts."

f   A LL hail, Adorèd Trinity ;
      All hail, Eternal Unity ;
    O God the Father, God the Son,
    And God the Spirit, ever One.

mf Behold to Thee, this festal day,
    We meekly pour our thankful lay ;
    O let our work accepted be,
    That sweetest work of praising Thee.

f   Three Persons praise we evermore,
    One only God our hearts adore ;
    In Thy sure mercy ever kind
    May we our true protection find.

p   O Trinity ! O Unity !
    Be present as we worship Thee ;
cr And with the songs that Angels sing
    Unite the hymns of praise we bring.

J. D. Chambers and Compilers·
from the Latin.

Alternative Tune, Hymn **682.**

Hymn 159. Faith.—10 10 10 10.10 12.

H. Smart·

A-men.

(122)

Trinity Sunday.

" O praise God in His holiness."

mf WITH hearts renew'd, and cleansed from guilt of sin,
Send we our voices pealing to the skies ;
Let a pure conscience echo joy within,
And all our powers in emulation rise :
To FATHER, SON, and HOLY SPIRIT'S praise,
THREE Whom One Essence joins, one anthem here we raise.

Maker of all, the FATHER uncreate,
Of Him from everlasting born, the SON,
And the Blest SPIRIT of co-equal state
From Both proceeding, are of Substance One :
So in this TRINITY the Persons THREE
One Perfect Being are, ONE GOD, One Majesty.

Yet, none the less, each Person of the Trine
GOD, in His attributes distinct, we own ;
Vainly would reason grasp the things Divine,
p   Man can but bend adoring at GOD'S Throne :
cr O may the FATHER, SON, and SPIRIT be
Our help in time of need, our joy eternally.

D. T. MORGAN : from the Latin.

The following Hymns are suitable for this Festival :

160 Holy, Holy, Holy ! LORD GOD Almighty.
161 Bright the vision that delighted.
162 Have mercy on us, GOD most High.
163 THREE in ONE, and ONE in THREE.
509 Be near us, HOLY TRINITY.
654 Sound aloud Jehovah's praises.
655 I bind unto myself to-day.

General Hymns.

Hymn 160. NICÆA.—11 12 12 10.   Rev. J. B. DYKES.

A-men.

*" They rest not day and night, saying, Holy, Holy, Holy, Lord God Almighty, Which was,
and is, and is to come."*

p   HOLY, Holy, Holy ! (*mf*) LORD GOD Almighty !
    Early in the morning our song shall rise to Thee :
p   Holy, Holy, Holy ! (*mf*) Merciful and Mighty !
f   GOD in THREE Persons, Blessèd TRINITY !

p   Holy, Holy, Holy ! (*mf*) all the Saints adore Thee,
    Casting down their golden crowns around the glassy sea :
Cherubim and Seraphim falling down before Thee,
    Which wert, and art, and evermore shalt be.

p   Holy, Holy, Holy ! though the darkness hide Thee,
    Though the eye of sinful man Thy glory may not see,
mf Only Thou art Holy, there is none beside Thee
    Perfect in power, in love, and purity.

p   Holy, Holy, Holy ! (*mf*) LORD GOD Almighty !
ff   All Thy works shall praise Thy Name, in earth, and sky, and sea :
mf Holy, Holy, Holy ! Merciful and Mighty !
f   GOD in THREE Persons, Blessèd TRINITY !   Bishop HEBER, 1826.

General Hymns.

Hymn 161. Laus Deo.—8 7 8 7.

R. REDHEAD.

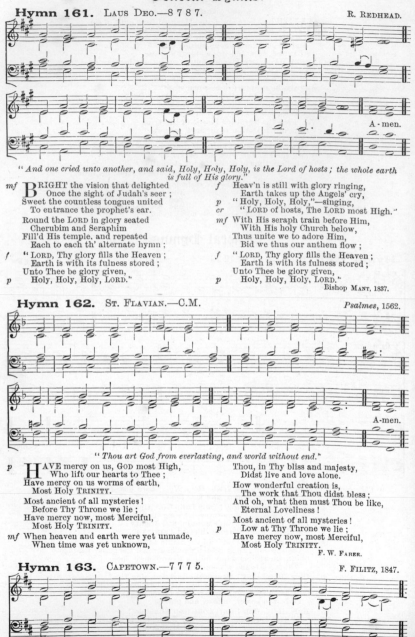

A-men.

"And one cried unto another, and said, Holy, Holy, Holy, is the Lord of hosts; the whole earth is full of His glory."

mf BRIGHT the vision that delighted
 Once the sight of Judah's seer ;
Sweet the countless tongues united
 To entrance the prophet's ear.

Round the LORD in glory seated
 Cherubim and Seraphim
Fill'd His temple, and repeated
 Each to each th' alternate hymn ;

f " LORD, Thy glory fills the Heaven ;
 Earth is with its fulness stored ;
Unto Thee be glory given,
p Holy, Holy, Holy, LORD."

f Heav'n is still with glory ringing,
 Earth takes up the Angels' cry,
p " Holy, Holy, Holy,"—singing,
cr " LORD of hosts, The LORD most High."

mf With His seraph train before Him,
 With His holy Church below,
Thus unite we to adore Him,
 Bid we thus our anthem flow ;

f " LORD, Thy glory fills the Heaven ;
 Earth is with its fulness stored ;
Unto Thee be glory given,
p Holy, Holy, Holy, LORD."

Bishop MANT, 1837.

Hymn 162. St. Flavian.—C.M.

Psalmes, 1562.

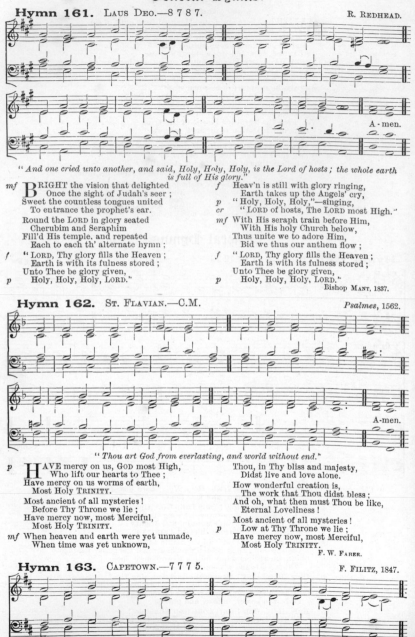

A-men.

" Thou art God from everlasting, and world without end."

p HAVE mercy on us, GOD most High,
 Who lift our hearts to Thee ;
Have mercy on us worms of earth,
 Most Holy TRINITY.

Most ancient of all mysteries !
 Before Thy Throne we lie ;
Have mercy now, most Merciful,
 Most Holy TRINITY.

mf When heaven and earth were yet unmade,
 When time was yet unknown,

Thou, in Thy bliss and majesty,
 Didst live and love alone.

How wonderful creation is,
 The work that Thou didst bless ;
And oh, what then must Thou be like,
 Eternal Loveliness !

Most ancient of all mysteries !
p Low at Thy Throne we lie ;
Have mercy now, most Merciful,
 Most Holy TRINITY.

F. W. FABER.

Hymn 163. Capetown.—7 7 7 5.

F. FILITZ, 1847.

General Hymns.

rall.

A-men.

" Sing unto the Lord, and praise His Name."

mf THREE in ONE, and ONE in THREE,
  Ruler of the earth and sea,
Hear us, while we lift to Thee
  Holy chant and psalm.

Light of lights ! with morning shine ;
Lift on us Thy Light Divine ;
And let charity benign
p Breathe on us her balm.

Light of lights ! when falls the even,
Let it close on sin forgiven ;
Fold us in the peace of Heav'n ;
  Shed a holy calm.

mf THREE in ONE, and ONE in THREE,
  Dimly here we worship Thee ;
cr With the Saints hereafter we
  Hope to bear the palm.

G. RORISON.

Hymn 164. RIVAULX.—L.M. (*First Tune.*)

Rev. J. B. DYKES.

p   *mf*

A - men.

Hymn 164. CHARNWOOD.—L.M. (*Second Tune.*)

Rev. C. E. MOBERLY.

A-men.

A higher setting of this Tune is given at Hymn 664.

" Let us therefore come boldly unto the throne of grace, that we may obtain mercy, and find grace to help in time of need."

mf FATHER of Heav'n, Whose love profound
  A ransom for our souls hath found,
p Before Thy Throne we sinners bend,
mf To us Thy pardoning love extend.

 Almighty SON, Incarnate WORD,
 Our Prophet, Priest, Redeemer, LORD,
p Before Thy Throne we sinners bend,
mf To us Thy saving grace extend.

Eternal SPIRIT, by Whose breath
The soul is raised from sin and death,
p Before Thy Throne we sinners bend,
mf To us Thy quickening power extend.

 Thrice Holy ! FATHER, SPIRIT, SON ;
 Mysterious GODHEAD, THREE in ONE,
p Before Thy Throne we sinners bend,
mf Grace, pardon, life to us extend.

E. COOPER, 1805.

(125)

General Hymns.

Hymn 165. ST. ANNE.—C.M.

W. CROFT, 1708.

A - men.

"Lord, Thou hast been our refuge from one generation to another."

f O GOD, our help in ages past,
　　　Our hope for years to come,
　Our shelter from the stormy blast,
　　And our eternal home ;

mf Beneath the shadow of Thy Throne
　　Thy Saints have dwelt secure ;
　Sufficient is Thine Arm alone,
　　And our defence is sure.

　Before the hills in order stood,
　　Or earth received her frame,
cr From everlasting Thou art GOD,
　　To endless years the Same.

p A thousand ages in Thy sight
　　Are like an evening gone ;
　Short as the watch that ends the night
　　Before the rising sun.

　Time, like an ever-rolling stream,
　　Bears all its sons away ;
　They fly forgotten, as a dream
　　Dies at the opening day.

f O GOD, our help in ages past,
　　Our hope for years to come,
　Be Thou our guard while troubles last,
　　And our eternal home.

I. WATTS, 1719.

Hymn 166. OLD 100TH.—L.M. *(First Version.)*

L. BOURGEOIS, 1551.

A - men.

Hymn 166. OLD 100TH.—L.M. *(Second Version.)*

L. BOURGEOIS, 1551.

A - men.

A lower setting of this Tune is given at Hymn 435.

(126)

General Hymns.

Hymn 166. OLD 100TH.—L.M. *(Third Version.)*

CONGREGATION.

Harmonised by J. DOWLAND, 1563–1626.

CHOIR.

Hymn 166. OLD 100TH.—L.M. *(Fourth Version.)*

CONGREGATION.

Harmonised by T. RAVENSCROFT, 1621.

CHOIR.

Either of the above Versions may be used for verses 2 and 4 in alternation with the First Version.

"O be joyful in the Lord, all ye lands."

f   ALL people that on earth do dwell,
      Sing to the LORD with cheerful voice ;
Him serve with fear, His praise forth tell,
Come ye before Him, and rejoice.

mf   The LORD, ye know, is GOD indeed ;
Without our aid He did us make ;
We are His folk, He doth us feed,
And for His sheep He doth us take.

f   O enter then His gates with praise,
Approach with joy His courts unto ;

Praise, laud, and bless His Name always,
For it is seemly so to do.

mf   For why? the LORD our GOD is good ;
His mercy is for ever sure ;
His truth at all times firmly stood,
And shall from age to age endure.

ff   To FATHER, SON, and HOLY GHOST,
The GOD Whom Heav'n and earth adore,
From men and from the Angel-host
Be praise and glory evermore.

W. KETHE, 1561.

(127)

General Hymns.

Hymn 167. OLD 104TH.—5 5 5 5.6 5 6 5. RAVENSCROFT, *Psalmes*, 1621.

A-men.

" Praise the Lord, O my soul : O Lord my God, Thou art become exceeding glorious ;
Thou art clothed with majesty and honour."

f   O WORSHIP the King All-glorious above ;
    O gratefully sing His power and His love ;
Our Shield and Defender, the Ancient of days,
Pavilion'd in splendour, and girded with praise.

    O tell of His might, O sing of His grace,
Whose robe is the light, Whose canopy space ;
His chariots of wrath the deep thunder clouds form,
And dark is His path on the wings of the storm.

mf   The earth with its store of wonders untold,
Almighty, Thy power hath founded of old ;
Hath stablish'd it fast by a changeless decree,
And round it hath cast, like a mantle, the sea.

    Thy bountiful care what tongue can recite ?
It breathes in the air, it shines in the light ;
It streams from the hills, it descends to the plain,
And sweetly distils in the dew and the rain.

p   Frail children of dust, and feeble as frail,
In Thee do we trust, nor find Thee to fail ;
cr   Thy mercies how tender ! how firm to the end !
Our Maker, Defender, Redeemer, and Friend.

f   O measureless Might, ineffable Love,
While Angels delight to hymn Thee above,
Thy ransom'd creation, (*p*) though feeble their lays,
cr   With true adoration shall sing to Thy praise.

Sir R. GRANT, 1833.

ALTERNATIVE TUNE, HYMN 431.

Hymn 168. ST. FLAVIAN.—C.M. (*First Tune.*) *Psalmes*, 1562.

A-men.

General Hymns.

"The invisible things of Him from the creation of the world are clearly seen, being understood by the things that are made."

mf THERE is a book, who runs may read,
Which heav'nly truth imparts,
And all the lore its scholars need,
Pure eyes and Christian hearts.

The works of GOD above, below,
Within us and around,
Are pages in that book, to show
How GOD Himself is found.

The glorious sky, embracing all,
Is like the Maker's love,
Wherewith encompass'd, great and small
In peace and order move.

The Moon above, the Church below,
A wondrous race they run ;
But all their radiance, all their glow,
Each borrows of its Sun.

The Saviour lends the light and heat
That crown His holy hill ;
The Saints, like stars, around His seat
Perform their courses still.

p The dew of heav'n is like Thy grace,
It steals in silence down ;
cr But where it lights, the favour'd place
By richest fruits is known.

f One Name, above all glorious names,
With its ten thousand tongues
The everlasting sea proclaims,
Echoing Angelic songs.

The raging fire, the roaring wind
Thy boundless power display ;
p But in the gentler breeze we find
Thy SPIRIT'S viewless way.

mf Two worlds are ours : 'tis only sin
Forbids us to descry
The mystic Heav'n and earth within,
Plain as the sea and sky.

Thou, Who hast given me eyes to see
And love this sight so fair,
Give me a heart to find out Thee,
And read Thee everywhere.

J. KEBLE.

Hymn 168. TRANMERE.—D.C.M. *(Second Tune.)* W. HAYES, *c.* 1774.

A - men.

"The invisible things of Him from the creation of the world are clearly seen, being understood by the things that are made."

mf THERE is a book, who runs may read,
Which heav'nly truth imparts,
And all the lore its scholars need,
Pure eyes and Christian hearts.

The works of GOD above, below,
Within us and around,
Are pages in that book, to show
How GOD Himself is found.

The glorious sky, embracing all,
Is like the Maker's love,
Wherewith encompass'd, great and small
In peace and order move.

The Moon above, the Church below,
A wondrous race they run ;
But all their radiance, all their glow,
Each borrows of its Sun.

The Saviour lends the light and heat
That crown His holy hill ;
The Saints, like stars, around His seat
Perform their courses still.

p The dew of heav'n is like Thy grace,
It steals in silence down ;
cr But where it lights, the favour'd place
By richest fruits is known.

f One Name, above all glorious names,
With its ten thousand tongues
The everlasting sea proclaims,
Echoing Angelic songs.

The raging fire, the roaring wind
Thy boundless power display ;
p But in the gentler breeze we find
Thy SPIRIT'S viewless way.

mf Two worlds are ours : 'tis only sin
Forbids us to descry
The mystic Heav'n and earth within,
Plain as the sea and sky.

Thou, Who hast given me eyes to see
And love this sight so fair,
Give me a heart to find out Thee,
And read Thee everywhere.

J. KEBLE.

F

General Hymns.

Hymn 169. WESTMINSTER.—C.M.   J. TURLE.

A - men.

"Thus saith the high and lofty One that inhabiteth eternity, Whose name is Holy: I dwell in the high and holy place, with him also that is of a contrite and humble spirit."

mf MY GOD, how wonderful Thou art,
  Thy majesty how bright,
How beautiful Thy mercy-seat,
  In depths of burning light!

p How dread are Thine eternal years,
  O everlasting LORD,
By prostrate spirits day and night
  Incessantly adored!

mf How wonderful, how beautiful,
  The sight of Thee must be,
Thine endless wisdom, boundless power,
  And awful purity!

p Oh, how I fear Thee, Living GOD,
  With deepest, tenderest fears,

And worship Thee with trembling hope,
  And penitential tears!

cr Yet I may love Thee too, O LORD,
  Almighty as Thou art,
For Thou hast stoop'd to ask of me
dim The love of my poor heart.

mf No earthly father loves like Thee,
  No mother, e'er so mild,
Bears and forbears as Thou hast done
  With me Thy sinful child.

FATHER of JESUS, love's reward,
  What rapture will it be,
Prostrate before Thy Throne to lie,
  And gaze and gaze on Thee.

F. W. FABER.

ALTERNATIVE TUNE, HYMN 633 (SECOND TUNE).

Hymn 170. KNIGHTON.—D.C.M.   W. H. MONK.

A - men.

General Hymns.

" In the beginning was the Word, and the Word was with God, and the Word was God.
All things were made by Him."

f JESUS is GOD : (*mf*) the solid earth,
   The ocean broad and bright,
   The countless stars, like golden dust,
    That strew the skies at night,
f The wheeling storm, the dreadful fire,
mf The pleasant wholesome air,
   The summer's sun, the winter's frost,
    His own creations were.

f JESUS is GOD : (*mf*) the glorious bands
   Of golden Angels sing
   Songs of adoring praise to Him,
    Their Maker and their King.

He was true GOD in Bethlehem's crib,
   On Calvary's Cross true GOD ;
He, Who in heaven Eternal reign'd,
   In time on earth abode.

f JESUS is GOD : (*p*) let sorrow come,
   And pain, and every ill,
cr All are worth while, for all are means
   His glory to fulfil ;
mf Worth while a thousand years of woe
   To speak one little word,
f If by that " I believe " we own
   The GODHEAD of our LORD.

F. W. FABER.

Hymn 171. OLD 113TH.—8 8 8.8 8 8 D.   *Kirchenampt* (Strasburg, 1525).

A - men.

" Worthy is the Lamb that was slain to receive power, and riches, and wisdom, and strength,
and honour, and glory, and blessing."

f FROM highest Heav'n the Eternal SON,
   With GOD the FATHER ever ONE,
p Came down to suffer and to die ;
mf For love of sinful man He bore
   Our human griefs and troubles sore,
p Our load of guilt and misery.

f Rejoice, ye Saints of GOD, and praise
   The LAMB Who died, His flock to raise
   From sin and everlasting woe ;
   With Angels round the Throne above
   O tell the wonders of His love,
   The joys that from His mercy flow.

p In darkest shades of night we lay,
   Without a beam to guide our way,
   Or hope of aught beyond the grave ;
mf But He has brought us life and light,
   And open'd Heaven to our sight,
f And lives for ever strong to save.

ff Rejoice, ye Saints of GOD, rejoice ;
   Sing out, and praise with cheerful voice
   The LAMB Whom Heav'n and earth adore ;
   To Him Who gave His only SON,
   To GOD the SPIRIT, with Them ONE,
   Be praise and glory evermore.

Sir H. W. BAKER.

General Hymns.

Hymn 172. GERONTIUS.—C.M. (*First Tune.*)   Rev. J. B. DYKES.

A - men.

Hymn 172. RICHMOND.—C.M. (*Second Tune.*)   Rev. T. HAWEIS, 1792.

A - men.

A higher setting of this Tune is given at Hymn **705.**

" The second Man is the Lord from heaven."

f   PRAISE to the Holiest in the height,
     And in the depth be praise ;
In all His words most wonderful,
     Most sure in all His ways.

mf   O loving wisdom of our GOD !
p   When all was sin and shame,
cr   A second Adam to the fight
f   And to the rescue came.

mf   O wisest love ! that flesh and blood,
p   Which did in Adam fail,
cr   Should strive afresh against the foe,
f   Should strive and should prevail ;

mf   And that a higher gift than grace
     Should flesh and blood refine,

p   GOD'S Presence and His very Self,
     And Essence all-divine.

mf   O generous love ! that He, Who smote
     In Man for man the foe,
The double agony in Man
     For man should undergo ;

p   And in the garden secretly,
     And on the Cross on high,
cr   Should teach His brethren, and inspire
     To suffer and to die.

f   Praise to the Holiest in the height,
     And in the depth be praise ;
In all His words most wonderful,
     Most sure in all His ways.

Cardinal J. H. NEWMAN.

Hymn 173. LEIPSIC (EISENACH).—L.M.   J. H. SCHEIN, 1628.

General Hymns.

An Alternative Version in a lower key is given at Hymn 479.

" The love of Christ which passeth knowledge."

mf O LOVE, how deep ! how broad ! how high !
   It fills the heart with ecstasy,
That GOD, the SON of GOD, should take
Our mortal form for mortals' sake.

He sent no Angel to our race
Of higher or of lower place,
p But wore the robe of human frame
Himself, and to this lost world came.

f For us He was baptized, and bore
His holy fast, and hunger'd sore ;
For us temptations sharp He know ;
mf For us the tempter overthrew.

For us He pray'd, for us He taught,
For us His daily works He wrought,

By words, and signs, and actions, thus
Still seeking not Himself but us.

p For us to wicked men betray'd,
Scourged, mock'd, in purple robe array'd,
He bore the shameful Cross and death ;
For us at length gave up His breath.

f For us He rose from death again,
For us He went on high to reign,
For us He sent His SPIRIT here
To guide, to strengthen, and to cheer.

To Him Whose boundless love has won
Salvation for us through His SON,
To GOD the FATHER, glory be
Both now and through eternity.

B. WEBB : from Thomas à Kempis.

Hymn 174. CREDO.—8 8 8 8.8 8.

Sir J. STAINER.

a little slower.

" Blessed are they that have not seen, and yet have believed."

mf WE saw Thee not when Thou didst come
   To this poor world of sin and death,
Nor e'er beheld Thy cottage-home
   In that despiséd Nazareth ;
f But we believe Thy footsteps trod
   Its streets and plains, Thou SON of GOD.

mf We did not see Thee lifted high
   Amid that wild and savage crew,
dim Nor heard Thy meek, imploring cry,
   " Forgive, they know not what they do ; "
f Yet we believe the deed was done,
dim Which shook the earth and veil'd the sun.

mf We stood not by the empty tomb
   Where late Thy sacred Body lay,
cr Nor sat within that upper room,

   Nor met Thee in the open way ;
f But we believe that Angels said,
   " Why seek the living with the dead ? "

mf We did not mark the chosen few,
   When Thou didst through the clouds ascend,
First lift to Heav'n their wondering view,
p Then to the earth all prostrate bend ;
f Yet we believe that mortal eyes
Beheld that journey to the skies.

And now that Thou dost reign on high,
   And thence Thy waiting people bless,
mf No ray of glory from the sky
   Doth shine upon our wilderness ;
ff But we believe Thy faithful Word,
And trust in our Redeeming LORD.

J. HAMPDEN GURNEY. 1851.

ALTERNATIVE TUNE, HYMN 370.

(133)

General Hymns.

Hymn 175. INNOCENTS.—7 7 7 7 *The Parish Choir, 1850.*

A - men.

A lower setting of this Tune is given at Hymns 33, 343.

" Thou shalt call His Name Jesus, for He shall save His people from their sins."

mf CONQUERING kings their titles take
  From the foes they captive make :
f JESUS, by a nobler deed,
  From the thousands He hath freed.

mf Yes : none other name is given
  Unto mortals under heaven,
  Which can make the dead arise,
  And exalt them to the skies.

That which CHRIST so hardly wrought,
That which He so dearly bought,
That salvation, brethren, say,
Shall we madly cast away ?

Rather gladly for that Name
Bear the cross, endure the shame :
Joyfully for Him to die
Is not death but victory.

p JESU, Who dost condescend
  To be call'd the sinner's Friend,
  Hear us, as to Thee we pray,
cr Glorying in Thy Name to-day.

f Glory to the FATHER be,
  Glory, Holy SON, to Thee,
  Glory to the HOLY GHOST,
  From the Saints and Angel-host.

J. CHANDLER : from the Latin.

Hymn 176. ST. PETER.—C.M. A. R. REINAGLE, 1799–1877.

A - men.

A lower setting of this Tune is given at Hymn 596.

" Unto you therefore which believe He is precious."

mf HOW sweet the Name of JESUS sounds
  In a believer's ear !
It soothes his sorrows, heals his wounds,
And drives away his fear.

It makes the wounded spirit whole,
  And calms the troubled breast ;
'Tis manna to the hungry soul,
p And to the weary rest.

mf Dear Name ! the rock on which I build,
  My shield and hiding-place,
My never-failing treasury fill'd
  With boundless stores of grace.

JESUS ! my Shepherd, Husband, Friend,
  My Prophet, Priest, and King,
My Lord, my Life, my Way, my End,
  Accept the praise I bring.

p Weak is the effort of my heart,
  And cold my warmest thought ;
cr But when I see Thee as Thou art,
  I'll praise Thee as I ought.

f Till then I would Thy love proclaim
  With every fleeting breath :
dim And may the music of Thy Name
p Refresh my soul in death.

J. NEWTON, 1779.

(134)

General Hymns.

Hymn 177. JESU DULCIS MEMORIA.—L.M. (*First Tune.*) (*First Version.*)

Proper Sarum Melody.

To be sung in Unison.

A - men.

For Alternative Version of this Tune see page 136.

Hymn 177. ST. BERNARD.—L.M. (*Second Tune.*)

W. H. MONK.

A - men.

" Thy Name is as ointment poured forth."

p	JESU ! the very thought is sweet ;
	In that dear Name all heart-joys meet ;
cr	But oh ! than honey sweeter far
	The glimpses of His Presence are.

mf No word is sung more sweet than this,
No sound is heard more full of bliss,
No thought brings sweeter comfort nigh,
Than JESUS, SON of GOD most High.

JESU, the hope of souls forlorn,
How good to them for sin that mourn !
To them that seek Thee, oh how kind !
cr But what art Thou to them that find?

mf No tongue of mortal can express,
No pen can write the blessedness,
He only who hath proved it knows
What bliss from love of JESUS flows.

f O JESU, King of wondrous might !
O Victor, glorious from the fight !
mf Sweetness that may not be express'd,
And altogether loveliest !

p Abide with us, O LORD, to-day,
Fulfil us with Thy grace, we pray ;
cr And with Thine own true sweetness feed
Our souls from sin and darkness freed.

J. M. NEALE and Compilers :
from the Latin.

(135)

General Hymns.

Hymn 177. JESU DULCIS MEMORIA.—L.M. (*First Tune.*) (*Alternative Version.*)

" Thy Name is as ointment poured forth."

Proper Sarum Melody.

JE -	SU!	the	ve -	ry thought	is . .	sweet;	In	that	dear	Name
No	word	is	sung	more sweet	than .	this,	No	sound	is	heard
JE -	SU,	the	hope	of souls	for -	lorn,	How	good	to	them
No	tongue	of	mor -	tal can	ex -	press,	No	pen	can	write
O	JE -	SU,	King	of won -	drous	might!	O	Vic -	tor,	glo -
A -	bide	with	us,	O LORD,	to -	day,	Ful -	fil	us	with

all	heart -	joys .	meet;	But	oh!	than hon -	ey sweet -	er	far
more	full	of .	bliss,	No thought	brings sweet -	er com -	fort	nigh,
for	sin	that	mourn!	To them	that seek	Thee, oh	how	kind!
the	bless -	ed -	ness,	He	on -	ly who	hath proved	it	knows
- rious	from	the .	fight!	Sweet-ness	that may	not be	ex -	press'd,
Thy	grace,	we .	pray;	And with	Thine own	true sweet -	ness	feed

The	glimp -	ses	of	His	Pre -	sence	are.
Than	JE -	SUS,	SON	of	GOD	most	High.
But	what	art	Thou	to	them	that	find?
What	bliss	from	love	of	JE -	SUS	flows.
And	al -	to -	geth -	er	love -	li -	est!
Our	souls	from	sin	and	dark -	ness	freed.

A - men.

J. M. NEALE and Compilers : from the Latin.

Hymn 178. ST. AGNES.—C.M. (*First Tune.*)

REV. J. B. DYKES.

General Hymns.

"*Thy Name is as ointment poured forth.*"

mf JESU, the very thought of Thee
　　With sweetness fills the breast ;
But sweeter far Thy Face to see,
　And in Thy Presence rest.

No voice can sing, no heart can frame,
　Nor can the memory find
A sweeter sound than JESU'S Name,
　The Saviour of mankind.

O Hope of every contrite heart,
　O Joy of all the meek,
To those who ask how kind Thou art,
　How good to those who seek !

But what to those who find ? Ah ! this
　Nor tongue nor pen can show ;
The love of JESUS, what it is
　None but His loved ones know.

f JESU, our only Joy be Thou,
　　As Thou our Prize wilt be ;
In Thee be all our glory now,
　And through eternity.

PART 2.

f O JESU, King most wonderful,
　　Thou Conqueror renown'd,
mf Thou Sweetness most ineffable,
　　In Whom all joys are found !

When once Thou visitest the heart,
　Then truth begins to shine,
Then earthly vanities depart,
　Then kindles love Divine.

f O JESU, Light of all below,
　　Thou Fount of living fire,

Surpassing all the joys we know,
　And all we can desire :

mf JESU, may all confess Thy Name,
　　Thy wondrous love adore,
And, seeking Thee, themselves inflame
　To seek Thee more and more.

Thee, JESU, may our voices bless,
　Thee may we love alone,
And ever in our lives express
　The Image of Thine Own.

PART 3.

mf O JESU, Thou the Beauty art
　　Of Angel-worlds above ;
Thy Name is music to the heart,
　Inflaming it with love.

Celestial Sweetness unalloy'd,
　Who eat Thee hunger still ;
Who drink of Thee still feel a void
　Which only Thou canst fill.

p O most sweet JESU, hear the sighs
　　Which unto Thee we send ;
To Thee our inmost spirit cries,
　To Thee our prayers ascend.

cr Abide with us, and let Thy Light
　　Shine, LORD, on every heart ;
Dispel the darkness of our night,
　And joy to all impart.

f JESU, our Love and Joy, to Thee,
　　The Virgin's Holy Son,
All might, and praise, and glory be,
　While endless ages run.

E. CASWALL : from the Latin.

General Hymns.

A - men.

A lower setting of this Tune is given at Hymn **396.**

"There is none other name under heaven given among men whereby we must be saved."

f   TO the Name of our Salvation
      Laud and honour let us pay,
p   Which for many a generation
      Hid in GOD's foreknowledge lay,
f   But with holy exultation
      We may sing aloud to-day.

mf JESUS is the Name we treasure,
      Name beyond what words can tell ;
   Name of gladness, Name of pleasure,
      Ear and heart delighting well ;
   Name of sweetness passing measure,
      Saving us from sin and hell.

   'Tis the Name for adoration,
      Name for songs of victory,
   Name for holy meditation
      In this vale of misery,
   Name for joyful veneration
      By the citizens on high.

   'Tis the Name that whoso preacheth
      Speaks like music to the ear ;
p   Who in prayer this Name beseecheth
      Sweetest comfort findeth near ;
cr   Who its perfect wisdom reacheth
mf   Heavenly joy possesseth here.

f   JESUS is the Name exalted
      Over every other name ;
   In this Name, whene'er assaulted,
      We can put our foes to shame ;
   Strength to them who else had halted,
      Eyes to blind, and feet to lame.

p   Therefore we in love adoring
      This most blessèd Name revere,
cr   Holy JESU, Thee imploring
      So to write it in us here,
   That hereafter heavenward soaring
f   We may sing with Angels there.

J. M. NEALE and Compilers:
from the Latin.

(138)

General Hymns.

Hymn 180.   St. George.—S.M.   H. J. Gauntlett.

A - men.

A lower setting of this Tune is given at Hymn 351.

" The everlasting Father, the Prince of peace."

mf   TO CHRIST, the Prince of peace,
       And SON of GOD most High,
The FATHER of the world to come,
       We lift our joyful cry.

p   Deep in His Heart for us
       The wound of love He bore,
cr   That love which He enkindles still
       In hearts that Him adore.

mf   O JESU, Victim Blest,
       What else but love Divine

Could Thee constrain to open thus
       That sacred Heart of Thine ?

O wondrous Fount of love,
       O Well of waters free,
O heavenly Flame, refining Fire,
       O burning Charity !

p   Hide us in Thy dear Heart,
       JESU, our Saviour Blest,
mf   So shall we find Thy plenteous grace,
       And Heav'n's eternal rest.

E. CASWALL and Compilers :
from the Latin.

Hymn 181.   Sellinge.—S.M.   J. Hullah.

A - men.

" Thou hast been my succour : leave me not, neither forsake me, O God of my salvation."

mf   WE know Thee Who Thou art,
       LORD JESUS, Mary's Son ;
We know the yearnings of Thy Heart
To end Thy work begun.

That sacred Fount of grace,
       'Mid all the bliss of heaven,
Has joy whenc'er we seek Thy Face,
And kneel to be forgiven.

p   Brought home from ways perverse,
       At peace Thine Arms within,

We pray Thee, shield us from the curse
       Of falling back to sin.

mf   We dare not ask to live
       Henceforth from trials free ;
But oh ! when next they tempt us, give
More strength to cling to Thee.

We know Thee Who Thou art,
       Our own redeeming LORD ;
Be Thou by will, and mind, and heart,
Accepted, loved, adored.

W. BRIGHT.

General Hymns.

Hymn 182. CANTERBURY.—7 7 7 7.   O. GIBBONS, 1623.

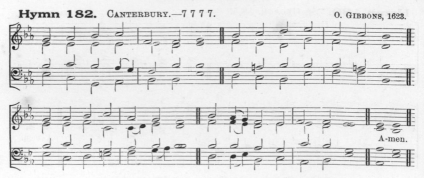

A-men.

An Alternative Version of this Tune is given at Hymn 151.

" Thou art a place to hide me in."

p	JESU, grant me this, I pray,
	Ever in Thy Heart to stay ;
	Let me evermore abide
	Hidden in Thy wounded Side.
mf	If the evil one prepare,
	Or the world, a tempting snare,
cr	I am safe when I abide
p	In Thy Heart and wounded Side.

mf	If the flesh, more dangerous still,
	Tempt my soul to deeds of ill,
cr	Nought I fear when I abide
p	In Thy Heart and wounded Side.
	Death will come one day to me ;
mf	JESU, cast me not from Thee :
p	Dying let me still abide
	In Thy Heart and wounded Side.

Sir H. W. BAKER : from the Latin.

Hymn 183. ST. BERNARD.—C.M.   *Tochter Sion* (Cologne, 1741).

A-men.

A lower setting of this Tune is given at Hymn 112.

" Lord, to whom shall we go ? "

p	WHEN wounded sore the stricken heart
	Lies bleeding and unbound,
cr	One only Hand, (*p*) a piercèd Hand,
mf	Can salve the sinner's wound.
p	When sorrow swells the laden breast,
	And tears of anguish flow,
cr	One only Heart, (*p*) a broken Heart,
mf	Can feel the sinner's woe.
p	When penitential grief has wept
	Over some foul dark spot,

cr	One only Stream, (*p*) a Stream of Blood,
mf	Can wash away the blot.
	'Tis JESUS' Blood that washes white,
	His Hand that brings relief,
cr	His Heart is touch,d with all our joys,
p	And feels for all our grief.
mf	Lift up Thy bleeding Hand, O LORD,
	Unseal that cleansing Tide ;
	We have no shelter from our sin
p	But in Thy wounded Side.

MRS. ALEXANDER.

(140)

General Hymns.

Hymn 184. PETRA.—7 7.7 7.7 7.

R. REDHEAD.

A-men.

" That rock was Christ."

mf ROCK of ages, cleft for me,
　Let me hide myself in Thee ;
Let the Water and the Blood,
From Thy riven Side which flow'd,
Be of sin the double cure,
Cleanse me from its guilt and power.

Not the labours of my hands
Can fulfil Thy law's demands ;
Could my zeal no respite know,
Could my tears for ever flow,
All for sin could not atone ;
Thou must save, and Thou alone.

p Nothing in my hand I bring,
Simply to Thy Cross I cling ;
Naked, come to Thee for dress ;
Helpless, look to Thee for grace ;
Foul, I to the Fountain fly ;
cr Wash me, Saviour, (*p*) or I die.

mf While I draw this fleeting breath,
p When my eyelids close in death,
cr When I soar through tracts unknown,
See Thee on Thy Judgment Throne ;
p Rock of ages, cleft for me,
pp Let me hide myself in Thee.

A. M. TOPLADY, 1775

Hymn 185. ST. PAUL'S.—S.M.

Sir J. STAINER.

A-men.

" O look Thou upon me, and be merciful unto me."

p LORD JESUS, think on me,
　And purge away my sin ;
cr From earthborn passions set me free,
And make me pure within.

p LORD JESUS, think on me,
With many a care opprest ;
cr Let me Thy loving servant be,
And taste Thy promised rest.

mf LORD JESUS, think on me,
Nor let me go astray ;

Through darkness and perplexity
cr Point Thou the heavenly way.

p LORD JESUS, think on me,
That, when the flood is past,
cr I may the eternal Brightness see,
And share Thy joy at last.

mf LORD JESUS, think on me,
cr That I may sing above
f Praise to the FATHER, and to THEE,
And to the HOLY DOVE.

A. W. CHATFIELD : from the
Greek of Synesius.

General Hymns.

Hymn 186. MAGDALENA.—7 6 7 6. 7 6 7 6. Sir J. STAINER.

A - men.

" Without Me ye can do nothing."

mf I COULD not do without Thee,
    O Saviour of the lost,
cr Whose precious Blood redeem'd me
dim At such tremendous cost ;
mf Thy righteousness, Thy pardon,
    Thy precious Blood must be
My only hope and comfort,
    My glory and my plea.

I could not do without Thee,
    I cannot stand alone,
I have no strength or goodness,
    No wisdom of my own ;
cr But Thou, belovèd Saviour,
    Art all in all to me,
And weakness will be power
    If leaning hard on Thee.

mf I could not do without Thee,
p   For, oh, the way is long,
And I am often weary,
    And sigh replaces song ;
How could I do without Thee?
    I do not know the way ;
cr Thou knowest, and Thou leadest,
    And wilt not let me stray.

mf I could not do without Thee,
    O JESUS, Saviour dear ;
E'en when my eyes are holden,
    I know that Thou art near ;
How dreary and how lonely
    This changeful life would be
Without the sweet communion,
    The secret rest with Thee.

I could not do without Thee ;
    No other friend can read
The spirit's strange deep longings,
    Interpreting its need ;
No human heart could enter
    Each dim recess of mine,
dim And soothe, and hush, and calm it,
cr   O Blessèd LORD, but Thine.

mf I could not do without Thee,
p   For years are fleeting fast,
And soon in solemn loneness
    The river must be pass'd ;
cr But Thou wilt never leave me,
    And though the waves roll high,
f I know Thou wilt be near me,
p   And whisper, " It is I."

FRANCES R. HAVERGAL.

ALTERNATIVE TUNE, HYMN **769.**

General Hymns.

Hymn 187. Ecce Agnus.—6 6 6 4.8 8 4. (*First Tune.*)   From Old Melody.

A-men.

Hymn 187. St. John.—6 6 6 4.8 8 4. (*Second Tune.*)   Rev. J. B. Dykes.

A - men.

"*Behold the Lamb of God, which taketh away the sin of the world.*"

mf BEHOLD the Lamb of God!
p   O Thou for sinners slain,
  Let it not be in vain
    That Thou hast died :
mf Thee for my Saviour let me take,
  My only refuge let me make
    p Thy piercèd Side.

mf Behold the Lamb of God!
p Into the sacred flood
  Of Thy most precious Blood
    My soul I cast :
mf Wash me and make me clean within
  And keep me pure from every sin,
    p Till life be past.

mf Behold the Lamb of God!
  All hail, Incarnate Word,
  Thou everlasting Lord,
    Saviour most Blest ;
  Fill us with love that never faints,
  Grant us with all Thy blessèd Saints
    p Eternal rest.

mf Behold the Lamb of God!
f Worthy is He alone
  To sit upon the Throne
    Of God above ;
  One with the Ancient of all days,
  One with the Comforter in praise,
    All Light and Love.

M. Bridges, 1848.

General Hymns.

Hymn 188. ST. MARTIN.—6 6 6 6.　　　　ETT, *Cantica Sacra*, 1840.

A-men.

" I, if I be lifted up from the earth, will draw all men unto Me."

mf JESU, meek and lowly,
　　　Saviour, pure and holy,
On Thy love relying
Hear me humbly crying.

　　Prince of life and power,
　　My salvation's tower,
p　On the Cross I view Thee
　　Calling sinners to Thee.

mf There behold me gazing
　　At the sight amazing ;
p　Bending low before Thee,
　　Helpless I adore Thee.

　　By Thy red Wounds streaming,
　　With Thy Life-blood gleaming,
　　Blood for sinners flowing,
　　Pardon free bestowing ;

　　By that Fount of blessing,
　　Thy dear love expressing,
　　All my aching sadness
cr　Turn Thou into gladness.

mf LORD, in mercy guide me,
　　Be Thou e'er beside me ;
　　In Thy ways direct me,
　　'Neath Thy wings protect me.

　　　　　　　　　　H. COLLINS.

Hymn 189. ST. FULBERT.—C.M.　　　　H. J. GAUNTLETT.

A - men.

A higher setting of this Tune is given at Hymn 125.

" I have loved thee with an everlasting love ; therefore with loving-kindness have I drawn thee."

mf JESU, Thy mercies are untold
　　　Through each returning day ;
Thy love exceeds a thousandfold
Whatever we can say ;

p　That love which in Thy Passion drain'd
　　For us Thy precious Blood :
mf That love whereby the Saints have gain'd
　　The vision of their GOD.

　　'Tis Thou hast loved us from the womb,
　　Pure Source of all our bliss,
　　Our only hope of life to come,
　　Our happiness in this.

p　LORD, grant us, while on earth we stay,
cr　Thy love to feel and know ;
p　And, when from hence we pass away,
mf　To us Thy glory show.

　　　　　　　E. CASWALL : from the Latin.

Hymn 190. EALING.—L.M.　　　　Sir H. OAKELEY.

General Hymns.

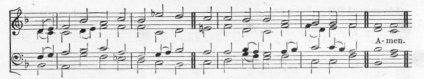

A-men.

"He is altogether lovely."

mf JESU, Thou Joy of loving hearts !
    Thou Fount of life, Thou Light of men !
From the best bliss that earth imparts
We turn unfill'd to Thee again.

Thy truth unchanged hath ever stood ;
Thou savest those that on Thee call ;
To them that seek Thee Thou art good ;
To them that find Thee All in all.

We taste Thee, O Thou Living Bread,
And long to feast upon Thee still ;

We drink of Thee, the Fountain-head,
And thirst our souls from Thee to fill.

p Our restless spirits yearn for Thee,
    Where'er our changeful lot is cast ;
cr Glad when Thy gracious smile we see,
    Blest, when our faith can hold Thee fast.

p O Jesu, ever with us stay ;
    Make all our moments calm and bright ;
cr Chase the dark night of sin away ;
    Shed o'er the world Thy holy light.

R. PALMER : from the Latin.

Hymn 191. ST. MATTHIAS.—8 8.8 8.8 8.   W. H. MONK.

A-men.

A lower setting of this Tune is given at Hymn 28.

"Whom have I in heaven but Thee? and there is none upon earth that I desire in comparison of Thee."

mf JESU, my LORD, my GOD, my All,
    Hear me, Blest Saviour, when I call ;
Hear me, and from Thy dwelling-place
Pour down the riches of Thy grace ;
    JESU, my LORD, I Thee adore,
cr   O make me love Thee more and more.

p JESU, too late I Thee have sought,
    How can I love Thee as I ought ?
And how extol Thy matchless fame,
mf The glorious beauty of Thy Name ?
    JESU, my LORD, I Thee adore,
cr   O make me love Thee more and more.

p JESU, what didst Thou find in me,
    That Thou hast dealt so lovingly?
f How great the joy that Thou hast brought,
    So far exceeding hope or thought !
mf   JESU, my LORD, I Thee adore,
cr   O make me love Thee more and more.

f JESU, of Thee shall be my song,
    To Thee my heart and soul belong ;
All that I have or am is Thine,
And Thou, Blest Saviour, Thou art mine.
mf   JESU, my LORD, I Thee adore,
cr   O make me love Thee more and more.

H. COLLINS.

ALTERNATIVE TUNE, HYMN 721.

(145)

General Hymns.

Hymn 192. BREMEN.—8 8.8 8.8 8. G. NEUMARK, 1657.

A-men.

" God is Love."

mf O LOVE, Who formedst me to wear
The image of Thy GODHEAD here;
p Who soughtest me with tender care
Thro' all my wanderings wild and drear;
cr O LOVE, I give myself to Thee,
mf Thine ever, only Thine to be.

O LOVE, Who ere life's earliest dawn
On me Thy choice hast gently laid;
p O LOVE, Who here as Man wast born,
And wholly like to us wast made;
cr O LOVE, I give myself to Thee,
mf Thine ever, only Thine to be.

p O LOVE, Who once in time wast slain,
Pierced through and through with bitter woe;
O LOVE, Who wrestling thus didst gain
That we eternal joy might know;
cr O LOVE, I give myself to Thee,
mf Thine ever, only Thine to be.

O LOVE, Who lovest me for aye,
Who for my soul dost ever plead;
p O LOVE, Who didst that ransom pay
Whose power sufficeth in my stead;
cr O LOVE, I give myself to Thee,
mf Thine ever, only Thine to be.

O LOVE, Who once shalt bid me rise
From out this dying life of ours;
O LOVE, Who once o'er yonder skies
Shalt set me in the fadeless bowers;
cr O LOVE, I give myself to Thee,
Thine ever, only Thine to be.

CATHERINE WINKWORTH: from
the German of J. Scheffler.

ALTERNATIVE TUNE, HYMN 720.

General Hymns.

Hymn 193.   HOLLINGSIDE.—7 7 7 7. 7 7 7 7.   Rev. J. B. DYKES.

A-men.

" A Man shall be as an hiding place from the wind, and a covert from the tempest."

p   JESU, Lover of my soul,
        Let me to Thy Bosom fly,
cr While the gathering waters roll,
      While the tempest still is high :
mf Hide me, O my Saviour, hide,
      Till the storm of life is past ;
dim Safe into the haven guide,
p   O receive my soul at last.

mf Other refuge have I none ;
      Hangs my helpless soul on Thee ;
p   Leave, ah ! leave me not alone,
      Still support and comfort me.
cr All my trust on Thee is stay'd,
      All my help from Thee I bring ;
    Cover my defenceless head
p   With the shadow of Thy wing.

mf Plenteous grace with Thee is found,
      Grace to cleanse from every sin ;
cr Let the healing streams abound ;
f   Make and keep me pure within ;
    Thou of Life the Fountain art ;
    Freely let me take of Thee ;
    Spring Thou up within my heart,
      Rise to all eternity.

                        C. WESLEY, 1740.

ALTERNATIVE TUNE, HYMN 251 (SECOND TUNE).

General Hymns.

Hymn 194. St. Constantine.—6 5 6 5.   W. H. Monk.

"Lord, save us."

p JESU, meek and gentle,
　　SON of GOD most High,
Pitying, loving Saviour,
　　Hear Thy children's cry.

Pardon our offences,
　　Loose our captive chains,
Break down every idol
　　Which our soul detains.

mf Give us holy freedom,
　　Fill our hearts with love,
Draw us, Holy JESUS,
　　To the realms above.

p　Lead us on our journey,
cr　Be Thyself the Way
　　Through terrestrial darkness
f　To celestial day.

p　JESU, meek and gentle,
　　SON of GOD most High,
　　Pitying, loving Saviour,

Hear Thy chil-dren's cry. A-men.

G. R. Prynne.

Hymn 195. Purleigh.—8 8 6.8 8 6. *(First Tune.)*   A. H. Brown.

· A - men.

Hymn 195. Cornwall.—8 8 6.8 8 6. *(Second Tune.)*   S. S. Wesley.

General Hymns.

"Mary hath chosen that good part, which shall not be taken away from her."

mf O LOVE Divine, how sweet thou art !
  When shall I find my willing heart
  All taken up by thee?
cr I thirst, I faint, I die to prove
  The greatness of redeeming love,
  The love of CHRIST to me.

mf Stronger His love than death or hell ;
  Its riches are unsearchable ;
  The first-born sons of light
  Desire in vain its depths to see ;
  They cannot reach the mystery,
  The length, and breadth, and height.

GOD only knows the love of GOD ;
O that it now were shed abroad
In this poor stony heart !
For love I sigh, for love I pine ;
This only portion, LORD, be mine,
Be mine this better part.

For ever would I take my seat
With Mary at the Master's feet ;
Be this my happy choice ;
My only care, delight, and bliss,
cr My joy, my heaven on earth, be this,
To hear the Bridegroom's voice.

C. WESLEY, 1746.

Hymn 196. PILGRIMAGE.—8 7 8 7.4 7. Sir G. J. ELVEY.

"This God is our God for ever and ever ; He shall be our guide unto death."

mf GUIDE me, O Thou great Redeemer,
  Pilgrim through this barren land ;
p I am weak, but (*f*) Thou art mighty,
  Hold me with Thy powerful hand ;
p Bread of Heaven,
cr Feed me now and evermore.

mf Open now the crystal fountain,
  Whence the healing streams do flow :
  Let the fiery cloudy pillar

Lead me all my journey through ;
f Strong Deliverer,
Be Thou still my Strength and Shield.

p When I tread the verge of Jordan,
  Bid my anxious fears subside :
f Death of death, and he'l's Destruction,
  Land me safe on Canaan's side ;
ff Songs of praises
I will ever give to Thee.

W. WILLIAMS, 1745.

ALTERNATIVE TUNE, HYMN 741.

(149)

General Hymns.

Hymn 197. Dominus regit me.—8 7 8 7.   Rev. J. B. Dykes.

"The Lord is my Shepherd."

mf THE King of love my Shepherd is,
    Whose goodness faileth never ;
I nothing lack if I am His
    And He is mine for ever.

Where streams of living water flow
    My ransom'd soul He leadeth,
And, where the verdant pastures grow,
    With food celestial feedeth.

p Perverse and foolish oft I stray'd,
cr   But yet in love He sought me,
dim And on His Shoulder gently laid,
f   And home, rejoicing, brought me.

p In death's dark vale I fear no ill
cr   With Thee, dear Lord, beside me ;
Thy rod and staff my comfort still,
    Thy Cross before to guide me.

mf Thou spread'st a Table in my sight ;
    Thy Unction grace bestoweth ;
f And oh, what transport of delight
    From Thy pure Chalice floweth !

mf And so through all the length of days
    Thy goodness faileth never ;
cr Good Shepherd, may I sing Thy praise
    Within Thy house for ever.

Sir H. W. Baker.

Hymn 198. St. Catherine.—7 6 7 6.7 6 7 6.   Rev. R. F. Dale.

"Behold, I stand at the door and knock."

p O JESU, Thou art standing
    Outside the fast-closed door,
In lowly patience waiting
    To pass the threshold o'er ;
f Shame on us, Christian brethren,
    His Name and sign who bear,
Oh shame, thrice shame upon us
p   To keep Him standing there !

O JESU, Thou art knocking ;
    And lo ! that Hand is scarr'd,
And thorns Thy Brow encircle,
    And tears Thy Face have marr'd :

cr O love that passeth knowledge
    So patiently to wait !
dim O sin that hath no equal
p   So fast to bar the gate !

O JESU, Thou art pleading
    In accents meek and low,
"I died for you, My children,
cr   And will ye treat me so ? "
mf O LORD, with shame and sorrow
    We open now the door :
Dear Saviour, enter, enter,
    And leave us never more.

Bishop W. Walsham How.

General Hymns.

Hymn 199. St. James.—C.M.　　　　R. Courteville, 1697.

A - men.

" Jesus saith unto him, I am the Way, the Truth, and the Life."

mf THOU art the Way; by Thee alone
　　From sin and death we flee :
And he who would the FATHER seek
　Must seek Him, LORD, by Thee.

Thou art the Truth ; Thy Word alone
　True wisdom can impart ;
Thou only canst inform the mind,
　And purify the heart.

Thou art the Life ; (*f*) the rending tomb
　Proclaims Thy conquering arm ;
mf And those who put their trust in Thee
　Nor death nor hell shall harm.

Thou art the Way, the Truth, the Life,
p　Grant us that Way to know,
That Truth to keep, that Life to win,
mf　Whose joys eternal flow.
　　　　　　　　　　Bishop Doane.

Hymn 200. Breslau.—L.M.　　　　*Geistliche Gesänge* (Leipzig, 1625).

A - men.

A higher setting of this Tune is given at Hymns **46, 246.**

"God forbid that I should glory, save in the Cross of our Lord Jesus Christ."

mf WE sing the praise of Him Who died,
p　　Of Him Who died upon the Cross ;
cr The sinner's hope let men deride,
For this we count the world but loss.

mf Inscribed upon the Cross we see
In shining letters, "GOD is Love ; "
p He bears our sins upon the Tree ;
cr He brings us mercy from above.

f The Cross ! it takes our guilt away ;
It holds the fainting spirit up ;
It cheers with hope the gloomy day,
And sweetens every bitter cup.

It makes the coward spirit brave,
And nerves the feeble arm for fight ;
It takes its terror from the grave,
And gilds the bed of death with light ;

The balm of life, the cure of woe,
The measure and the pledge of love,
The sinner's refuge here below,
The Angels' theme in Heav'n above.

mf To CHRIST, Who won for sinners grace
p By bitter grief and anguish sore,
f Be praise from all the ransom'd race
For ever and for evermore.
　　　　　　　　　　T. Kelly, 1815.

Alternative Tune, Hymn **658.**

General Hymns.

Hymn 201. COMMANDMENTS.—L.M.

L. BOURGEOIS, 1547.

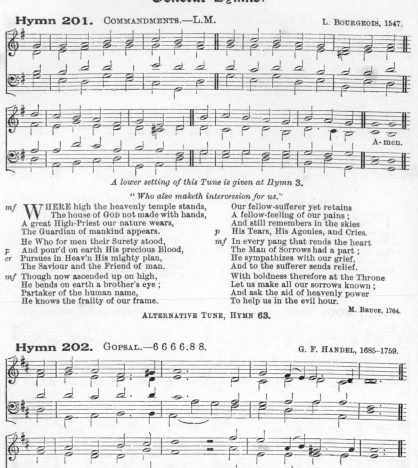

A-men.

A lower setting of this Tune is given at Hymn 3.

" Who also maketh intercession for us."

mf WHERE high the heavenly temple stands,
The house of GOD not made with hands,
A great High-Priest our nature wears,
The Guardian of mankind appears.

He Who for men their Surety stood,
F And pour'd on earth His precious Blood,
cr Pursues in Heav'n His mighty plan,
The Saviour and the Friend of man.

mf Though now ascended up on high,
He bends on earth a brother's eye ;
Partaker of the human name,
He knows the frailty of our frame.

Our fellow-sufferer yet retains
A fellow-feeling of our pains ;
And still remembers in the skies
p His Tears, His Agonies, and Cries.

mf In every pang that rends the heart
The Man of Sorrows had a part ;
He sympathizes with our grief,
And to the sufferer sends relief.

With boldness therefore at the Throne
Let us make all our sorrows known ;
And ask the aid of heavenly power
To help us in the evil hour.

M. BRUCE, 1764.

ALTERNATIVE TUNE, HYMN 63.

Hymn 202. GOPSAL.—6 6 6 6.8 8.

G. F. HANDEL, 1685–1759.

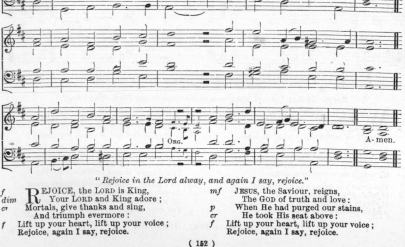

A-men.

" Rejoice in the Lord alway, and again I say, rejoice."

f REJOICE, the LORD is King,
dim Your LORD and King adore ;
cr Mortals, give thanks and sing,
And triumph evermore :
f Lift up your heart, lift up your voice ;
Rejoice, again I say, rejoice.

mf JESUS, the Saviour, reigns,
The GOD of truth and love ;
p When He had purged our stains,
cr He took His seat above :
f Lift up your heart, lift up your voice ;
Rejoice, again I say, rejoice.

(152)

General Hymns.

mf   His Kingdom cannot fail;
     He rules o'er earth and Heav'n;
     The keys of death and hell
     Are to our JESUS given:
f   Lift up your heart, lift up your voice;
     Rejoice, again I say, rejoice.

mf   He sits at GOD'S right hand
     Till all His foes submit,
     And bow to His command,
     And fall beneath His feet:
f   Lift up your heart, lift up your voice;
ff   Rejoice, again I say, rejoice.

C. WESLEY, 1746.

ALTERNATIVE TUNE, HYMN 414.

Hymn 203.   BEVERLEY.—8 7.8 8 7.7 7 7 7.   W. H. MONK.

"He . . . saith, Surely I come quickly. Amen. Even so, come, Lord Jesus."

f   THOU art coming, O my Saviour,
     Thou art coming, O my King,
mf   In Thy beauty all-resplendent,
cr   In Thy glory all-transcendent;
f   Well may we rejoice and sing;
p   Coming! (cr) In the opening east
     Herald brightness slowly swells;
p   Coming! (cr) O my glorious Priest,
dim   Hear we not Thy golden bells?

mf   Thou art coming, Thou art coming;
     We shall meet Thee on Thy way,
     We shall see Thee, we shall know Thee,
cr   We shall bless Thee, we shall show Thee
     All our hearts could never say;
mf   What an anthem that will be
     Ringing out our love to Thee,
     Pouring out our rapture sweet
cr   At Thine own all-glorious Feet.

mf   Thou art coming; at Thy Table
     We are witnesses for this;
p   While remembering hearts Thou meetest
     In communion clearest, sweetest,
cr   Earnest of our coming bliss,

mf   Showing not Thy death alone,
     And Thy love exceeding great,
cr   But Thy coming, and Thy Throne,
dim   All for which we long and wait.

mf   Thou art coming; we are waiting
     With a hope that cannot fail,
     Asking not the day or hour,
     Resting on Thy word of power,
     Anchor'd safe within the veil.
p   Time appointed may be long,
cr   But the vision must be sure;
     Certainty shall make us strong,
     Joyful patience can endure.

f   O the joy to see Thee reigning,
     Thee, my own belovèd LORD!
     Every tongue Thy Name confessing,
     Worship, honour, glory, blessing
     Brought to Thee with one accord,
p   Thee, my Master, and my Friend,
f   Vindicated and enthroned,
cr   Unto earth's remotest end
     Glorified, adored, and own'd!

FRANCES R. HAVERGAL.

General Hymns.

Hymn 204. VENI CITO.—8 8.8 8.8 8.

Rev. J. B. DYKES.

"*He . . . saith, Surely I come quickly. Amen. Even so, come, Lord Jesus*"

mf O QUICKLY come, dread Judge of all ;
p For, awful though Thine Advent be,
cr All shadows from the truth will fall,
dim And falsehood die, in sight of Thee :
cr O quickly come : for doubt and fear
Like clouds dissolve when Thou art near.

mf O quickly come, great King of all ;
Reign all around us, and within ;
Let sin no more our souls enthral,
Let pain and sorrow die with sin :
cr O quickly come : for Thou alone
Canst make Thy scatter'd people one.

mf O quickly come, true Life of all ;
p For death is mighty all around ;
On every home his shadows fall,
On every heart his mark is found :
cr O quickly come : for grief and pain
f Can never cloud Thy glorious reign.

mf O quickly come, sure Light of all,
p For gloomy night broods o'er our way ;
And weakly souls begin to fall
With weary watching for the day :
cr O quickly come : for round Thy Throne
f No eye is blind, no night is known.

L. TUTTIETT.

ALTERNATIVE TUNE, HYMN 644.

(154)

General Hymns.

Hymn 205. SOUTHWELL.—S.M.   DAMON, *Psalmes*, 1579.

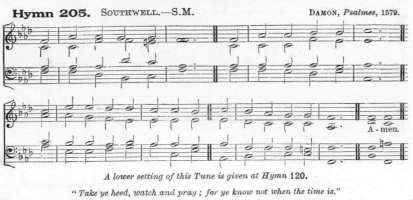

A-men.

A lower setting of this Tune is given at Hymn 120.

"Take ye heed, watch and pray; for ye know not when the time is."

p THOU Judge of quick and dead,
  Before Whose bar severe
mf With holy joy, or (p) guilty dread,
  We all shall soon appear ;

mf Our waken'd souls prepare
  For that tremendous day,
And fill us now with watchful care,
And stir us up to pray :

  To pray, and wait the hour,
p The awful hour unknown,
cr When, robed in majesty and power,
  Thou shalt from Heav'n come down,

mf Th' immortal SON of Man,
  To judge the human race,
With all Thy FATHER'S dazzling train,
With all Thy glorious grace.

p To sober earthly joys,
  To quicken holy fears,
cr For ever let the Archangel's voice
  Be sounding in our ears ;

p The solemn midnight cry,
f "Ye dead, the Judge is come !
Arise, and meet Him in the sky,
And meet your instant doom !"

p O may we thus be found
  Obedient to His Word,
cr Attentive to the trumpet's sound,
  And looking for our LORD.

mf O may we thus insure
  Our lot among the blest, ·
And watch a moment, to secure
An everlasting rest.

C. WESLEY, 1749.

Hymn 206. ABBOTSFORD.—L.M. *Catholische Geistliche Gesänge* (Andernach, 1608).

A-men.

"The day of the Lord will come as a thief in the night."

mf THAT day of wrath, that dreadful day,
  When heaven and earth shall pass away,
What power shall be the sinner's stay?
How shall he meet that dreadful day ?

When, shrivelling like a parchèd scroll,
The flaming heavens together roll ;

cr When louder yet, and yet more dread,
ff Swells the high trump that wakes the dead ;

p Oh, on that day, that wrathful day,
  When man to judgment wakes from clay,
cr Be Thou, O CHRIST, the sinner's stay,
dim Though heaven and earth shall pass away.

Sir W. SCOTT, 1771-1832.

ALTERNATIVE TUNE, HYMN 88 (SECOND TUNE)

General Hymns.

Hymn 207. St. Cuthbert.—8 6 8 4.

Rev. J. B. DYKES.

A - men.

" If I go not away, the Comforter will not come unto you ; but if I depart, I will send Him unto you."

p OUR Blest Redeemer, ere He breathed
His tender last farewell,
A Guide, a Comforter, bequeath'd
With us to dwell.

mf He came sweet influence to impart,
A gracious willing Guest,
While He can find one humble heart
Wherein to rest.

p And His that gentle voice we hear,
Soft as the breath of even,
That checks each fault, that calms each fear,
And speaks of Heav'n.

cr And every virtue we possess,
And every conquest won,
And every thought of holiness,
mf Are His alone.

SPIRIT of purity and grace,
Our weakness, pitying, see :
O make our hearts Thy dwelling-place,
And worthier Thee.

HARRIET AUBER, 1829.

Hymn 208. Tallis.—C.M.

T. TALLIS, 1567.

A - men.

A higher setting of this Tune is given at Hymn 72.

" The communion of the Holy Ghost."

mf O HOLY SPIRIT, LORD of grace,
Eternal Fount of love,
Inflame, we pray, our inmost hearts
With fire from Heav'n above.

As Thou in bond of love dost join
The FATHER and the SON,
So fill us all with mutual love,
And knit our hearts in one.

f All glory to the FATHER be,
All glory to the SON,
All glory, HOLY GHOST, to Thee,
While endless ages run.

J. CHANDLER and Compilers:
from the Latin of C. Coffin.

(156)

General Hymns.

Hymn 209. HAWKHURST.—L.M.   H. J. GAUNTLETT.

A - men.

"*As many as are led by the Spirit of God, they are the sons of God.*"

mf   COME, gracious SPIRIT, heavenly Dove,
     With light and comfort from above ;
Be Thou our Guardian, Thou our Guide,
O'er every thought and step preside.

The light of truth to us display,
And make us know and choose Thy way ;
p   Plant holy fear in every heart,
cr   That we from GOD may ne'er depart.

mf   Lead us to CHRIST, the living Way,
Nor let us from His pastures stray ;
Lead us to holiness, the road
That we must take to dwell with GOD.

Lead us to Heav'n, that we may share
Fulness of joy for ever there ;
Lead us to GOD, our final rest,
To be with Him for ever blest.

S. BROWNE, 1720.

Hymn 210. CHARITY.—7 7 7 5.   Sir J. STAINER.

rall.   Voices in Unison.

ORG.   A - men.

"*And now abideth faith, hope, charity, these three ; but the greatest of these is charity.*"

mf   GRACIOUS SPIRIT, HOLY GHOST,
     Taught by Thee, we covet most
Of Thy gifts at Pentecost,
   Holy, heavenly love.

Love is kind, and suffers long,
Love is meek, and thinks no wrong,
Love than death itself more strong ;
   Therefore give us love.

Prophecy will fade away,
Melting in the light of day ;
Love will ever with us stay ;
   Therefore give us love.

Faith will vanish into sight ;
Hope be emptied in delight ;
cr   Love in Heav'n will shine more bright ;
   Therefore give us love.

mf   Faith and hope and love we see
Joining hand in hand agree ;
cr   But the greatest of the three,
   And the best, is love.

p   From the overshadowing
Of Thy gold and silver wing
Shed on us, who to Thee sing,
   Holy, heavenly love.

Bishop C. WORDSWORTH.

General Hymns.

Hymn 211. St. Timothy.—C.M.   Rev. Sir H. W. Baker.

A - men.

A lower setting of this Tune is given at Hymn 5.

" Awake, O north wind ; and come, thou south ; blow upon my garden, that the spices thereof may flow out."

mf O HOLY GHOST, Thy people bless
    Who long to feel Thy might,
And fain would grow in holiness
    As children of the light.

To Thee we bring, Who art the LORD,
    Ou' selves to be Thy throne ;
Let every thought, and deed, and word
    Thy pure dominion own.

    Life-giving SPIRIT, o'er us move,
dim As on the formless deep ;
cr Give life and order, light and love,
p   Where now is death or sleep.

f Great Gift of our ascended King,
    His saving truth reveal ;
Our tongues inspire His praise to sing,
    Our hearts His love to feel.

mf True Wind of Heav'n, from south or north,
    For joy (*dim*) or chastening, blow ;
cr The garden-spices shall spring forth
    If Thou wilt bid them flow.

f O HOLY GHOST, of sevenfold might,
    All graces come from Thee ;
p Grant us to know and serve aright
    ONE GOD in Persons THREE.

Sir H. W. Baker.

Hymn 212. SALES.—8 8 6.   Sir F. Champneys.

A - men.

" He is faithful."

mf TO Thee, O Comforter Divine,
    For all Thy grace and power benign,
f   Sing we Alleluia !

To Thee, Whose faithful love had place
In GOD's great covenant of grace,
    Sing we Alleluia !

mf To Thee, Whose faithful voice doth win
    The wandering from the ways of sin,
f   Sing we Alleluia !

To Thee, Whose faithful power doth heal,
Enlighten, sanctify, and seal,
    Sing we Alleluia !

mf To Thee, Whose faithful truth is shown
    By every promise made our own,
f   Sing we Alleluia !

To Thee, our Teacher and our Friend,
Our faithful Leader to the end,
    Sing we Alleluia !

mf To Thee, by JESUS CHRIST sent down,
f Of all His gifts the sum and crown,
ff   Sing we Alleluia !

f To Thee, Who art with GOD the SON
    And GOD the FATHER ever ONE,
ff   Sing we Alleluia !

FRANCES R. HAVERGAL.

General Hymns.

Hymn 213. STOCKTON.—C.M.   T. WRIGHT.

A - men.

A higher setting of this Tune is given at Hymn 549.

" And he shewed me a pure river of water of life, clear as crystal, proceeding out of the Throne of God and of the Lamb."

mf A LIVING stream, as crystal clear,
  Welling from out the Throne
Of GOD and of the LAMB on high,
  The LORD to man hath shown.

This stream doth water Paradise,
  It makes the Angels sing :
cr One precious drop within the heart
  Is of all joy the spring :

f Joy past all speech, of glory full,
dim But stored where none may know,
As manna hid in dewy heaven,
  As pearls in ocean low.

p Eye hath not seen, nor ear hath heard,
  Nor to man's heart hath come

What for those loving Thee in truth
  Thou hast in love's own home.

mf But by His SPIRIT He to us
  The secret doth reveal :
cr Faith sees and hears : but O for wings
  That we might taste, and feel ;

Wings like a dove to waft us on
  High o'er the flood of sin !
p LORD of the Ark, put forth Thine hand,
  And take Thy wanderers in.

f O praise the FATHER, praise the SON,
  The LAMB for sinners given,
And HOLY GHOST, through Whom alone
  Our hearts are raised to Heav'n.

J. KEBLE : based on J. Mason.

ALTERNATIVE TUNE, HYMN 478 (SECOND TUNE).

Hymn 214. CLOISTERS.—11 11 11 5.   Sir J. BARNBY.

A - men.

" Help us, O God of our salvation, for the glory of Thy Name."

mf LORD of our life, and GOD of our salvation,
  Star of our night, and Hope of every nation,
p Hear and (*cr*) receive Thy Church's supplication,
  f LORD GOD Almighty.

mf See round Thine ark the hungry billows curling ;
  See how Thy foes their banners are unfurling ;
p LORD, while their (*cr*) darts envenom'd they are hurling,
  f Thou canst preserve us.

mf LORD, Thou canst help when earthly armour faileth,
  LORD, Thou canst save when deadly sin assaileth,
p LORD, o'er Thy (*cr*) Church nor death nor hell prevaileth ;
  p Grant us Thy peace, LORD.

mf Grant us Thy help till foes are backward driven,
  Grant them Thy truth, that they may be forgiven,
p Grant peace on earth, (*cr*) and, after we have striven,
      pp Peace in Thy Heaven.   P. PUSEY.

(159)

General Hymns.

Hymn 215.   Aurelia.—7 6 7 6. 7 6 7 6.   S. S. Wesley.

" He is the Head of the body, the Church."

mf THE Church's one foundation
    Is Jesus Christ her Lord ;
She is His new creation
    By water and the Word :
From Heav'n He came and sought her
    To be His holy Bride ;
p   With His own Blood He bought her,
pp   And for her life He died.

mf Elect from every nation,
    Yet one o'er all the earth,
Her charter of salvation
    One Lord, one Faith, one Birth,
One Holy Name she blesses,
    Partakes one Holy Food,
And to one hope she presses
    With every grace endued.

p Though with a scornful wonder
    Men see her sore opprest,
By schisms rent asunder,
    By heresies distrest,
cr Yet Saints their watch are keeping,
    Their cry goes up, " How long? "
mf And soon the night of weeping
cr Shall be the morn of song.

mf Mid toil, and tribulation,
    And tumult of her war,
She waits the consummation
p   Of peace for evermore ;
cr Till with the vision glorious
    Her longing eyes are blest,
f And the great Church victorious
dim Shall be the Church at rest.

mf Yet she on earth hath union
    With God the Three in One,
And mystic sweet communion
    With those whose rest is won :
f O happy ones and holy !
p Lord, give us grace that we,
Like them the meek and lowly,
cr On high may dwell with Thee.

                S J. Stone.

General Hymns.

Hymn 216. OLD 44TH.—D.C.M.   *Psalmes*, 1556.

A-men.

"That they all may be one."

p WHAT time the evening shadows fall
    Around the Church on earth,
When darker forms of doubt appal,
    And new false lights have birth;
cr Then closer should her faithful band
    For Truth together hold,
Hell's last devices to withstand,
    And safely guard her fold.

p O FATHER, in that hour of fear
    The Church of England keep,
mf Thine Altar to the last to rear,
    And feed Thy fainting sheep;
May she the holy truths attest
    Apostles taught of yore,
Nor quit the Faith by saints confest,
    Though tempted ne'er so sore.

p O CHRIST, Who for Thy flock didst pray
    That all might be as one,
mf Unite us all ere fades the day,
    Thou Sole-Begotten SON;
The East, the West, together bind
    In love's unbroken chain;
cr Give each one hope, one heart, one mind,
    One glory, and one gain.

f O SPIRIT, LORD of light and life,
    The Church with strength renew,
p Compose the angry voice of strife,
    All jealousies subdue:
cr Do Thou in ever-quickening streams
    Upon Thy saints descend,
And warm them with reviving beams,
    And guide them to the end.

mf Great THREE in ONE, Great ONE in THREE,
    Our hymns of prayer receive,
And teach us all from sin to flee,
    And live as we believe;
cr So, pure in faith, our thoughts and speech
    And acts that faith shall own;
f So shall we to Thy Presence reach,
    And know as we are known.

J. W. HEWETT

(161)   6

General Hymns.

Hymn 217. St. Cecilia.—6 6 6 6.   Rev. L. G. Hayne.

A - men.

" Thy Kingdom come."

mf THY kingdom come, O God,
     Thy rule, O Christ, begin ;
Break with Thine iron rod
The tyrannies of sin.

p Where is Thy reign of peace,
     And purity, and love?
When shall all hatred cease,
     As in the realms above?

When comes the promised time
     That war shall be no more,
And lust, oppression, crime
     Shall flee Thy Face before?

mf We pray Thee, Lord, arise,
     And come in Thy great might ;
Revive our longing eyes,
     Which languish for Thy sight.

p Men scorn Thy sacred Name,
     And wolves devour Thy fold ;
By many deeds of shame
     We learn that love grows cold.

O'er heathen lands afar
     Thick darkness broodeth yet :
cr Arise, O morning Star,
f   Arise, and never set.

              L. Hensley.

Hymn 218. Heathlands.—7 7.7 7 7.7 7.   H. Smart.

A - men.

" God be merciful unto us, and bless us ; and shew us the light of His countenance."

mf GOD of mercy, God of grace,
     Show the brightness of Thy Face ;
Shine upon us, Saviour, shine,
Fill Thy Church with light Divine ;
And Thy saving health extend
Unto earth's remotest end.

f Let the people praise Thee, Lord ;
Be by all that live adored ;
Let the nations shout and sing

Glory to their Saviour King ;
p At Thy feet their tribute pay,
And Thy holy Will obey.

f Let the people praise Thee, Lord ;
Earth shall then her fruits afford ;
God to man His blessing give,
Man to God devoted live ;
All below, and all above,
One in joy, and light, and love.

              H. F. Lyte, 1834.

General Hymns.

Hymn 219. CRÜGER.—7 6 7 6.7 6 7 6.   J. CRÜGER, 1598–1662.

A-men.

A higher setting of this Tune is given at Hymn 604.

"All the earth shall be filled with His Majesty."

f   HAIL to the LORD's Anointed,
     Great David's greater Son !
Hail, in the time appointed,
     His reign on earth begun !
He comes to break oppression,
     To set the captive free,
To take away transgression,
     And rule in equity.

mf He shall come down like showers
     Upon the fruitful earth,
And joy and hope, like flowers,
     Spring in His path to birth :
Before Him on the mountains
p   Shall peace, the herald, go ;
cr From hill to vale the fountains
     Of righteousness o'erflow

mf Kings shall bow down before Him,
     And gold and incense bring ;
All nations shall adore Him,
     His praise all people sing ;
To Him shall prayer unceasing
     And daily vows ascend ;
His kingdom still increasing,
     A kingdom without end.

f   O'er every foe victorious,
     He on His Throne shall rest ;
From age to age more glorious,
     All-blessing and all-blest :
The tide of time shall never
     His covenant remove ;
His Name shall stand for ever,
p   His changeless Name of love.

J. MONTGOMERY, 1821.

General Hymns.

Hymn 220. GALILEE.—L.M.   P. ARMES.

A - men.

" The kingdoms of this world are become the kingdoms of our Lord and of His Christ;
and He shall reign for ever and ever."

f   JESUS shall reign where'er the sun
       Doth his successive journeys run ;
   His kingdom stretch from shore to shore,
   Till moons shall wax and wane no more.

mf People and realms of every tongue
     Dwell on His love with sweetest song,
p   And infant voices shall proclaim
cr   Their early blessings on His Name.

f   Blessings abound where'er He reigns ;
     The prisoner leaps to lose his chains ;
dim The weary find eternal rest,
cr   And all the sons of want are blest.

f   Let every creature rise and bring
     Peculiar honours to our King ;
     Angels descend with songs again,
     And earth repeat the loud Amen.

                    I. WATTS, 1719.

Hymn 221. DUNDEE.—C.M.   *Psalms* (Edinburgh, 1615).

A - men.

A higher setting of this Tune is given at Hymns 41, 80.

Hymn 221. DUNDEE.—C.M.   *(Alternative Version.)*

Harmonised by T. RAVENSCROFT, 1621.

(164)

General Hymns.

The Alternative Version may be used for verses 2 and 4.

"Of Whom the whole family in heaven and earth is named."

mf LET saints on earth in concert sing
    With those whose work is done ;
For all the servants of our King
    In Heav'n and earth are one.

One family, we dwell in Him,
    One Church, above, beneath ;
dim Though now divided by the stream,
p   The narrow stream of death.
mf One army of the living GOD,
    To His command we bow ;

p Part of the host have cross'd the flood,
    And part are crossing now.
E'en now to their eternal home
    There pass some spirits blest ;
While others to the margin come,
    Waiting their call to rest.
mf JESU, be Thou our constant Guide ;
    Then, when the word is given,
    Bid Jordan's narrow stream divide,
cr And bring us safe to Heav'n.

C. WESLEY, 1759.

Hymn 222. ALFORD.—7 6 8 6. 7 6 8 6.
REV. J. B. DYKES.

A-men.

"God shall wipe away all tears from their eyes."

f TEN thousand times ten thousand,
    In sparkling raiment bright,
The armies of the ransom'd Saints
    Throng up the steeps of light :
mf 'Tis finish'd ! all is finish'd,
    Their fight with death and sin ;
f Fling open wide the golden gates,
    And let the victors in.

What rush of Alleluias
    Fills all the earth and sky !
What ringing of a thousand harps
    Bespeaks the triumph nigh !
O day, for which creation
    And all its tribes were made !
O joy, for all its former woes
    A thousand-fold repaid !

mf Oh, then what raptured greetings
    On Canaan's happy shore,
What knitting sever'd friendships up,
    Where partings are no more !
f Then eyes with joy shall sparkle
p That brimm'd with tears of late ;
cr Orphans no longer fatherless,
    Nor widows desolate.

p Bring near Thy great Salvation,
    Thou LAMB for sinners slain,
cr Fill up the roll of Thine elect,
f Then take Thy power and reign :
mf Appear, Desire of nations,
p Thine exiles long for home ;
cr Show in the heavens Thy promised sign ;
f Thou Prince and Saviour, come.

H. ALFORD.

(165)

Hymn 223. VOX ANGELICA.—11 10 11 10.9 11. *(First Tune.)*

Rev. J. B. DYKES.

mf

p *cres.* *pp*

An-gels of JE - SUS, An - gels of light, Sing-ing to wel-come the pilgrims of the night, night, Sing-

cres. *pp* *rall.* . . . .

ing

Sing - ing to wel - come the pil-grims, the pil - grims of the night. A - men.

" The night is far spent, the day is at hand."

HARK ! hark, my soul ! Angelic songs are swelling
    O'er earth's green fields, and ocean's wave-beat shore :
How sweet the truth those blessèd strains are telling
    Of that new life when sin shall be no more.
Angels of JESUS, Angels of light,
Singing to welcome the pilgrims of the night !

Onward we go, for still we hear them singing,
    " Come, weary souls, for JESUS bids you come : "
And through the dark, its echoes sweetly ringing,
    The music of the Gospel leads us home.
Angels of JESUS, Angels of light,
Singing to welcome the pilgrims of the night !

Far, far away, like bells at evening pealing,
    The voice of JESUS sounds o'er land and sea,
And laden souls, by thousands meekly stealing,
    Kind Shepherd, turn their weary steps to Thee.
Angels of JESUS, Angels of light,
Singing to welcome the pilgrims of the night !

Rest comes at length ; though life be long and dreary,
    The day must dawn, and darksome night be past ;
Faith's journey ends in welcome to the weary,
    And Heav'n, the heart's true home, will come at last.
Angels of JESUS, Angels of light,
Singing to welcome the pilgrims of the night !

Angels ! sing on, your faithful watches keeping,
    Sing us sweet fragments of the songs above ;
Till morning's joy shall end the night of weeping,
    And life's long shadows break in cloudless love.
Angels of JESUS, Angels of light,
Singing to welcome the pilgrims of the night !

F. W. FABER.

General Hymns.

Hymn 223. PILGRIMS.—11 10 11 10.9 11. (*Second Tune.*) H. SMART.

A - men.

"*The night is far spent, the day is at hand.*"

mf HARK! hark, my soul! Angelic songs are swelling
    O'er earth's green fields, and ocean's wave-beat shore:
  How sweet the truth those blessèd strains are telling
    Of that new life when sin shall be no more.
p   Angels of JESUS, (*cr*) Angels of light,
f   Singing to welcome (*p*) the pilgrims of the night!

mf Onward we go, for still we hear them singing,
p   "Come, weary souls, for JESUS bids you come:"
cr And through the dark, its echoes sweetly ringing,
    The music of the Gospel leads us home.
p   Angels of JESUS, (*cr*) Angels of light,
f   Singing to welcome (*p*) the pilgrims of the night!

p   Far, far away, like bells at evening pealing,
    The voice of JESUS sounds o'er land and sea,
  And laden souls, by thousands meekly stealing,
cr   Kind Shepherd, turn their weary steps to Thee.
p   Angels of JESUS, (*cr*) Angels of light,
f   Singing to welcome (*p*) the pilgrims of the night!

mf Rest comes at length; though life be long and dreary,
    The day must dawn, and darksome night be past;
  Faith's journey ends in welcome to the weary,
    And Heav'n, the heart's true home, will come at last.
p   Angels of JESUS, (*cr*) Angels of light,
f   Singing to welcome (*p*) the pilgrims of the night!

mf Angels! sing on, your faithful watches keeping,
    Sing us sweet fragments of the songs above;
  Till morning's joy shall end the night of weeping,
or   And life's long shadows break in cloudless love.
p   Angels of JESUS, (*cr*) Angels of light,
f   Singing to welcome the pilgrims of the night!

                          F. W. FABER.

General Hymns.

Hymn 224. KOCHER.—7 6 7 6.

J. H. KNECHT, 1752–1817.

A - men.

"The fellowship of His sufferings."

mf O HAPPY band of pilgrims,
If onward ye will tread
With JESUS as your Fellow
To JESUS as your Head!

O happy if ye labour
As JESUS did for men:
O happy if ye hunger
As JESUS hunger'd then !

p The Cross that JESUS carried
He carried as your due:
f The Crown that JESUS weareth
He weareth it for you.

mf The faith by which ye see Him,
The hope in which ye yearn,

The love that through all troubles
To Him alone will turn.

p The trials that beset you,
The sorrows ye endure,
The manifold temptations
That death alone can cure,

cr What are they but His jewels
Of right celestial worth ?
What are they but the ladder
Set up to Heav'n on earth?

f O happy band of pilgrims,
Look upward to the skies,
dim Where such a light affliction
f Shall win so great a prize.

J. M. NEALE.

Hymn 225. ST. ALPHEGE.—7 6 7 6. *(First Tune.)*

H. J. GAUNTLETT.

A - men.

A higher setting of this Tune is given at Hymn **350.**

Hymn 225. HIC BREVE VIVITUR.—7 6 7 6. *(Second Tune.)*

A. PETTET, c. 1815.

Slow.

A-men.

(168)

General Hymns.

p BRIEF life is here our portion ;
 Brief sorrow, short-lived care ;
cr The life that knows no ending,
 The tearless life, is there.

mf O happy retribution !
 Short toil, eternal rest ;
For mortals and for sinners
 A mansion with the blest !

And now we fight the battle,
f   But then shall wear the crown
Of full and everlasting
 And passionless renown ;

p And now we watch and struggle,
 And now we live in hope,
And Sion in her anguish
 With Babylon must cope ;

mf But He, Whom now we trust in,
 Shall then be seen and known ;

And they that know and see Him
 Shall have Him for their own.

cr The morning shall awaken,
 The shadows shall decay,
And each true-hearted servant
 Shall shine as doth the day. :

f There GOD, our King and Portion,
 In fulness of His grace,
Shall we behold for ever,
p   And worship face to face.

mf O sweet and blessèd country,
 The home of GOD'S elect !
O sweet and blessèd country
 That eager hearts expect ! .

p JESU, in mercy bring us
 To that dear land of rest ;
mf Who art, with GOD the FATHER
 And SPIRIT, ever Blest.

J. M. NEALE : from the Latin
of Bernard of Murles.

Hymn 226. PEARSALL.—7 6 7 6.7 6 7 6.

R. L. PEARSALL.

A - men.

mf THE world is very evil,
 The times are waxing late,
p Be sober and keep vigil,
 The Judge is at the gate ;
The Judge Who comes in mercy,
cr   The Judge Who comes with might,
Who comes to end the evil,
f   Who comes to crown the right.

mf Arise, arise, good Christian,
 Let right to wrong succeed ;
p Let penitential sorrow
cr   To heavenly gladness lead,
To light that has no evening,
 That knows nor moon nor sun,
The light so new and golden,
 The light that is but one.

mf O home of fadeless splendour,
 Of flowers that bear no thorn,
Where they shall dwell as children
p   Who here as exiles mourn ;

mf 'Midst power that knows no limit,
 Where wisdom has no bound,
p The Beatific Vision
cr   Shall glad the Saints around.

mf O happy, holy portion,
 Refection for the blest,
True vision of true beauty,
 True cure of the distrest !

f Strive, man, to win that glory ;
 Toil, man, to gain that light ;
Send hope before to grasp it,
 Till hope be lost in sight.

mf O sweet and blessèd country,
 The home of GOD'S elect !
O sweet and blessèd country
 That eager hearts expect !

p JESU, in mercy bring us
 To that dear land of rest ;
mf Who art, with GOD the FATHER
 And SPIRIT, ever Blest.

J. M. NEALE : from the Latin
of Bernard of Murles.

G 2

General Hymns.

Hymn 227.   JENNER.—7 6 7 6. 7 6 7 6.   (*First Tune.*)   Bishop JENNER.

A - men.

Hymn 227.   TOURS.—7 6 7 6. 7 6 7 6.   (*Second Tune.*)   B. TOURS.

A - men.

[*For copyright, see* p. iv.]

"*A better country, that is, an heavenly.*"

mf FOR thee, O dear, dear country,
        Mine eyes their vigils keep ;
For very love, beholding
        Thy happy name, they weep.
The mention of thy glory
        Is unction to the breast,
And medicine in sickness,
        And love, and life, and rest.

O one, O only mansion !
        O Paradise of joy !
Where tears are ever banish'd,
        And smiles have no alloy ;
f The LAMB is all thy splendour ;
        The Crucified thy praise ;
His laud and benediction
        Thy ransom'd people raise.

(170)

General Hymns.

With jasper glow thy bulwarks,
    Thy streets with emeralds blaze ;
The sardius and the topaz
    Unite in thee their rays ;
Thine ageless walls are bonded
    With amethyst unpriced ;
The Saints build up thy fabric,
    And the corner-stone is CHRIST.

mf Thou hast no shore, fair ocean !
    Thou hast no time, bright day !
Dear fountain of refreshment
    To pilgrims far away !

f Upon the Rock of ages
    They raise thy holy tower ;
Thine is the victor's laurel,
    And thine the golden dower.

mf O sweet and blessèd country,
    The home of GOD's elect !
O sweet and blessèd country
    That eager hearts expect !
p JESU, in mercy bring us
    To that dear land of rest ;
mf Who art, with GOD the FATHER
    And SPIRIT, ever Blest.

ALTERNATIVE TUNE, HYMN 769.

J. M. NEALE : from the Latin
of Bernard of Murles.

Hymn 228.   EWING.—7 6 7 6. 7 6 7 6.   A. EWING.

A men.

" And the city was pure gold."

mf JERUSALEM the golden,
    With milk and honey blest,
Beneath thy contemplation
dim   Sink heart and voice opprest.
cr I know not, oh, I know not
    What joys await us there,
What radiancy of glory,
p   What bliss beyond compare.

f They stand, those halls of Sion,
    All jubilant with song,
And bright with many an Angel,
    And all the Martyr throng ;
The Prince is ever in them,
    The daylight is serene ;
The pastures of the blessèd
p   Are deck'd in glorious sheen.

mf There is the throne of David ;
    And there, from care released,
The shout of them that triumph,
    The song of them that feast ;
f And they, who with their Leader
    Have conquer'd in the fight,
For ever and for ever
p   Are clad in robes of white.

mf O sweet and blessèd country,
    The home of GOD's elect !
O sweet and blessèd country
    That eager hearts expect !
p JESU, in mercy bring us
    To that dear land of rest ;
mf Who art, with GOD the FATHER
p   And SPIRIT, ever Blest.

J. M. NEALE : from the Latin
of Bernard of Murles.

General Hymns.

Hymn 229. THE ROSEATE HUES.—D.C.M. (*First Tune.*) Sir J. STAINER.

A - men.

Hymn 229. AMBERLEY.—D.C.M. (*Second Tune.*) Sir H. PARRY.

General Hymns.

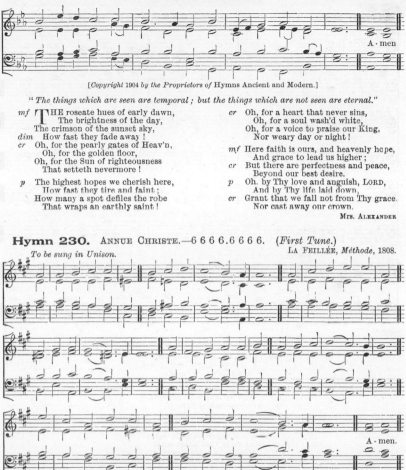

A·men

"The things which are seen are temporal; but the things which are not seen are eternal."

mf THE roseate hues of early dawn,
 The brightness of the day,
 The crimson of the sunset sky,
dim How fast they fade away!
cr Oh, for the pearly gates of Heav'n,
 Oh, for the golden floor,
 Oh, for the Sun of righteousness
 That setteth nevermore!

p The highest hopes we cherish here,
 How fast they tire and faint;
 How many a spot defiles the robe
 That wraps an earthly saint!

cr Oh, for a heart that never sins,
 Oh, for a soul wash'd white,
 Oh, for a voice to praise our King,
 Nor weary day or night!

mf Here faith is ours, and heavenly hope,
 And grace to lead us higher;
cr But there are perfectness and peace,
 Beyond our best desire.

p Oh, by Thy love and anguish, LORD,
 And by Thy life laid down,
cr Grant that we fall not from Thy grace,
 Nor cast away our crown.

      MRS. ALEXANDER

Hymn 230. ANNUE CHRISTE.—6 6 6 6.6 6 6 6. (*First Tune.*)

           LA FEILLÉE, *Méthode*, 1808.

To be sung in Unison.

A·men.

"There remaineth therefore a rest to the people of God."

mf THERE is a blessèd home
 Beyond this land of woe,
 Where trials never come,
 Nor tears of sorrow flow;
cr Where faith is lost in sight,
 And patient hope is crown'd,
f And everlasting light
 Its glory throws around.

p There is a land of peace,
 Good Angels know it well;
cr Glad songs that never cease
 Within its portals swell;
mf Around its glorious Throne
 Ten thousand Saints adore
 CHRIST, with the FATHER ONE
 And SPIRIT, evermore.

f O joy all joys beyond,
 To see the LAMB Who died,
p And count each sacred Wound
 In Hands, and Feet, and Side;
mf To give to Him the praise
 Of every triumph won,
cr And sing through endless days
 The great things He hath done.

mf Look up, ye saints of GOD,
 Nor fear to tread below
 The path your Saviour trod
p Of daily toil and woe;
cr Wait but a little while
 In uncomplaining love,
mf His own most gracious smile
 Shall welcome you above.

      Sir H. W. BAKER.

(173)

General Hymns.

Hymn 230. THE BLESSED HOME.—6 6 6 6.6 6 6 6. *(Second Tune.)*

Sir J. STAINER.

"There remaineth therefore a rest to the people of God."

mf THERE is a blessèd home
    Beyond this land of woe,
Where trials never come,
    Nor tears of sorrow flow ;
cr Where faith is lost in sight,
    And patient hope is crown'd,
f And everlasting light
    Its glory throws around.

p There is a land of peace,
    Good Angels know it well ;
cr Glad songs that never cease
    Within its portals swell ;
mf Around its glorious Throne
    Ten thousand Saints adore
CHRIST. with the FATHER ONE
    And SPIRIT, evermore.

f O joy all joys beyond,
    To see the LAMB Who died,
p And count each sacred Wound
    In Hands, and Feet, and Side ;
mf To give to Him the praise
    Of every triumph won,
cr And sing through endless days
    The great things He hath done.

mf Look up, ye saints of GOD,
    Nor fear to tread below
The path your Saviour trod
p   Of daily toil and woe ;
cr Wait but a little while
    In uncomplaining love,
mf His own most gracious smile
    Shall welcome you above.

Sir H. W. BAKER.

(174)

General Hymns.

Hymn 231. Nearer Home.—D.S.M.   J. Woodbury (arr. by Sir A. Sullivan).

"And so shall we ever be with the Lord."

mf "FOR ever with the Lord!"
p   Amen; so let it be;
cr Life from the dead is in that word,
     'Tis immortality.
p Here in the body pent,
     Absent from Him I roam,
cr Yet nightly pitch my moving tent
     A day's march nearer home.

mf My Father's house on high,
     Home of my soul, how near
   At times to faith's foreseeing eye
     Thy golden gates appear!
p *Ah! then my spirit faints
     To reach the land I love,
cr The bright inheritance of Saints,
     Jerusalem above.

f "For ever with the Lord!"
mf   Father, if 'tis Thy Will,
   The promise of that faithful word
     Even here to me fulfil.
   Be Thou at my right hand,
     Then can I never fail;
cr Uphold Thou me, and I shall stand,
     Fight, and I must prevail.

p So when my latest breath
     Shall rend the veil in twain,
cr By death I shall escape from death,
f   And life eternal gain.
mf Knowing as I am known,
     How shall I love that word,
cr And oft repeat before the Throne,
     "For ever with the Lord!"

J. Montgomery, 1835.

Verse 2, lines 5 and 6.

General Hymns.

Hymn 232. URBS BEATA.—8 7.8 7.8 7. *(First Tune.)*

To be sung in Unison.

Sarum Melody.

An Alternative Version of this Tune is given at Hymn 396, and also a lower setting of this Version.

Hymn 232. REGENT SQUARE.—8 7.8 7.8 7. *(Second Tune.)*

H. SMART.

General Hymns.

" Eye hath not seen, nor ear heard, neither have entered into the heart of man, the things which God hath prepared for them that love Him. But God hath revealed them unto us by His Spirit."

mf LIGHT'S abode, celestial Salem,
   Vision whence true peace doth spring,
Brighter than the heart can fancy,
Mansion of the Highest King;
f Oh, how glorious are the praises
   Which of thee the prophets sing!

mf There for ever and for ever
   Alleluia is out-pour'd;
For unending, for unbroken
Is the feast-day of the LORD;
p All is pure and all is holy
   That within thy walls is stored.

There no cloud nor passing vapour
   Dims the brightness of the air;
mf Endless noon-day, glorious noon-day,
   From the Sun of suns is there;
There no night brings rest from labour,
   For unknown are toil and care.

f Oh, how glorious and resplendent,
   Fragile body, shalt thou be,
When endued with so much beauty,
Full of health, and strong, and free,
Full of vigour, full of pleasure
   That shall last eternally!

mf Now with gladness, now with courage,
   Bear the burden on thee laid,
p That hereafter these thy labours
   May with endless gifts be paid;
cr And in everlasting glory
   Thou with brightness be array'd.

f Laud and honour to the FATHER,
   Laud and honour to the SON,
Laud and honour to the SPIRIT,
   Ever THREE and ever ONE,
Consubstantial, Co-eternal,
   While unending ages run.

           J. M. NEALE: from Thomas à Kempis.

Hymn 233. CHRISTCHURCH.—6 6 6 6. 4 4 4 4.
C. STEGGALL.

A-men.

" Our conversation is in heaven."

mf JERUSALEM on high
   My song and city is,
My home whene'er I die,
The centre of my bliss:
f O happy place!
   When shall I be,
   My GOD, with Thee,
p To see Thy Face?

mf There dwells my LORD, my King,
p Judged here unfit to live;
mf There Angels to Him sing,
   And lowly homage give:
f O happy place!
   When shall I be,
   My GOD, with Thee,
p To see Thy Face?

mf The Patriarchs of old
   There from their travels cease;
The Prophets there behold
   Their longed-for Prince of peace:
f O happy place!
   When shall I be,
   My GOD, with Thee,
p To see Thy Face?

mf The LAMB'S Apostles there
   I might with joy behold,
The harpers I might hear
   Harping on harps of gold:
f O happy place!
   When shall I be,
   My GOD, with Thee,
p To see Thy Face?

p The bleeding Martyrs, they
   Within those courts are found,
cr Clothèd in pure array,
   Their scars with glory crown'd:
f O happy place!
   When shall I be,
   My GOD, with Thee,
p To see Thy Face?

Ah me! ah me! that I
   In Kedar's tents here stay;
No place like that on high;
cr LORD, thither guide my way:
f O happy place!
   When shall I be,
   My GOD, with Thee,
p To see Thy Face?

           S. CROSSMAN.

General Hymns.

Hymn 234. PARADISE. No. 1.—8 6 8 6.6 6 6 6. (*First Tune.*) H. SMART.

A - men.

Hymn 234. PARADISE. No. 2.—8 6 8 6.6 6 6 6. (*Second Tune.*)

Rev. J. B. DYKES.

A - men.

" The Paradise of God."

mf O PARADISE ! O Paradise !
Who doth not crave for rest ?
Who would not seek the happy land
Where they that loved are blest ;
f   Where loyal hearts and true
Stand ever in the light,
All rapture through and through,
dim In GOD'S most holy sight ?

mf O Paradise ! O Paradise !
p   The world is growing old ;
cr Who would not be at rest and free
Where love is never cold ;
f   Where loyal hearts and true
Stand ever in the light,
All rapture through and through,
dim In GOD'S most holy sight ?

General Hymns.

mf O Paradise ! O Paradise !
p   'Tis weary waiting here ;
cr I long to be where JESUS is,
        To feel, to see Him near ;
f   Where loyal hearts and true
           Stand ever in the light,
        All rapture through and through,
dim In GOD'S most holy sight.

mf O Paradise ! O Paradise !
     . I want to sin no more,
     I want to be as pure on earth
        As on thy spotless shore :
f   Where loyal hearts and true
           Stand ever in the light,
        All rapture through and through,
dim In GOD'S most holy sight.

mf O Paradise ! O Paradise !
        I greatly long to see
     The special place my dearest LORD
        In love prepares for me ;
f   Where loyal hearts and true
           Stand ever in the light,
        All rapture through and through,
dim In GOD'S most holy sight.

p   LORD JESU, King of Paradise,
        O keep me in Thy love,
cr And guide me to that happy land
        Of perfect rest above ;
f   Where loyal hearts and true
           Stand ever in the light.
        All rapture through and through,
dim In GOD'S most holy sight.

F. W. FABER (last verse by Compilers).

Hymn 235.   O QUANTA QUALIA.—10 10 10 10.   LA FEILLÉE, *Méthode*, 1808.

* *For the 1st verse, the slur is better over the 3rd and 4th notes of this bar.*

" There remaineth therefore a rest to the people of God."

mf OH, what the joy and the glory must be,
        Those endless Sabbaths the blessèd ones see ;
      Crown for the valiant, (*p*) to weary ones rest ;
cr GOD shall be All and in all ever Blest.

mf What are the Monarch, His Court, and His Throne?
      What are the peace and the joy that they own ?
      O that the blest ones, who in it have share,
      All that they feel could as fully declare !

      Truly Jerusalem name we that shore,
p   Vision of peace, (*cr*) that brings joy evermore ;
mf Wish and fulfilment can sever'd be ne'er,
      Nor the thing pray'd for come short of the prayer.

p   There, where no troubles distraction can bring,
cr We the sweet anthems of Sion shall sing,
      While for Thy grace, LORD, their voices of praise
      Thy blessèd people eternally raise.

mf There dawns no Sabbath, no Sabbath is o'er,
      Those Sabbath-keepers have one evermore ;
f   One and unending is that triumph-song
      Which to the Angels and us shall belong.

p   Now in the meanwhile, with hearts raised on high,
      We for that country must yearn and must sigh ;
      Seeking Jerusalem, dear native land,
      Through our long exile on Babylon's strand.

mf Low before Him with our praises we fall,
      Of Whom, and in Whom, and through Whom are all ;
f   Of Whom, the FATHER ; and in Whom, the SON ;
      Through Whom, the SPIRIT, with Them ever ONE.

J. M. NEALE : from the Latin of Abelard.

ALTERNATIVE TUNE, HYMN 423.

(179)

General Hymns.

Hymn 236. SOUTHWELL.—C.M.   H. S. IRONS.

A-men.

" When shall I come to appear before the presence of God?"

mf JERUSALEM, my happy home,
    Name ever dear to me,
When shall my labours have an end?
    Thy joys when shall I see?

When shall these eyes thy heaven-built walls
    And pearly gates behold?
Thy bulwarks with salvation strong,
    And streets of shining gold?

f Apostles, Martyrs, Prophets, there
    Around my Saviour stand;

And all I love in CHRIST below
    Will join the glorious band.

mf Jerusalem, my happy home,
    When shall I come to thee?
When shall my labours have an end?
    Thy joys when shall I see?

p O CHRIST, do Thou my soul prepare
    For that bright home of love;
cr That I may see Thee and adore,
    With all Thy Saints above.

Adapted from F. B. P. (c. 1600).

Hymn 237. YORK.—C.M.   *Psalms* (Edinburgh, 1615).

A-men.

Hymn 237. YORK.—C.M. *(Alternative Version.)*

CONGREGATION.   Harmonised by S. STUBBS, 1621.

CHOIR.

General Hymns.

The Alternative Version may be used for verses 2 and 4.

" O how amiable are Thy dwellings, Thou Lord of hosts."

mf O GOD of hosts, the mighty LORD,
　　How lovely is the place,
Where Thou enthroned in glory, show'st
The brightness of Thy Face !

p　My longing soul faints with desire
　　To view Thy blest abode ;
My panting heart and flesh cry out
For Thee the living GOD.

mf　For in Thy courts one single day
　　'Tis better to attend,

Than, LORD, in any place besides
A thousand days to spend.

O LORD of hosts, my King and GOD,
How highly blest are they
Who in Thy temple always dwell,
And there Thy praise display !

f　To FATHER, SON, and HOLY GHOST,
　　The GOD Whom we adore,
Be glory, as it was, is now,
And shall be evermore.

N. TATE and N. BRADY, 1696.

Hymn 238. MARTYRDOM.—C.M.　　　　H. WILSON, 1766–1824.

A - men.

A lower setting of this Tune is given at Hymn 630.

" Like as the hart desireth the water-brooks, so longeth my soul after Thee, O God."

p　AS pants the hart for cooling streams
　　When heated in the chase,
So longs my soul, O GOD, for Thee,
And Thy refreshing grace.

For Thee my GOD, the living GOD,
　　My thirsty soul doth pine :
cr　O when shall I behold Thy Face,
Thou Majesty Divine ?

p　Why restless, why cast down, my soul ?
cr　Hope still, and thou shalt sing
f　The praise of Him Who is thy GOD,
Thy health's eternal Spring.

To FATHER, SON, and HOLY GHOST,
The GOD Whom we adore,
Be glory, as it was, is now,
And shall be evermore.

N. TATE and N. BRADY, 1696.

General Hymns.

Hymn 239. HAREWOOD.—6 6 6 6. 4 4 4 4.
S. S. WESLEY, 1839.

A-men.

*"The Lord said unto him, . . . I have hallowed this house . . . to put My Name there for ever,
and Mine eyes and Mine heart shall be there perpetually."*

mf CHRIST is our corner-stone,
  On Him alone we build ;
With His true Saints alone
  The courts of Heav'n are fill'd :
cr On His great love
    Our hopes we place
    Of present grace
    And joys above.

f Oh, then with hymns of praise
  These hallow'd courts shall ring ;
Our voices we will raise
  The THREE in ONE to sing ;
    And thus proclaim
    In joyful song,
    Both loud and long,
    That glorious Name.

mf Here, gracious GOD, do Thou
  For evermore draw nigh ;
  Accept each faithful vow,
p And mark each suppliant sigh ;
mf In copious shower
    On all who pray
    Each holy day
    Thy blessings pour.

Here may we gain from Heav'n
  The grace which we implore ;
And may that grace, once given,
  Be with us evermore,
p Until that day
    When all the blest
cr To endless rest
dim Are call'd away.

J. CHANDLER : from the Latin.

Hymn 240. MAIDSTONE.—7 7 7 7. 7 7 7 7.
W. B. GILBERT.

A men.

General Hymns.

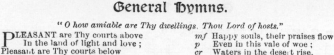

" O how amiable are Thy dwellings, Thou Lord of hosts."

mf PLEASANT are Thy courts above
    In the land of light and love ;
p Pleasant are Thy courts below
    In this land of sin and woe :
cr Oh, my spirit longs and faints
    For the converse of Thy Saints,
    For the brightness of Thy Face,
    For Thy fulness, GOD of grace.

mf Happy birds that sing and fly
    Round Thy Altars, O most High ;
p Happier souls that find a rest
    In a heavenly FATHER'S breast ;
    Like the wandering dove that found
    No repose on earth around,
cr They can to their ark repair,
    And enjoy it ever there.

mf Happy souls, their praises flow
p Even in this vale of woe ;
cr Waters in the desert rise,
    Manna feeds them from the skies ;
f On they go from strength to strength,
    Till they reach Thy Throne at length,
p At Thy feet adoring fall,
mf Who hast led them safe through all.

p LORD, be mine this prize to win,
    Guide me through a world of sin,
    Keep me by Thy saving grace,
    Give me at Thy side a place ;
mf Sun and Shield alike Thou art,
    Guide and guard my erring heart ;
f Grace and glory flow from Thee ;
dim Shower, O shower them, LORD, on me.

H. F. LYTE, 1834.

ALTERNATIVE TUNE, HYMN **544** (SECOND TUNE).

Hymn 241. HOSANNA.—8 8 8 8 7. (*Fi st Tune.*) J. W. ELLIOTT.

Unison.   *Harmony.*

rit.   A - men.

Hymn 241. PRAISES.—8 8 8 8 7. (*Second Tune.*) B. LUARD SELBY.

A - men.

[*Copyright* 1904 *by the Proprietors of* Hymns Ancient and Modern.]

" Hosanna in the highest."

mf HOSANNA to the living LORD !
    Hosanna to the Incarnate WORD,
    To CHRIST, Creator, Saviour, King,
    Let earth, let heaven Hosanna sing,
    f Hosanna in the highest !

p O Saviour, with protecting care
    Abide in this Thy house of prayer,
    Where we Thy parting promise claim,
    Assembled in Thy sacred Name.
    f Hosanna in the highest !

mf But, chiefest, in our cleansèd breast,
    ETERNAL, bid Thy SPIRIT rest ;
    And make our secret soul to be
    A temple pure and worthy Thee.
        Hosanna in the highest !

f To GOD the FATHER, GOD the SON,
    And GOD the SPIRIT, THREE in ONE,
cr Be honour, praise, and glory given
    By all on earth and all in heaven.
    ff Hosanna in the highest !

Bishop HEBER, 1811

(183)

General Hymns.

Hymn 242. QUAM DILECTA.—6 6 6 6.   Bishop JENNER.

A - men.

" Lord, I have loved the habitation of Thy house; and the place where Thine honour dwelleth."

mf WE love the place, O GOD,
       Wherein Thine honour dwells;
The joy of Thine abode
  All earthly joy excels.

It is the house of prayer,
  Wherein Thy servants meet;
And Thou, O LORD, art there
  Thy chosen flock to greet.

We love the sacred Font;
  For there the HOLY DOVE
To pour is ever wont
  His blessings from above.

We love Thine Altar, LORD;
  Oh, what on earth so dear?

p   For there, in faith adored,
cr   We find Thy Presence near.

mf We love the Word of life,
       The Word that tells of peace,
p   Of comfort in the strife,
cr   And joys that never cease.

f   We love to sing below
       For mercies freely given;
cr But, oh, we long to know
       The triumph-song of Heav'n.

p   LORD JESUS, give us grace
       On earth to love Thee more,
f   In Heav'n to see Thy Face,
dim   And with Thy Saints adore.

W. BULLOCK and Sir H. W. BAKER.

Hymn 243. RAVENSHAW.—6 6 6 6.   Traditional German Melody.

A - men.

" Thy Word is a lantern unto my feet, and a light unto my paths."

mf LORD, Thy Word abideth,
       And our footsteps guideth;
Who its truth believeth
  Light and joy receiveth.

p   When our foes are near us,
cr Then Thy Word doth cheer us
Word of consolation,
  Message of salvation.

p   When the storms are o'er us,
       And dark clouds before us,
cr Then its light directeth,
       And our way protecteth.

mf Who can tell the pleasure,
       Who recount the treasure
By Thy Word imparted
  To the simple-hearted?

Word of mercy, giving
  Succour to the living;
Word of life, supplying
p   Comfort to the dying!

mf O that we discerning
       Its most holy learning,
LORD, may love and fear Thee,
  Evermore be near Thee.

Sir H. W. BAKER.

General Hymns.

Hymn 244. ST. EDMUND.—C.M.

W. S. HOYTE.

A-men.

" A broken and contrite heart, O God, shalt Thou not despise."

p   LORD, when we bend before Thy Throne,
    And our confessions pour,
Teach us to feel the sins we own,
    And hate what we deplore.

Our broken spirits pitying see ;
    True penitence impart ;
cr   Then let a kindling glance from Thee
    Beam hope upon the heart.

mf When we disclose our wants in prayer,
    May we our wills resign,
And not a thought our bosoms share
    Which is not wholly Thine.

May faith each weak petition fill,
    And waft it to the skies,
And teach our hearts 'tis goodness still
    That grants it or denies.

J. D. CARLYLE.

Hymn 245. ST. SEPULCHRE.—L.M.

G. COOPER.

A-men.

" If any man sin, we have an Advocate with the Father, Jesus Christ the Righteous."

p   WHEN at Thy footstool, LORD, I bend,
    And plead with Thee for mercy there,
cr   Think of the sinner's dying Friend,
    And for His sake receive my prayer.

p   O think not of my shame and guilt,
    My thousand stains of deepest dye ;
cr   Think of the Blood which JESUS spilt,
    And let that Blood my pardon buy.

mf   Think, LORD, how I am still Thine own,
p   The trembling creature of Thy hand ;
Think how my heart to sin is prone,
    And what temptations round me stand.

mf O think upon Thy holy Word,
    And every plighted promise there ;
How prayer should evermore be heard,
    And how Thy glory is to spare.

p   O think not of my doubts and fears,
    My strivings with Thy grace Divine ;
Think upon JESUS' woes and tears,
cr   And let His Merits stand for mine.

mf Thine eye, Thine ear, they are not dull ;
Thine arm can never shorten'd be :
Behold me here ; my heart is full ;
p   Behold, and spare, and succour me.

H. F. LYTE, 1833.

(185)

General Hymns.

Hymn 246. Breslau.—L.M. (*First Tune.*) Geistliche Gesänge (Leipzig, 1625).

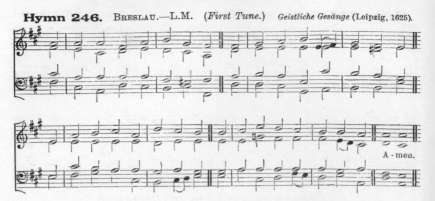

A - men.

A higher setting of this Tune is given at Hymn 46, and a lower setting at Hymn 200.

Hymn 246. Crowborough.—L.M. (*Second Tune.*) Rev. W. G. Whinfield.

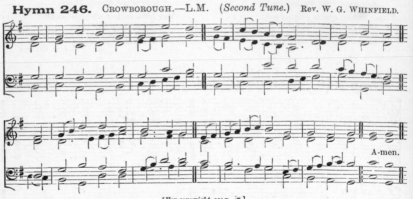

A-men.

[*For copyright, see p. iv*]

"*Men ought always to pray, and not to faint.*"

mf WHAT various hindrances we meet
In coming to the Mercy-seat;
Yet who, that knows the worth of prayer,
But wishes to be often there?

Prayer makes the darken'd cloud withdraw,
Prayer climbs the ladder Jacob saw,
Gives exercise to faith and love,
Brings every blessing from above.

p Restraining prayer, we cease to fight;
cr Prayer makes the Christian's armour bright;
And Satan trembles when he sees
The weakest saint upon his knees.

mf When Moses stood with arms spread wide,
Success was found on Israel's side;
p But when through weariness they fail'd,
That moment Amelek prevail'd.

mf Have we no words? ah, think again;
Words flow apace when we complain,
And fill our fellow-creature's ear
With the sad tale of all our care.

Were half the breath thus vainly spent
To Heav'n in supplication sent,
Our cheerful song would oftener be,
f "Hear what the LORD hath done for me."

mf O LORD, increase our faith and love,
That we may all Thy goodness prove,
And gain from Thy exhaustless store
The fruits of prayer for evermore.

W. Cowper (1779) and Compilers.

(186)

General Hymns.

Hymn 247. St. Hugh.—C.M.

E. J. Hopkins.

A-men.

A higher setting of this Tune is given at Hymn 39.

" Thou preparest their heart, and Thine ear hearkeneth thereto."

mf LORD, teach us how to pray aright
　　 With reverence and with fear ;
p Though dust and ashes in Thy sight,
cr 　 We may, we must draw near.

mf We perish if we cease from prayer ;
　 O grant us power to pray ;
And, when to meet Thee we prepare,
LORD, meet us by the way.

GOD of all grace, we bring to Thee
p 　 A broken contrite heart ;
mf Give, what Thine eye delights to see,
Truth in the inward part ;

Faith in the only Sacrifice
　 That can for sin atone ;
To cast our hopes, to fix our eyes,
cr 　 On CHRIST, on CHRIST alone ;

p Patience to watch, and wait, and weep,
　 Though mercy long delay ;
cr Courage our fainting souls to keep,
　 And trust Thee though Thou slay ;

mf Give these, and then Thy Will be done ;
　 Thus, strengthen'd with all might,
We, through Thy SPIRIT and Thy SON,
　 Shall pray, and pray aright.

　　　　　　J. MONTGOMERY, 1818.

Hymn 248. St. Etheldreda.—C.M.

Bishop TURTON, 1860.

A-men.

" And he said, I will not let Thee go, except Thou bless me."

mf SHEPHERD Divine, our wants relieve
　　 In this our evil day ;
To all Thy tempted followers give
The power to watch and pray.

p Long as our fiery trials last,
　 Long as the cross we bear,
cr O let our souls on Thee be cast
In never-ceasing prayer.

mf The Spirit of interceding grace
Give us in faith to claim ;
To wrestle till we see Thy Face,
And know Thy hidden Name.

Till Thou Thy perfect love impart,
　 Till Thou Thyself bestow,
Be this the cry of every heart,
　 "I will not let Thee go."

I will not let Thee go, unless
　 Thou tell Thy Name to me ;
With all Thy great Salvation bless,
　 And make me all like Thee.

Then let me on the mountain-top
　 Behol'd Thine open Face ;
f Where faith in sight is swallow'd up,
　 And prayer in endless praise.

　　　　　　C. WESLEY, 1740.

(187)

General Hymns.

Hymn 249. St. Bride.—S.M.

S. Howard, 1710–1782.

A - men.

" Have mercy upon me, O God, after Thy great goodness ; according to the multitude of Thy mercies do away mine offences."

p HAVE mercy, Lord, on me,
　　As Thou wert ever kind ;
Let me, opprest with loads of guilt,
　Thy wonted mercy find.

Wash off my foul offence,
　And cleanse me from my sin ;
For I confess my crime, and see
　How great my guilt has been.

mf The joy Thy favour gives
　　Let me again obtain,
And Thy free Spirit's firm support
　My fainting soul sustain.

f To God the Father, Son,
　　And Spirit glory be,
As 'twas, and is, and shall be so
　To all eternity.

N. Tate and N. Brady, 1696.

Hymn 250. Aston.—S.M.

J. Heywood.

A - men.

' Out of the deep have I called unto Thee, O Lord.'

p OUT of the deep I call
　　To Thee, O Lord, to Thee ;
Before Thy Throne of grace I fall ;
　Be merciful to me.

Out of the deep I cry,
　The woful deep of sin,
Of evil done in days gone by,
　Of evil now within.

Out of the deep of fear,
　And dread of coming shame,
From morning watch till night is near
cr　I plead the Precious Name.

mf Lord, there is mercy now,
　　As ever was, with Thee ;
Before Thy Throne of grace I bow ;
p　Be merciful to me.

Sir H. W. Baker

Hymn 251. Miserere.—7 7 7 7. 7 7 7 7. *(First Tune.)*

W. H. Monk.

General Hymns.

rall.

A - men.

Hymn 251. ABERYSTWITH.—7 7 7 7. 7 7 7 7. (*Second Tune.*)   J. PARRY.

A - men.

[*For copyright, see p.* **lv.**]

"*Jesus, Master, have mercy on us.*"

p SAVIOUR, when in dust to Thee
        Low we bow the adoring knee ;
    When, repentant, to the skies
    Scarce we lift our weeping eyes,
    Oh, by all Thy pains and woe
    Suffer'd once for man below,
    Bending from Thy Throne on high,
    Hear our solemn litany.

mf By Thy helpless infant years,
    By Thy life of want and tears,
    By Thy days of sore distress
    In the savage wilderness,
    By the dread mysterious hour
    Of the insulting tempter's power ;
    Turn, O turn a favouring eye ;
p   Hear our solemn litany.

mf By the sacred griefs that wept
    O'er the grave where Lazarus slept ;
    By the boding tears that flow'd
    Over Salem's loved abode ;

    By the mournful word that told
    Treachery lurk'd within Thy fold ;
    From Thy Seat above the sky
p   Hear our solemn litany.

    By Thine hour of whelming fear ;
    By Thine agony of prayer ;
    By the cross, the nail, the thorn,
    Piercing spear, and torturing scorn ;
    By the gloom that veil'd the skies
    O'er the dreadful Sacrifice ;
    Listen to our humble cry ;
    Hear our solemn litany.

pp By Thy deep expiring groan ;
    By the sad sepulchral stone ;
    By the vault whose dark abode
cr Held in vain the rising GOD ;
f   Oh, from earth to Heav'n restored,
    Mighty, re-ascended LORD,
mf Listen, listen to the cry
p   Of our solemn litany.
                Sir R. GRANT, 1815.

(189)

General Hymns.

Hymn 252. DALKEITH.—10 10 10 10. *(First Tune.)* T. HEWLETT.

A - men.

Hymn 252. St. CYPRIAN.—10 10 10 10. *(Second Tune.)* Sir J. STAINER.

A - men.

" In Whom we have redemption through His Blood, the forgiveness of sins."

p   WEARY of earth and láden with my sin,
         I look at Heav'n and long to enter in ;
       But there no evil thing may find a home,
cr   And yet I hear a voice that bids me, " Come."

p   So vile I am, how dáre I hope to stand
      In the pure glory of that holy land?
      Before the whiteness óf that Throne appear ?
cr   Yet there are Hands stretch'd out to draw me near.

p   The while I fain would tréad the heavenly way,
      Evil is ever with me day by day ;
cr   Yet on mine ears the grácious tidings fall,
      " Repent, confess, thou shalt be loosed from all."

mf   It is the voice of JÉSUS that I hear,
      His are the Hands stretch'd out to draw me near.
      And His the Blood that cán for all atone,
      And set me faultless there before the Throne.

      'Twas He Who found me ón the deathly wild,
      And made me heir of Heav'n, the FATHER'S child,
      And day by day, wherebý my soul may live,
      Gives me His grace of pardon, and will give.

p   O great Absolver, gránt my soul may wear
      The lowliest garb of penitence and prayer,
cr   That in the FATHER'S coúrts my glorious dress
      May be the garment of Thy righteousness.

mf   Yea, Thou wilt answer fór me, Righteous LORD ;
      Thine all the merits, mine the great reward ;
p   Thine the sharp thorns, and *(mf)* mine the golden crown ;
      Mine the life won, and *(p)* Thine the life laid down.

mf   Nought can I bring, dear LÓRD, for all I owe,
      Yet let my full heart what it can bestow ;
cr   Like Mary's gift, let mý devotion prove,
      Forgiven greatly, how I greatly love.   S. J. STONE.

ALTERNATIVE TUNE, HYMN 715 (FIRST TUNE).

Hymn 253. BURFORD.—C.M.   CHETHAM, *Psalms*, 1718.

A men.

"When he thought thereon, he wept."

p O JESU CHRIST, if aught there be
That, more than all beside,
In ever-painful memory
Must in my heart abide,

It is that deep ingratitude
Which I to Thee have shown,
Who didst for me in Tears and Blood
Upon the Cross atone.

Alas, how with my actions all
Has this defect entwined ;
How has it poison'd with its gall
My spirit, heart, and mind !

mf Alas, through this, how many a gem
I've rudely cast away,
That might have form'd my diadem
In everlasting day !

p Yet though the time be past and gone,
Though little more remains ;
Though nought is all that can be done,
E'en with my utmost pains ;

mf Still will I strive, O Saviour mine,
To do what in me lies ;
For never did Thy glance Divine
A contrite heart despise.

E. CASWALL.

Hymn 254. CHRISTUS CONSOLATOR.—8 5 8 3. *(First Tune.)*
With expression.   Rev. J. B. DYKES.

ORG.

rall.   Last Verse.

Be at rest. Yes. A - men.

Be at rest.

ORG.

"Come unto Me, all ye that labour and are heavy laden, and I will give you rest."

p ART thou weary, art thou languid,
Art thou sore distrest ?
mf "Come to Me," saith One, "and coming
p Be at rest !"

mf Hath He marks to lead me to Him,
If He be my Guide ?
p "In His Feet and Hands are Wound-prints,
And His Side."

mf Hath He diadem as Monarch
That His Brow adorns ?
"Yea, a Crown, in very surety,
p But of thorns."

mf If I find Him, if I follow,
What His guerdon here ?
p "Many a sorrow, many a labour,
Many a tear."

mf If I still hold closely to Him,
What hath He at last ?
f "Sorrow vanquish'd, labour ended,
Jordan past."

mf If I ask Him to receive me,
Will He say me nay ?
f "Not till earth, and not till Heaven
Pass away."

mf Finding, following, keeping, struggling,
Is He sure to bless ?
ff "Angels, Martyrs, Prophets, Virgins,
Answer, Yes !"

J. M. NEALE.

General Hymns.

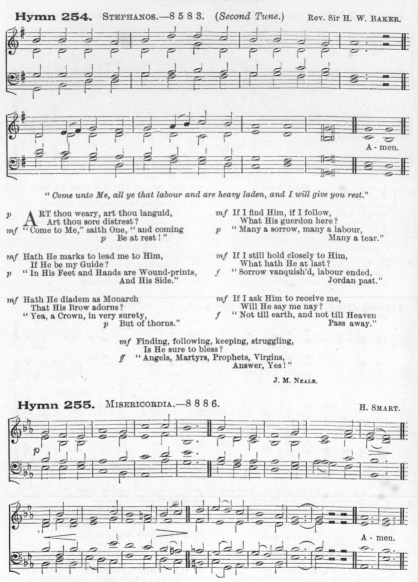

Hymn 254. STEPHANOS.—8 5 8 3. (*Second Tune.*) Rev. Sir H. W. BAKER.

A - men.

" Come unto Me, all ye that labour and are heavy laden, and I will give you rest."

p   A RT thou weary, art thou languid,
      Art thou sore distrest?
mf " Come to Me," saith One, " and coming
      p   Be at rest ! "

mf Hath He marks to lead me to Him,
      If He be my Guide?
p " In His Feet and Hands are Wound-prints,
      And His Side."

mf Hath He diadem as Monarch
      That His Brow adorns?
" Yea, a Crown, in very surety,
      p   But of thorns."

mf If I find Him, if I follow,
      What His guerdon here?
p " Many a sorrow, many a labour,
      Many a tear."

mf If I still hold closely to Him,
      What hath He at last?
f " Sorrow vanquish'd, labour ended,
      Jordan past."

mf If I ask Him to receive me,
      Will He say me nay?
f " Not till earth, and not till Heaven
      Pass away."

mf Finding, following, keeping, struggling,
      Is He sure to bless?
ff " Angels, Martyrs, Prophets, Virgins,
      Answer, Yes ! "

J. M. NEALE.

Hymn 255. MISERICORDIA.—8 8 8 6. H. SMART.

A - men.

" Him that cometh to Me I will in no wise cast out."

p   J UST as I am, without one plea
      But that Thy Blood was shed for me,
And that Thou bidd'st me come to Thee,
      O LAMB of GOD, I come.

Just as I am, though toss'd about
With many a conflict, many a doubt,
Fightings and fears within, without,
      O LAMB of GOD, I come.

General Hymns.

Just as I am, poor, wretched, blind ;
er Sight, riches, healing of the mind,
Yea all I need, in Thee to find,
p   O LAMB of GOD, I come.

Just as I am, (*mf*) Thou wilt receive,
Wilt welcome, pardon, cleanse, relieve ;
cr Because Thy promise I believe,
  O LAMB of GOD, I come.

p   Just as I am, (*mf*) (Thy love unknown
Has broken every barrier down),
cr Now to be Thine, yea, Thine alone,
  O LAMB of GOD, I come.

p   Just as I am, (*mf*) of that free love [prove,
The breadth, length, depth, and height to
cr Here for a season, then above,
p   O LAMB of GOD, I come.

CHARLOTTE ELLIOTT.

Hymn 256.   COME UNTO ME. —7 6 7 6. 7 6 7 6.   Rev. J. B. DYKES.

NOTE.—*It is suggested that the first two lines of each verse should be sung by Tenors and Basses only, but if necessary they may be sung in Octaves by all the voices.*

" Him that cometh to Me I will in no wise cast out."

mf " COME unto Me, ye weary,
    And I will give you rest."
p O blessèd voice of JESUS,
cr   Which comes to hearts opprest ;
mf It tells of benediction,
    Of pardon, grace, and peace,
f Of joy that hath no ending,
    Of love which cannot cease.

mf " Come unto Me, ye wanderers,
    And I will give you light."
p O loving voice of JESUS,
cr   Which comes to cheer the night ;
p Our hearts were fill'd with sadness,
    And we had lost our way ;
f But He has brought us gladness
    And songs at break of day.

mf " Come unto Me, ye fainting,
    And I will give you life."
O cheering voice of JESUS,
cr   Which comes to aid our strife ;
mf The foe is stern and eager,
    The fight is fierce and long ;
f But He has made us mighty,
    And stronger than the strong.

mf " And whosoever cometh,
    I will not cast him out."
O welcome voice of JESUS,
cr   Which drives away our doubt ;
mf Which calls us very sinners,
p   Unworthy though we be
cr Of love so free and boundless,
p   To come, dear LORD, to Thee.

W. C. DIX.

General Hymns.

Hymn 257. Vox Dilecti.—D.C.M.

Rev. J. B. DYKES.

" He that cometh to Me shall never hunger ; and he that believeth on Me shall never thirst."

p   I HEARD the voice of JESUS say,
mf   "Come unto Me and rest ;
cr Lay down, thou weary one, lay down
     Thy head upon My Breast :"
p   I came to JESUS as I was,
     Weary, and worn, and sad ;
cr I found in Him a resting-place,
ff   And He has made me glad.

p   I heard the voice of JESUS say,
mf   "Behold, I freely give
cr The living water, thirsty one,
     Stoop down, and drink, and live :'

p   *I came to JESUS, and I drank
cr   Of that life-giving stream ;
     My thirst was quench'd, my soul revived,
ff   And now I live in Him.

p   I heard the voice of JESUS say,
mf   "I am this dark world's Light ;
cr Look unto Me, thy morn shall rise,
     And all thy day be bright :"
p   *I look'd to JESUS, and I found
cr   In Him my Star, my Sun ;
     And in that Light of life I'll walk
dim Till travelling days are done.

H. BONAR.

* In verses 2 and 3, for music of lines 5 and 6, substitute the following :—

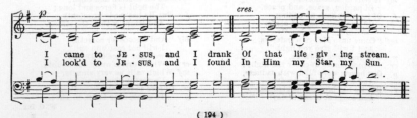

I came to JE-SUS, and I drank Of that life-giv-ing stream.
I look'd to JE-SUS, and I found In Him my Star, my Sun.

Hymn 258. In viam rectam.—D.S.M.

H. J. GAUNTLETT.

ritenuto.

A - men.

" When he hath found it, he layeth it on his shoulders rejoicing."

p   I WAS a wandering sheep,
     I did not love the fold,
I did not love my Shepherd's voice,
   I would not be controll'd.
   I was a wayward child,
   I did not love my home,
I did not love my FATHER'S voice,
   I loved afar to roam.

mf The Shepherd sought His sheep,
   The FATHER sought His child,
They follow'd me o'er vale and hill,
   O'er deserts waste and wild ;
   They found me (p) nigh to death,
   Famish'd, and faint, and lone ;
cr They bound me with the bands of love,
   They saved the wandering one.

mf They spoke in tender love,
   They raised my drooping head,
They gently closed my bleeding wounds,
   My fainting soul they fed ;
   They wash'd my filth away,
   They made me clean and fair ;
cr They brought me to my home in peace,
dim The long-sought wanderer.

f   JESUS my Shepherd is,
   'Twas He that loved my soul,
'Twas He that wash'd me in His Blood,
   'Twas He that made me whole ;
   'Twas He that sought the lost,
dim That found the wandering sheep ;
cr 'Twas He that brought me to the fold,
   'Tis He that still doth keep.

   p I was a wandering sheep,
     I would not be controll'd ;
  f But now I love my Shepherd's voice,
     I love, I love the fold.
   p I was a wayward child,
     I once preferr'd to roam ;
  f But now I love my FATHER'S voice,
     I love, I love His home.

H. BONAR.

Hymn 259. THY LIFE WAS GIVEN FOR ME.—6 6 6 6.6 6.

Sir G. A. MACFARREN.

For the last verse only. ..me, I give my-self .. to Thee. A-men.

" What reward shall I give unto the Lord for all the benefits that He hath done unto me ! "

p	THY Life was given for me,
	Thy Blood, O LORD, was shed,
cr	That I might ransom'd be,
	And quicken'd from the dead ;
p	Thy Life was given for me ;
	What have I given for Thee?

Thou, LORD, hast borne for me
   More than my tongue can tell
Of bitterest agony,
   To rescue me from hell ;
Thou suff'redst all for me ;
   What have I borne for Thee?

Long years were spent for me
   In weariness and woe,
cr That through eternity
   Thy glory I might know ;
p Long years were spent for me ;
   Have I spent one for Thee?

mf And Thou hast brought to me
   Down from Thy Home above
cr Salvation full and free,
   Thy pardon and Thy love ;
mf Great gifts Thou broughtest me ;
p What have I brought to Thee?

mf Thy FATHER'S Home of light,
   Thy rainbow-circled Throne,
dim Were left for earthly night,
   For wanderings sad and lone ;
p Yea, all was left for me ;
   Have I left aught for Thee?

mf O let my life be given,
   My years for Thee be spent ;
World-fetters all be riven,
   And joy with suffering blent ;
cr Thou gav'st Thyself for me,
   I give myself to Thee.

FRANCES R. HAVERGAL.

General Hymns.

Hymn 260. St. Bees.—7 7 7 7.

Rev. J. B. Dykes.

" Lovest thou Me ? "

A- men.

mf HARK, my soul! it is the LORD;
'Tis thy Saviour, hear His Word;
JESUS speaks, and speaks to thee,
p "Say, poor sinner, lov'st thou Me?

mf "I deliver'd thee when bound,
And, when bleeding, heal'd thy wound;
Sought thee wandering, set thee right,
Turn'd thy darkness into light.

"Can a woman's tender care
Cease towards the child she bare?
p Yes, she may forgetful be,
cr Yet will I remember thee.

mf "Mine is an unchanging love,
Higher than the heights above,
Deeper than the depths beneath,
cr Free and faithful, strong as death.

f "Thou shalt see My glory soon,
mf When the work of grace is done;
cr Partner of My Throne shalt be;
p Say, poor sinner, (*cr*) lov'st thou Me?"

mf LORD, it is my chief complaint
That my love is weak and faint;
cr Yet I love Thee, (*dim*) and adore;
cr O for grace to love Thee more.

W. Cowper. 1768

ALTERNATIVE TUNE, HYMN 645 (SECOND TUNE).

Hymn 261. Franconia.—S.M.

Harmonischer Liederschatz, 1738.

A- men.

A lower setting of this Tune is given at Hymn 48, and a higher setting at Hymn 488.

" Blessed are the pure in heart, for they shall see God."

mf BLESS'D are the pure in heart,
For they shall see our GOD;
The secret of the LORD is theirs,
Their soul is CHRIST'S abode.

p The LORD, Who left the heavens
Our life and peace to bring,
To dwell in lowliness with men,
Their Pattern and their King;

Still to the lowly soul
He doth Himself impart,
cr And for His dwelling and His Throne
Chooseth the pure in heart.

p LORD, we Thy Presence seek;
May ours this blessing be;
cr Give us a pure and lowly heart,
A temple meet for Thee.

J. Keble (altered with his permission).

(197)

General Hymns.

Hymn 262. CHAPEL ROYAL.—8 8 6.8 8 6. W. BOYCE, 1710–1779.

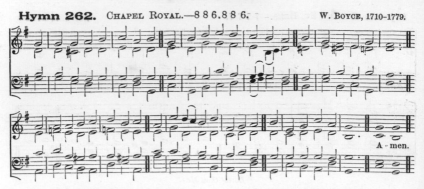

A - men.

" Now abideth faith, hope, charity, these three; but the greatest of these is charity."

mf GREAT Mover of all hearts, Whose Hand
Doth all the secret springs command
Of human thought and will,
Thou, since the world was made, dost bless
Thy Saints with fruits of holiness,
Their order to fulfil.

Faith, hope, and love here weave one chain;
But love alone shall then remain
When this short day is gone:

f O Love, O Truth, O endless Light,
When shall we see Thy Sabbath bright
With all our labours done?

p We sow 'mid perils here and tears;
cr There the glad hand the harvest bears,
dim Which here in grief hath sown:
mf Great THREE in ONE, the increase give;
Thy gifts of grace, by which we live,
cr With heavenly glory crown.

I. WILLIAMS: from the Latin of C. Coffin.

Hymn 263. BRESLAU.—L.M. *Geistliche Gesänge* (Leipzig, 1625).

A - men.

Lower settings of this Tune are given at Hymns 200 and 246.

" If any man will come after Me, let him deny himself, and take up his cross, and follow Me."

mf TAKE up thy cross, the Saviour said,
If thou wouldst My disciple be;
Deny thyself, the world forsake,
And humbly follow after Me.

Take up thy cross; let not its weight
Fill thy weak spirit with alarm;
His strength shall bear thy spirit up,
And brace thy heart, and nerve thine arm.

Take up thy cross, nor heed the shame,
Nor let thy foolish pride rebel;
p Thy LORD for thee the Cross endured,
cr To save thy soul from death and hell.

mf Take up thy cross then in His strength,
And calmly every danger brave;
'Twill guide thee to a better home,
cr And lead to victory o'er the grave.

mf Take up thy cross, and follow CHRIST,
Nor think till death to lay it down;
For only he who bears the cross
cr May hope to wear the glorious crown.

f To Thee, Great LORD, the ONE in THREE,
All praise for evermore ascend;
dim O grant us in our Home to see
f The heavenly life that knows no end.

C. W. EVEREST.

(198)

General Hymns.

Hymn 264. TROYTE'S CHANT, No. 1.—8 8 8 4.　　A. H. DYKE TROYTE.

rall.

p　　　　A - men.

" Thy will be done."

mf MY GOD, my FATHER, while I stray,
　　　Far from my home, on life's rough
O teach me from my heart to say,　　[way,
　　p　" Thy Will be done."

Though dark my path, and sad my lot,
Let me be still and murmur not,
Or breathe the prayer divinely taught,
　　" Thy Will be done."

What though in lonely grief I sigh
For friends beloved no longer nigh,
Submissive would I still reply,
　　" Thy Will be done."

If Thou shouldst call me to resign
What most I prize, it ne'er was mine ;
I only yield Thee what is Thine ;
　　" Thy Will be done."

mf Let but my fainting heart be blest
With Thy sweet SPIRIT for its guest,
My GOD, to Thee I leave the rest ;
　　p　" Thy Will be done."

mf Renew my will from day to day,
Blend it with Thine, and take away
All that now makes it hard to say,
　　p　" Thy Will be done."

CHARLOTTE ELLIOTT.

ALTERNATIVE TUNE, HYMN 275.

Hymn 265. IBSTONE.—6 6 6 6.　　Miss M. TIDDEMAN.

A - men.

" Not as I will, but as Thou wilt."

mf THY way, not mine, O LORD,
　　　However dark it be ;
Lead me by Thine own Hand,
　　Choose out the path for me.

Smooth let it be or rough,
　　It will be still the best ;
Winding or straight, it leads
　　Right onward to Thy rest.

p　I dare not choose my lot ;
　　I would not if I might ;
mf Choose Thou for me, my GOD,
　　So shall I walk aright.

The kingdom that I seek
　Is Thine, so let the way

That leads to it be Thine,
p　Else I must surely stray.

mf Take Thou my cup, and it
　　With joy or sorrow fill,
　　As best to Thee may seem ;
　　Choose Thou my good and ill.

Choose Thou for me my friends,
　　My sickness or my health ;
p　Choose Thou my cares for me,
　　My poverty or wealth.

mf Not mine, not mine the choice
　　In things or great or small ;
cr Be Thou my Guide, my Strength,
f　　My Wisdom, and my All.

H. BONAR.

General Hymns.

Hymn 266. LUX BENIGNA.— 10 4 10 4. 10 10. (*First Tune.*)

Rev. J. B. DYKES.

A - men.

Hymn 266. SANDON.— 10 4 10 4. 10 10. (*Second Tune.*) C. H. PURDAY, 1860.

General Hymns.

A - men.

" In the day time also He led them with a cloud, and all the night through with a light of fire."

mf   L EAD, kindly Light, amid the encircling gloom,
          Lead Thou me on ;
p   The night is dark, and I am far from home,
        Lead Thou me on.
cr   Keep Thou my feet ; I do not ask to see
     The distant scene ; (p) one step enough for me.

mf   I was not ever thus, nor pray'd that Thou
        Shouldst lead me on ;
    I loved to choose and see my path ; (p) but now
        Lead Thou me on.
cr   I loved the garish day, and, spite of fears,
     Pride ruled my will : (p) remember not past years.

mf   So long Thy power hath blest me, sure it still
        Will lead me on,
    O'er moor and fen, o'er crag and torrent, (p) till
        The night is gone ;
cr   And with the morn those Angel faces smile,
     Which I have loved long since, (p) and lost awhile.

                        Cardinal J. H. NEWMAN.

Hymn 267.   WINDSOR.—C.M.   *(First Tune.)*   DAMON, *Psalms*, 1591.

A - men.

An Alternative Version of this Tune is given at Hymn 90.

" Let this mind be in you, which was also in Christ Jesus."

p   L ORD, as to Thy dear Cross we flee,
        And plead to be forgiven,
cr   So let Thy Life our pattern be,
    And form our souls for Heav'n.

mf   Help us, through good report and ill,
      Our daily cross to bear ,
    Like Thee, to do our FATHER's Will,
p   Our brethren's griefs to share.

mf   Let grace our selfishness expel,
    Our earthliness refine ;

And kindness in our bosoms dwell,
    As free and true as Thine.

If joy shall at Thy bidding fly,
p   And grief's dark day come on,
    We in our turn would meekly cry,
pp   " FATHER, Thy Will be done."

mf   Kept peaceful in the midst of strife.
     Forgiving and forgiven,
cr   O may we lead the pilgrim's life,
    And follow Thee to Heav'n.

               J. HAMPDEN GURNEY, 1838.

H 2

General Hymns.

Hymn 267. WESTMINSTER NEW.—C.M. *(Second Tune.)* J. NARES, 1762.

A - men.

" Let this mind be in you, which was also in Christ Jesus."

p LORD, as to Thy dear Cross we flee,
    And plead to be forgiven,
cr So let Thy Life our pattern be,
    And form our souls for Heav'n.

mf Help us, through good report and ill,
    Our daily cross to bear ;
    Like Thee, to do our FATHER'S Will,
p Our brethren's griefs to share.

mf Let grace our selfishness expel,
    Our earthliness refine ;

And kindness in our bosoms dwell,
    As free and true as Thine.

If joy shall at Thy bidding fly,
    And grief's dark day come on,
p We in our turn would meekly cry,
pp " FATHER, Thy Will be done."

mf Kept peaceful in the midst of strife,
    Forgiving and forgiven,
cr O may we lead the pilgrim's life,
    And follow Thee to Heav'n.

J. HAMPDEN GURNEY, 1838.

Hymn 268. NARENZA.—S.M. LEISENTRIT, *Catholicum Hymnologium*, 1587.

A - men.

A higher setting of this Tune is given at Hymn **504.**

" Blessed are those servants whom the Lord when He cometh shall find watching."

mf YE servants of the LORD,
    Each in his office wait,
Observant of His heavenly Word,
And watchful at His gate.

Let all your lamps be bright,
And trim the golden flame ;
Gird up your loins as in His sight,
For awful is His Name.

Watch ! 'tis your LORD's command,
And while we speak, He's near ;
Mark the first signal of His Hand,
And ready all appear.

Oh, happy servant he,
In such a posture found !
He shall his LORD with rapture see,
And be with honour crown'd.

CHRIST shall the banquet spread
With His own royal Hand,
And raise that faithful servant's head
Amid the Angelic band.

f All glory, LORD, to Thee,
Whom Heav'n and earth adore,
To FATHER, SON, and HOLY GHOST,
ONE GOD for evermore.

P. DODDRIDGE, 1755.

General Ibymns.

Hymn 269. VIGILATE.—7 7 7 3. W. H. MONK.

A - men.

" Watch and pray."

mf "CHRISTIAN! seek not yet repose,"
p   Hear thy guardian Angel say ;
mf Thou art in the midst of foes ;
   p   "Watch and pray."

mf Principalities and powers,
  Mustering their unseen array,
  Wait for thy unguarded hours :
   p   "Watch and pray."

mf Gird thy heavenly armour on,
  Wear it ever night and day ;
cr Ambush'd lies the evil one ;
   p   "Watch and pray."

f   Hear the victors who o'ercame ;
dim Still they mark each warrior's way ;
cr All with one sweet voice exclaim,
    "Watch and pray."

mf Hear, above all, hear thy LORD,
  Him thou lovest to obey ;
p Hide within thy heart His Word,
   "Watch and pray."

mf Watch, as if on that alone
  Hung the issue of the day ;
  Pray, that help may be sent down ;
    "Watch and pray."
      CHARLOTTE ELLIOTT.

Hymn 270. ST. ETHELWALD.—S.M. W. H. MONK.

A - men

" Put on the whole armour of God."

f   SOLDIERS of CHRIST, arise,
   And put your armour on ;
Strong in the strength which GOD supplies,
Through His Eternal SON ;

  Strong in the LORD of Hosts,
  And in His mighty power ;
p Who in the strength of JESUS trusts
cr Is more than conqueror.

f   Stand then in His great might,
  With all His strength endued ;
mf And take, to arm you for the fight,
  The panoply of GOD.

  From strength to strength go on,
  Wrestle, and fight, and pray ;
cr Tread all the powers of darkness down,
ff   And win the well-fought day.

mf   That having all things done,
  And all your conflicts past,
Ye may obtain, through CHRIST alone,
cr   A crown of joy at last.

p   JESU, Eternal SON,
cr   We praise Thee and adore,
f   Who art with GOD the FATHER ONE
  And SPIRIT evermore.
      C. WESLEY, 1749.

General Hymns.

Hymn 271. Day of Rest.—7 6 7 6. 7 6 7 6. *(First Tune.)* J. W. Elliott.

Voices in Unison. In Harmony.

A - men.

Man. Ped.

Hymn 271. Llanberis.—7 6 7 6. 7 6 7 6. *(Second Tune.)* S. Wesley, 1839.

(204)

General Hymns.

A-men.

"If any man serve Me, let him follow Me ; and where I am, there shall also My servant be."

mf O JESUS, I have promised
  To serve Thee to the end ;
Be Thou for ever near me,
 My Master and my Friend ;
I shall not fear the battle
 If Thou art by my side,
Nor wander from the pathway,
 If Thou wilt be my Guide.

O let me feel Thee near me :
 The world is ever near ;
I see the sights that dazzle,
 The tempting sounds I hear ;
p My foes are ever near me,
 Around me and within ;
cr But, JESUS, draw Thou nearer,
 And shield my soul from sin.

mf O let me hear Thee speaking
 In accents clear and still,
Above the storms of passion,
 The murmurs of self-will ;
O speak to re-assure me,
 To hasten or control ;
O speak, and make me listen,
 Thou Guardian of my soul.

O JESUS, Thou hast promised
 To all who follow Thee,
That where Thou art in glory
 There shall Thy servant be ;
And, JESUS, I have promised
 To serve Thee to the end ;
O give me grace to follow,
 My Master and my Friend.

p O let me see Thy foot-marks,
 And in them plant mine own ;
 My hope to follow duly
 Is in Thy strength alone ;
cr O guide me, call me, draw me,
 Uphold me to the end ;
 And then in Heav'n receive me,
 My Saviour and my Friend.

      J. E. BODE.

Hymn 272. CHESHIRE.—C.M.

ESTE, *Psalmes*, 1592.

A-men.

"Christ in you, the hope of glory."

mf O SAVIOUR, may we never rest
  Till Thou art form'd within,
Till Thou hast calm'd our troubled breast,
 And crush'd the power of sin.

p O may we gaze upon Thy Cross,
cr Until the wondrous sight
Makes earthly treasures seem but dross,
p And earthly sorrows light :

mf Until, released from carnal ties,
 Our spirit upward springs,
And sees true peace above the skies,
 True joy in heavenly things.

p There as we gaze, may we become
 United, LORD, to Thee,
cr And, in a fairer, happier home,
 Thy perfect beauty see.

     W. H. BATHURST, 1831.

General Hymns.

Hymn 273. MELCOMBE.—L.M. (*First Tune.*)   S. WEBBE, 1782.

A-men.

Lower settings of this Tune are given at Hymns 4 and 363.

Hymn 273. ALMSGIVING.—L.M. (*Second Tune.*)   S. S. WESLEY.

A - men.

[*For copyright, see p. lv.*]

" Behold, how good and joyful a thing it is, brethren, to dwell together in unity !"

mf   O LORD, how joyful 'tis to see
      The brethren join in love to Thee !
On Thee alone their heart relies,
Their only strength Thy grace supplies.

How sweet within Thy holy place
With one accord to sing Thy grace,
Besieging Thine attentive ear
With all the force of fervent prayer !

O may we love the House of GOD,
p   Of peace and joy the blest abode ;
cr   O may no angry strife destroy
That sacred peace, that holy joy.

mf   The world without may rage, but we
Will only cling more close to Thee,
With hearts to Thee more wholly given,
More wean'd from earth, more fix'd on Heav'n.

p   LORD, shower upon us from above
The sacred gift of mutual love ;
Each other's wants may we supply,
cr   And reign together in the sky.

f   Praise GOD, from Whom all blessings flow,
Praise Him, all creatures here below,
Praise Him above, Angelic host,
Praise FATHER, SON, and HOLY GHOST.

J. CHANDLER : from the Latin of C. Coffin.

(206)

General Hymns.

Hymn 274. ST. OSWALD.—8 7 8 7. *(First Tune.)*   Rev. J. B. DYKES.

A · men.

Hymn 274. RUSTINGTON.—8 7 8 7. 8 7 8 7. *(Second Tune.)*   Sir H. PARRY.

A · men.

[For copyright, see p. lv.]

"One hope of your calling."

nf THROUGH the night of doubt and sorrow
    Onward goes the pilgrim band,
Singing songs of expectation,
    Marching to the Promised Land.

Clear before us through the darkness
    Gleams and burns the guiding Light;
Brother clasps the hand of brother,
    Stepping fearless through the night.

One the Light of GOD'S own Presence
    O'er His ransom'd people shed,
Chasing far the gloom and terror,
    Brightening all the path we tread:

One the object of our journey,
    One the faith which never tires,
One the earnest looking forward,
    One the hope our GOD inspires:

One the strain that lips of thousands
    Lift as from the heart of one;
One the conflict, one the peril,
    One the march in GOD begun:

f   One the gladness of rejoicing
    On the far eternal shore,
Where the One Almighty FATHER
    Reigns in love for evermore.

mf Onward, therefore, pilgrim brothers,
    Onward with the Cross our aid;
Bear its shame, and fight its battle,
p   Till we rest beneath its shade.

cr Soon shall come the great awaking,
    Soon the rending of the tomb;
f Then the scattering of all shadows,
    And the end of toil and gloom.

S. BARING-GOULD: from the Danish
of B. S. Ingemann.

(207)

General Ibymns.

Hymn 275. RISEHOLME.—8 8 8 4.   H. J. GAUNTLETT.

A - men.

"That they all may be one."

mf FATHER of all, from land and sea
    The nations sing, "Thine, LORD, are we,
Countless in number, but in Thee
        May we be one."

    O SON of GOD, Whose love so free
p For men did make Thee Man to be,
cr United to our GOD in Thee
        May we be one.

p Thou, LORD, didst once for all atone ;
mf Thee may both Jew and Gentile own
Of their two walls the Corner Stone,
        Making them one.

    In Thee we are GOD's Israel,
Thou art the world's Emmanuel,
In Thee the Saints for ever dwell,
        Millions, but one.

    Thou art the Fountain of all good,
p Cleansing with Thy most precious Blood,

cr And feeding us with Angels' Food,
        Making us one.

mf Join high and low, join young and old
    In love that never waxes cold ;
cr Under one Shepherd, in one Fold,
        Make us all one.

p O SPIRIT Blest, Who from above
Cam'st gently gliding like a dove,
Calm all our strife, give faith and love ;
        O make us one.

mf O TRINITY in UNITY,
ONE only GOD, in Persons THREE,
Dwell ever in our hearts ; like Thee
        May we be one.

f So, when the world shall pass away,
May we awake with joy and say,
"Now in the bliss of endless day
        We all are one."

             Bishop C. WORDSWORTH.

Hymn 276. INNSBRUCK.—8 8 6. 8 8 6. *(First Tune.)*

                        Old Volkslied. H. ISAAK (?).

A - men.

A lower setting of this Tune is given at Hymn 86.

(208)

General Hymns.

Hymn 276. BRIDEHEAD.—8 8 6.8 8 6. (*Second Tune.*) A. H. D. TROYTE.

Hymn 276. ANSTICE.—8 8 6.8 8 6. (*Third Tune.*) G. P. WEIMAR, 1734 1800.

A-men.

"Casting all your care upon Him; for He careth for you."

mf O LORD, how happy should we be
  If we could cast our care on Thee,
  If we from self could rest ;
  And feel at heart that One above,
  In perfect wisdom, perfect love,
  Is working for the best.

p How far from this our daily life,
  How oft disturb'd by anxious strife,
  By sudden wild alarms ;
cr Oh, could we but relinquish all
  Our earthly props, and simply fall
  On Thy Almighty arms !

p Could we but kneel, and cast our load,
  E'en while we pray, upon our GOD,
cr Then rise with lighten'd cheer ;

mf Sure that the FATHER, Who is nigh
  To still the famish'd raven's cry,
  Will hear in that we fear.

p We cannot trust Him as we should ;
  So chafes weak nature's restless mood
  To cast its peace away ;
cr But birds and flowerets round us preach,
  All, all the present evil teach
  Sufficient for the day.

mf LORD, make these faithless hearts of ours
  Such lessons learn from birds and flowers ;
  Make them from self to cease ;
  Leave all things to a FATHER'S Will,
  And taste, before Him lying still,
p E'en in affliction, peace.

J. ANSTICE, 1836.

General Hymns.

Hymn 277. HORBURY.—6 4 6 4. 6 6 4. *(First Tune.)*   Rev. J. B. DYKES.

Hymn 277. COMMUNION.—6 4 6 4. 6 6 4. *(Second Tune.)*   S. S. WESLEY.

" Whom have I in heaven but Thee? and there is none upon earth that I desire in comparison of Thee."

mf   NEARER, my GOD, to Thee,
      Nearer to Thee ;
p   E'en though it be a cross
      That raiseth me ;
cr   Still all my song shall be,
dim   Nearer, my GOD, to Thee,
      Nearer to Thee.

p   Though, like the wanderer,
      The sun gone down,
  Darkness comes over me,
      My rest a stone ;
cr   Yet in my dreams I'd be
dim   Nearer, my GOD, to Thee,
      Nearer to Thee.

mf   There let my way appear
      Steps unto Heav'n,
  All that Thou sendest me
      In mercy given,
cr   Angels to beckon me
dim   Nearer, my GOD, to Thee,
      Nearer to Thee.

mf   Then, with my waking thoughts
      Bright with Thy praise,
  Out of my stony griefs
      Beth-el I'll raise ;
cr   So by my woes to be
dim   Nearer, my GOD, to Thee,
      Nearer to Thee.

MRS. ADAMS, 1841.

General Hymns.

Hymn 278. ST. LEONARD.—C.M.   H. SMART.

A-men.

A lower setting of this Tune is given at Hymn 572.

" And the Apostles said unto the Lord, Increase our faith."

mf O FOR a faith that will not shrink,
    Though press'd by many a foe ;
That will not tremble on the brink
    Of poverty or woe ;

p That will not murmur nor complain
    Beneath the chastening rod ;
cr But in the hour of grief or pain
    Can lean upon its GOD ;

mf A faith that shines more bright and clear
    When tempests rage without ;

That when in danger knows no fear,
    In darkness feels no doubt ;

A faith that keeps the narrow way
    Till life's last spark is fled,
And with a pure and heavenly ray
    Lights up the dying bed.

p LORD, give me such a faith as this,
    And then, whate'er may come,
cr I taste e'en now the hallow'd bliss
    Of an eternal home.

                              W. H. BATHURST.

Hymn 279. BEDFORD.—C.M.   W. WHEALE, c. 1715.

A-men.

" Lord, help me."

p O HELP us, LORD ; each hour of need
    Thy heavenly succour give ;
mf Help us in thought, and word, and deed,
    Each hour on earth we live.

p O help us, when our spirits bleed
    With contrite anguish sore ;
And when our hearts are cold and dead,
cr O help us, LORD, the more.

mf O help us, through the prayer of faith
    More firmly to believe ;
For still the more the servant hath,
    The more shall he receive.

O help us, JESU, from on high,
    We know no help but Thee ;
O help us so to live and die
cr As Thine in Heav'n to be.

                              H. H. MILMAN, 1827.

General Hymns.

Hymn 280. EVERMORE.—7 7 7 7. *(First Tune.)*   H. J. GAUNTLETT.

A - men.

Hymn 280. NEWINGTON.—7 7 7 7. *(Second Tune.)*   Archbishop MACLAGAN.

A - men.

" And they shall be Mine, saith the Lord of hosts, in that day when I make up My jewels."

mf THINE for ever ! GOD of love,
Hear us from Thy Throne above ;
Thine for ever may we be
Here and in eternity.

Thine for ever ! LORD of life,
Shield us through our earthly strife ;
Thou the Life, the Truth, the Way,
Guide us to the realms of day.

Thine for ever ! oh, how blest
They who find in Thee their rest !
Saviour, Guardian, Heavenly Friend,
O defend us to the end.

Thine for ever ! Saviour, keep
p Us Thy frail and trembling sheep ;
Safe alone beneath Thy care,
cr Let us all Thy goodness share.

mf Thine for ever ; Thou our Guide,
All our wants by Thee supplied,
All our sins by Thee forgiven,
cr Lead us, LORD, from earth to Heav'n.

Mrs. MAUDE.

General Hymns.

Hymn 281.   MANNHEIM.—8 7 8 7 8 7.   F. FILITZ, 1847.

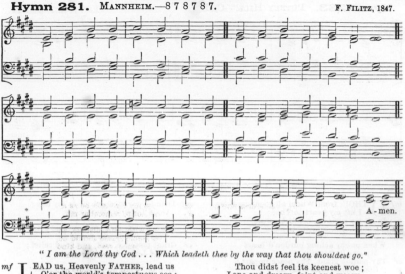

A - men.

" I am the Lord thy God . . . Which leadeth thee by the way that thou shouldest go."

mf LEAD us, Heavenly FATHER, lead us
       O'er the world's tempestuous sea ;
Guard us, guide us, keep us, feed us,
   For we have no help but Thee ;
Yet possessing every blessing,
   If our GOD our FATHER be.

p SAVIOUR, breathe forgiveness o'er us,
       All our weakness Thou dost know ;
Thou didst tread this earth before us,

Thou didst feel its keenest woe ;
Lone and dreary, faint and weary,
   Through the desert Thou didst go.

mf SPIRIT of our GOD, descending,
       Fill our hearts with heavenly joy,
Love with every passion blending,
   Pleasure that can never cloy ;
Thus provided, pardon'd, guided,
   Nothing can our peace destroy.

                              J. EDMESTON.

Hymn 282.   ABRIDGE.—C.M.   I. SMITH, 1770.

A - men.

" O hold Thou up my goings in Thy paths ; that my footsteps slip not."

mf BE Thou my Guardian and my Guide,
       And hear me when I call ;
Let not my slippery footsteps slide,
   And hold me lest I fall.

p The world, the flesh, and Satan dwell
       Around the path I tread ;
cr O save me from the snares of hell,
f   Thou Quickener of the dead.

p And if I tempted am to sin,
       And outward things are strong,
cr Do Thou, O LORD, keep watch within,
       And save my soul from wrong.

mf Still let me ever watch and pray,
p   And feel that I am frail ;
That if the Tempter cross my way,
cr   Yet he may not prevail.

                              I. WILLIAMS.

(213)

General Hymns.

Hymn 283. PUTNEY HILL.—C.M.

Rev. F. A. J. HERVEY.

A-men.

" Lord, remember me."

mf O THOU, from Whom all goodness flows,
     I lift my heart to Thee ;
p In all my sorrows, conflicts, woes,
     Good LORD, remember me.

When on my aching burden'd heart
     My sins lie heavily,
cr Thy pardon grant, Thy peace impart ;
p Good LORD, remember me.

When trials sore obstruct my way,
     And ills I cannot flee,

mf Then let my strength be as my day ;
p Good LORD, remember me.

If worn with pain, disease, and grief
     This feeble frame should be,
cr Grant patience, rest, and kind relief ;
p Good LORD, remember me.

And, oh, when in the hour of death
     I bow to Thy decree,
JESU, receive my parting breath ;
pp Good LORD, remember me.

T. HAWEIS, 1792.

ALTERNATIVE TUNE, HYMN 112.

Hymn 284. LYTE.—S.M.

J. WILKES.

A-men.

*" My soul thirsteth for Thee, my flesh also longeth after Thee ; in a barren and dry land
where no water is."*

p FAR from my heavenly home,
     Far from my FATHER'S breast,
Fainting I cry, " Blest SPIRIT, come,
cr And speed me to my rest."

mf My spirit homeward turns,
     And fain would thither flee ;
dim My heart, O Sion, droops and yearns
     When I remember thee.

mf To thee, to thee I press,
p A dark and toilsome road ;
     When shall I pass the wilderness,
cr And reach the Saints' abode ?

mf GOD of my life, be near ;
     On Thee my hopes I cast ;
p O guide me through the desert here,
cr And bring me home at last.

H. F. LYTE, 1834.

(214)

General Hymns.

Hymn 285. ST. AËLRED.—8 8 8 3.   Rev. J. B. DYKES.

"And He arose and rebuked the wind, and said unto the sea, Peace, be still."

f   FIERCE raged the tempest o'er the deep,
        Watch did Thine anxious servants keep,
dim But Thou wast wrapp'd in guileless sleep,
            pp Calm and still.

mf   "Save, LORD, we perish," was their cry,
        "O save us in our agony!"
cr   Thy Word above the storm rose high,
            p "Peace, be still."

pp   The wild winds hush'd; (*f*) the angry deep
dim Sank, like a little child, to sleep;
        The sullen billows ceased to leap,
            cr At Thy Will.

mf   So, when our life is clouded o'er,
        And storm-winds drift us from the shore,
        Say, lest we sink to rise no more,
            pp "Peace, be still."

                                    G. THRING.

Hymn 286. CLEWER.—6 5 6 5.   F. FILITZ, 1847.

"Our light affliction, which is but for a moment, worketh for us a far more exceeding and eternal weight of glory."

mf O LET him, whose sorrow
        No relief can find,
    Trust in GOD, and borrow
        Ease for heart and mind.

p   Where the mourner weeping
        Sheds the secret tear,
cr GOD His watch is keeping,
dim Though none else be near.

mf GOD will never leave thee,
        All thy wants He knows,
    Feels the pains that grieve thee,
        Sees thy cares and woes.

    Raise thine eyes to Heav'n
        When thy spirits quail,

    When, by tempests driven,
        Heart and courage fail.

p   When in grief we languish,
cr   He will dry the tear,
    Who His children's anguish
        Soothes with succour near.

p   All our woe and sadness,
        In this world below,
cr Balance not the gladness
        We in Heav'n shall know.

p   JESU, Holy Saviour,
cr   In the realms above,
mf Crown us with Thy favour,
        Fill us with Thy love.

                    FRANCES E. COX: from the
                    German of H. S. Oswald.

(215)

General Hymns.

Hymn 287. ST. RAPHAEL.—8 7 8 7.4 7.

E. J. HOPKINS.

A - men.

" Let my supplication come before Thee ; deliver me, according to Thy Word."

mf   JESUS, LORD of life and glory,
  Bend from Heav'n Thy gracious ear ;
While our waiting souls adore Thee,
  Friend of helpless sinners, hear :
p   By Thy mercy,
  O deliver us, good LORD.

mf   From the depths of nature's blindness,
  From the hardening power of sin,
From all malice and unkindness,
  From the pride that lurks within,
p   By Thy mercy,
  O deliver us, good LORD.

When temptation sorely presses,
  In the day of Satan's power,
In our times of deep distresses,
  In each dark and trying hour,
  By Thy mercy,
  O deliver us, good LORD.

mf   When the world around is smiling,
  In the time of wealth and ease,
Earthly joys our hearts beguiling,
  In the day of health and peace,
p   By Thy mercy,
  O deliver us, good LORD.

In the weary hours of sickness,
  In the times of grief and pain,
When we feel our mortal weakness,
  When the creature's help is vain,
  By Thy mercy,
  O deliver us, good LORD.

In the solemn hour of dying,
  In the awful judgment day,
cr   May our souls, on Thee relying,
  Find Thee still our Hope and Stay :
p   By Thy mercy,
  O deliver us, good LORD.

J. J. CUMMINS.

(216)

General Hymns.

Hymn 288. CHALVEY.—D.S.M.

Rev. L. G. HAYNE.

" The time is short."

mf A FEW more years shall roll,
A few more seasons come,
dim And we shall be with those that rest
p Asleep within the tomb:
Then, O my LORD, prepare (*cr*)
My soul for that great day;
cr e dim O wash me in Thy precious Blood,
p And take my sins away.

mf A few more suns shall set
O'er these dark hills of time,
And we shall be where suns are not,
A far serener clime:
p Then, O my LORD, prepare (*cr*)
My soul for that bright day;
cr e dim O wash me in Thy precious Blood,
p And take my sins away.

mf A few more storms shall beat
On this wild rocky shore,
cr And we shall be where tempests cease,
And surges swell no more:
p Then, O my LORD, prepare (*cr*)
My soul for that calm day;
cr e dim O wash me in Thy precious Blood,
p And take my sins away.

A few more struggles here,
A few more partings o'er,
A few more toils, a few more tears,
cr And we shall weep no more:
p Then, O my LORD, prepare (*cr*)
My soul for that blest day;
cr e dim O wash me in Thy precious Blood,
p And take my sins away.

mf 'Tis but a little while
And He shall come again,
p Who died that we might live, (*f*) Who lives
That we with Him may reign:
p Then, O my LORD, prepare (*cr*)
My soul for that glad day;
cr e dim O wash me in Thy precious Blood,
p And take my sins away.

H. BONAR.

(217)

General Hymns.

Hymn 289. ST. SYLVESTER.—8 7 8 7 and 8 8 8 9. Rev. J. B. DYKES.

"So soon passeth it away, and we are gone."

mf DAYS and moments quickly flying;
    Blend the living with the dead;
p   Soon will you and I be lying
    Each within our narrow bed.

    Soon our souls to GOD Who gave them
    Will have sped their rapid flight:
cr Able now by grace to save them,
    Oh, that while we can we might!

mf JESU, Infinite Redeemer,
    Maker of this mighty frame,
*dim*Teach, O teach us to remember
    What we are, and whence we came;

    Whence we came, and whither wending;
p   Soon we must through darkness go,
f   To inherit bliss unending,
p   Or eternity of woe.

After the 4th verse.

mf O by Thy power grant, LORD, that we *dim.* At our last hour

fall not from Thee; *cres.* Saved by Thy grace, Thine may we be

All through the days of e · ter · · · · · ni · ty. A · men.

E. CASWALL. Last verse by Compilers.

General Hymns.

Hymn 290. WILTSHIRE.—C.M. Sir G. SMART, 1798.

A - men.

A lower setting of this Tune is given at Hymn 633.

" I will alway give thanks unto the Lord : His praise shall ever be in my mouth."

mf THROUGH all the changing scenes of life,
   In trouble and in joy,
The praises of my GOD shall still
   My heart and tongue employ.

O magnify the LORD with me,
   With me exalt His Name ;
p When in distress to Him I call'd,
f He to my rescue came.

mf The Hosts of GOD encamp around
   The dwellings of the just ;
Deliverance He affords to all
   Who on His succour trust.

O make but trial of His love,
   Experience will decide
How bless'd are they, and only they,
   Who in His truth confide.

Fear Him, ye saints, and you will then
   Have nothing else to fear ;
Make you His service your delight,
   Your wants shall be His care.

f To FATHER, SON, and HOLY GHOST,
   The GOD Whom we adore,
Be glory, as it was, is now,
   And shall be evermore.

N. TATE and N. BRADY, 1696.

Hymn 291. UNIVERSITY COLLEGE.—7 7 7 7. H. J. GAUNTLETT.

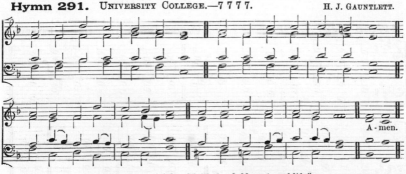

A - men.

" Fight the good fight of faith, lay hold on eternal life."

mf OFT in danger, oft in woe,
   Onward, Christians, onward go ;
Bear the toil, maintain the strife,
Strengthen'd with the Bread of Life !

Let not sorrow dim your eye,
cr Soon shall every tear be dry ;
mf Let not fears your course impede,
f Great your strength, if (*dim*) great your need.

mf Let your drooping hearts be glad ;
March in heavenly armour clad ;

Fight, nor think the battle long,
f Soon shall victory wake your song.

Onward then in battle move ;
   More than conquerors ye shall prove ;
dim Though opposed by many a foe,
f Christian soldiers, onward go !

Hymns of glory and of praise,
mf FATHER, unto Thee we raise :
HOLY JESUS, praise to Thee
With the SPIRIT ever be.

H. KIRKE WHITE (1785–1806) and others.

(219)

General Hymns.

Hymn 292.   AUSTRIA.— 8 7 8 7. 8 7 8 7.   *(First Tune.)*   J. HAYDN, 1797.

A-men.

A lower setting of this Tune is given at Hymn **545.**

Hymn 292.   LANGDALE.—8 7 8 7.   *(Second Tune.)*   R. REDHEAD.

A-men.

" O praise the Lord of heaven, praise Him in the height."

ff PRAISE the LORD ! ye heavens, adore Him,
     Praise Him, Angels, in the height ;
Sun and moon, rejoice before Him,
     Praise Him, all ye stars and light :
f Praise the LORD ! for He hath spoken,
     Worlds His mighty voice obey'd ;
ff Laws, which never shall be broken,
     For their guidance He hath made.

f Praise the LORD ! for He is glorious ;
     Never shall His promise fail ;
ff GOD hath made His Saints victorious,
     Sin and death shall not prevail.
Praise the GOD of our salvation !
     Hosts on high, His power proclaim ;
Heav'n and earth, and all creation,
     Laud and magnify His Name !

J. KEMPTHORNE, 1796.

General Hymns.

Hymn 293. Erk.—8 7 8 7. 8 8 7. *(First Tune.)* *Etlich Cristliche Lyeder*, 1524.

A - men.

" O that men would therefore praise the Lord for His goodness."

f SING praise to God Who reigns above,
  The God of all creation,
The God of power, (*p*) the God of love,
f   The God of our salvation ;
mf With healing balm my soul He fills,
And every faithless murmur stills ;
f   To God all praise and glory.

mf The Angel-host, O King of kings,
  Thy praise for ever telling,
In earth and sky all living things
  Beneath Thy shadow dwelling,
Adore the wisdom which could span,
And power which form'd creation's plan :
f   To God all praise and glory.

mf What God's Almighty power hath made
  His gracious mercy keepeth ;
cr By morning glow (*p*) or evening shade
  His watchful eye ne'er sleepeth ;
mf Within the kingdom of His might
Lo ! all is just, and all is right ;
f   To God all praise and glory.

mf The Lord is never far away,
p   But, through all grief distressing,
cr An ever-present help and stay,
  Our peace and joy and blessing ;
dim As with a mother's tender hand,
cr He leads His own, His chosen band ;
f   To God all praise and glory.

mf Thus all my toilsome way along
cr   I sing aloud Thy praises,
  That men may hear the grateful song
  My voice unwearied raises ;
f   Be joyful in the Lord, my heart ;
  Both soul and body bear your part ;
ff   To God all praise and glory.

Frances E. Cox : from the
German of J. J. Schütz.

General Hymns.

Hymn 293. SAVING HEALTH.—8 7 8 7. 8 8 7. (*Second Tune.*)

Etlich Cristliche Lyeder, 1524.

Verses 1, 3, 5 in Unison.

" O that men would therefore praise the Lord for His goodness."

f SING praise to GOD Who reigns above,
    The GOD of all creation,
The GOD of power, (*p*) the GOD of love,
f   The GOD of our salvation ;
mf With healing balm my soul He fills,
    And every faithless murmur stills ;
f   To GOD all praise and glory.

mf What GOD'S Almighty power hath made
    His gracious mercy keepeth ;
cr By morning glow (*p*) or evening shade
    His watchful eye ne'er sleepeth ;
mf Within the kingdom of His might
    Lo ! all is just, and all is right ;
f   To GOD all praise and glory.

mf The Angel-host, O King of kings,
    Thy praise for ever telling,
In earth and sky all living things
    Beneath Thy shadow dwelling,
Adore the wisdom which could span,
And power which form'd creation's plan :
f   To GOD all praise and glory.

mf The LORD is never far away,
p   But, through all grief distressing,
cr An ever-present help and stay,
    Our peace and joy and blessing ;
dim As with a mother's tender hand,
cr He leads His own, His chosen band :
f   To GOD all praise and glory

mf Thus all my toilsome way along
cr   I sing aloud Thy praises,
    That men may hear the grateful song
    My voice unwearied raises :
f   Be joyful in the LORD, my heart ;
    Both soul and body bear your part ;
ff   To GOD all praise and glory.

FRANCES E. COX : from the
German of J. J. Schütz.

(222)

General Hymns.

Hymn 294. St. Ursula.—D.C.M.

F. Westlake.

A - men.

" Who led His people through the wilderness ; for His mercy endureth for ever."

f O PRAISE our Great and Gracious Lord,
      And call upon His Name ;
    To strains of joy tune every chord,
      His mighty acts proclaim ;
mf Tell how He led His chosen race
      To Canaan's promised land ;
    Tell how His covenant of grace
f   Unchanged shall ever stand.

mf He gave the shadowing cloud by day,
      The moving fire by night ;
    To guide His Israel on their way,
      He made their darkness light ;
    And have not we a sure retreat,
      A Saviour ever nigh,
cr The same clear light to guide our feet,
      The Day-spring from on high ?

mf We too have Manna from above,
      The Bread that came from Heav'n ;
    To us the same kind hand of love
      Hath living waters given ;
    A Rock we have, from whence the spring
      In rich abundance flows ;
f   That Rock is Christ, our Priest, our King,
      Who life and health bestows.

mf O may we prize this blessèd Food,
      And trust our heavenly Guide ;
p   So shall we find death's fearful flood
      Serene as Jordan's tide,
cr And safely reach that happy shore,
p   The land of peace and rest,
cr Where Angels worship and adore
      In God's own Presence blest.

Harriet Auber, 1829.

General Hymns.

Hymn 295. TROYTE'S CHANT, No. 2.—Irregular. *(First Tune.)*

"All Thy works praise Thee, O Lord."

A. H. DYKE TROYTE.

f The strain upraise of joy and praise, Alle-	-lu - - ia !	To the glory of their King Let the ransom'd	peo - ple sing
And the choirs that . . .	dwell on high	Swell the chorus	in the sky,
mf Ye, through the fields of .	Paradise that roam,	Ye blessèd ones, repeat through	that bright home
(Unison.) Ye planets glittering on your	heaven-ly way,	Ye shining constellations,	join and say
(Harmony.) *p* Ye clouds that onward sweep, Ye winds on	pin - ions light,	*f* Ye thunders, echoing loud and deep, Ye lightnings,	wildly bright,
mf Ye floods and ocean billows, Ye storms and	win - ter snow,	Ye days of cloudless beauty, Hoar frost and	summer glow,
(Trebles only.) *p* First let the birds, with painted	plum-age gay,	Exalt their great Creator's	praise, and say
(Men only.) Then let the beasts of earth, with	vary-ing strain,	Join in creation's hymn, and	cry a - gain
(Men only.) *f* Here let the mountains thunder forth so-	-nor - - ous	Alle - - - - - - -	-lu - - ia !
(Men only.) *mf* Thou jubilant abyss of . .	o - cean, cry	Alle - - - - - - -	-lu - - ia !
(Harmony.) To GOD, Who all cre - - - -	-a - tion made,	The frequent hymn be . .	du - ly paid,
This is the strain, the eternal strain, the LORD of	all things loves,	Alle - - - - - - -	-lu - - ia !
Wherefore we sing, both heart and voice a-	-wak - - ing,	Alle - - - - - - -	-lu - - ia !
(Unison.) Now from all men	be out - pour'd	Alleluia - - - - - -	to the LORD ;
(Harmony.) *ff* Praise be done to the . . .	THREE in ONE.	Alle - - - - - - -	-lu - - ia !

(224)

General Hymns.

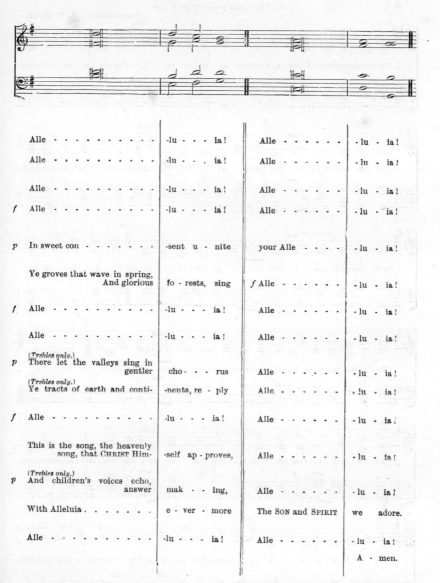

	Alle - - - - - - - - - - -	-lu - - ia!	Alle - - - - - - -lu - ia!
	Alle - - - - - - - - - -	-lu - - ia!	Alle - - - - - -lu - ia!
	Alle - - - - - - - - -	-lu - - ia!	Alle - - - - - -lu - ia!
f	Alle - - - - - - - - -	-lu - - ia!	Alle - - - - - -lu - ia!
p	In sweet con - - - - - - -	-sent u - nite	your Alle - - - - -lu - ia!
	Ye groves that wave in spring, And glorious	fo - rests, sing	*f* Alle - - - - - -lu - ia!
f	Alle - - - - - - - - - -	-lu - - ia!	Alle - - - - - -lu - ia!
	Alle - - - - - - - - -	-lu - - ia!	Alle - - - - - -lu - ia!
p	*(Trebles only.)* There let the valleys sing in gentler	cho - - rus	Alle - - - - - -lu - ia!
	(Trebles only.) Ye tracts of earth and conti-	-nents, re - ply	Alle - - - - - -lu - ia!
f	Alle - - - - - - - - -	-lu - - ia!	Alle - - - - - -lu - ia!
	This is the song, the heavenly song, that CHRIST Him-	-self ap - proves,	Alle - - - - - -lu - ia!
p	*(Trebles only.)* And children's voices echo, answer	mak - - ing,	Alle - - - - - -lu - ia!
	With Alleluia . - - - - - -	e - ver - more	The SON and SPIRIT we adore.
	Alle - - - - - - - - -	-lu - - ia!	Alle - - - - - -lu - ia!
			A - men.

J. M. NEALE: from Godescalcus.

General Hymns.

" All Thy works praise Thee, O Lord."

Harmonised by W. H. MONK.

(f) The strain up-raise of joy and praise, Al - le - lu - ia! To the glo - ry of their King

Let the ran-som'd peo - ple sing Al - le - lu - ia! And the choirs that dwell on high

Swell the cho - rus in the sky, . . Al - le - lu - ia! (mf) Ye, thro' the fields of

Pa - ra-dise that roam, Ye bless-ed ones, re-peat through that bright home Al - le - lu - ia!

Ye pla - nets glit-t'ring on your heav'n-ly way, Ye shin-ing con - stel - la-tions, join

and say (f) Al - le - lu - - ia! (p) Ye clouds that on-ward sweep, Ye winds on pin-ions light,

General Hymns.

CAN. DEC. FULL.

(*f*) Ye thunders, echo-ing loud and deep, Ye light-nings, wild-ly bright,(*p*) In sweet con-sent

CAN. DEC.

u - nite your Al - le - lu - ia! (*mf*) Ye floods and o - cean bil-lows, Ye storms and

CAN. DEC. CAN.

win - ter snow, Ye days of cloud-less beau-ty, Hoar frost and sum-mer glow, Ye groves that

DEC. FULL. CAN.

wave in spring, And glorious forests, sing(*f*)Al - le - lu - ia !(*p*) First let the birds, with painted

DEC.

plumage gay, Ex-alt their great Cre-a-tor's praise, and say(*f*)Al - le - lu - ia ! Then let the beasts

of earth, with vary-ing strain, Join in cre - a - tion's hymn, and cry a-gain Al - le - lu - ia !

General Hymns.

(f) Here let the mountains thunder forth so-nor-ous Al-le-lu-ia! (p) There let the val-leys

sing in gen-tler cho-rus Al-le-lu-ia! (mf) Thou ju-bi-lant a-byss of o-cean,

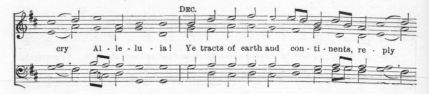

cry Al-le-lu-ia! Ye tracts of earth and con-ti-nents, re-ply

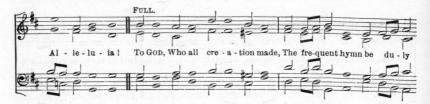

Al-le-lu-ia! To GOD, Who all cre-a-tion made, The fre-quent hymn be du-ly

paid, . . (f) Al-le-lu-ia! This is the strain, th' e-ter-nal strain, the LORD

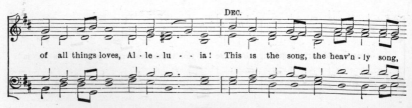

of all things loves, Al-le-lu-ia! This is the song, the heav'n-ly song,

General Hymns.

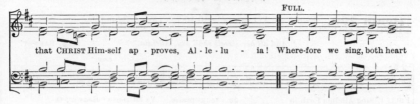

that CHRIST Him-self ap - proves, Al - le - lu - ia! Where-fore we sing, both heart

and voice a - wak - ing, Al - le - lu - ia! (p) And children's voi - ces e - cho, an - swer

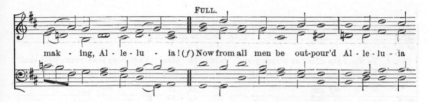

mak - ing, Al - le - lu - ia! (f) Now from all men be out-pour'd Al - le - lu - ia

to the LORD; With Al - le - lu - ia ev - er-more The SON and SPI-RIT we a - dore.

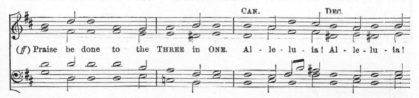

(ff) Praise be done to the THREE in ONE. Al - le - lu - ia! Al - le - lu - ia!

Al - le - lu - ia! Al - le - lu - ia! Al - le - lu - ia! Al - le - lu - ia! . . .

J. M. NEALE: from Godescalcus.

General Hymns.

Hymn 296. ENDLESS ALLELUIA.—10 10 7. (*First Tune.*)

"And all her streets shall say, Alleluia."   Sir J. BARNBY.

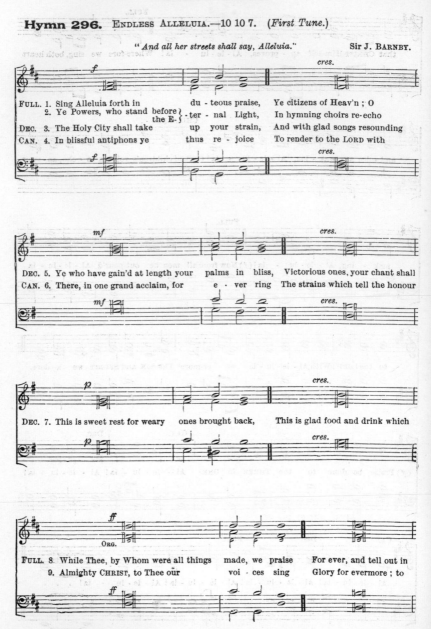

FULL. 1. Sing Alleluia forth in du - teous praise, Ye citizens of Heav'n ; O
2. Ye Powers, who stand before the E- ter - nal Light, In hymning choirs re-echo
DEC. 3. The Holy City shall take up your strain, And with glad songs resounding
CAN. 4. In blissful antiphons ye thus re - joice To render to the LORD with

DEC. 5. Ye who have gain'd at length your palms in bliss, Victorious ones, your chant shall
CAN. 6. There, in one grand acclaim, for e - ver ring The strains which tell the honour

DEC. 7. This is sweet rest for weary ones brought back, This is glad food and drink which

FULL. 8. While Thee, by Whom were all things made, we praise For ever, and tell out in
9. Almighty CHRIST, to Thee our voi - ces sing Glory for evermore ; to

(230)

General Hymns.

sweet - ly raise An end - less Al - le - lu - ia.
to the height An end - less Al - le - lu - ia.
wake a - gain An end - less Al - le - lu - ia.
thank - ful voice An end - less Al - le - lu - ia.

still be this, An end - less Al - le - lu - ia.
of your King, An end - less Al - le - lu - ia.

ne'er shall lack, An end - less Al - le - lu - ia.

sweet - est lays An end - less Al - le - lu - ia.
Thee we bring An end - less Al - le - lu - ia. A - men.

J. ELLERTON: from the Latin.

General Hymns.

Hymn 296. ALLELUIA PERENNE.—10 10 7. (*Second Tune.*)

W. H. MONK.

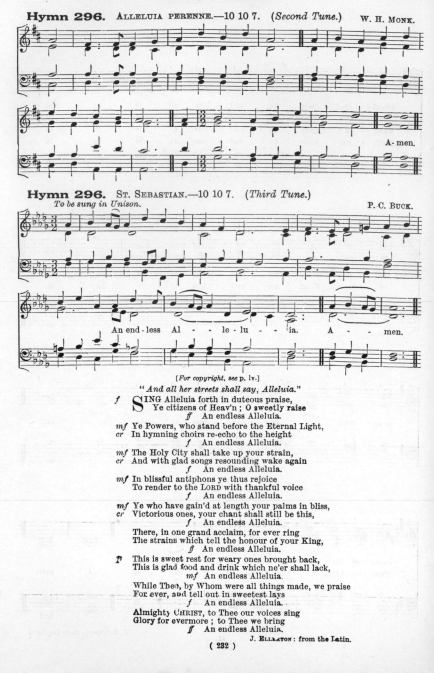

A - men.

Hymn 296. ST. SEBASTIAN.—10 10 7. (*Third Tune.*)

To be sung in Unison.

P. C. BUCK.

An end - less Al - le - lu - ia. A - men.

[*For copyright, see p. lv.*]

"And all her streets shall say, Alleluia."

f SING Alleluia forth in duteous praise,
Ye citizens of Heav'n ; O sweetly raise
    ff An endless Alleluia.

mf Ye Powers, who stand before the Eternal Light,
cr In hymning choirs re-echo to the height
    f An endless Alleluia.

mf The Holy City shall take up your strain,
cr And with glad songs resounding wake again
    f An endless Alleluia.

mf In blissful antiphons ye thus rejoice
To render to the LORD with thankful voice
    f An endless Alleluia.

mf Ye who have gain'd at length your palms in bliss,
cr Victorious ones, your chant shall still be this,
    f An endless Alleluia.

There, in one grand acclaim, for ever ring
The strains which tell the honour of your King,
    ff An endless Alleluia.

p This is sweet rest for weary ones brought back,
This is glad food and drink which ne'er shall lack,
    mf An endless Alleluia.

While Thee, by Whom were all things made, we praise
For ever, and tell out in sweetest lays
    f An endless Alleluia.

Almighty CHRIST, to Thee our voices sing
Glory for evermore ; to Thee we bring
    ff An endless Alleluia.

J. ELLERTON : from the Latin.

(232)

General Hymns.

Hymn 297. CULBACH.—7 7 7 7.　　　SCHEFFLER, *Heilige Seelenlust*, 1657.

A-men.

*A lower setting of this Tune is given at Hymn **73**.*

" When I laid the foundations of the earth . . . when the morning stars sang together, and all the sons of God shouted for joy."

mf SONGS of praise the Angels sang,
　　Heav'n with Alleluias rang,
When creation was begun,
When GOD spake and it was done.

　Songs of praise awoke the morn
p　When the Prince of peace was born;
cr　Songs of praise arose when He
f　Captive led captivity.

p　Heav'n and earth must pass away,
mf　Songs of praise shall crown that day;
　GOD will make new heavens and earth,
f　Songs of praise shall hail their birth.

p　And will man alone be dumb
　　Till that glorious kingdom come?
cr　No, the Church delights to raise
f　Psalms and hymns and songs of praise.

mf　Saints below, with heart and voice,
　　Still in songs of praise rejoice;
　　Learning here, by faith and love,
　　Songs of praise to sing above.

f　Hymns of glory, songs of praise,
　　FATHER, unto Thee we raise,
　　JESU, glory unto Thee,
　　With the SPIRIT, ever be.

J. MONTGOMERY, 1819.

Hymn 298. ALLELUIA DULCE CARMEN.—8 7 8 7. 8 7. (*First Tune.*)
Essay on the Church Plain Chant, 1782.

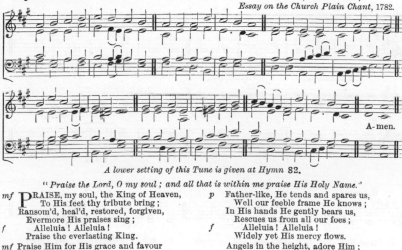

A-men.

*A lower setting of this Tune is given at Hymn **82**.*

" Praise the Lord, O my soul; and all that is within me praise His Holy Name."

mf PRAISE, my soul, the King of Heaven,
　　To His feet thy tribute bring;
Ransom'd, heal'd, restored, forgiven,
　Evermore His praises sing;
f　Alleluia! Alleluia!
　Praise the everlasting King.

mf Praise Him for His grace and favour
　To our fathers in distress;
Praise Him still the same as ever,
　Slow to chide, and swift to bless;
f　Alleluia! Alleluia!
　Glorious in His faithfulness.

p　Father-like, He tends and spares us,
　　Well our feeble frame He knows;
　In His hands He gently bears us,
　　Rescues us from all our foes;
f　Alleluia! Alleluia!
　Widely yet His mercy flows.

　Angels in the height, adore Him;
　　Ye behold Him face to face;
　Saints triumphant, bow before Him,
　　Gather'd in from every race;
ff　Alleluia! Alleluia!
　Praise with us the GOD of grace.

H. F. LYTE, 1834.

(233)

I 2

General Hymns.

Hymn 298. PRAISE, MY SOUL.—8 7 8 7.8 7. *(Second Tune.)*

" Praise the Lord, O my soul ; and all that is within me praise His Holy Name."

In Unison.   Sir J. GOSS.

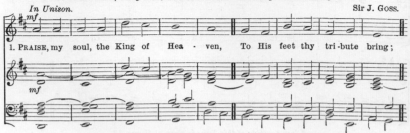

1. PRAISE, my soul, the King of Hea - ven, To His feet thy tri - bute bring;

Ran-som'd, heal'd, re - stored, for - giv - en, Ev - er - more His prais - es sing;

Al - le - lu - ia! Al - le - lu - ia! Praise the ev - er - last - ing King.

HARMONY.

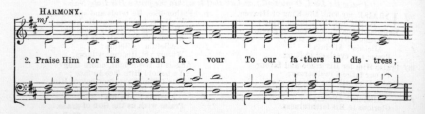

2. Praise Him for His grace and fa - vour To our fa - thers in dis - tress;

General Hymns.

Praise Him still the same as ev - er, Slow to chide, and swift to bless;

Al - le - lu - ia! Al - le - lu - ia! Glo - rious in His faith-ful - ness.

TREBLES ONLY.
Slower.

3. Fa - ther - like, He tends and spares us, Well our fee - ble frame He knows;

In His hands He gen - tly bears us, Res - cues us from all our foes;

Al - le - lu - ia! Al - le - lu - ia! Wide - ly yet His mer - cy flows.

General Hymns.

UNISON.

4. An - gels in the height, a - dore Him; Ye be - hold Him

face to face; Saints tri - um - phant, bow be - fore Him,

Gath - er'd in from ev - 'ry race; Al - le - lu - ia!

Al - le - lu - ia! Praise with us the GOD of grace.

In Harmony.

A - men.

H. F. Lyte, 1834.

General Hymns.

Hymn 299. NATIVITY.—C.M. *(First Tune.)*   H. LAHEE, 1855.

A - men.

Hymn 299. LOUGHTON.—C.M. *(Second Tune.)*   B. MILGROVE, 1781.

A - men.

" I heard the voice of many angels . . . saying, . . . Worthy is the Lamb that was slain to receive power, and riches, and wisdom, and strength, and honour, and glory, and blessing."

f   COME, let us join our cheerful songs
         With Angels round the Throne ;
     Ten thousand thousand are their tongues,
         But all their joys are one.

     "Worthy the LAMB that died," they cry,
         "To be exalted thus ;"
     "Worthy the LAMB," our lips reply,
p   "For He was slain for us."

mf JESUS is worthy to receive
         Honour and power Divine ;
cr   And blessings, more than we can give,
         Be, LORD, for ever Thine.

f   Let all creation join in one
         To bless the sacred Name
     Of Him that sits upon the Throne,
p   And to adore the LAMB.

                 I. WATTS, 1707.

General Hymns.

Hymn 300. St. Miles Lane.—C.M. (*First Tune.*)   W. Shrubsole, 1779.

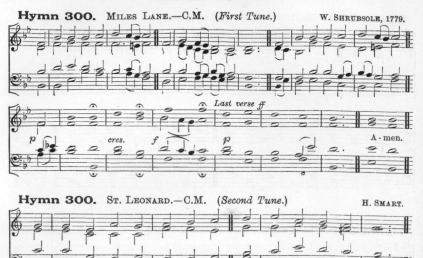

Last verse ff

A - men.

Hymn 300. St. Leonard.—C.M. (*Second Tune.*)   H. Smart.

A - men.

A lower setting of this Tune is given at Hymn 572.

" King of kings, and Lord of lords."

f   **A**LL hail the power of Jesus' Name ;
dim   Let Angels prostrate fall ;
cr   Bring forth the royal diadem
    And crown Him Lord of all.

mf   Crown Him, ye morning stars of light,
    Who fix'd this floating ball ;
f   Now hail the Strength of Israel's might,
    And crown Him Lord of all.

mf   Crown Him, ye Martyrs of your God,
    Who from His Altar call ;
    Extol the Stem-of-Jesse's Rod,
    And crown Him Lord of all.

    Ye seed of Israel's chosen race,
    Ye ransom'd of the fall,

cr   Hail Him Who saves you by His grace,
    And crown Him Lord of all.

mf   Hail Him, ye heirs of David's line,
    Whom David Lord did call,
p   The God Incarnate, Man Divine,
    And crown Him Lord of all.

    Sinners, whose love can ne'er forget
    The wormwood and the gall,
cr   Go spread your trophies at His feet,
    And crown Him Lord of all.

f   Let every tribe and every tongue
    Before Him prostrate fall,
    And shout in universal song
    The crownèd Lord of all.

E. Perronet, 1779.

In First Tune the last line of every verse is to be sung as marked in the music.

Hymn 301. St. Magnus.—C.M.   J. Clarke, 1670–1707.

General Hymns.

A. men.

A lower setting of this Tune is given at Hymn 751.

"To him that overcometh will I grant to sit with Me in My throne, even as I also overcame, and am set down with My Father in His throne."

p
f THE Head that once was crown'd with
    Is crown'd with glory now: [thorns
A royal diadem adorns
    The mighty Victor's Brow.

The highest place that Heav'n affords
    Is His, is His by right,
The King of kings, and LORD of Lords,
    And Heav'n's eternal Light.

mf The Joy of all who dwell above,
    The Joy of all below,
To whom He manifests His love,
    And grants His Name to know.

p To them the Cross, with all its shame,
cr   With all its grace, is given:
f Their name an everlasting name,
    Their joy the joy of Heav'n.

p They suffer with their LORD below,
f   They reign with Him above ;
mf Their profit and their joy to know
    The mystery of His love.

The Cross He bore is life and health,
    Though shame and death to Him ;
His people's hope, His people's wealth,
f   Their everlasting theme.

                T. KELLY, 1820.

Hymn 302.   UNSER HERRSCHER.—8 7. 8 7. 8 7.   J. NEANDER, 1680.

A. men.

"The four beasts and four and twenty elders fell down before the Lamb, having every one of them harps, and golden vials full of odours, which are the prayers of saints."

f COME, ye faithful, raise the anthem,
    Cleave the skies with shouts of praise ;
Sing to Him Who found the ransom,
    Ancient of eternal days,
GOD of GOD, the WORD Incarnate,
    Whom the Heav'n of Heav'n obeys.

mf Ere He raised the lofty mountains,
    Form'd the seas, or built the sky,
    Love eternal, free, and boundless,
p Moved the LORD of Life to die,
cr Fore-ordain'd the Prince of princes
p   For the Throne of Calvary.

There, for us and our redemption,
    See Him all His Life-blood pour !
cr There He wins our full salvation,
    Dies that we may die no more ;
f Then, arising, lives for ever,
ff   Reigning where He was before.

f High on yon celestial mountains
    Stands His gem-built Throne, all bright,
Midst unending Alleluias
    Bursting from the sons of light ;
Sion's people tell His praises,
ff   Victor after hard-won fight.

mf Bring your harps, and bring your odours,
    Sweep the string and pour the lay ;
f Let the earth proclaim His wonders,
    King of that celestial day ;
p He the LAMB once slain is worthy,
    Who was dead, (*f*) and lives for aye.

ff Laud and honour to the FATHER,
    Laud and honour to the SON,
Laud and honour to the SPIRIT,
    Ever THREE and ever ONE,
Consubstantial, Co-eternal,
    While unending ages run.

           J. HUPTON and J. M. NEALE.

General Hymns.

Hymn 303. LAUDES DOMINI.—6 6 6.6 6 6. (*First Tune.*) Sir J. BARNBY.

" In everything give thanks."

mf WHEN morning gilds the skies,
My heart awaking cries,
f May JESUS CHRIST be praised :
p Alike at work and prayer
cr To JESUS I repair ;
May JESUS CHRIST be praised.

mf Whene'er the sweet church bell
Peals over hill and dell,
f May JESUS CHRIST be praised :
p O hark to what it sings,
cr As joyously it rings,
May JESUS CHRIST be praised.

mf My tongue shall never tire
Of chanting with the choir,
f May JESUS CHRIST be praised :
p This song of sacred joy,
cr It never seems to cloy,
May JESUS CHRIST be praised.

p When sleep her balm denies,
My silent spirit sighs,
mf May JESUS CHRIST be praised :
p When evil thoughts molest,
cr With this I shield my breast,
May JESUS CHRIST be praised.

p Does sadness fill my mind?
cr A solace here I find,
mf May JESUS CHRIST be praised :
p Or fades my earthly bliss ?
cr My comfort still is this,
May JESUS CHRIST be praised.

mf The night becomes as day,
When from the heart we say,
f May JESUS CHRIST be praised :
p The powers of darkness fear,
cr When this sweet chant they hear,
May JESUS CHRIST be praised.

f In Heav'n's eternal bliss
The loveliest strain is this,
ff May JESUS CHRIST be praised :
f Let earth, and sea, and sky
cr From depth to height reply,
May JESUS CHRIST be praised.

mf Be this, while life is mine,
My canticle Divine,
f May JESUS CHRIST be praised :
Be this the eternal song
Through ages all along,
cr May JESUS CHRIST be praised.

E. CASWALL : from the German.

Hymn 303. OLD 122ND.—6 6 7. 12 lines. (*Second Tune.*) L. BOURGEOIS, 1551.

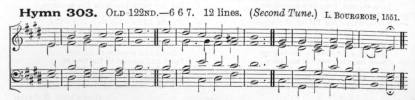

General Hymns.

A - men.

"In everything give thanks."

mf WHEN morning gilds the skies,
   My heart awaking cries,
f   May JESUS CHRIST be praisèd :
p Alike at work and prayer
cr To JESUS I repair ;
      May JESUS CHRIST be praisèd.
mf Whene'er the sweet church bell
   Peals over hill and dell,
f   May JESUS CHRIST be praisèd ;
p O hark to what it sings,
cr As joyously it rings,
      May JESUS CHRIST be praisèd.

mf My tongue shall never tire
   Of chanting with the choir,
f   May JESUS CHRIST be praisèd :
p This song of sacred joy,
cr It never seems to cloy,
      May JESUS CHRIST be praisèd.
p When sleep her balm denies,
   My silent spirit sighs,
mf   May JESUS CHRIST be praisèd :
p When evil thoughts molest,
cr With this I shield my breast,
      May JESUS CHRIST be praisèd.

p Does sadness fill my mind?
cr A solace here I find,
mf   May JESUS CHRIST be praisèd :
p Or fades my earthly bliss?
cr My comfort still is this,
      May JESUS CHRIST be praisèd.
mf The night becomes as day,
   When from the heart we say,
f   May JESUS CHRIST be praisèd :
p The powers of darkness fear,
cr When this sweet chant they hear,
      May JESUS CHRIST be praisèd.

f In Heav'n's eternal bliss
   The loveliest strain is this,
ff   May JESUS CHRIST be praisèd :
f Let earth, and sea, and sky
cr From depth to height reply,
      May JESUS CHRIST be praisèd.
mf Be this, while life is mine,
   My canticle Divine,
f   May JESUS CHRIST be praisèd :
   Be this the eternal song
   Through ages all along,
cr   May JESUS CHRIST be praisèd.

E. CASWALL : from the German.

(241)

General Hymns.

Hymn 304. DIADEMATA.—D.S.M.

Sir G. J. ELVEY.

A- men.

" And on His Head were many crowns."

f CROWN Him with many crowns,
The LAMB upon His Throne;
Hark! how the heavenly anthem drowns
All music but its own:
Awake, my soul, and sing
p Of Him Who died for thee,
cr And hail Him as thy matchless King
Through all eternity.

f Crown Him the Virgin's Son,
p The GOD Incarnate born,
cr Whose Arm those crimson trophies won
Which now His Brow adorn:
p Fruit of the mystic Rose,
cr As of that Rose the Stem;
mf The Root whence mercy ever flows,
p The Babe of Bethlehem.

mf Crown Him the LORD of love;
p Behold His Hands and Side,
cr Those Wounds yet visible above
In beauty glorified:
p No Angel in the sky
pp rit But downward bends his burning eye
At mysteries so bright.

mf Crown Him the LORD of peace,
cr Whose power a sceptre sways
From pole to pole, that wars may cease,
And all be prayer and praise:
f His reign shall know no end,
p And round His piercèd Feet
Fair flowers of Paradise extend
cr Their fragrance ever sweet.

f Crown Him the LORD of years,
The Potentate of time,
Creator of the rolling spheres,
Ineffably Sublime:
All hail, Redeemer, hail!
p For Thou hast died for me;
ff Thy praise shall never, never fail
Throughout eternity.

M. BRIDGES, 1851.

(242)

Hymn 305. EDINA.—6 5 6 5. 6 5 6 5. (*First Tune.*) Sir H. OAKELEY.

"Every day will I give thanks unto Thee, and praise Thy Name for ever and ever."

mf SAVIOUR, Blessèd Saviour,
    Listen whilst we sing,
  Hearts and voices raising
    Praises to our King;
p All we have we offer;
    All we hope to be,
f Body, soul, and spirit,
    All we yield to Thee.

p Nearer, ever nearer,
    CHRIST, we draw to Thee,
  Deep in adoration
    Bending low the knee;
  Thou for our redemption
    Cam'st on earth to die;
f Thou, that we might follow,
    Hast gone up on high.

mf Great and ever greater
    Are Thy mercies here;
f True and everlasting
    Are the glories there;
p Where no pain, nor sorrow,
    Toil, nor care, is known,
f Where the Angel-legions
    Circle round Thy Throne.

p Dark and ever darker
    Was the wintry past,
cr Now a ray of gladness
    O'er our path is cast;
p Every day that passeth,
    Every hour that flies,
f Tells of love unfeignèd,
    Love that never dies.

mf Clearer still and clearer
    Dawns the light from Heav'n,
  In our sadness bringing
    News of sin forgiven;
  Life has lost its shadows,
    Pure the light within;
f Thou hast shed Thy radiance
    On a world of sin.

Brighter still and brighter
  Glows the western sun,
  Shedding all its gladness
    O'er our work that's done;
p Time will soon be over,
    Toil and sorrow past,
mf May we, Blessèd Saviour,
    Find a rest at last.

Onward, ever onward,
  Journeying o'er the road
cr Worn by Saints before us,
    Journeying on to GOD;
p Leaving all behind us,
cr May we hasten on,
  Backward never looking
    Till the prize is won.

f Bliss, all bliss excelling,
    When the ransom'd soul,
  Earthly toils forgetting,
    Finds its promised goal;
p Where in joys unheard of
cr Saints with Angels sing,
f Never weary raising
    Praises to their King.

G. THRING.

General Hymns.

Hymn 305. BLESSED SAVIOUR.—6 5 6 5. 6 5 6 5. *(Second Tune.)* J. E. WEST.

Voices in Unison.

ORG.

Harmony.

A-men.

[*Copyright* 1910 *by* Novello and Company, Limited.]

Hymn 305. BOHEMIA.—6 5 6 5. 6 5 6 5. *(Third Tune.)* German Melody.

A-men.

"*Every day will I give thanks unto Thee, and praise Thy Name for ever and ever.*"

mf SAVIOUR, Blessèd Saviour,
　　Listen whilst we sing,
　Hearts and voices raising
　　Praises to our King;
p　All we have we offer;
　　All we hope to be,
f　Body, soul, and spirit,
　　All we yield to Thee.

p　Nearer, ever nearer,
　　CHRIST, we draw to Thee,
　Deep in adoration
　　Bending low the knee;
　Thou for our redemption
　　Cam'st on earth to die;
f　Thou, that we might follow,
　　Hast gone up on high.

mf Great and ever greater
　　Are Thy mercies here;
f　True and everlasting
　　Are the glories there;
p　Where no pain, nor sorrow,
　　Toil, nor care, is known,
f　Where the Angel-legions
　　Circle round Thy Throne.

p　Dark and ever darker
　　Was the wintry past,
cr Now a ray of gladness
　　O'er our path is cast;
p　Every day that passeth,
　　Every hour that flies,
f　Tells of love unfeignèd,
　　Love that never dies.

mf Clearer still and clearer
　　Dawns the light from Heav'n,
　In our sadness bringing
　　News of sin forgiven;
　Life has lost its shadows,
　　Pure the light within;
f　Thou hast shed Thy radiance
　　On a world of sin.

　Brighter still and brighter
　　Glows the western sun,
　Shedding all its gladness
　　O'er our work that's done;
p　Time will soon be over,
　　Toil and sorrow past,
mf May we, Blessèd Saviour,
　　Find a rest at last.

f

Onward, ever onward,
   Journeying o'er the road
cr Worn by Saints before us,
   Journeying on to GOD ;
p Leaving all behind us,
cr May we hasten on,
   Backward never looking
   Till the prize is won.

f Bliss, all bliss excelling,
   When the ransom'd soul,
   Earthly toils forgetting,
   Finds its promised goal ;
p Where in joys unheard of
cr Saints with Angels sing,
f Never weary raising
   Praises to their King.

G. THRING.

Hymn 306. EVELYNS.—6 5 6 5. 6 5 6 5.

W. H. MONK.

A-men.

" Wherefore God also hath highly exalted Him, and given Him a Name which is above every name : that at the Name of Jesus every knee should bow."

mf AT the Name of JESUS
   Every knee shall bow,
cr Every tongue confess Him
f King of glory now ;
mf 'Tis the FATHER'S pleasure
   We should call Him LORD,
cr Who from the beginning
   Was the Mighty WORD.

f At His voice creation
   Sprang at once to sight,
   All the Angel faces,
   All the hosts of light,
   Thrones and Dominations,
   Stars upon their way,
   All the heavenly Orders,
   In their great array.

p Humbled for a season,
   To receive a Name
   From the lips of sinners
   Unto whom He came,
cr Faithfully He bore it
   Spotless to the last,
   Brought it back victorious,
   When from death He pass'd :

f Bore it up triumphant
p With its human light,
cr Through all ranks of creatures,
   To the central height ;

f To the Throne of GODHEAD,
   To the FATHER'S breast,
   Fill'd it with the glory
dim Of that perfect rest.

f Name Him, brothers, name Him,*
   With love as strong as death,
p But with awe and wonder,
pp And with bated breath ;
p He is GOD the Saviour,
   He is CHRIST the LORD,
cr Ever to be worshipp'd,
   Trusted, and adored.

mf In your hearts enthrone Him ;
   There let Him subdue
   All that is not holy,
   All that is not true :
cr Crown Him as your Captain
   In temptation's hour ;
   Let His Will enfold you
   In its light and power.

f Brothers, this LORD JESUS
   Shall return again,
   With His FATHER'S glory,
   With His Angel train ;
ff For all wreaths of empire
   Meet upon His Brow,
   And our hearts confess Him
rall King of glory now.

CAROLINE M. NOEL.

* *In verse 5 sing this chord to the first word of line 2, dividing the ♩ of the melody into two ♪ ♪*

General Hymns.

A - men.

"So shall the King have pleasure in thy beauty: for He is thy Lord God, and worship thou Him."

mf O SAVIOUR, precious Saviour,
    Whom yet unseen we love,
cr O Name of might and favour,
    All other names above !
p We worship Thee, (*cr*) we bless Thee,
    To Thee alone we sing ;
f We praise Thee, and confess Thee
    Our holy LORD and King.

mf O Bringer of salvation,
    Who wondrously hast wrought,
Thyself the revelation
    Of love beyond our thought ;
p We worship Thee, (*cr*) we bless Thee,
    To Thee alone we sing ;
f We praise Thee, and confess Thee
dim Our gracious LORD and King.

f In Thee all fulness dwelleth,
    All grace and power Divine ;
The glory that excelleth,
    O SON of GOD, is Thine ;
p We worship Thee, (*cr*) we bless Thee,
    To Thee alone we sing ;
f We praise Thee, and confess Thee
    Our glorious LORD and King.

mf O grant the consummation
    Of this our song above
In endless adoration,
    And everlasting love ;
f Then shall we praise and bless Thee
    Where perfect praises ring,
And evermore confess Thee
    Our Saviour and our King.

FRANCES R. HAVERGAL.

H. J. GAUNTLETT.

A-men.

General Hymns.

" O praise the Lord."

f O PRAISE ye the LORD!
 Praise Him in the height ;
Rejoice in His Word,
 Ye Angels of light ;
Ye heavens, adore Him
 By Whom ye were made,
p And worship before Him,
cr In brightness array'd.

f O praise ye the LORD !
 Praise Him upon earth,
mf In tuneful accord,
 Ye sons of new birth ;
f Praise Him Who hath brought you
 His grace from above,
Praise Him Who hath taught you
 To sing of His love.

O praise ye the LORD,
 All things that give sound ;
Each jubilant chord,
 Re-echo around ;
Loud organs, His glory
 Forth tell in deep tone,
p And sweet harp, the story
 Of what He hath done.

f O praise ye the LORD !
 Thanksgiving and song
To Him be outpour'd
 All ages along :
mf For love in creation,
cr For heaven restored,
f For grace of salvation
 O praise ye the LORD !

Sir H. W. BAKER.

Hymn 308.   LAUDATE DOMINUM.—5 5 5 5.6 5 6 5.   *(Second Tune.)*

Vigorously.   Sir H. PARRY.

[*Copyright* 1915 *by* Novello and Company, Limited.]

" O praise the Lord."

f O PRAISE ye the LORD !
 Praise Him in the height ;
Rejoice in His Word,
 Ye Angels of light ;
Ye heavens, adore Him
 By Whom ye were made,
p And worship before Him,
cr In brightness array'd.

f O praise ye the LORD !
 Praise Him upon earth,
mf In tuneful accord,
 Ye sons of new birth ;

f Praise Him Who hath brought you
 His grace from above,
Praise Him Who hath taught you
 To sing of His love.

O praise ye the LORD,
 All things that give sound ;
Each jubilant chord,
 Re-echo around ;
Loud organs, His glory
 Forth tell in deep tone,
p And sweet harp, the story
 Of what He hath done.

See next page for verse 4.

General Hymns.

VERSE 4. *Voices in Unison.*

O praise ye the LORD! Thanks-giv-ing and song
To Him be out-pour'd All a-ges a-
long: For love in cre-a-tion, For
hea-ven re-stored, For grace of sal-

General Hymns.

- va - tion O praise ye the LORD! A - men, A - - men.

Holy Communion.

Sir H. W. BAKER.

Hymn 309. PANGE LINGUA.—8 7. 8 7. 8 7. (*First Tune.*) (*First Version.*)
Proper Sarum Melody.

A - men. . .

For Alternative Version of this Tune, see page 250. A higher setting is given at Hymn **97.**

"*The cup of blessing which we bless, is it not the communion of the Blood of Christ? The
bread which we break, is it not the communion of the Body of Christ?*"

mf NOW, my tongue, the mystery telling
　　Of the glorious Body sing,
And the Blood, all price excelling,
　　Which the Gentiles' LORD and King,
p　In a Virgin's womb once dwelling,
　　Shed for this world's ransoming.

mf Given for us, and condescending
p　To be born for us below,
cr He, with men in converse blending,
　　Dwelt the seed of truth to sow,
Till He closed with wondrous ending
p　His most patient life of woe.

rif That last night, at supper lying,
　　'Mid the Twelve, His chosen band,
JESUS, with the law complying,
　　Keeps the feast its rites demand;
Then, more precious Food supplying,
　　Gives Himself with His own Hand.

p WORD-made-Flesh true bread He maketh
cr　By His Word His Flesh to be;
p Wine His Blood; (*mf*) which whoso taketh
　　Must from carnal thoughts be free;
f Faith alone, though (*dim*) sight forsaketh,
mf　Shows true hearts the mystery.

PART 2.

p Therefore we, before Him bending,
　　This great Sacrament revere;
cr Types and shadows have their ending,
　　For the newer rite is here;
mf Faith, our outward sense befriending,
　　Makes our inward vision clear.

f Glory let us give, and blessing
　　To the FATHER, and the SON,
Honour, might, and praise addressing,
　　While eternal ages run;
Ever too His love confessing,
　　Who from Both with Both is ONE.

E. CASWALL and Compilers:
from St. Thomas Aquinas

(249)

Holy Communion.

Hymn 309. Pange lingua.—8 7. 8 7. 8 7. (*First Tune.*) (*Alternative Version.*)
Proper Sarum Melody.

mf Now, my tongue, the mys-tery tell - ing Of the glo-rious Bo-dy sing,

And the Blood, all price ex - cell - ing, Which the Gen-tiles' LORD and King,

p In a Vir-gin's womb once dwell-ing, Shed for this world's ran-som -ing. A - men.

Hymn 309. Milano.—8 7. 8 7. 8 7. (*Second Tune.*)

F. BONAGGI.

A - men.

(250)

Holy Communion.

Hymn 309. ST. THOMAS.—8 7.8 7.8 7. *(Third Tune.)* Traditional Melody.

A - men.

A higher setting of this Tune is given at Hymn 51.

Hymn 309. TANTUM ERGO.—8 7.8 7.8 7. *(Fourth Tune.)* French Melody.

Slow.

A - men.

" The cup of blessing which we bless, is it not the communion of the Blood of Christ ? The bread which we break, is it not the communion of the Body of Christ ? "

mf NOW, my tongue, the mystery telling
 Of the glorious Body sing,
And the Blood, all price excelling,
 Which the Gentiles' LORD and King,
p In a Virgin's womb once dwelling,
 Shed for this world's ransoming.

mf Given for us, and condescending,
p To be born for us below,
cr He, with men in converse blending,
 Dwelt the seed of truth to sow,
 Till He closed with wondrous ending
p His most patient life of woe.

mf That last night, at supper lying,
 'Mid the Twelve, His chosen band,
JESUS, with the law complying,
 Keeps the feast its rites demand ;
Then, more precious Food supplying,
 Gives Himself with His own Hand.

p WORD-made-Flesh true bread He maketh
cr By His Word His Flesh to be ;
p Wine His Blood ; *(mf)* which whoso taketh
 Must from carnal thoughts be free ;
f Faith alone, though *(dim)* sight forsaketh,
mf Shows true hearts the mystery.

PART 2.

p Therefore we, before Him bending,
 This great Sacrament revere ;
cr Types and shadows have their ending,
 For the newer rite is here ;
mf Faith, our outward sense befriending,
 Makes our inward vision clear.

f Glory let us give, and blessing
 To the FATHER, and the SON,
Honour, might, and praise addressing,
 While eternal ages run ;
Ever too His love confessing,
 Who from Both with Both is ONE.

E. CASWALL and Compilers:
from St. Thomas Aquinas.

Holy Communion.

Hymn 310. ECCE PANIS.—Irregular. (*First Tune.*)

" So man did eat angels' food."

Rev. J. B. DYKES.

With expression.

mf 1. Lo! the An-gels' Food is giv - en To the pil - grim who hath stri - ven;
2. Truth the ancient types ful - fill - ing, I - saac bound, a vic - tim will - ing,

See the children's Bread from Hea - ven, Which on dogs may ne'er be spent:
Pas-chal Lamb its life-blood spill - ing, Man - na to the fa - thers sent.

Ve - ry Bread, Good Shep-herd, tend . . . us; JE - SU, of Thy love be -

- friend . . . us, Thou re-fresh us, Thou de - fend us,

cres.

Thine e - ter - nal good-ness send us In the land of life to see: . . ORG.

Thou Who all things canst and know - est, Who on earth such Food be - stow - est,

(252)

Holy Communion.

Grant us with Thy Saints, though low - est, Where the heav'nly Feast Thou show - est,

Fel - low heirs and guests .. to be. A - - men.

dim. *rall.*

Compilers: from St. Thomas Aquinas.

Hymn 310. AQUINAS.—8 8 8 8 7. (*Second Tune.*) J. A. HILLER, 1793.

Slow.

A-men.

"*So man did eat angels' food.*"

PART 2.

pp VERY Bread, Good Shepherd, tend us ;
JESU, of Thy love befriend us ;
cr Thou refresh us, Thou defend us,
Thine eternal goodness send us
f In the land of life to see :
p Thou Who all things canst and knowest,
Who on earth such Food bestowest,
cr Grant us with Thy Saints, though lowest,
Where the heav'nly Feast Thou showest,
Fellow heirs (*dim*) and guests to be.

Compilers: from St. Thomas Aquinas.

(253)

Holy Communion.

Hymn 311.*   O Salutaris.—L.M.   (*First Tune.*)

To be sung in Unison.

Proper Mechlin Melody.

A - men.

Hymn 311.   O Salutaris.—L.M.   (*First Tune.*)   (*Alternative Version.*)

Proper Mechlin Melody.

A - men...

Hymn 311.   St. Vincent.—L.M.   (*Second Tune.*)

J. Uglow.

A - men.

* *The Tune "Melcombe" (Hymn 4) may also be sung to this Hymn, for which it was composed.*

"*As the living Father hath sent Me, and I live by the Father; so he that eateth Me, even he shall live by Me.*"

mf   THE Heavenly Word proceeding forth,
     Yet leaving not the Father's side,
     Accomplishing His work on earth
p   Had reach'd at length life's eventide.

mf   By false disciple to be given
     To foemen for His life athirst,
     Himself, the very Bread of Heav'n,
     He gave to His disciples first.

     He gave Himself in either kind,
     His precious Flesh, His precious Blood;
cr   In love's own fulness thus design'd
     Of the whole man to be the Food.

p   By Birth their Fellow-man was He;
cr   Their Meat, when sitting at the Board;
p   He died, their Ransomer to be;
f   He ever reigns, their great Reward.

Holy Communion.

p O Saving Victim, (*cr*) opening wide
mf The gate of heaven to (*dim*) man below,
cr Our foes press on from every side,
mf Thine aid supply, Thy strength (*dim*) bestow.

mf All praise and thanks to Thee ascend
For evermore, Blest ONE in THREE ;
p O grant us life that shall not end
cr In our true native land with Thee.

J. M. NEALE and Compilers:
from St. Thomas Aquinas.

Hymn 312. ADORO TE DEVOTE.—10 10 10 10. (*First Tune.*)

Traditional Melody.

A - men.

Hymn 312. ADORO TE DEVOTE.—10 10 10 10. (*First Tune.*) (*Alternative Version.*)

Traditional Melody.

A - men.

"Jesus said unto them, I am the Bread of Life."

p THEE we adore, O hidden Saviour, Thee,
Who in Thy Sacrament dost deign to be ;
Both flesh and spirit at Thy Presence fail,
Yet here Thy Presence we devoutly hail.

mf O blest Memorial of our dying LORD,
Who living Bread to men doth here afford !
O may our souls for ever feed on Thee,
And Thou, O CHRIST, for ever precious be.

Fountain of goodness, JESU, LORD and GOD,
p Cleanse us, unclean, with Thy most cleansing Blood ;
cr Increase our faith and love, that we may know
The hope and peace which from Thy Presence flow.

p O CHRIST, Whom now beneath a veil we see,
May what we thirst for soon our portion be,
cr To gaze on Thee unveil'd, and see Thy Face,
f The vision of Thy glory and Thy grace.

Bishop WOODFORD and Compilers:
from St. Thomas Aquinas.

Holy Communion.

Hymn 312. EUCHARISTIC CHANT.—10 10 10 10. *(Second Tune.)*

W. H. MONK.

A-men.

Hymn 312. ST. SACRAMENT.—10 10 10 10. *(Third Tune.)*

W. H. MONK.

A-men.

" Jesus said unto them, I am the Bread of Life."

p THEE we adore, O hidden Sáviour, Thee,
Who in Thy Sacrament dost deign to be ;
Both flesh and spirit át Thy Presence fail,
Yet here Thy Presence wé devoutly hail.

mf O blest Memorial of our dýing LORD,
Who living Bread to men doth hére afford !
O may our souls for éver feed on Thee,
And Thou, O CHRIST, for éver precious be.

Fountain of goodness, JESU, LÓRD and GOD,
p Cleanse us, unclean, with Thy most cléansing Blood ;
cr Increase our faith and lóve, that we may know
The hope and peace which fróm Thy Presence flow.

p O CHRIST, Whom now beneath a véil we see,
May what we thirst for soon our pórtion be,
cr To gaze on Thee unvéil'd, and see Thy Face,
f The vision of Thy glóry and Thy grace.

Bishop WOODFORD and Compilers : from St. Thomas Aquinas.

ALTERNATIVE TUNES, HYMNS 31 and 715.

Hymn 313. LAMMAS.—10 10. *(First Tune.)*

A. H. BROWN.

A-men.

Hymn 313. CŒNA DOMINI.—10 10. *(Second Tune.)*

Sir A. SULLIVAN.

A-men.

holy Communion.

Hymn 313. SANCTI VENITE.—10 10. *(Third Tune.)* Rev. J. B. DYKES.

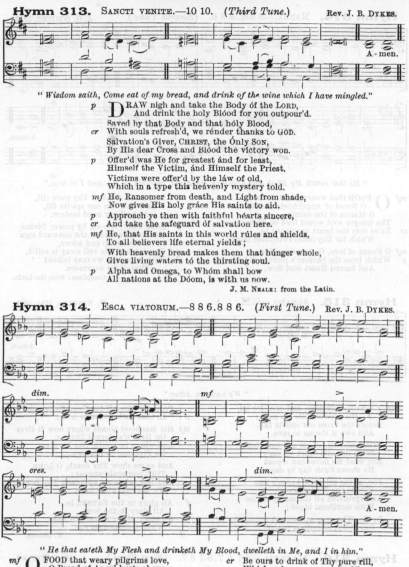

" Wisdom saith, Come eat of my bread, and drink of the wine which I have mingled."

  p DRAW nigh and take the Body óf the LORD,
       And drink the holy Blóod for you outpour'd.
    Saved by that Body and that hóly Blood,
  cr With souls refresh'd, we rénder thanks to GOD.
    Salvation's Giver, CHRIST, the Ónly SON,
    By His dear Cross and Blóod the victory won.

  p Offer'd was He for greatest ánd for least,
    Himself the Victim, ánd Himself the Priest.
    Victims were offer'd by the láw of old,
    Which in a type this heávenly mystery told.

  mf He, Ransomer from death, and Líght from shade,
    Now gives His holy gráce His saints to aid.
  p Approach ye then with faithful héarts sincere,
  cr And take the safeguard óf salvation here.

  mf He, that His saints in this world rúles and shields,
    To all believers life eternal yields ;
    With heavenly bread makes them that húnger whole,
    Gives living waters tó the thirsting soul.

  p Alpha and Omega, to Whóm shall bow
    All nations at the Dóom, is with us now.

                   J. M. NEALE: from the Latin.

Hymn 314. ESCA VIATORUM.—8 8 6.8 8 6. *(First Tune.)* Rev. J. B. DYKES.

" He that eateth My Flesh and drinketh My Blood, dwelleth in Me, and I in him."

  mf O FOOD that weary pilgrims love,
    O Bread of Angel-hosts above,
    O Manna of the Saints,
    The hungry soul would feed on Thee ;
  cr Ne'er may the heart unsolaced be
    Which for Thy *(dim)* sweetness faints.

  mf O Fount of love, O cleansing Tide,
  p Which from the Saviour's piercèd Side
    And Sacred Heart dost flow,

  cr Be ours to drink of Thy pure rill,
    Which only can our spirits fill,
    And all our need bestow.

  p LORD JESU, Whom, by power Divine
    Now hidden 'neath the outward sign,
    We worship and adore.
  mf Grant, when the veil away is roll'd,
  cr With open face we may behold
    Thyself for evermore.

                   Compilers: from the Latin.

Holy Communion.

Hymn 314. MANNA.—8 8 6. 8 8 6. *(Second Tune.)*   J. G. SCHICHT, 1819.

A-men.

" He that eateth My Flesh and drinketh My Blood, dwelleth in Me, and I in him."

mf O FOOD that weary pilgrims love,
    O Bread of Angel-hosts above,
    O Manna of the Saints,
    The hungry soul would feed on Thee ;
cr Ne'er may the heart unsolaced be
    Which for Thy *(dim)* sweetness faints.

mf O Fount of love, O cleansing Tide,
p Which from the Saviour's piercèd Side
    And Sacred Heart dost flow,

cr Be ours to drink of Thy pure rill,
    Which only can our spirits fill,
    And all our need bestow.

p LORD JESU, Whom, by power Divine
    Now hidden 'neath the outward sign
    We worship and adore,
mf Grant, when the veil away is roll'd,
cr With open face we may behold
    Thyself for evermore.

Compilers : from the Latin.

Hymn 315. ALBANO.—C.M.   V. NOVELLO, 1781–1861.

Amen.

" We have an Altar."

mf ONCE, only once, and once for all,
    His precious life He gave ;
Before the Cross our spirits fall,
    And own it strong to save.

"One offering, single and complete,
    With lips and heart we say ;
But what He never can repeat
    He shows forth day by day.

For, as the priest of Aaron's line
    Within the Holiest stood,
And sprinkled all the mercy-shrine
    With sacrificial blood ;

So He, Who once atonement wrought,
    Our Priest of endless power,

Presents Himself for those He bought
p In that dark noontide hour.

mf His Manhood pleads where now It lives
    On Heav'n's eternal Throne,
And where in mystic rite He gives
    Its Presence to His own.

And so we show Thy death, O LORD,
    Till Thou again appear ;
And feel, when we approach Thy Board,
    We have an Altar here.

f All glory to the FATHER be,
    All glory to the SON,
All glory, HOLY GHOST, to Thee,
    While endless ages run.

W. BRIGHT.

Hymn 316. ALLELUIA.—8 7 8 7. 8 7 8 7. *(First Tune.)*   S. S. WESLEY.

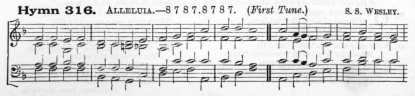

Holy Communion.

A-men.

Hymn 316. ADORATION.—8 7 8 7 . 8 7 8 7 . (*Second Tune.*) B. LUARD SELBY.

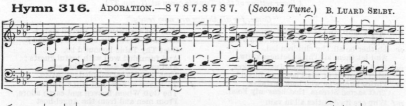

A - men.

" Thou art a Priest for ever."

f　ALLELUIA ! sing to JESUS !
　　His the Sceptre, His the Throne !
　Alleluia ! His the triumph,
　　His the victory alone ;
p　Hark ! the songs of peaceful Sion
cr　Thunder like a mighty flood ;
f　JESUS out of every nation
　　Hath redeem'd us (*p*) by His Blood.

mf　Alleluia ! not as orphans
　　Are we left in sorrow now ;
　Alleluia ! He is near us,
　　Faith believes, nor questions how :
　Though the cloud from sight received Him,
　　When the forty days were o'er,
cr　Shall our hearts forget His promise,
　　" I am with you evermore "?

mf　Alleluia ! Bread of Angels,
　　Thou on earth our Food, our Stay ;
　Alleluia ! (*p*) here the sinful
　　Flee to Thee from day to day ;

　　Intercessor, Friend of sinners,
cr　Earth's Redeemer, plead for me,
　Where the songs of all the sinless
　　Sweep across the crystal sea.

mf　Alleluia ! King Eternal,
　　Thee the LORD of lords we own ;
　Alleluia ! (*p*) born of Mary,
cr　Earth Thy footstool, Heav'n Thy Throne :
mf　Thou within the veil hast enter'd,
　　Robed in flesh, our great High Priest ;
　Thou on earth both Priest and Victim
　　In the Eucharistic Feast.

f　Alleluia ! sing to JESUS !
　　His the Sceptre, His the Throne ;
　Alleluia ! His the triumph,
　　His the victory alone ;
p　Hark ! the songs of peaceful Sion
cr　Thunder like a mighty flood ;
f　JESUS out of every nation
　　Hath redeem'd us (*p*) by His Blood.

W. C. DIX.

Holy Communion.

Hymn 317. ROCKINGHAM.—L.M.

E. MILLER, 1735–1807.

A-men.

A lower setting of this Tune is given at Hymn 371.

"*Come, for all things are now ready.*"

p **M**Y GOD, and is Thy Table spread,
  And doth Thy Cup with love o'erflow?
cr Thither be all Thy children led,
  And let them all Thy sweetness know.

mf Hail, sacred Feast, which JESUS makes,
  Rich banquet of His Flesh and Blood!
cr Thrice happy he who here partakes
  That sacred Stream, that heavenly Food.

mf Why are its dainties all in vain
  Before unwilling hearts display'd?

Was not for them the Victim slain?
Are they forbid the children's Bread?
O let Thy Table honour'd be,
And furnish'd well with joyful guests;
And may each soul salvation see,
That here its sacred pledges tastes.

f To FATHER, SON, and HOLY GHOST,
The GOD Whom heaven and earth adore,
From men and from the Angel-host
Be praise and glory evermore.

P. DODDRIDGE, 1755.

Hymn 318. BREAD OF HEAVEN.—7 7.7 7.7 7. (*First Tune.*)

Archbishop MACLAGAN.

A-men.

Hymn 318. NICHT SO TRAURIG.—7 7.7 7.7 7. (*Second Tune.*)

J. S. BACH, 1685–1750.

A-men.

Holy Communion.

Hymn 318. HOUGHTON-LE-SPRING.—7 7.7 7.7 7. *(Third Tune.)*

S. S. WESLEY, 1860.

A-men.

" This do in remembrance of Me."

mf BREAD of Heav'n, on Thee we feed,
For Thy Flesh is meat indeed ;
Ever may our souls be fed
With this true and living Bread ;
cr Day by day with strength supplied
dim Through the life of Him Who died.

mf Vine of Heav'n, Thy Blood supplies
This blest Cup of Sacrifice ;
p LORD, Thy Wounds our healing give,
To Thy Cross we look and live :
cr JESUS, may we ever be
Grafted, rooted, built in Thee.

J. CONDER.

Hymn 319. AUTHOR OF LIFE.—6 6 6 6.8 8. *(First Tune.)* Sir J. STAINER.

rall.

A - men.

" The Lord's Table."

mf AUTHOR of life Divine,
Who hast a Table spread,
Furnish'd with mystic Wine
And everlasting Bread,
cr Preserve the life Thyself hast given,
And feed and train us up for Heav'n.

mf Our needy souls sustain
With fresh supplies of love,
Till all Thy life we gain,
And all Thy fulness prove,
cr And, strengthen'd by Thy perfect grace,
dim Behold without a veil Thy Face.

J. WESLEY, 1745.

Holy Communion.

Hymn 319. Auctor Vitæ.—6 6 6 6. 8 8. *(Second Tune.)*

"The Lord's Table."

Sir Walford Davies.

1. AU - THOR of life Di - vine, Who hast a Ta - ble spread,
2. Our need - y souls sus - tain With fresh sup - plies of love,

Fur-nish'd with mys - tic Wine And ev - er - last - - ing Bread, Pre - serve the life
Till all Thy life we gain, And all Thy ful - - ness prove, And, strengthen'd by

Thy - self . . hast given, And feed and train us up . . . for Heav'n.
Thy per - fect grace, Be - hold with - out a veil . . Thy Face. A - men.

J. Wesley, 1745.

Hymn 320. St. Flavian.—C.M. *(First Tune.)*

Psalmes, 1562.

A - men.

(262)

holy Communion.

Hymn 320. ST. FLAVIAN.—C.M. *(First Tune.)* *(Alternative Version.)*
Harmonised by T. RAVENSCROFT, 1621.

The above may be used for verses 2 and 4.

Hymn 320. IRISH.—C.M. *(Second Tune.)*
Hymns and Sacred Poems (Dublin, 1749).

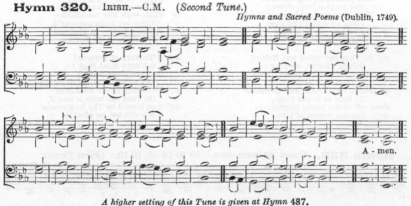

A - men.

A higher setting of this Tune is given at Hymn 487.

" My Flesh is meat indeed, and My Blood is drink indeed."

p O GOD, unseen yet ever near,
　　Thy Presence may we feel ;
And, thus inspired with holy fear,
　　Before Thine Altar kneel.

mf Here may Thy faithful people know
　　The blessings of Thy love,
The streams that through the desert flow,
　　The manna from above.

We come, obedient to Thy Word,
　　To feast on heavenly Food ;
Our meat the Body of the LORD,
　　Our drink His precious Blood.

p　Thus may we all Thy Word obey,
cr　For we, O GOD, are Thine ;
f　And go rejoicing on our way,
　　Renew'd with strength Divine.

E. OSLER, 1836.

Holy Communion.

Hymn 321.   Dies Dominica.—7 6 7 6. 7 6 7 6.   Rev. J. B. Dykes.

A-men.

" I love them that love Me : and those that seek Me early shall find Me."

mf   WE pray Thee, heavenly Father,
    To hear us in Thy love,
  And pour upon Thy children
    The unction from above ;
    That so in love abiding,
    From all defilement free,
cr   We may in pureness offer
    Our Eucharist to Thee.

mf   Be Thou our Guide and Helper,
    O Jesu Christ, we pray ;
  So may we well approach Thee,
    If Thou wilt be the Way :
cr   Thou, very Truth, hast promised
    To help us in our strife,
dim Food of the weary pilgrim,
cr   Eternal Source of Life.

mf   And Thou, Creator Spirit,
    Look on us, we are Thine ;
  Renew in us Thy graces,
    Upon our darkness shine ;
cr   That, with Thy benediction
    Upon our souls outpour'd,
  We may receive in gladness
p   The Body of the Lord.

mf   O Trinity of Persons !
    O Unity most High !
  On Thee alone relying
    Thy servants would draw nigh :
p   Unworthy in our weakness,
cr   On Thee our hope is stay'd,
mf   And bless'd by Thy forgiveness
    We will not be afraid.

                        V. S. S. Coles.

Hymn 322.   Unde et memores.—10 10 10 10. 10 10.   (*First Tune.*)

                                          W. H. Monk.

Holy Communion.

A-men.

Hymn 322. Song 24.—10 10 10 10. 10 10. *(Second Tune.)* O. Gibbons, 1623.

A-men.

"In every place incense shall be offered unto My Name, and a pure offering."

 p AND now, O FATHER, mindful of the love
    That bought us, once for all, on Calvary's Tree,
   And having with us Him that pleads above,
 cr We here present, we here spread forth to Thee
 mf That only Offering perfect in Thine eyes,
    The one true, pure, immortal Sacrifice.

 p Look, FATHER, look on His Anointed Face,
    And only look on us as found in Him ;
   Look not on our misusings of Thy grace,
    Our prayer so languid, and our faith so dim ;
 cr For lo ! between our sins and their reward
    We set the Passion of Thy SON our LORD.

 p And then for those, our dearest and our best,
    By this prevailing Presence we appeal ;
 cr O fold them closer to Thy mercy's breast,
    O do Thine utmost for their souls' true weal :
   From tainting mischief keep them white and clear,
    And crown Thy gifts with strength to persevere.

 p And so we come ; O draw us to Thy Feet,
    Most patient Saviour, Who canst love us still ;
 cr And by this Food, so awful and so sweet,
    Deliver us from every touch of ill :
 f In Thine own service make us glad and free,
    And grant us never more to part with Thee.

           W. BRIGHT.

Holy Communion.

Hymn 323. LEICESTER.—C.M.

W. HURST.

A-men.

"The centurion answered and said, Lord, I am not worthy that Thou shouldest come under my roof; but speak the word only, and my servant shall be healed."

p I AM not worthy, Holy LORD,
  That Thou shouldst come to me ;
cr Speak but the Word ; one gracious Word
  Can set the sinner free.

p I am not worthy ; cold and bare
  The lodging of my soul ;
  How canst Thou deign to enter there ?
cr LORD, speak, and make me whole.

p I am not worthy ; (*cr*) yet, my GOD,
  How can I say Thee nay ;
  Thee, Who didst give Thy Flesh and Blood
  My ransom-price to pay ?

mf O come ! in this sweet morning hour
  Feed me with Food Divine ;
  And fill with all Thy love and power
p This worthless heart of mine.

Sir H. W. BAKER.

ALTERNATIVE TUNE, HYMN 705.

Hymn 324. EUCHARISTICUS.—6 5 6 5.

Sir J. STAINER.

rall.

A-men.

"He that eateth Me, even he shall live by Me."

p JESU, gentlest Saviour,
  Thou art in us now,
cr Fill us with Thy Goodness,
  Till our hearts o'erflow.

p Multiply our graces,
  Chiefly love and fear,
cr And, dear LORD, the chiefest,
  Grace to persevere.

mf Oh, how can we thank Thee
  For a Gift like this,
  Gift that truly maketh
  Heav'n's eternal bliss !

p Ah ! when wilt Thou always
  Make our hearts Thy home ?
cr We must wait for Heaven,
  Then the day will come.

F. W. FABER.

ALTERNATIVE TUNE, HYMN 773.

The following Hymns are suitable :

Holy Baptism.

Hymn 325. ST. FRANCIS.—10 6 10 6. 8 8 4. Sir A. SULLIVAN.

A-men.

"Ask, and it shall be given you; seek, and ye shall find; knock, and it shall be opened unto you."

mf O FATHER, Thou Who hast created all
In wisest love, we pray,
Look on this babe, who at Thy grácious call
Is entering on life's way;

p Bend o'er *him* in Thy tenderness,
Thine image on *his* soul impress;
cr O FATHER, hear!

p O SON of GOD, Who diedst for ús, behold,
We bring our child to Thee;
Thou tender Shepherd, take *him* tó Thy fold,
Thine own for aye to be;
Defend *him* through this earthly strife,
cr And lead *him* on the path of life,
f O SON of GOD!

mf O HOLY GHOST, Who broodedst ó'er the wave,
Descend upon this child;
Give *him* undying life, *his* spirit lave
With waters undefiled;

p Grant *him*, while yet a babe, to be
cr A child of GOD, a home for Thee,
O HOLY GHOST!

mf O TRIUNE GOD, what Thou commánd'st is done;
We speak, but Thine the might;
This child hath scarce yet seen óur éarthly sun,
Yet pour on *him* Thy light,
cr In faith and hope, in joy and love,
f Thou Sun of all below, above,
O TRIUNE GOD!

CATHERINE WINKWORTH: from
the German of A. Knapp.

Hymn 326. KENILWORTH.—8 8 6. 8 8 6. E. HULTON.

A-men.

"Baptizing them in the Name of the Father, and of the Son, and of the Holy Ghost."

mf WITHIN the Church's sacred fold,
By holy Sacrament enroll'd,
Another lamb we lay:
p An heir before of sin and shame,
cr Now in the Holy TRIUNE Name
His guilt is wash'd away.

mf O loving FATHER, Thee we pray
Look on this babe new-born to-day,
Thine own adopted child;
An Angel guard do Thou bestow
To lead *him* in Thy paths below,
And guide *him* through the wild.

O GOD the SON, Thou heavenly Vine,
Protect this tender branch of Thine
Through all that may betide;

For ever nourish'd may *he* be
With sap Divine that flows from Thee,
In Thee for aye abide.

Blest SPIRIT, Whose indwelling grace
Has given this little one a place
Among the heirs of life;
O breathe Thy sevenfold gifts within,
And keep Thy temple pure from sin
In midst of worldly strife.

So, Holy TRINITY, by Thee
Divinely train'd this babe may be
In faith and hope and love;
cr So may *he* gain, earth's waves o'erpast,
His bright inheritance at last
With all Thy Saints above.

KATHERINE D. CORNISH.

ALTERNATIVE TUNE, HYMN 262.

(267)

Holy Baptism.

Hymn 327. WINCHESTER NEW.—L.M. *Musikalisch Handbuch (Hamburg, 1690).*

A-men.

A higher setting of this Tune is given at Hymn 50.

"The washing of regeneration."

mf 'TIS done! that new and heavenly birth,
Which re-creates the sons of earth,
Has cleansed from guilt of Adam's sin
A soul which JESUS (*p*) died to win.

mf 'Tis done! the Cross upon the brow
Is mark'd for weal or sorrow now,
cr To shine with heavenly lustre bright,
pp Or burn in everlasting night.

mf O ye who came that babe to lay
Within a Saviour's Arms to-day,
Watch well and guard with careful eye
The heir of immortality.

Teach *him* to know a FATHER'S love,
And seek for happiness above,
To CHRIST *his* heart and treasure give,
And in the SPIRIT ever live;

cr That so before the judgment-seat
In joy and triumph ye may meet;
f The battle fought, the struggle o'er,
The kingdom yours for evermore.

Praise GOD, from Whom all blessings flow,
Praise Him, all creatures here below,
Praise Him above, Angelic host,
Praise FATHER, SON, and HOLY GHOST.

Sir H. W. BAKER.

Hymn 328. ST. STEPHEN.—C.M. Rev. W. JONES, 1726–1800.

A-men.

" Be not thou therefore ashamed of the testimony of our Lord."

mf IN token that thou shalt not fear
CHRIST Crucified to own,
We print the Cross upon thee here,
And stamp thee His alone.

In token that thou shalt not blush
To glory in His Name,
We blazon here upon thy front
His glory (*dim*) and His shame.

mf In token that thou shalt not flinch
CHRIST'S quarrel to maintain,

But 'neath His banner manfully
Firm at thy post remain;

In token that thou too shalt tread
The path He travell'd by,
Endure the cross, despise the shame,
cr And sit thee down on high;

mf Thus outwardly and visibly
We seal thee for His own;
And may the brow that wears His Cross
cr Hereafter share His Crown.

H. ALFORD.

*This Hymn may also be sung when a child who has been privately baptized is received
into the congregation; and at the baptism of an adult.*

The following Hymns are suitable for Holy Baptism:

561 With CHRIST we share a mystic grave.   **563** FATHER, SON, and HOLY GHOST.
562 O FATHER, bless the children.   **725** Grant to this child the inward grace.

(268)

For the Young.

Hymn 329. IRBY.—8 7 8 7.7.7.   H. J. GAUNTLETT.

A - men.

"The Child Jesus."

mf ONCE in royal David's city
Stood a lowly cattle shed,
p Where a Mother laid her Baby
In a manger for His bed;
mf Mary was that Mother mild,
p JESUS CHRIST her little Child.

He came down to earth from Heaven
f Who is GOD and LORD of all,
p And His shelter was a stable,
And His cradle was a stall;
With the poor, and mean, and lowly,
Lived on earth our Saviour Holy.

mf And, through all His wondrous Childhood,
He would honour and obey,
Love, and watch the lowly Maiden,
In whose gentle arms He lay;
Christian children all must be
Mild, obedient, good as He.

For He is our childhood's pattern,
Day by day like us He grew;
p He was little, weak, and helpless,
Tears and smiles like us He knew;
And He feeleth for our sadness,
cr And He shareth in our gladness.

f And our eyes at last shall see Him,
Through His own redeeming love,
p For that Child so dear and gentle
f Is our LORD in Heav'n above;
And He leads His children on
To the place where He is gone.

mf Not in that poor lowly stable,
With the oxen standing by,
We shall see Him; (*f*) but in Heaven,
Set at GOD's right hand on high;
When like stars His children crown'd
All in white shall wait around.

MRS. ALEXANDER.

(269)

For the Young.

Hymn 330. I LOVE TO HEAR THE STORY.—7 6 7 6. 7 6 7 6.   H. J. GAUNTLETT.

I love to hear the sto-ry Which An-gel voi-ces tell,

How once the King of glo-ry Came down on earth to dwell. A-men. FINE.

I am both weak and sin-ful, But this I sure-ly know,

The LORD came down to save me, Be-cause He loved me so.

" The love of Christ."

mf I LOVE to hear the story
    Which Angel voices tell,
p How once the King of glory
    Came down on earth to dwell.
  I am both weak and sinful,
c) But this I surely know,
  The LORD came down to save me,
    Because He loved me so.
mf   I love to hear the story
    Which Angel voices tell,
  How once the King of glory
    Came down on earth to dwell.

  I'm glad my Blessèd SAVIOUR
    Was once a Child like me,
  To show how pure and holy
    His little ones might be ;
  And if I try to follow
    His footsteps here below,

He never will forget me,
  Because He loves me so.
  I love to hear the story
    Which Angel voices tell,
  How once the King of glory
    Came down on earth to dwell.

f To sing His love and mercy
    My sweetest songs I'll raise ;
mf And though I cannot see Him
    I know He hears my praise ;
  For He has kindly promised
    That even I may go
cr To sing among His Angels,
    Because He loves me so.
f I love to hear the story
    Which Angel voices tell,
p How once the King of glory
    Came down on earth to dwell.

MRS. MILLER.

For the Young.

Hymn 331.   ALSTONE.—L.M.

C. E. WILLING.

A - men.

"Even a child is known by his doings."

mf   WE are but little children weak,
        Nor born in any high estate ;
      What can we do for JESUS' sake,
cr   Who is so High and Good and Great ?

mf   We know the Holy Innocents
      Laid down for Him their infant life,
      And Martyrs brave, and patient Saints
      Have stood for Him in fire and strife.

      We wear the cross they wore of old,
      Our lips have learn'd like vows to make ;
      We need not die ; we cannot fight ;
      What may we do for JESUS' sake ?

      Oh, day by day, each Christian child
      Has much to do, without, within ;
      A death to die for JESUS' sake,
      A weary war to wage with sin.

p   When deep within our swelling hearts
      The thoughts of pride and anger rise,
      When bitter words are on our tongues,
      And tears of passion in our eyes ;

cr   Then we may stay the angry blow,
      Then we may check the hasty word,
p   Give gentle answers back again,
f   And fight a battle for our LORD.

mf   With smiles of peace, and looks of love,
      Light in our dwellings we may make,
      Bid kind good humour brighten there,
p   And still do all for JESUS' sake.

mf   There's not a child so small and weak
      But has his little cross to take,
      His little work of love and praise
p   That he may do for JESUS' sake.

MRS. ALEXANDER.

ALTERNATIVE TUNE, HYMN 449 (SECOND TUNE).

(271)

For the Young.

Hymn 332. HORSLEY.—C.M.

W. HORSLEY.

A-men.

" While we were yet sinners, Christ died for us."

mf THERE is a green hill far away,
     Without a city wall,
p Where the dear LORD was crucified,
     Who died to save us all.

We may not know, we cannot tell
What pains He had to bear,
But we believe it was for us
He hung and suffer'd there.

mf He died that we might be forgiven,
     He died to make us good,

cr That we might go at last to Heav'n,
p Saved by His precious Blood.

mf There was no other good enough
     To pay the price of sin,
He only could unlock the gate
Of Heav'n, and let us in.

Oh, dearly, dearly has He loved,
And we must love Him too,
And trust in His redeeming Blood,
And try His works to do.

MRS. ALEXANDER.

Hymn 333. PASTOR BONUS.—6 5 6 5. 6 5 6 5.

Sir J. STAINER.

A-men.

" He took them up in His Arms."

f CHRIST, Who once amongst us
    As a Child did dwell,
Is the children's SAVIOUR,
And He loves us well ;
mf If we keep our promise
     Made Him at the Font,
f He will be our Shepherd,
    And we shall not want.

mf There it was they laid us
     In those tender Arms,
Where the lambs are carried
Safe from all alarms ;
If we trust His promise,
He will let us rest
In His Arms for ever,
Leaning on His Breast.

Though we may not see Him
For a little while,
We shall know He holds us,
Often feel His smile ;

p Death will be to slumber
    In that sweet embrace,
f And we shall awaken
    To behold His Face.

mf He will be our Shepherd
     After as before,
By still heavenly waters
Lead us evermore,
Make us lie in pastures
Beautiful and green,
Where none thirst or hunger,
And no tears are seen.

p JESUS, our good Shepherd,
    Laying down Thy life,
Lest Thy sheep should perish
In the cruel strife,
cr Help us to remember
     All Thy love and care,
f Trust in Thee, and love Thee
    Always, everywhere.

ALTERNATIVE TUNE, HYMN 726.

W. ST. HILL BOURNE.

(272)

For the Young.

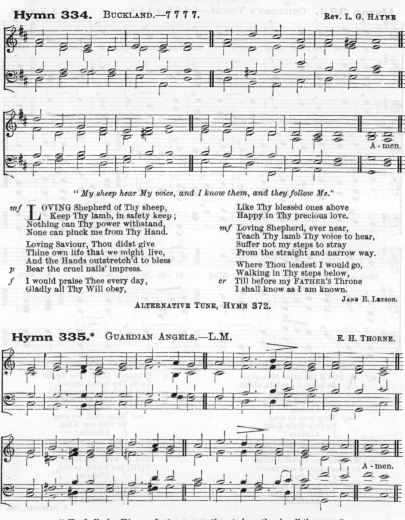

Hymn 334. BUCKLAND.—7 7 7 7.   Rev. L. G. HAYNE

A-men.

" My sheep hear My voice, and I know them, and they follow Me."

mf LOVING Shepherd of Thy sheep,
  Keep Thy lamb, in safety keep ;
Nothing can Thy power withstand,
None can pluck me from Thy Hand.

Loving Saviour, Thou didst give
Thine own life that we might live,
And the Hands outstretch'd to bless
p Bear the cruel nails' impress.

f I would praise Thee every day,
Gladly all Thy Will obey,

Like Thy blessèd ones above
Happy in Thy precious love.

mf Loving Shepherd, ever near,
Teach Thy lamb Thy voice to hear,
Suffer not my steps to stray
From the straight and narrow way.

Where Thou leadest I would go,
Walking in Thy steps below,
cr Till before my FATHER'S Throne
I shall know as I am known.

          JANE E. LEESON.

ALTERNATIVE TUNE, HYMN 372.

Hymn 335.* GUARDIAN ANGELS.—L.M.   E. H. THORNE.

A-men.

" He shall give His angels charge over thee, to keep thee in all thy ways."

mf AROUND the Throne of GOD a band
  Of glorious Angels ever stand ; [hold,
cr Bright things they see, sweet harps they
f And on their heads are crowns of gold.

mf Some wait around Him, ready still
To sing His praise and do His Will ;
And some, when He commands them, go
To guard His servants here below.

LORD, give Thy Angels every day
Command to guide us on our way,
And bid them every evening keep
p Their watch around us while we sleep.

mf So shall no wicked thing draw near,
To do us harm or cause us fear ;
cr And we shall dwell, when life is past,
f With Angels round Thy Throne at last.

          J. M. NEALE.

* This Tune may be sung in Two Parts (Treble and Alto), if preferred ; or in the absence
of the other voices."

(273)

For the Young.

Hymn 336. CHILDREN'S VOICES.—6 6 6 6. 4 4 4 4.   E. J. HOPKINS.

A - bove the clear blue sky, ... In hea - ven's bright a - bode, .. The

An - gel host on high Sing prais - es to .. their GOD: Al - le - lu - ia!

They love to sing To GOD their King Al - le - lu - - ia! .. A - men.

" Praise our God, all ye His servants, and ye that fear Him, both small and great."

mf ABOVE the clear blue sky,
    In heaven's bright abode,
The Angel host on high
Sing praises to their GOD :
    f Alleluia !
   mf They love to sing
     To GOD their King
    f Alleluia !

mf But GOD from infant tongues
    On earth receiveth praise ;
cr We then our cheerful songs
    In sweet accord will raise :
    f Alleluia !
   mf We too will sing
     To GOD our King
    f Alleluia !

p O Blessèd LORD, Thy Truth
    To us Thy babes impart,
cr And teach us in our youth
    To know Thee as Thou art.
    f Alleluia !
   mf Then shall we sing
     To GOD our King
    f Alleluia !

mf O may Thy holy Word
    Spread all the world around ;
And all with one accord
Uplift the joyful sound,
    f Alleluia !
   mf All then shall sing
     To GOD their King
    f Alleluia !

J. CHANDLER, 1841.

Hymn 337. IN MEMORIAM.—8 6 7 6. 7 6 7 6.   Sir J. STAINER.

There's a Friend for lit - tle chil - dren A - bove the bright blue

For the Young.

sky, A Friend Who ne-ver chan-ges, Whose love will ne-ver

die; Our earth-ly friends may fail us, And change with chang-ing

years, This Friend is al-ways wor-thy Of that dear Name He bears. A-men.

" Jesus . . . took a child, and set him by Him."

mf THERE'S a Friend for little children
Above the bright blue sky,
A Friend Who never changes,
Whose love will never die ;
p Our earthly friends may fail us,
And change with changing years,
f This Friend is always worthy
Of that dear Name He bears.

mf There's a rest for little children
Above the bright blue sky,
Who love the Blessèd Saviour,
And to the FATHER cry ;
p A rest from every turmoil,
From sin and sorrow free,
Where every little pilgrim
Shall rest eternally.

mf There's a home for little children
Above the bright blue sky,
f Where JESUS reigns in glory,
A home of peace and joy ;
mf No home on earth is like it,
Nor can with it compare ;
f For every one is happy,
Nor could be happier, there.

There's a crown for little children
Above the bright blue sky,
mf And all who look for JESUS
Shall wear it by and by ;
f A crown of brightest glory,
Which He will then bestow
mf On those who found His favour
And loved His Name below.

f There's a song for little children
Above the bright blue sky,
A song that will not weary,
Though sung continually ;
mf A song which even Angels
Can never, never sing ;
They know not CHRIST as SAVIOUR,
But worship Him as King.

f There's a robe for little children
Above the bright blue sky ;
And a harp of sweetest music,
And palms of victory.
All, all above is treasured,
And found in CHRIST alone ;
p LORD, grant Thy little children
To know Thee as their own.

A. MIDLANE.

(275)

For the Young.

Hymn 338. IONA.—8 7 8 7 . 8 7 8 7. *(First Tune.)* Sir J. STAINER.

A higher setting of this Tune is given at Hymn **359.**

Hymn 338. LUGANO.—8 7 8 7 . 8 7 8 7. *(Second Tune.)*
Catholic Hymn Tunes, 1849.

For the Young.

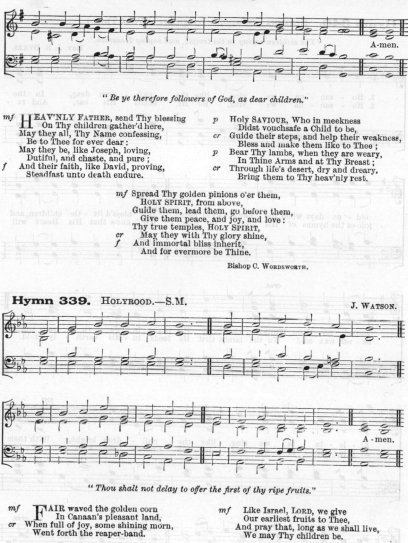

A-men.

" Be ye therefore followers of God, as dear children."

mf HEAV'NLY FATHER, send Thy blessing
    On Thy children gather'd here,
May they all, Thy Name confessing,
    Be to Thee for ever dear:
May they be, like Joseph, loving,
    Dutiful, and chaste, and pure ;
f And their faith, like David, proving,
    Steadfast unto death endure.

p Holy SAVIOUR, Who in meekness
    Didst vouchsafe a Child to be,
cr Guide their steps, and help their weakness,
    Bless and make them like to Thee ;
p Bear Thy lambs, when they are weary,
    In Thine Arms and at Thy Breast ;
cr Through life's desert, dry and dreary.
    Bring them to Thy heav'nly rest.

mf Spread Thy golden pinions o'er them,
    HOLY SPIRIT, from above,
Guide them, lead them, go before them,
    Give them peace, and joy, and love :
    Thy true temples, HOLY SPIRIT,
cr May they with Thy glory shine,
f And immortal bliss inherit,
    And for evermore be Thine.

Bishop C. WORDSWORTH.

Hymn 339. HOLYROOD.—S.M.

J. WATSON.

A-men.

" Thou shalt not delay to offer the first of thy ripe fruits."

mf FAIR waved the golden corn
    In Canaan's pleasant land,
cr When full of joy, some shining morn,
    Went forth the reaper-band.

f To GOD so good and great
    Their cheerful thanks they pour ;
Then carry to His temple-gate
    The choicest of their store.

mf Like Israel, LORD, we give
    Our earliest fruits to Thee,
And pray that, long as we shall live,
    We may Thy children be.

Thine is our youthful prime,
    And life and all its powers ;
Be with us in our morning time,
p And bless our evening hours.

cr In wisdom let us grow,
    As years and strength are given,
That we may serve Thy Church below,
f And join Thy Saints in Heav'n.

J. HAMPDEN GURNEY.

Hymn 340. HOSANNA WE SING.—Irregular. *(First Tune.)*

"The children crying in the temple, and saying Hosanna."

Rev. J. B. DYKES.

1. Ho - san - na we sing, like the chil - dren dear, In the old - en days when the LORD lived here; He bless'd lit - tle children, and smiled on them, While they chant - ed His praise in Je - ru - sa - lem.

2. Ho - san - na we sing, for He bends His ear, And re - joic-es the hymns of His own to hear; We know that His Heart will ne - ver wax cold To the lambs that He feeds in His earth - ly fold.

Al - le - lu - ia we sing, like the chil - dren bright, With their harps of gold and their rai - ment white, As they fol - low their Shepherd with

Al - le - lu - ia we sing, in the Church we love, Al - le - lu - ia re-sounds in the Church a - bove; To Thy lit - tle ones, LORD, may such

This may be sung as an accompanied Melody, or in Harmony.

For the Young.

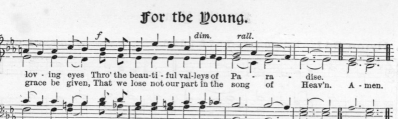

lov - ing eyes Thro' the beau-ti - ful val-leys of Pa - ra - dise.
grace be given, That we lose not our part in the song of Heav'n. A - men.

G. S. HODGES.

Hymn 340. AIRLIE.—10 10 10 10. *(Second Tune.)*

To be sung in Unison.

S. H. NICHOLSON.

A - men.

"The children crying in the temple, and saying Hosanna."

    f   HOSANNA we sing, like the children dear,
        In the olden days when the LORD lived here ;
    p He bless'd little children, and smiled on them,
    cr While they chanted His praise in Jerusalem.

    f Alleluia we sing, like the children bright,
        With their harps of gold and their raiment white,
        As they follow their Shepherd with loving eyes
        Through the beautiful valleys of Paradise.

        Hosanna we sing, for He bends His ear,
        And rejoices the hymns of His own to hear ;
    p We know that His Heart will never wax cold
    cr To the lambs that He feeds in His earthly fold.

    f Alleluia we sing in the Church we love,
        Alleluia resounds in the Church above ;
        To Thy little ones, LORD, may such grace be given,
        That we lose not our part in the song of Heav'n.

G. S. HODGES.

For the Young.

Hymn 341. ELLACOMBE.—7 6 7 6. 7 6 7 6.

Würtemburg Gesangbuch, 1784.

A-men.

" My song shall be alway of the loving-kindness of the Lord."

f COME, sing with holy gladness,
   High Alleluias sing,
Uplift your loud Hosannas
   To JESUS, LORD and King ;
Sing, boys, in joyful chorus
   Your hymn of praise to-day,
p And sing, ye gentle maidens,
cr   Your sweet responsive lay.

mf 'Tis good for boys and maidens
   Sweet hymns to CHRIST to sing,
'Tis meet that children's voices
   Should praise the children's King ;
For JESUS is salvation,
   And glory, grace, and rest ;
To babe, and boy, and maiden
   The one Redeemer Blest.

O boys, be strong in JESUS,
   To toil for Him is gain,
And JESUS wrought with Joseph
   With chisel, saw, and plane ;
O maidens, live for JESUS,
   Who was a maiden's Son ;
Be patient, pure, and gentle,
   And perfect grace begun.

f Soon in the golden city
   The boys and girls shall play,
And through the dazzling mansions
   Rejoice in endless day ;
p O CHRIST, prepare Thy children
cr   With that triumphant throng
f To pass the burnish'd portals,
   And sing th' eternal song.

J. J. DANIELL.

Hymn 342. ST. BEDE.—8 7. 8 7. 8 7.

P. ARMES.

(280)

For the Young.

A-men.

"He shall feed His flock like a shepherd; He shall gather the lambs with His arm, and carry them in His bosom."

mf **G**RACIOUS SAVIOUR, gentle Shepherd,
　　Little ones are dear to Thee;
　Gather'd with Thine Arms, and carried
　　In Thy Bosom may we be;
p　Sweetly, fondly, safely tended,
cr　From all want and danger free.

mf　Tender Shepherd, never leave us
　　From Thy fold to go astray;
　By Thy look of love directed
　　May we walk the narrow way;
　Thus direct us, and protect us,
　　Lest we fall an easy prey.

　Cleanse our hearts from sinful folly
　　In the stream Thy love supplied,
p　Mingled stream of Blood and Water,

　　Flowing from Thy wounded Side;
cr　And to heavenly pastures lead us,
　　Where Thine own still waters glide.

mf　Let Thy holy Word instruct us;
　　Guide us daily by its light;
　Let Thy love and grace constrain us
　　To approve whate'er is right,
cr　Strengthen'd with Thy heavenly might.

mf　Taught to lisp the holy praises
　　Which on earth Thy children sing,
　Both with lips and hearts unfeignèd
　　May we our thank-offerings bring;
f　Then with all the Saints in glory
　　Join to praise our LORD and King.

　　　　　　JANE E. LEESON and J. WITTEMORE.

ALTERNATIVE TUNE, HYMN 385 (SECOND TUNE).

Hymn 343. INNOCENTS.—7 7 7 7.　　　　*The Parish Choir*, 1850.

A-men.

A lower setting of this Tune is given at Hymn 33, and a higher setting at Hymn 175.

"Out of the mouth of babes and sucklings Thou hast perfected praise."

f　**G**OD Eternal, Mighty King,
　　Unto Thee our praise we bring;
　All the earth doth worship Thee,
　　We amid the throng would be.

pp　Holy, Holy, Holy! cry
p　Angels round Thy Throne on high;
cr　LORD of all the heavenly powers,
　　Be the same loud anthem ours.

f　Glorified Apostles raise
　　Night and day continual praise;
mf　Hast not Thou a mission too
　　For Thy children here to do?

　With the Prophets' goodly line
　We in mystic bond combine;
　For Thou hast to babes reveal'd
　Things that to the wise were seal'd.

　Martyrs, in a noble host,
　Of the Cross are heard to boast;
p　O that we our cross may bear,
f　And a crown of glory wear.

ff　GOD Eternal, Mighty King,
　Unto Thee our praise we bring;
　To the FATHER, and the SON,
　And the SPIRIT, THREE in ONE.

　　　　　　　　　J. E. MILLARD.

For the Young.

Hymn 344. St. Helena.—S.M.

B. Milgrove (Mount Ephraim), 1769.

A-men.

A higher setting of this Tune is given at Hymn 69.

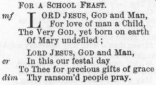

"*Thy Holy Child Jesus.*"

For a School Feast.

mf LORD JESUS, GOD and Man,
    For love of man a Child,
The Very GOD, yet born on earth
    Of Mary undefiled ;

    LORD JESUS, GOD and Man,
cr In this our festal day
To Thee for precious gifts of grace
dim Thy ransom'd people pray.

mf We pray for childlike hearts,
    For gentle holy love,
For strength to do Thy Will below
    As Angels do above.

    We pray for simple faith,
    For hope that never faints,

cr For true communion evermore
    With all Thy blessèd Saints.

mf On friends around us here
    O let Thy blessing fall ;
cr We pray for grace to love them well,
    But Thee beyond them all.

f   O joy to live for Thee !
    O joy in Thee to die !
ff O very joy of joys to see
    Thy Face eternally !

p   LORD JESUS, GOD and Man,
cr We praise Thee and adore,
Who art with GOD the FATHER ONE
    And SPIRIT evermore.

Sir H. W. Baker.

Hymn 345. Bickley.—8 8 8 8.8 8. (*First Tune.*)

W. H. Monk.

A-men.

Hymn 345. Eaton.—8 8 8 8.8 8. (*Second Tune.*)

Z. Wyvill, 1802.

For the Young.

A-men.

" In Him was Life, and the Life was the Light of men."

mf O LIGHT, Whose beams illumine all
From twilight dawn to perfect day,
Shine Thou before the shadows fall
dim That lead our wand'ring feet astray:
mf At morn and eve Thy radiance pour,
cr That youth may love, and age adore.

mf O Way, through Whom our souls draw near
To you eternal home of peace,
f Where perfect love shall cast out fear,
And earth's vain toil and wand'ring cease ;
mf In strength or weakness may we see
cr Our heav'nward path, O LORD, through Thee.

mf O Truth, before Whose shrine we bow,
Thou priceless pearl for all who seek,
To Thee our earliest strength we vow,

Thy love will bless the pure and meek ;
p When dreams or mists beguile our sight,
cr Turn Thou our darkness into light.
mf O Life, the well that ever flows
To slake the thirst of those that faint,
f Thy power to bless what Seraph knows?
Thy joy supreme what words can paint?
y In earth's last hour of fleeting breath
cr Be Thou our Conqueror over death.
f O Light, O Way, O Truth, O Life,
O JESU, born mankind to save,
p Give Thou Thy peace in deadliest strife,
Shed Thou Thy calm on stormiest wave ;
f Be Thou our Hope, our Joy, our Dread,
LORD of the living (*dim*) and the dead.

E. H. PLUMPTRE.

Hymn 346. EUDOXIA.—6 5 6 5.   Rev. S. BARING-GOULD.

A-men.

A lower setting of this Tune is given at Hymn 750.

' *When thou liest down thou shalt not be afraid ; yea, thou shalt lie down and thy sleep shall be sweet.*'

EVENING.

p NOW the day is over,
Night is drawing nigh,
Shadows of the evening
Steal across the sky.

Now the darkness gathers,
Stars begin to peep,
Birds, and beasts, and flowers
Soon will be asleep.

mf JESU, give the weary
Calm and sweet repose :
p With Thy tenderest blessing
May mine eyelids close.

cr Grant to little children
Visions bright of Thee ;
Guard the sailors tossing
On the deep blue sea.

p Comfort every sufferer
Watching late in pain ;
Those who plan some evil
cr From their sin restrain.

p Through the long night watches
May Thine Angels spread
Their white wings above me,
cr Watching round my bed.

mf When the morning wakens,
Then may I arise
Pure, and fresh, and sinless
In Thy Holy Eyes.

f Glory to the FATHER,
Glory to the SON,
And to Thee, Blest SPIRIT,
Whilst all ages run.

S. BARING-GOULD.

Confirmation.

Hymn 347. MELCOMBE.—L.M. (*First Tune.*) S. WEBBE, 1782.

A - men.

Lower settings of this Tune are given at Hymns 4 and 363.

Hymn 347. VENI CREATOR.—L.M. (*Second Tune.*) Proper Sarum Melody.

A - men.

An Alternative Version of this Tune is given at Hymn 157.

"The Comforter Which is the Holy Ghost."

mf COME, HOLY GHOST, Creator Blest,
Vouchsafe within our souls to rest;
Come with Thy grace and heavenly aid,
And fill the hearts which Thou hast made.

p To Thee, the Comforter, we cry,
To Thee, the Gift of GOD most High,
The Fount of life, the Fire of love,
The soul's Anointing from above.

mf O Finger of the Hand Divine,
The sevenfold gifts of grace are Thine;
True promise of the FATHER Thou,
Who dost the tongue with power endow.

cr Thy light to every sense impart,
And shed Thy love in every heart;
f Thine own unfailing might supply
dim To strengthen our infirmity.

mf Drive far away our ghostly foe,
And Thine abiding peace bestow;
If Thou be our preventing Guide,
No evil can our steps betide.

Grant us through Thee, O HOLY ONE,
To know the FATHER and the SON;
And this be our unchanging creed,
That Thou dost from Them Both proceed.

f Praise we the FATHER, and the SON,
And HOLY SPIRIT with Them ONE;
p And may the SON on us bestow
cr The gifts that from the SPIRIT flow.

E. CASWALL and Compilers: from
the Latin of Rabanus Maurus.

ALTERNATIVE TUNE, HYMN 698.

Confirmation.

W. H. Monk.

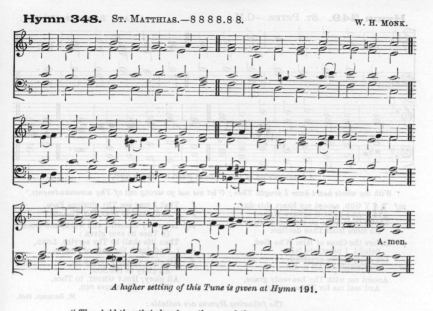

A-men.

A higher setting of this Tune is given at Hymn 191.

" *Then laid they their hands on them, and they received the Holy Ghost.*"

mf BEHOLD us, LORD, before Thee met
    Whom each bright Angel serves and fears,
  Who on Thy Throne rememberest yet
p   Thy spotless Boyhood's quiet years ;
  Whose Feet the hills of Nazareth trod,
cr Who art true Man and perfect GOD.

mf To Thee we look, in Thee confide,
    Our help is in Thine own dear Name ;
cr For who on JESUS e'er relied,
    And found not JESUS still the same ?
mf Thus far Thy love our souls hath brought ;
cr O stablish well what Thou hast wrought.

mf From Thee was our baptismal grace,
    The holy seed by Thee was sown ;
  And now before our FATHER's Face
    We make the three great vows our own,
  And ask, in Thine appointed way,
  Confirm us in Thy grace to-day.

  We need Thee more than tongue can speak,
    'Mid foes that well might cast us down ;
cr But thousands, (*dim*) once as young and weak,
cr   Have fought the fight, and won the crown ;
p We ask the help that (*cr*) bore them through ;
  We trust the Faithful and the True.

mf So bless us with the gift complete
    By hands of Thy chief Pastors given,
p That awful Presence kind and sweet
    Which comes in sevenfold might from Heav'n ;
pp Eternal CHRIST, to Thee we bow :
cr Give us Thy SPIRIT here and now.

W. Bright.

Confirmation.

Hymn 349. St. Peter.—C.M.   A. R. Reinagle, 1799-1877.

A - men.

A lower setting of this Tune is given at Hymn 596.

" With my whole heart have I sought Thee ; O let me not go wrong out of Thy commandments."

mf MY GOD, accept my heart this day,
  And make it always Thine,
That I from Thee no more may stray,
  No more from Thee decline.

p Before the Cross of Him Who died,
  Behold, I prostrate fall ;
Let every sin be crucified,
cr And CHRIST be All in all.

Anoint me with Thy heavenly grace,
  And seal me for Thine own ;

f That I may see Thy glorious Face,
p And worship near Thy Throne.

mf Let every thought, and work, and word
  To Thee be ever given ;
Then life shall be Thy service, LORD,
cr And death the gate of Heav'n.

f All glory to the FATHER be,
  All glory to the SON,
All glory, HOLY GHOST, to Thee,
  While endless ages run.

M. Bridges, 1848.

The following Hymns are suitable :

156 Come, Thou HOLY SPIRIT, come.
157 Come, HOLY GHOST, our souls inspire.
207 Our Blest Redeemer, ere He breathed.
733 Once pledged by the Cross.

270 Soldiers of CHRIST, arise.
271 O JESUS, I have promised.
280 Thine for ever ! GOD of love.

Holy Matrimony.

Hymn 350. St. Alphege.—7 6 7 6. *(First Tune.)*   H. J. Gauntlett.

A - men.

A lower setting of this Tune is given at Hymn 225.

Hymn 350. Matrimony.—7 6 7 6. *(Second Tune.)*   Sir J. Stainer.

Holy Matrimony.

" A threefold cord is not quickly broken."

mf THE voice that breathed o'er Eden,
   That earliest wedding day,
The primal marriage blessing,
   It hath not pass'd away :

Still in the pure espousal
   Of Christian man and maid
The Holy THREE are with us,
   The threefold grace is said,

For dower of blessèd children,
   For love and faith's sweet sake,
For high mysterious union
   Which nought on earth may break.

p Be present, awful FATHER,
cr   To give away this bride,
As Eve Thou gav'st to Adam
   Out of his own pierced side ;

p Be present, SON of Mary,
cr   To join their loving hands,
As Thou didst bind two natures
   In Thine Eternal bands ;

p Be present, Holiest SPIRIT,
cr   To bless them as they kneel,
As Thou for CHRIST, the Bridegroom,
   The heavenly spouse dost seal.

mf O spread Thy pure wing o'er them,
   Let no ill power find place,
When onward to Thine Altar
   The hallow'd path they trace,

f To cast their crowns before Thee
   In perfect sacrifice,
Till to the home of gladness
   With CHRIST'S own Bride they rise.

                              J. KEBLE

Hymn 351. ST. GEORGE.—S.M.

                              H. J. GAUNTLETT.

A higher setting of this Tune is given at Hymn 58.

" Both Jesus was called, and His disciples, to the marriage."

mf HOW welcome was the call,
   And sweet the festal lay,
cr When JESUS deign'd in Cana's hall
   To bless the marriage day !

mf And happy was the Bride,
   And glad the Bridegroom's heart,
For He Who tarried at their side
   Bade grief and ill depart.

His gracious power Divine
   The water vessels knew ;
cr And plenteous was the mystic wine
   The wondering servants drew.

p O LORD of life and love,
   Come Thou again to-day ;
cr And bring a blessing from above
   That ne'er shall pass away.

mf O bless, as erst of old,
   The Bridegroom and the Bride ;
Bless with the holier stream that flow'd
p Forth from Thy piercèd Side.

Before Thine Altar-throne
   This mercy we implore ;
cr As Thou dost knit them, LORD, in one,
f So bless them evermore.

                         Sir H. W. BAKER.

The following Hymns are suitable for Holy Matrimony :

578 O perfect Love, all human thought transcending.   **579** O FATHER, all creating.

Ember Days.

Hymn 352. St. David.—C.M.

RAVENSCROFT, *Psalmes,* 1621.

A-men.

"As My Father hath sent Me, even so send I you."

mf CHRIST is gone up; yet ere He pass'd
　　From earth, in Heav'n to reign,
He form'd one holy Church to last
　　Till He should come again.

His Twelve Apostles first He made
　　His ministers of grace;
And they their hands on others laid,
　　To fill in turn their place.

So age by age, and year by year,
　　His grace was handed on;
And still the holy Church is here,
　　Although her LORD is gone.

p Let those find pardon, LORD, from Thee,
　　Whose love to her is cold:
cr Bring wanderers in, and let there be
　　One Shepherd and one fold.

J. M. NEALE.

Hymn 353. St. Lawrence.—L.M.

Rev. L. G. HAYNE.

A-men.

*"He gave some Apostles . . . and some Pastors and Teachers, for the perfecting of the Saints,
for the work of the ministry, for the edifying of the Body of Christ."*

mf O THOU Who makest souls to shine
　　With light from lighter worlds above,
And droppest glistening dew Divine
　　On all who seek a Saviour's love;

Do Thou Thy benediction give
　　On all who teach, on all who learn,
That so Thy Church may holier live,
　　And every lamp more brightly burn.

Give those, who teach, pure hearts and wise,
　　Faith, hope, and love, all warm'd by prayer;
Themselves first training for the skies,
　　They best will raise their people there.

Give those, who learn, the willing ear,
　　The spirit meek, the guileless mind;
Such gifts will make the lowliest here
　　Far better than a kingdom find.

cr O bless the shepherd; bless the sheep;
　　That guide and guided both be one,
One in the faithful watch they keep,
　　Until this hurrying life be done.

mf If thus, Good LORD, Thy grace be given,
　　In Thee to live, (*p*) in Thee to die,
cr Before we upward pass to Heav'n,
f We taste our immortality.

Bishop ARMSTRONG.

(288)

Ember Days.

Hymn 354. MANCHESTER NEW.—C.M. R. WAINWRIGHT, 1774.

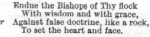

" The harvest truly is plenteous, but the labourers are few."

mf THE earth, O LORD, is one wide field
    Of all Thy chosen seed;
    The crop prepared its fruit to yield;
p   The labourers few indeed.

    We therefore come before Thee now
    With fasting, and with prayer,
cr Beseeching of Thy love that Thou
    Wouldst send more labourers there.

mf Not for our land alone we pray,
    Though that above the rest;
    The realms and islands far away,
    O let them all be blest.

Endue the Bishops of Thy flock
    With wisdom and with grace,
cr Against false doctrine, like a rock,
    To set the heart and face.

mf To all Thy Priests Thy truth reveal,
    And make Thy judgments clear;
    Make Thou Thy Deacons full of zeal,
    And humble, and sincere:

And give their flocks a lowly mind
    To hear and to obey;
    That each and all may mercy find
    At Thine appearing-day.

J. M. NEALE.

ALTERNATIVE TUNE, HYMN 549 (SECOND TUNE).

Hymn 355. LUDBOROUGH.—L.M. Rev. T. R. MATTHEWS.

" Let Thy priests be clothed with righteousness."

mf LORD, pour Thy SPIRIT from on high,
    And Thine ordainèd servants bless;
Graces and gifts to each supply,
And clothe Thy Priests with righteousness.

Within Thy temple when they stand,
To teach the truth as taught by Thee,
cr Saviour, like stars in Thy right hand,
Let all Thy Church's Pastors be.

mf Wisdom, and zeal, and faith impart,
Firmness with meekness, from above,

To bear Thy people in their heart,
And love the souls whom Thou dost love:

p To watch, and pray, and never faint,
    By day and night their guard to keep,
    To warn the sinner, cheer the saint,
    To feed Thy lambs, and tend Thy sheep.

mf So, when their work is finish'd here,
    May they in hope their charge resign;
cr So, when their Master shall appear,
    May they with crowns of glory shine.

J. MONTGOMERY, 1833.

These Hymns for Ember Days are also suitable for meetings of Clergy.

(289)

L

Lay Helpers.

Hymn 356. MELCOMBE.—L.M.

S. WEBBE, 1782.

A - men.

Lower settings of this Tune are given at Hymns 4 and 363.

"*My helpers in Christ Jesus.*"

mf LORD, speak to me, that I may speak
In living echoes of Thy tone;
As Thou hast sought, so let me seek
Thy erring children lost and lone.

O lead me, LORD, that I may lead
The wandering and the wavering feet;
O feed me, LORD, that I may feed
Thy hungering ones with manna sweet.

O strengthen me, that while I stand
Firm on the Rock, and strong in Thee,
I may stretch out a loving hand
To wrestlers with the troubled sea.

O teach me, LORD, that I may teach
The precious things Thou dost impart;

And wing my words, that they may reach
The hidden depths of many a heart.

p O give Thine own sweet rest to me,
That I may speak with soothing power
A word in season, as from Thee,
To weary ones in needful hour.

f O fill me with Thy fulness, LORD,
Until my very heart o'erflow
In kindling thought and glowing word,
Thy love to tell, Thy praise to show.

mf O use me, LORD, use even me,
Just as Thou wilt, and when, and where;
cr Until Thy Blessèd Face I see,
Thy rest, Thy joy, Thy glory share.

FRANCES R. HAVERGAL.

ALTERNATIVE TUNE, HYMN 760.

Hymn 357. ST. MATTHEW.—D.C.M.

W. CROFT, 1708.

A - men.

The original form of this Tune is given with Hymn 369.

(290)

Lay Helpers.

"If any man serve Me, let him follow Me; and where I am, there shall also My servant be."

mf HOW blessèd, from the bonds of sin
 And earthly fetters free,
In singleness of heart and aim
Thy servant, LORD, to be;
The hardest toil to undertake
 With joy at Thy command,
p The meanest office to receive
 With meekness at Thy hand.

mf With willing heart and longing eyes
 To watch before Thy gate,
Ready to run the weary race,
 To bear the heavy weight;
No voice of thunder to expect,
p But follow calm and still;
cr For love can easily divine
 The One Belovèd's Will.

mf Thus may I serve Thee, gracious LORD;
 Thus ever Thine alone,
My soul and body given to Thee,
 The purchase Thou hast won,
Through evil or through good report
 Still keeping by Thy side,
By life or death, in this poor flesh,
 Let CHRIST be magnified.

f How happily the working days
 In this dear service fly,
p How rapidly the closing hour,
 The time of rest, draws nigh,
cr When all the faithful gather home,
f A joyful company,
And ever where the Master is
 Shall His blest servants be.

ALTERNATIVE TUNE, HYMN 375.

JANE BORTHWICK: from the German of C. J. P. Spitta.

Missions.

Hymn 358. AURELIA.—7 6 7 6. 7 6 7 6. *(First Tune.)* S. S. WESLEY, 1864.

A men.

" Come over . . . and help us."

mf FROM Greenland's icy mountains,
 From India's coral strand,
Where Afric's sunny fountains
 Roll down their golden sand,
From many an ancient river,
 From many a palmy plain,
They call us to deliver
 Their land from error's chain.

What though the spicy breezes
 Blow soft o'er Ceylon's isle,
Though every prospect pleases
dim And only man is vile,
mf In vain with lavish kindness
 The gifts of GOD are strown,
p The heathen in his blindness
 Bows down to wood and stone.

mf Can we, whose souls are lighted
 With wisdom from on high,
Can we to men benighted
 The lamp of life deny?
f Salvation! oh, salvation!
 The joyful sound proclaim,
Till each remotest nation
 Has learn'd Messiah's name.

ff Waft, waft, ye winds, His story,
 And you, ye waters, roll,
Till, like a sea of glory,
 It spreads from pole to pole;
p Till o'er our ransom'd nature
 The LAMB for sinners slain,
cr Redeemer, King, Creator,
f In bliss returns to reign.

Bishop HEBER, 1819.

Missions.

Hymn 358. GREENLAND.—7 6 7 6.7 6 7 6. *(Second Tune.)* T. CLARK, 1828.

A - men.

" Come over . . . and help us."

mf FROM Greenland's icy mountains,
From India's coral strand,
Where Afric's sunny fountains
Roll down their golden sand,
From many an ancient river,
From many a palmy plain,
They call us to deliver
Their land from error's chain.

What though the spicy breezes
Blow soft o'er Ceylon's isle,
Though every prospect pleases
dim And only man is vile,
mf In vain with lavish kindness
The gifts of GOD are strown,
p The heathen in his blindness
Bows down to wood and stone.

mf Can we, whose souls are lighted
With wisdom from on high,
Can we to men benighted
The lamp of life deny?
f Salvation! oh, salvation!
The joyful sound proclaim,
Till each remotest nation
Has learn'd Messiah's name.

ff Waft, waft, ye winds, His story,
And you, ye waters, roll,
Till, like a sea of glory,
It spreads from pole to pole;
p Till o'er our ransom'd nature
The LAMB for sinners slain,
cr Redeemer, King, Creator,
f In bliss returns to reign.

Bishop HÉBER, 1819.

Hymn 359. IONA.—8 7 8 7.8 7 8 7. Sir J. STAINER.

Missions.

A lower setting of this Tune is given at Hymn 338.

" So shall He sprinkle many nations."

mf SAVIOUR, sprinkle many nations,
 Fruitful lot Thy sorrows be ;
By Thy pains and consolations
 Draw the Gentiles unto Thee :
Of Thy Cross the wondrous story,
 Be it to the nations told ;
f Let them see Thee in Thy glory,
 And Thy mercy manifold.

mf Far and wide, though all unknowing,
 Pants for Thee each mortal breast ;
p Human tears for Thee are flowing,
 Human hearts in Thee would rest ;

Thirsting, as for dews of even,
cr Thee they seek, as GOD of Heaven,
dim Thee, as Man, for sinners slain.

mf Saviour, lo ! the isles are waiting,
 Stretch'd the hand, and strain'd the sight,
For Thy SPIRIT new creating,
 Love's pure flame and wisdom's light ;
cr Give the word, and of the preacher
 Speed the foot, and touch the tongue,
f Till on earth by every creature
 Glory to the LAMB be sung.

        Bishop COXE.

ALTERNATIVE TUNE, HYMN 338 (SECOND TUNE).

Hymn 360.   FIAT LUX.—6 6 4. 6 6 6 4.   (*First Tune.*)

                    Rev. J. B. DYKES.

" And God said, Let there be light ; and there was light."

mf THOU, Whose Almighty Word
 Chaos and darkness heard,
  And took their flight ;
p Hear us, we humbly pray,
cr And where the Gospel-day
 Sheds not its glorious ray,
  Let there be light.

mf Thou, Who didst come to bring
 On Thy redeeming wing
  Healing and sight,
 Health to the sick in mind,
 Sight to the inly blind,
cr Oh ! now to all mankind
f Let there be light.

mf SPIRIT of truth and love,
 Life-giving, HOLY DOVE,
  Speed forth Thy flight ;
p Move on the waters' face,
cr Bearing the lamp of grace,
 And in earth's darkest place
f Let there be light.

mf Holy and Blessèd THREE,
 Glorious TRINITY,
  Wisdom, Love, Might ;
f Boundless as ocean's tide,
 Rolling in fullest pride,
cr Through the earth, far and wide,
ff Let there be light.

        J. MARRIOTT, 1813.

Missions.

Hymn 360. Moscow.—6 6 4.6 6 6 4. (*Second Tune.*) F. GIARDINI, 1769.

A - men.

"*And God said, Let there be light; and there was light.*"

mf THOU, Whose Almighty Word
    Chaos and darkness heard,
      And took their flight;
p   Hear us, we humbly pray,
cr And where the Gospel-day
    Sheds not its glorious ray,
      Let there be light.

mf Thou, Who didst come to bring
    On Thy redeeming wing
      Healing and sight,
    Health to the sick in mind,
    Sight to the inly blind,
cr Oh! now to all mankind
f   Let there be light.

mf SPIRIT of truth and love,
    Life-giving, HOLY DOVE,
      Speed forth Thy flight;
p   Move on the waters' face,
cr Bearing the lamp of grace,
    And in earth's darkest place
f   Let there be light.

mf Holy and Blessèd THREE,
    Glorious TRINITY,
      Wisdom, Love, Might;
f   Boundless as ocean's tide
    Rolling in fullest pride,
cr Through the earth, far and wide,
ff   Let there be light.

J. MARRIOTT, 1813.

Hymn 361. MACEDON.—8 8.8 8.8 8. (*First Tune.*) C. A. BARRY.

A - men.

Missions.

Hymn 361. Matlock.—8 8.8 8 8.8 8. *(Second Tune.)* M. WISE, 1684.

A - men.

A higher setting of this Tune is given at Hymn **743.**

"Come over into Macedonia, and help us."

p   THROUGH midnight gloom from Macedon
     The cry of myriads as of one,
  The voiceful silence of despair,
  Is eloquent in awful prayer,
cr The soul's exceeding bitter cry,
  "Come o'er and help us, *(dim)* or we die."

p   How mournfully it echoes on!
  For half the earth is Macedon;
mf These brethren to their brethren call,
  And by the Love which loved them all,
  And by the whole world's Life they cry,
cr "O ye that live, *(dim)* behold we die!"

mf By other sounds the world is won
  Than that which wails from Macedon;
  The roar of gain is round it roll'd,
  Or men unto themselves are sold,
  And cannot list the alien cry,
p   "O hear and help us, lest we die!"

mf Yet with that cry from Macedon
  The very car of CHRIST rolls on;
  "I come; who would abide My day
  In yonder wilds prepare My way;
  My voice is crying in their cry;
  Help ye the dying, lest ye die."

  JESU, for men of Man the Son,
  Yea, Thine the cry from Macedon;
cr O by the kingdom and the power
  And glory of Thine Advent hour,
  Wake heart and will to hear their cry;
  Help us to help them, lest we die!

S. J. STONE.

Missions.

Hymn 362. EVERTON.—8 7 8 7.8 7 8 7. H. SMART.

A - men.

" Waiting for the coming of our Lord Jesus Christ."

p L ORD, her watch Thy Church is keeping ;
cr   When shall earth Thy rule obey ?
When shall end the night of weeping?
  When shall break the promised day ?

p See the whitening harvest languish,
  Waiting still the labourers' toil ;
cr Was it vain, Thy SON'S deep anguish?
  Shall the strong retain the spoil ?

p Tidings, sent to every creature,
  Millions yet have never heard ;
cr Can they hear without a preacher ?
  LORD Almighty, give the Word :

mf Give the Word ; in every nation
  Let the Gospel-trumpet sound,
Witnessing a world's salvation
cr   To the earth's remotest bound

f Then the end : Thy Church completed,
  All Thy chosen gather'd in,
With their King in glory seated,
  Satan bound, and banish'd sin ;
p Gone for ever parting, weeping,
  Hunger, sorrow, death, and pain ;
cr Lo ! her watch Thy Church is keeping ;
  Come, LORD JESUS, come to reign.

H. DOWNTON.

Hymn 363. INTERCESSION.—L.M. (*First Tune.*)

Easy Music for Church Choirs, 1853.

A - men.

Hymn 363. MELCOMBE.—L.M. (*Second Tune.*) S. WEBBE, 1782.

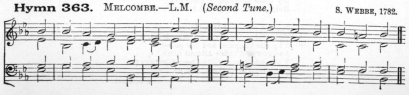

Missions.

A-men.

A lower setting of this Tune is given at Hymn 4, and a higher setting at Hymn 273.

"*Turn us then, O God our Saviour.*"

mf ALMIGHTY GOD, Whose only SON
O'er sin and death the triumph won,
And ever lives to intercede
For souls who Thy sweet mercy need ;
In His dear Name to Thee we pray
For all who err and go astray,
For sinners, wheresoe'er they be,
Who do not serve and honour Thee.

p There are who never yet have heard
The tidings of Thy blessèd Word,
But still in heathen darkness dwell,
Without one thought of Heav'n or hell ;

And some within Thy sacred fold
To holy things are dead and cold,

And waste the precious hours of life
In selfish ease, or toil, or strife ;
And many a quicken'd soul within
There lurks the secret love of sin,
A wayward will, or anxious fears,
Or lingering taint of bygone years.

mf O give repentance true and deep
To all Thy lost and wandering sheep,

or And kindle in their hearts the fire
Of holy love and pure desire.

f That so from Angel-hosts above
May rise a sweeter song of love,
And we, with all the Blest, adore
Thy Name, O GOD, for evermore.

Sir H. W. BAKER.

Hymn 364. HAARLEM.—7 7 7 5.

B. TOURS.

rall.

A-men.

"*That Thy way may be known upon earth, Thy saving health among all nations.*"

p GOD of grace, O let Thy light
Bless our dim and blinded sight ;
cr Like the day-spring on the night,
Bid Thy grace to shine.

mf To the nations led astray
Thine eternal love display ;
cr Let Thy truth direct their way
Till the world be Thine.

f Praise to Thee, the faithful LORD ;
Let all tongues in glad accord
Learn the good thanksgiving word,
Ever praising Thee.

mf Let them moved to gladness sing,
Owning Thee their Judge and King ;

Righteous truth shall bloom and spring
Where Thy rule shall be.

ff Praise to Thee, all faithful LORD ;
Let all tongues in glad accord
Speak the good thanksgiving word,
Heart-rejoicing praise.

mf So the fruitful earth's increase,
Bounty of the GOD of peace,
Never in its course shall cease
Through the length of days ;

While His grace our life shall cheer,
Furthest lands shall own His fear,
Brought to Him in worship near,
Taught His mercy's ways.

E. CHURTON.

ALTERNATIVE TUNE, HYMN 163.

The following Hymns are suitable :

(297)

L 2

Almsgiving.

Hymn 365. ALMSGIVING.—8 8 8 4.

Rev. J. B. DYKES.

A - men.

" Freely ye have received, freely give."

f O LORD of Heav'n, and earth, and sea,
    To Thee all praise and glory be ;
  How shall we show our love to Thee,
    Who givest all?

mf The golden sunshine, vernal air,
    Sweet flowers and fruit, Thy love declare ;
  When harvests ripen, Thou art there,
    Who givest all.

  For peaceful homes, and healthful days,
  For all the blessings earth displays,
cr We owe Thee thankfulness and praise,
    Who givest all.

p Thou didst not spare Thine Only SON,
  But gav'st Him for a world undone,
cr And freely with that Blessèd One
    Thou givest all.

mf Thou giv'st the HOLY SPIRIT'S dower,
  SPIRIT of life, and love, and power,

And dost His sevenfold graces shower
    Upon us all.

For souls redeem'd, for sins forgiven,
For means of grace and hopes of Heav'n,
cr FATHER, what can to Thee be given,
    Who givest all?

p We lose what on ourselves we spend,
f We have as treasure without end
  Whatever, LORD, to Thee we lend,
    Who givest all.

mf Whatever, LORD, we lend to Thee
cr Repaid a thousandfold will be ;
f Then gladly will we give to Thee,
    Who givest all ;

  To Thee, from Whom we all derive
  Our life, our gifts, our power to give :
p O may we ever with Thee live,
    Who givest all.

Bishop C. WORDSWORTH.

Hymn 366. WE GIVE THEE BUT THINE OWN.—S.M.

E. H. THORNE.

A - men.

" Whoso hath this world's good, and seeth his brother have need, and shutteth up his bowels
of compassion from him, how dwelleth the love of God in him ? "

mf WE give Thee but Thine own,
    Whate'er the gift may be :
  All that we have is Thine alone,
  A trust, O LORD, from Thee.

  May we Thy bounties thus
  As stewards true receive,
  And gladly, as Thou blessest us,
  To Thee our first-fruits give.

p Oh, hearts are bruised and dead,
  And homes are bare and cold,
  And lambs, for whom the Shepherd bled,
  Are straying from the fold.

cr To comfort and to bless,
  To find a balm for woe,
  To tend the lone and fatherless,
  Is Angels' work below.

(298)

Almsgiving.

The captive to release,
To GOD the lost to bring,
To teach the way of life and peace.
It is a Christ-like thing.

And we believe Thy Word,
dim Though dim our faith may be ;

cr Whate'er for Thine we do, O LORD,
We do it unto Thee.

f All might, all praise be Thine,
FATHER, Co-equal SON,
And SPIRIT, Bond of love Divine,
While endless ages run.

Bishop W. WALSHAM HOW

Hymn 367. CHARITAS.—8 7 8 7.8 7 8 7. (*First Tune.*) Rev. J. B. DYKES.

rall.

A - men.

*" Ye ought . . . to remember the words of the Lord Jesus, how He said, It is more blessed
to give than to receive."*

mf LORD of glory, Who hast bought us
With Thy Life-blood as the price,
Never grudging for the lost ones
That tremendous Sacrifice,
And with that hast freely given
Blessings, countless as the sand,
To the unthankful and the evil
With Thine own unsparing hand ;

Grant us hearts, dear LORD, to yield Thee
Gladly, freely of Thine own ;
With the sunshine of Thy goodness
Melt our thankless hearts of stone ;
p Till our cold and selfish natures,
cr Warm'd by Thee, at length believe
That more happy and more blessèd
'Tis to give than to receive.

mf Wondrous honour hast Thou given
To our humblest charity
In Thine own mysterious sentence,
" Ye have done it unto Me."

p Can it be, O gracious Master,
Thou dost deign for alms to sue,
cr Saying by Thy poor and needy,
" Give as I have given to you " ?

p Yes : the sorrow and the suffering,
Which on every hand we see,
Channels are for tithes and offerings
Due by solemn right to Thee ;
cr Right of which we may not rob Thee,
Debt we may not choose but pay,
dim Lest that Face of love and pity
Turn from us another day.

mf LORD of glory, Who hast bought us
With Thy Life-blood as the price,
Never grudging for the lost ones
That tremendous Sacrifice.
cr Give us faith, to trust Thee boldly,
Hope, to stay our souls on Thee ;
f But O, best of all Thy graces,
dim Give us Thine own charity.

MRS. ALDERSON.

Almsgiving.

Hymn 367. ST. ASAPH.—8 7 8 7.8 7 8 7. (*Second Tune.*) W. S. BAMBRIDGE.

A - men.

" Ye ought . . . to remember the words of the Lord Jesus, how He said, It is more blessed to give than to receive."

mf LORD of glory, Who hast bought us
　　With Thy Life-blood as the price,
Never grudging for the lost ones
　　That tremendous Sacrifice,
And with that hast freely given
　　Blessings, countless as the sand,
To the unthankful and the evil
　　With Thine own unsparing hand ;

Grant us hearts, dear LORD, to yield Thee
　　Gladly, freely of Thine own ;
With the sunshine of Thy goodness
　　Melt our thankless hearts of stone ;
p　Till our cold and selfish natures,
cr　Warm'd by Thee, at length believe
That more happy and more blessèd
　　Tis to give than to receive.

mf Wondrous honour hast Thou given
　　To our humblest charity
In Thine own mysterious sentence,
　　" Ye have done it unto Me."
p　Can it be, O gracious Master,
　　Thou dost deign for alms to sue,
cr　Saying by Thy poor and needy,
　　" Give as I have given to you " ?

p　Yes : the sorrow and the suffering,
　　Which on every hand we see,
Channels are for tithes and offerings
　　Due by solemn right to Thee ;
cr　Right of which we may not rob Thee
　　Debt we may not choose but pay,
dim Lest that Face of love and pity
　　Turn from us another day.

mf LORD of glory, Who hast bought us
　　With Thy Life-blood as the price,
Never grudging for the lost ones
　　That tremendous Sacrifice,
cr　Give us faith, to trust Thee boldly,
　　Hope, to stay our souls on Thee ;
f　But O, best of all Thy graces,
dim　Give us Thine own charity.

MRS. ALDERSON.

The following Hymn is suitable :
259 Thy Life was given for me.

(300)

Hospitals.

Hymn 368. WALTHAM.—8 7 8 7. 7 7. (*First Tune.*)   H. ALBERT, 1642.

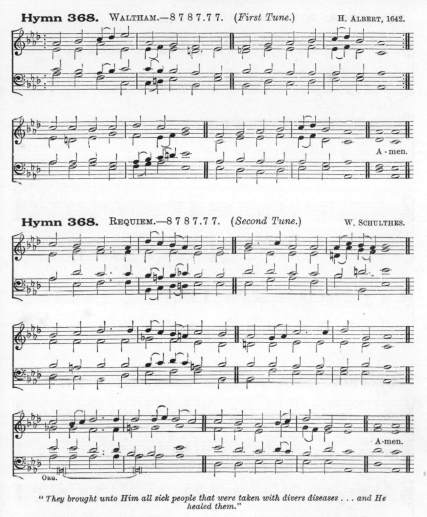

A-men.

Hymn 368. REQUIEM.—8 7 8 7. 7 7. (*Second Tune.*)   W. SCHULTHES.

A-men.

ORG.

" They brought unto Him all sick people that were taken with divers diseases . . . and He healed them."

mf THOU to Whom the sick and dying
    Ever came, nor came in vain,
  Still with healing word replying
    To the wearied cry of pain,
p   Hear us, JESU, as we meet
    Suppliants at Thy mercy-seat.

  Still the weary, sick, and dying
    Need a brother's, sister's care,
cr On Thy higher help relying
    May we now their burden share,
mf   Bringing all our offerings meet
    Suppliants at Thy mercy-seat.

May each child of Thine be willing,
    Willing both in hand and heart,
All the law of love fulfilling,
    Ever comfort to impart ;
    Ever bringing offerings meet
    Suppliant to Thy mercy-seat.

So may sickness, sin, and sadness
    To Thy healing virtue yield,
cr Till the sick and sad, in gladness,
    Rescued, ransom'd, cleansèd, heal'd,
f   One in Thee together meet,
p   Pardon'd at Thy judgment-seat.

G. THRING.

(301)

Hospitals.

Hymn 369. ST. MATTHEW.—D.C.M. *(Original Form.)* W. CROFT, 1708.

A - men

Hymn 369. ST. MATTHEW.—D.C.M. *(Modern Form.)* W. CROFT, 1708.

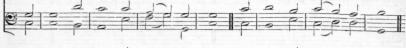

Hospitals.

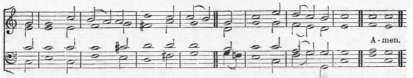

A - men.

"They brought unto Him all that were diseased, and besought Him that they might only touch the hem of His garment; and as many as touched were made perfectly whole."

f THINE arm, O LORD, in days of old,
　Was strong to heal and save;
It triumph'd o'er disease and death,
　O'er darkness and the grave;
p To Thee they went, the blind, the dumb,
　The palsied and the lame,
The leper with his tainted life,
　The sick with fever'd frame.

mf And lo: Thy touch brought life and health,
　Gave speech, and strength, and sight;
cr And youth renew'd and frenzy calm'd
　Own'd Thee, the LORD of light;

f And now, O LORD, be near to bless,
　Almighty as of yore,
In crowded street, by restless couch,
　As by Gennesareth's shore.

mf Be Thou our great Deliverer still,
　Thou LORD of life and death;
Restore and quicken, soothe and bless
　With Thine Almighty Breath;
To hands that work, and eyes that see,
　Give wisdom's heavenly lore,
f That whole and sick, and weak and strong
　May praise Thee evermore.

E. H. PLUMPTRE.

ALTERNATIVE TUNE, HYMN 216.

For those at Sea.

Hymn 370　MELITA.—8 8. 8 8. 8 8.　Rev. J. B. DYKES.

p　　　　　　　　　　　　　　　　　　　　A - men.

"These men see the works of the Lord, and His wonders in the deep."

mf ETERNAL FATHER, strong to save,
　Whose arm hath bound the restless
Who bidd'st the mighty ocean deep [wave,
　Its own appointed limits keep;
p O hear us (cr) when we cry to Thee
dim For those in peril on the sea.

mf O CHRIST, Whose voice the waters heard
p And hush'd their raging at Thy word,
cr Who walkedst on the foaming deep,
dim And calm amid the storm didst sleep;
p O hear us (cr) when we cry to Thee
dim For those in peril on the sea.

mf O HOLY SPIRIT, Who didst brood
　Upon the waters dark and rude,
And bid their angry tumult cease,
And give, for wild confusion, (p) peace;
O hear us (cr) when we cry to Thee
dim For those in peril on the sea.

mf O TRINITY of love and power,
　Our brethren shield in danger's hour;
From rock and tempest, fire and foe,
Protect them wheresoe'er they go;
cr Thus evermore shall rise to Thee
f Glad hymns of praise from land and sea.

W. WHITING.

For those at Sea.

Hymn 371. ROCKINGHAM.—L.M.   E. MILLER, 1735–1807.

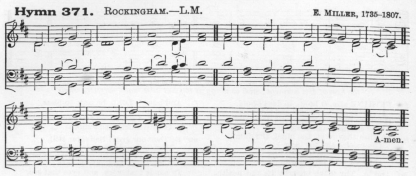

A-men.

A higher setting of this Tune is given at Hymn 108.

" Thou shalt shew us wonderful things in Thy righteousness, O God of our salvation: Thou that art the hope of all the ends of the earth, and of them that remain in the broad sea."

mf ALMIGHTY FATHER, hear our cry,
　　As o'er the trackless deep we roam ;
　Be Thou our haven always nigh,
　On homeless waters Thou our home.

p　O JESU, Saviour, at Whose Voice
　　The tempest sank to perfect rest,
cr　Bid Thou the fearful heart rejoice,
　　And cleanse and calm the troubled breast.

mf O HOLY GHOST, beneath Whose Power
　The ocean woke to life and light,
　Command Thy blessing in this hour,
　Thy fostering warmth, Thy quickening might.

f　Great GOD of our salvation, Thee
　We love, we worship, we adore ;
　Our Refuge on time's changeful sea,
　Our Joy on Heav'n's eternal shore.

Bishop E. H. BICKERSTETH.

Hymn 372. GERMAN HYMN.—7 7 7 7.   I. PLEYEL, 1757–1831.

A - men.

" They willingly received Him into the ship."

p　ON the waters dark and drear,
　　JESUS, Saviour, Thou art near,
cr　With our ship where'er it roam,
　　As with loving friends at home.

mf　Thou hast walk'd the heaving wave ;
f　Thou art mighty still to save ;
p　With one gentle word of peace
　　Thou canst bid the tempest cease.

mf　Safely from the boisterous main
　　Bring us back to port again :
　　In our haven we shall be,
　　JESU, if we have but Thee.

　　Only by Thy power and love
　　Fit us for the port above ;
*dim*Still the deadly storm within,
　　Gusts of passion, waves of sin.

f　So, when breaks the glorious dawn
　　Of the Resurrection morn,
p　When the night of toil is o'er,
cr　We shall see Thee on the shore.

f　Holy FATHER, Holy SON,
　　Holy SPIRIT, THREE in ONE,
　　Praise unending unto Thee,
　　Now and evermore shall be.

W. C. DIX.

The following Hymns are suitable:

285 Fierce raged the tempest o'er the deep.
592 O LORD, be with us when we sail.
593 O GOD, Who metest in Thine hand.
594 When through the torn sail the wild tempest is streaming.

595 Holy FATHER, in Thy mercy.
596 O Saviour ! when Thy loving Hand.
597 As near the wish'd-for port we draw.

In Times of Trouble.

Hymn 373. LONDON NEW.—C.M. *Psalms* (Edinburgh, 1635).

" What I do thou knowest not now ; but thou shalt know hereafter."

mf GOD moves in a mysterious way
  His wonders to perform ;
He plants His footsteps in the sea,
And rides upon the storm.

Deep in unfathomable mines
Of never-failing skill
He treasures up His bright designs,
And works His sovereign Will.

Ye fearful saints, fresh courage take ;
The clouds ye so much dread

Are big with mercy, and shall break
In blessings on your head.

Judge not the LORD by feeble sense,
  But trust Him for His grace ;
p Behind a frowning providence
cr He hides a smiling face.

mf Blind unbelief is sure to err,
  And scan His work in vain ;
cr GOD is His own interpreter,
  And He will make it plain.

W. COWPER, 1779.

Hymn 374. ST. BARTHOLOMEW.—L.M. E. H. THORNE.

" God is our hope and strength, a very present help in trouble."

p GOD of our life, to Thee we call,
  Afflicted at Thy feet we fall ;
When the great water-floods prevail,
Leave not our trembling hearts to fail.

Friend of the friendless and the faint,
Where should we lodge our deep complaint ?
cr Where but with Thee, Whose open door
Invites the helpless and the poor ?

p Did ever mourner plead with Thee,
cr And Thou refuse that mourner's plea ?
mf Does not the Word still fix'd remain,
  That none shall seek Thy Face in vain ?

p Then hear, O LORD, our humble cry,
And bend on us Thy pitying eye :
To Thee their prayer Thy people make,
Hear us for our REDEEMER'S sake.

W. COWPER, 1779.

ALTERNATIVE TUNE, HYMN 245.

(305)

In Times of Trouble.

Hymn 375. OLD 137TH.—D.C.M.   *Psalmes,* 1556.

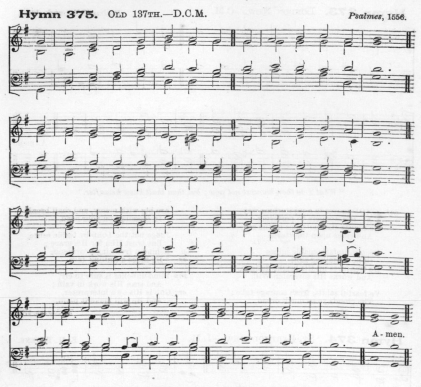

A - men.

'Thou that hearest the prayer; unto Thee shall all flesh come."

p   GREAT King of nations, hear our prayer,
        While at Thy feet we fall,
And humbly with united cry
    To Thee for mercy call ;
The guilt is ours, but grace is Thine,
    O turn us not away ;
cr But hear us from Thy lofty Throne,
        And help us when we pray.

p   Our fathers' sins were manifold,
        And ours no less we own,
mf Yet wondrously from age to age
        Thy goodness hath been shown ;
dim When dangers, like a stormy sea,
        Beset our country round,
cr To Thee we look'd, to Thee we cried,
        And help in Thee was found.

p   With one consent we meekly bow
        Beneath Thy chastening hand,
And, pouring forth confession meet,
        Mourn with our mourning land ;
cr With pitying eye behold our need,
        As thus we lift our prayer ;
p   Correct us with Thy judgments, LORD,
cr Then let Thy mercy spare.

                          J. HAMPDEN GURNEY, 1838.

In Times of Trouble.

Hymn 376. ROCKINGHAM.—L.M.   E. MILLER, 1735-1807.

A-men.

A lower setting of this Tune is given at Hymn 371.

" The Lord shall give His people the blessing of peace."

WAR.

mf O GOD of love, O King of peace,
    Make wars throughout the world to
The wrath of sinful man restrain,   [cease ;
p   Give peace, O GOD, give peace again.

mf Remember, LORD, Thy works of old,
    The wonders that our fathers told,
    Remember not our sin's dark stain,
p   Give peace, O GOD, give peace again.

mf Whom shall we trust but Thee, O LORD?
    Where rest but on Thy faithful Word?
cr   None ever call'd on Thee in vain,
p   Give peace, O GOD, give peace again.

f Where Saints and Angels dwell above,
    All hearts are knit in holy love ;
    O bind us in that heavenly chain,
p   Give peace, O GOD, give peace again.

Sir H. W. BAKER.

The following Hymns are suitable :

742 GOD the All-terrible! King, Who ordainest.   **743** LORD, while afar our brothers fight.

Hymn 377. SALISBURY.—C.M.   RAVENSCROFT, *Psalmes*, 1621.

A - men.

*" Thou shalt not be afraid . . . for the pestilence that walketh in darkness ; nor for the
sickness that destroyeth in the noon day."*

PESTILENCE.

p IN grief and fear to Thee, O LORD,
    We now for succour fly ;
    Thine awful judgments are abroad,
er e dim O shield us lest we die.

p The fell disease on every side
    Walks forth with tainted breath ;
And pestilence, with rapid stride,
    Bestrews the land with death.

mf O look with pity on the scene
    Of sadness and of dread ;
    And let Thine Angel stand between
dim   The living and the dead.

p With contrite hearts to Thee, our King,
    We turn who oft have stray'd ;
cr Accept the sacrifice we bring,
    And let the plague be stay'd.

W. BULLOCK.

ALTERNATIVE TUNES, HYMNS 112 AND 253.

In time of Famine or Scarcity the following Hymn is suitable :

389 What our FATHER does is well.

Thanksgiving.

Hymn 378. EIN' FESTE BURG.—8 7 8 7.6 6 6 6 7. (*First Version.*)

M. LUTHER, 1529.

A - men.

Hymn 378. EIN' FESTE BURG.—8 7 8 7.6 6 6 6 7. (*Second Version.*)

M. LUTHER, 1529.

A - men.

Thanksgiving.

"O praise the Lord, laud ye the Name of the Lord ; praise it, O ye servants of the Lord."

f   REJOICE to-day with one accord,
     Sing out with exultation ;
Rejoice and praise our mighty LORD,
   Whose arm hath brought salvation ;
   His works of love proclaim
   The greatness of His Name ;
   For He is GOD alone
   Who hath His mercy shown ;
dim   Let all His saints adore Him !

p   When in distress to Him we cried,
     He heard our sad complaining ;
cr   O trust in Him, whate'er betide,
     His love is all-sustaining ;
f   Triumphant songs of praise
   To Him our hearts shall raise ;
   Now every voice shall say,
   "O praise our GOD alway ;"
dim   Let all His saints adore Him !

ff   Rejoice to-day with one accord,
     Sing out with exultation ;
   Rejoice and praise our mighty LORD,
   Whose arm hath brought salvation ;
   His works of love proclaim
   The greatness of His Name ;
   For He is GOD alone
   Who hath His mercy shown ;
   Let all His saints adore Him !

Sir H. W. BAKER.

Hymn 379.   NUN DANKET.—6 7 6 7.6 6 6 6.   J. CRÜGER, 1648.

A-men.

"O clap your hands together, all ye people ; O sing unto God with the voice of melody."

f   NOW thank we all our GOD,
     With heart, and hands, and voices,
Who wondrous things hath done,
  In Whom His world rejoices ;
  Who from our mother's arms
   Hath bless'd us on our way
With countless gifts of love,
   And still is ours to-day.

mf   O may this bounteous GOD
Through all our life be near us,
  With ever joyful hearts
And blessèd peace to cheer us ;
  And keep us in His grace,
   And guide us when perplex'd,
  And free us from all ills
   In this world and the next.

f   All praise and thanks to GOD
  The FATHER now be given,
  The SON, and HIM Who reigns
  With Them in highest Heaven,
  The ONE Eternal GOD,
   Whom earth and Heav'n adore,
  For thus it was, is now,
   And shall be evermore.

CATHERINE WINKWORTH : from the
German of M. Rinkart.

Friendly Societies.

Hymn 380. ST. MICHAEL.—S.M. *Psalmes*, 1561.

A higher setting of this Tune is given at Hymn **152.**

" Bear ye one another's burdens, and so fulfil the law of Christ."

f   O PRAISE our GOD to-day,
    His constant mercy bless,
Whose love hath help'd us on our way,
And granted us success.

mf   His arm the strength imparts
    Our daily toil to bear ;
His grace alone inspires our hearts
    Each other's load to share.

    O happiest work below,
    Earnest of joy above,

To sweeten many a cup of woe
    By deeds of holy love !

    LORD, may it be our choice
    This blessed rule to keep,
cr   " Rejoice with them that do rejoice,
dim   And weep with them that weep."

f   O praise our GOD to-day,
    His constant mercy bless,
Whose love hath help'd us on our way,
    And granted us success.

Sir H. W. BAKER.

The following Hymns are suitable :

273   O LORD, how joyful 'tis to see.   **274**   Through the night of doubt and sorrow.

Harvest.

Hymn 381. MONKLAND.—7 7 7 7. Arranged by J. WILKES.

" Who giveth food to all flesh ; for His mercy endureth for ever."

f   PRAISE, O praise our GOD and King ;
    Hymns of adoration sing ;
    For His mercies still endure
    Ever faithful, ever sure.

mf   Praise Him that He made the sun
    Day by day his course to run ;
f   For His mercies still endure
    Ever faithful, ever sure ;

p   And the silver moon by night,
    Shining with her gentle light ;
f   For His mercies still endure
    Ever faithful, ever sure.

mf   Praise Him that He gave the rain
    To mature the swelling grain ;
f   For His mercies still endure
    Ever faithful, ever sure ;

(310)

Harvest.

mf And hath bid the fruitful field
Crops of precious increase yield ;
f For His mercies still endure
Ever faithful, ever sure.

ff Praise Him for our harvest-store,
He hath fill'd the garner-floor ;
For His mercies still endure
Ever faithful, ever sure ;

p And for richer Food than this,
cr Pledge of everlasting bliss ;
f For His mercies still endure
Ever faithful, ever sure.

ff Glory to our Bounteous King ;
Glory let creation sing ;
Glory to the FATHER, SON,
And Blest SPIRIT, THREE in ONE.

Sir H. W. BAKER.

Hymn 382. St. GEORGE.—7 7 7 7.7 7 7 7.　　　Sir G. J. ELVEY.

" They joy before Thee according to the joy in harvest."

f COME, ye thankful people, come,
Raise the song of Harvest-home :
All is safely gather'd in,
Ere the winter storms begin ;
mf GOD, our Maker, doth provide
For our wants to be supplied ;
f Come to GOD'S own Temple, come ;
Raise the song of Harvest-home.

mf All this world is GOD'S own field,
Fruit unto His praise to yield ;
Wheat and tares therein are sown,
Unto joy or sorrow grown ;
cr Ripening with a wondrous power
Till the final Harvest-hour :
p Grant, O LORD of life, that we
Holy grain and pure may be.

mf For we know that Thou wilt come,
And wilt take Thy people home ;
From Thy field wilt purge away
All that doth offend, that day ;
p And Thine Angels charge at last
In the fire the tares to cast,
f But the fruitful ears to store
In Thy garner evermore :

mf Come then, LORD of mercy, come,
Bid us sing Thy Harvest-home ;
cr Let Thy Saints be gather'd in,
Free from sorrow, free from sin ;
f All upon the golden floor
Praising Thee for evermore :
Come, with all Thine Angels come ;
Bid us sing Thy (*rall*) Harvest-home.

H. ALFORD.

harvest.

Hymn 383. WIR PFLÜGEN.—7 6 7 6. 7 6 7 6. 6 6 8 4.

J. A. P. SCHULTZ, 1747–1800.

A-men.

"The eyes of all wait upon Thee, O Lord, and Thou givest them their meat in due season."

mf WE plough the fields, and scatter
The good seed on the land,
But it is fed and water'd
By GOD'S Almighty Hand ;
He sends the snow in winter,
The warmth to swell the grain,
p The breezes, and the sunshine,
And soft refreshing rain.
f All good gifts around us
Are sent from Heav'n above,
ff Then thank the LORD, O thank the LORD,
For all His love.

mf He only is the Maker
Of all things near and far ;
He paints the wayside flower,
He lights the evening star ;
cr The winds and waves obey Him,
p By Him the birds are fed ;
cr Much more to us, His children,
He gives our daily bread.
f All good gifts around us
Are sent from Heav'n above,
ff Then thank the LORD, O thank the LORD,
For all His love.

mf We thank Thee then, O FATHER,
For all things bright and good,
The seed-time and the harvest,
Our life, our health, our food ;
Accept the gifts we offer
For all Thy love imparts,
And, what Thou most desirest,
p Our humble, thankful hearts.
f All good gifts around us
Are sent from Heav'n above,
ff Then thank the LORD, O thank the LORD,
For all His love.

JANE M. CAMPBELL : from the
German of M. Claudius.

Harvest.

Hymn 384. GOLDEN SHEAVES.—8 7 8 7. 8 7 8 7. Sir A. SULLIVAN.

A-men.

" Thou crownest the year with Thy goodness."

f   TO Thee, O LORD, our hearts we raise
      In hymns of adoration,
    To Thee bring sacrifice of praise
      With shouts of exultation ;
mf Bright robes of gold the fields adorn,
      The hills with joy are ringing,
    The valleys stand so thick with corn
f   That even they are singing.

mf And now, on this our festal day,
      Thy bounteous Hand confessing,
    Upon Thine Altar, LORD, we lay
      The first-fruits of Thy blessing ;
p   By Thee the souls of men are fed
      With gifts of grace supernal,
    Thou, Who dost give us earthly bread,
      Give us the Bread Eternal.

mf We bear the burden of the day,
      And often toil seems dreary ;
    But labour ends with sunset ray,
      And rest comes for the weary ;
    May we, the Angel-reaping o'er,
      Stand at the last accepted,
    CHRIST'S golden sheaves for evermore
      To garners bright elected.

f   Oh, blessèd is that land of GOD,
      Where Saints abide for ever ;
    Where golden fields spread far and broad,
      Where flows the crystal river :
p   The strains of all its holy throng
      With ours to-day are blending ;
f   Thrice blessèd is that harvest-song
      Which never hath an ending.

W. C. DIX.

Harvest.

Hymn 385. Neale.—8 7. 8 7. 8 7. (*First Tune.*)

W. H. Monk.

A - men.

Hymn 385. First Fruits.—8 7. 8 7. 8 7. (*Second Tune.*) Rev. J. B Dykes.

dim. *cres.* *ten.*

A - men.

" While the earth remaineth, seed-time and harvest . . . shall not cease."

mf GOD the FATHER ! Whose Creation
 Gives to flowers and fruits their birth,
Thou, Whose yearly operation
 Brings the hour of harvest mirth,
Here to Thee we make oblation
 Of the August-gold of earth.

 GOD the WORD ! the sun, maturing
  With his blessèd ray the corn,
cr Spake of Thee, O Sun enduring,
  Thee, O everlasting Morn !
p Thee in Whom our woes find curing,
cr Thee that liftest up our horn.

mf GOD the HOLY GHOST ! the showers
 That have fatten'd out the grain,
Types of Thy celestial powers,
 Symbols of baptismal rain,
Shadow'd out the grace that dowers
 All the faithful of Thy train.

When the harvest of each nation
 Severs righteousness from sin,
And Archangel-proclamation
 Bids to put the sickle in,
And each age and generation
 Sink to woe, or glory win ;

p Grant that we, or young, or hoary,
  Lengthen'd be our span or brief,
Whatsoe'er the life-long story
 Of our joy or of our grief,
cr May be garner'd up in glory
  As Thine own elected sheaf.

f Laud to Him to Whom Supernal
 Thrones and Virtues bend the knee ;
Laud to Him from Whom infernal
 Powers and Dominations flee ;
Laud to Him the Co-eternal
 Paraclete, for ever be.

J. M. NEALE.

(314)

Harvest.

Hymn 386. St. Beatrice.—7 6 7 6. 7 6 7 6. 7 6 7 6.   Sir J. F. Bridge.

A - men.

" Behold a sower went forth to sow."

mf THE sower went forth sowing,
p   The seed in secret slept
  Through weeks of faith and patience,
cr   Till out the green blade crept ;
  And warm'd by golden sunshine,
    And fed by silver rain,
  At last the fields were whiten'd
    To harvest once again.

f O praise the heavenly Sower,
    Who gave the fruitful seed,
  And watch'd and water'd duly,
    And ripen'd for our need.

mf Behold ! the heavenly Sower
    Goes forth with better seed,
  The Word of sure Salvation,
p   With Feet and Hands that bleed ;
mf Here in His Church 'tis scatter'd,
    Our spirits are the soil ;
  Then let an ample fruitage
    Repay His pain and toil.

f Oh, beauteous is the harvest
    Wherein all goodness thrives,
  And this the true thanksgiving,
    The first-fruits of our lives.

p Within a hallow'd acre
    He sows yet other grain,
  When peaceful earth receiveth
    The dead He died to gain ;
  For though the growth be hidden,
cr   We know that they shall rise ;
  Yea even now they ripen
    In sunny Paradise.

f O summer land of harvest,
    O fields for ever white
  With souls that wear Christ's raiment,
    With crowns of golden light !

mf One day the heavenly Sower
    Shall reap where He hath sown,
cr And come again rejoicing,
    And with Him bring His own ;
p And then the fan of judgment
    Shall winnow from His floor
  The chaff into the furnace
    That flameth evermore.

mf O holy, awful Reaper,
p   Have mercy in the day
  Thou puttest in Thy sickle,
rall e pp And cast us not away.

W. St. Hill Bourne.

Harvest.

Hymn 387. Preston.—8 8.8 8.8 8.

Bishop H. L. Jenner.

A-men.

" The harvest is the end of the world, and the reapers are the Angels."

mf LORD of the harvest, once again
We thank Thee for the ripen'd grain ;
For crops safe carried, sent to cheer
Thy servants through another year ;
For all sweet holy thoughts supplied
By seed-time, and by harvest-tide.

p The bare dead grain, in autumn sown,
cr Its robe of vernal green puts on ;
mf Glad from its wintry grave it springs,
Fresh garnish'd by the King of kings :
p So, LORD, to those who sleep in Thee
cr Shall new and glorious bodies be.

mf Nor vainly of Thy Word we ask
A lesson from the reaper's task :
So shall Thine Angels issue forth ;
The tares be burnt ; (*cr*) the just of earth,
To wind and storm exposed no more,
Be gather'd to their FATHER'S store.

mf Daily, O LORD, our prayers be said,
As Thou hast taught, for daily bread ;
But not alone our bodies feed,
Supply our fainting spirits' need :
cr O Bread of life, from day to day,
Be Thou their Comfort, Food, and Stay.

J. ANSTICE, 1836.

ALTERNATIVE TUNE, HYMN 345.

Hymn 388. St. James.—C.M.

R. COURTEVILLE, 1697.

A-men.

Harvest.

"Thou visitest the earth, and blessest it ; Thou makest it very plenteous."

mf FATHER of mercies, GOD of love,
 Whose gifts all creatures share,
The rolling seasons as they move
 Proclaim Thy constant care.

p When in the bosom of the earth
 The sower hid the grain,
cr Thy goodness mark'd its secret birth,
 And sent the early rain.

mf The spring's sweet influence, LORD, was Thine,
 The seasons knew Thy call ;
Thou mad'st the summer sun to shine,
 The summer dews to fall.

Thy gifts of mercy from above
 Matured the swelling grain ;
f And now the harvest crowns Thy love,
 And plenty fills the plain.

mf O ne'er may our forgetful hearts
 O'erlook Thy bounteous care,
But what our FATHER'S Hand imparts
 Still own in praise and prayer.

f To FATHER, SON, and HOLY GHOST,
 The GOD Whom we adore,
Be glory, as it was, is now,
 And shall be evermore.

MRS. FLOWERDEW, 1811.

Hymn 389.   CASSEL.—7 7.7 7.7 7.   *Christen-schatz* (Basle, 1745).

A-men.

"Although . . . the fields shall yield no meat . . . yet I will rejoice in the Lord, I will joy in the God of my salvation."

mf WHAT our FATHER does is well ;
 Blessèd truth His children tell !
dim Though He send, for plenty, want,
 Though the harvest-store be scant,
cr Yet we rest upon His love,
 Seeking better things above.

mf What our FATHER does is well ;
 Shall the wilful heart rebel?
dim If a blessing He withhold
 In the field, or in the fold,
cr Is it not Himself to be
 All our store eternally?

mf What our FATHER does is well ;
p Though He sadden hill and dell,
or Upward yet our praises rise

For the strength His Word supplies ;
 He has call'd us sons of GOD,
p Can we murmur at His rod?

mf What our FATHER does is well :
 May the thought within us dwell ;
dim Though nor milk nor honey flow
 In our barren Canaan now,
cr GOD can save us in our need,
 GOD can bless us, GOD can feed.

f Therefore unto Him we raise
 Hymns of glory, songs of praise ;
To the FATHER, and the SON,
 And the SPIRIT, THREE in ONE,
Honour, might, and glory be
 Now, and through eternity

Sir H. W. BAKER: from the
German of B. Schmolk.

This Hymn may be sung when there is a deficiency in the crops.

(317)

Processional.

Hymn 390.   Vexillum.—6565.6565.6565.   H. Smart.

" Behold, I have given Him for . . . a leader and commander to the people."

f   BRIGHTLY gleams our banner
      Pointing to the sky,
Waving wanderers onward
   To their home on high.
p   Journeying o'er the desert,
      Gladly thus we pray,
cr   And with hearts united
      Take our heavenward way.
     f   Brightly gleams our banner
        Pointing to the sky,
      Waving wanderers onward
        To their home on high.

mf   JESU, LORD and Master,
      At Thy sacred Feet,
Here with hearts rejoicing
   See Thy children meet ;
p   Often have we left Thee,
      Often gone astray ;
cr   Keep us, mighty SAVIOUR,
      In the narrow way.
     f Brightly gleams, &c.

mf   All our days direct us
      In the way we go,
f   Lead us on victorious
      Over every foe :
p   Bid Thine Angels shield us
      When the storm-clouds lour,
cr   Pardon, LORD, and save us
p   In the last dread hour.
     f Brightly gleams, &c.

mf   Then with Saints and Angels
      May we join above,
Offering prayers and praises
   At Thy Throne of love ;
p   When the toil is over,
      Then comes rest and peace,
cr   JESUS in His beauty,
f   Songs that never cease.
     ff   Brightly gleams our banner
        Pointing to the sky,
      Waving wanderers onward
        To their home on high.

T. J. Potter.

Processional.

Hymn 391. ONWARD, CHRISTIAN SOLDIERS.—6 5 6 5. 12 lines. (*First Tune.*)

H. J. GAUNTLETT.

A - men.

"*Be strong and of a good courage . . . And the Lord, He it is that doth go before thee.*"

f ONWARD, Christian soldiers,
    Marching as to war,
With the Cross of JESUS
    Going on before.
CHRIST the Royal Master
    Leads against the foe ;
Forward into battle,
    See, His banners go !
ff   Onward, Christian soldiers,
        Marching as to war,
        With the Cross of JESUS
        Going on before.

f At the sign of triumph
        Satan's host doth flee ;
On then, Christian soldiers,
        On to victory.
Hell's foundations quiver
        At the shout of praise ;
Brothers, lift your voices,
        Loud your anthems raise.
            ff Onward, &c.

f Like a mighty army
        Moves the Church of GOD ;
mf Brothers, we are treading
        Where the Saints have trod ;

We are not divided,
    All one body we,
cr One in hope and doctrine,
    One in charity.
        ff Onward, &c.

p Crowns and thrones may perish,
        Kingdoms rise and wane,
cr But the Church of JESUS
        Constant will remain ;
f Gates of hell can never
        'Gainst that Church prevail ;
We have CHRIST'S own promise,
    And that cannot fail.
        ff Onward, &c.

f Onward, then, ye people,
        Join our happy throng,
Blend with ours your voices
        In the triumph song ;
Glory, laud, and honour
Unto CHRIST the King,
This through countless ages
Men and Angels sing.
    ff   Onward, Christian soldiers,
            Marching as to war,
            With the Cross of JESUS
            Going on before.

S. BARING-GOULD.

(319)

Processional.

Hymn 391. St. Gertrude.—6 5 6 5. 6 5 6 5. 6 5 6 5.　(*Second Tune.*)

Sir A. SULLIVAN.

ff On-ward, Chris-tian sol - diers,

March-ing as to war. With the Cross of Je - sus Go-ing on be - fore. A-men.

war, With the Cross of Je - sus

war, With the Cross of Je - sus

[*For copyright, see p. 1v.*]

"*Be strong and of a good courage . . . And the Lord, He it is that doth go before thee.*"

f ONWARD, Christian soldiers,
　　Marching as to war,
With the Cross of Jesus
　Going on before.
Christ the Royal Master
　Leads against the foe;
Forward into battle,
　See, His banners go!
　　ff Onward, Christian soldiers,
　　　Marching as to war,
　　With the Cross of Jesus
　　　Going on before.

f At the sign of triumph
　Satan's host doth flee;
On then, Christian soldiers,
　On to victory.
Hell's foundations quiver
　At the shout of praise;
Brothers, lift your voices,
　Loud your anthems raise.
　　ff Onward, &c.

f Like a mighty army
　Moves the Church of God;
mf Brothers, we are treading
　Where the Saints have trod;

We are not divided,
　All one body we,
cr One in hope and doctrine,
　One in charity.
　　ff Onward, &c.

p Crowns and thrones may perish,
　Kingdoms rise and wane,
cr But the Church of Jesus
　Constant will remain;
f Gates of hell can never
　'Gainst that Church prevail;
We have Christ's own promise,
　And that cannot fail.
　　ff Onward, &c.

f Onward, then, ye people,
　Join our happy throng,
Blend with ours your voices
　In the triumph song;
Glory, laud, and honour
　Unto Christ the King,
This through countless ages
　Men and Angels sing.
　　ff Onward, Christian soldiers,
　　　Marching as to war,
　　With the Cross of Jesus
　　　Going on before.

S. Baring-Gould.

Processional.

Hymn 392. ST. BONIFACE.—6 5 6 5. 6 5 6 5. 6 5 6 5. (*First Tune.*)

H. GADSBY.

" Speak unto the children of Israel that they go forward."

mf FORWARD ! be our watchword,
　　Steps and voices join'd ;
Seek the things before us,
　Not a look behind ;
Burns the fiery pillar
　At our army's head ;
Who shall dream of shrinking,
　By our Captain led ?
　　f Forward through the desert,
　　　Through the toil and fight ;
　　　Jordan flows before us,
　　　Sion beams with light.

mf Forward, when in childhood
　　Buds the infant mind ;
All through youth and manhood,
　Not a thought behind ;
Speed through realms of nature,
　Climb the steps of grace ;
Faint not, till in glory
　Gleams our FATHER'S Face.
　　f Forward, all the life-time,
　　　Climb from height to height ;
　　　Till the head be hoary,
　　　Till the eve be light.

mf Forward, flock of JESUS,
　　Salt of all the earth,
Till each yearning purpose
　Spring to glorious birth ;
p Sick, they ask for healing,
　Blind, they grope for day ;
cr Pour upon the nations
　Wisdom's loving ray.
　　f Forward, out of error,
　　　Leave behind the night ;
　　　Forward through the darkness,
　　　Forward into light.

Glories upon glories
　Hath our GOD prepared,
By the souls that love Him
　One day to be shared ;
mf Eye hath not beheld them,
　　Ear hath never heard ;
Nor of these hath utter'd
　Thought or speech a word ;
　　f Forward, marching eastward
　　　Where the Heav'n is bright,
　　　Till the veil be lifted,
　　　Till our faith be sight.

mf Far o'er yon horizon
　　Rise the city towers,
Where our GOD abideth ;
　That fair home is ours :
Flash the streets with jasper,
　Shine the gates with gold ;
Flows the gladdening river
　Shedding joys untold.
　　f Thither, onward thither,
　　　In the SPIRIT'S might ;
　　　Pilgrims to your country,
　　　Forward into light.

mf Into GOD'S high temple
　　Onward as we press,
Beauty spreads around us,
　Born of holiness ;
Arch, and vault, and carving,
　Lights of varied tone,
p Soften'd words and holy,
　Prayer and praise alone :
　　f Every thought upraising
　　　To our city bright,
　　　Where the tribes assemble
　　　Round the Throne of light.

mf Nought that city needeth
　　Of these aisles of stone ;
Where the GODHEAD dwelleth,
　Temple there is none ;
All the Saints, that ever
　In these courts have stood,
p Are but babes, and feeding
　On the children's food.
　　f On through sign and token,
　　　Stars amidst the night,
　　　Forward through the darkness,
　　　Forward into light.

ff To the Eternal FATHER
　　Loudest anthems raise ;
To the SON and SPIRIT
　Echo songs of praise ;
To the LORD of glory,
　Blessed THREE in ONE,
Be by men and Angels
　Endless honours done :
　p Weak are earthly praises ;
　　Dull the songs of night ;
　cr Forward into triumph,
　f Forward into light !

H. ALFORD.

(321)

M

Processional.

Hymn 392. ESTHER.—6 5 6 5. 6 5 6 5. 6 5 6 5. *(Second Tune.)*

A. H. BREWER.

Processional.

A - men.

" Speak unto the children of Israel that they go forward."

mf FORWARD ! be our watchword,
    Steps and voices join'd ;
Seek the things before us,
    Not a look behind ;
Burns the fiery pillar
    At our army's head ;
Who shall dream of shrinking,
    By our Captain led ?
  f   Forward through the desert,
        Through the toil and fight ;
    Jordan flows before us,
        Sion beams with light.

mf Forward, when in childhood
    Buds the infant mind ;
All through youth and manhood,
    Not a thought behind ;
Speed through realms of nature,
    Climb the steps of grace ;
Faint not, till in glory
    Gleams our FATHER'S Face.
  f   Forward, all the life-time,
        Climb from height to height ;
    Till the head be hoary,
        Till the eve be light.

mf Forward, flock of JESUS,
    Salt of all the earth,
Till each yearning purpose
    Spring to glorious birth ;
p Sick, they ask for healing,
    Blind, they grope for day ;
cr Pour upon the nations
    Wisdom's loving ray.
  f   Forward, out of error,
        Leave behind the night ;
    Forward through the darkness,
        Forward into light.

Glories upon glories
    Hath our GOD prepared,
By the souls that love Him
    One day to be shared ;
mf Eye hath not beheld them,
    Ear hath never heard ;
Nor of these hath utter'd
    Thought or speech a word ;
  f   Forward, marching eastward
        Where the Heav'n is bright,
    Till the veil be lifted,
        Till our faith be sight.

mf Far o'er yon horizon
    Rise the city towers,
Where our GOD abideth ;
    That fair home is ours :
Flash the streets with jasper,
    Shine the gates with gold ;
Flows the gladdening river
    Shedding joys untold.
  f   Thither, onward thither,
        In the SPIRIT'S might ;
    Pilgrims to your country,
        Forward into light.

mf Into GOD's high temple
    Onward as we press,
Beauty spreads around us,
    Born of holiness ;
Arch, and vault, and carving,
    Lights of varied tone,
p Soften'd words and holy,
    Prayer and praise alone :
  f   Every thought upraising
        To our city bright,
    Where the tribes assemble
        Round the Throne of light.

mf Nought that city needeth
    Of these aisles of stone ;
Where the GODHEAD dwelleth,
    Temple there is none ;
All the Saints, that ever
    In these courts have stood,
p Are but babes, and feeding
    On the children's food.
  f   On through sign and token,
        Stars amidst the night,
    Forward through the darkness,
        Forward into light.

ff To the Eternal FATHER
    Loudest anthems raise ;
To the SON and SPIRIT
    Echo songs of praise ;
To the LORD of glory,
    Blessèd THREE in ONE,
Be by men and Angels
    Endless honours done :
p Weak are earthly praises ;
    Dull the songs of night ;
cr Forward into triumph,
  f   Forward into light !

H. ALFORD.

Processional.

Hymn 393. PETERBOROUGH.—S.M. (*First Tune.*)   W. H. MONK.

A-men.

Hymn 393. CARLISLE.—S.M. (*Second Tune.*)   C. LOCKHART, 1745–1815.

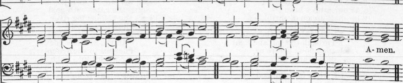

A-men.

A higher setting of this Tune is given at Hymn **706.**

" *Young men and maidens, old men and children, praise the Name of the Lord.*"

f   REJOICE, ye pure in heart,
     Rejoice, give thanks, and sing ;
Your festal banner wave on high,
     The Cross of CHRIST your King.

mf   Bright youth and snow-crown'd age,
     Strong men and maidens meek,
Raise high your free exulting song.
     GOD'S wondrous praises speak.

Yes onward, onward still,
     With hymn, and chant, and song,
Thro' gate, and porch, and column'd aisle,
     The hallow'd pathways throng.

With all the Angel choirs,
     With all the saints on earth,
Pour out the strains of joy and bliss,
     True rapture, noblest mirth.

f   Your clear Hosannas raise,
     And Alleluias loud ;
Whilst answering echoes upward float,
     Like wreaths of incense cloud.

With voice as full and strong
     As ocean's surging praise,

Send forth the hymns our fathers loved,
     The psalms of ancient days.

mf   Yes on, through life's long path,
     Still chanting as ye go,
From youth to age, by night and day,
     In gladness and in woe.

Still lift your standard high,
     Still march in firm array,
As warriors through the darkness toil
     Till dawns the golden day.

p   At last the march shall end,
     The wearied ones shall rest,
cr   The pilgrims find their FATHER'S house,
     Jerusalem the blest.

f   Then on, ye pure in heart,
     Rejoice, give thanks, and sing ;
Your festal banner wave on high,
     The Cross of CHRIST your King.

ff   Praise Him Who reigns on high,
     The LORD Whom we adore,
The FATHER, SON, and HOLY GHOST,
     ONE GOD for evermore.

E. H. PLUMPTRE.

The following Hymns are suitable :

(324)

Laying the Foundation Stone of a Church.

Hymn 394. MELCOMBE.—L.M.

S. WEBBE, 1782.

A - men.

A higher setting of this Tune is given at Hymn 155, a lower setting at Hymn 4.

*" The glory of Lebanon shall come unto thee, the fir tree, the pine tree, and the box together,
to beautify the place of My sanctuary."*

mf O LORD of hosts, Whose glory fills
 The bounds of the eternal hills,
And yet vouchsafes, in Christian lands,
To dwell in temples made with hands :

Grant that all we, who here to-day
Rejoicing this foundation lay,
May be in very deed Thine own,
Built on the precious Corner-stone.

Endue the creatures with Thy grace,
That shall adorn Thy dwelling-place ;
The beauty of the oak and pine,
The gold and silver, make them Thine.

To Thee they all belong ; to Thee
The treasures of the earth and sea ;
And when we bring them to Thy Throne,
We but present Thee with Thine own.

p The heads that guide endue with skill,
The hands that work preserve from ill,
cr That we, who these foundations lay,
May raise the topstone in its day.

mf Both now and ever, LORD, protect
The temple of Thine own elect ;
f Be Thou in them, and they in Thee,
O Ever-blessèd TRINITY !

J. M. NEALE.

Festival of the Dedication of a Church.

Hymn 395. ST. HELENA.—S.M. *(First Tune.)*

B. MILGROVE (Mount Ephraim), 1769.

A - men.

A lower setting of this Tune is given at Hymn 344.

" This is none other but the house of God, and this is the gate of Heaven."

f O WORD of GOD above,
 Who fillest all in all,
Hallow this house with Thy sure love,
And bless our Festival.

mf Here from the Font is pour'd
Grace on each sinful child ;
The blest Anointing of the LORD
Brightens the once defiled.

Here CHRIST to faithful hearts
p His Body gives for food ;
cr The LAMB of GOD Himself imparts
p The Chalice of His Blood.

Here guilty souls that pine
May health and pardon win ;

cr The Judge acquits, and grace Divine
Restores the dead in sin.

mf Yea, GOD enthroned on high
Here also dwells to bless ;
Here trains adoring souls that sigh
His mansions to possess.

f Against this holy home
Rude tempests harmless beat,
And Satan's angels fiercely come
But to endure defeat.

ff All might, all praise be Thine,
FATHER, Co-equal SON,
And SPIRIT, Bond of love Divine,
While endless ages run.

I. WILLIAMS : from the
Latin of C. Guiet.

(325)

Festival of the Dedication of a Church.

Hymn 395. DEDICATION.—S.M. (*Second Tune.*)

E. GILDING, 1762.

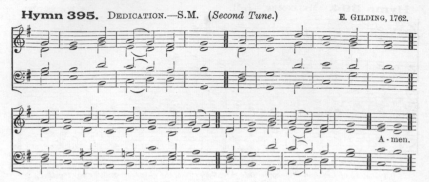

A - men.

"This is none other but the house of God, and this is the gate of Heaven."

f O WORD of GOD above,
Who fillest all in all,
Hallow this house with Thy sure love,
And bless our Festival.

mf Here from the Font is pour'd
Grace on each sinful child ;
The blest Anointing of the LORD
Brightens the once defiled.

Here CHRIST to faithful hearts
p His Body gives for food ;
cr The LAMB of GOD Himself imparts
p The Chalice of His Blood.

Here guilty souls that pine
May health and pardon win ;

cr The Judge acquits, and grace Divine
Restores the dead in sin.

mf Yea, GOD enthroned on high
Here also dwells to bless ;
Here trains adoring souls that sigh
His mansions to possess.

f Against this holy home
Rude tempests harmless beat,
And Satan's angels fiercely come
But to endure defeat.

ff All might, all praise be Thine,
FATHER, Co-equal SON,
And SPIRIT, Bond of love Divine,
While endless ages run.

I. WILLIAMS : from the
Latin of C. Guiet.

Hymn 396. URBS BEATA.—8 7.8 7.8 7. (*First Tune.*) (*First Version.*)

To be sung in Unison.

Proper Sarum Melody.

A-men.

A higher setting of this Tune is given at Hymn 232.

Festival of the Dedication of a Church.

Hymn 396. URBS BEATA.—8 7.8 7.8 7. *(First Tune.)* *(Alternative Version.)*
Proper Sarum Melody.

Bless - ed ci - ty, heav'n-ly Sa - lem, Vis - ion dear of peace and love,

Who of liv - ing stones art build - ed In the height of heav'n a - bove,

And, with An - gel hosts en - cir-cled, As a bride dost . . earthward move. A - men.

" I, John, saw the holy city, new Jerusalem, coming down from God out of heaven, prepared as a bride adorned for her husband."

PART 2.

mf BLESSÈD city, heav'nly Salem,
Vision dear of peace and love,
f Who of living stones art builded
In the height of heav'n above,
mf And, with Angel hosts encircled,
As a bride dost earthward move ;

cr From celestial realms descending,
Bridal glory round thee shed,
p Meet for Him Whose love espoused thee,
cr To thy LORD shalt thou be led ;
All thy streets, and all thy bulwarks
Of pure gold are fashionèd.

mf Bright thy gates of pearl are shining,
They are open evermore ;
cr And by virtue of His merits
Thither faithful souls do soar,
p Who for CHRIST'S dear Name in this world
Pain and tribulation bore.

Many a blow and biting sculpture
Polish'd well those stones elect,
cr In their places now compacted
By the heavenly Architect,
Who therewith hath will'd for ever
That His Palace should be deck'd.

f CHRIST is made the sure Foundation,
CHRIST the Head and Corner-stone,
mf Chosen of the LORD, and precious,
Binding all the Church in one,
f Holy Sion's help for ever,
And her confidence alone.

mf All that dedicated city,
Dearly lovèd of GOD on high,
f In exultant jubilation
Pours perpetual melody,
p GOD the ONE in THREE adoring
cr In glad hymns eternally.

mf To this Temple, where we call Thee,
Come, O LORD of hosts, to-day ;
With Thy wonted loving-kindness
Hear Thy servants, as they pray ;
cr And Thy fullest benediction
Shed within its walls alway.

p Here vouchsafe to all Thy servants
What they ask of Thee to gain,
cr What they gain from Thee for ever
With the Blessèd to retain,
f And hereafter in Thy glory
Evermore with Thee to reign.

The following may be sung at the end of each Part :
f Laud and honour to the FATHER,
Laud and honour to the SON,
Laud and honour to the SPIRIT,
Ever THREE, and ever ONE,
Consubstantial, Co-eternal,
While unending ages run.

J. M. NEALE and Compilers ; from the Latin.

(327)

Festival of the Dedication of a Church.

Hymn 396. ORIEL.—8 7.8 7.8 7. *(Second Tune.)* ETT, *Cantica Sacra*, 1840.

A - men.

A higher setting of this Tune is given at Hymn 179.

Hymn 396. URBS CÆLESTIS.—8 7.8 7.8 7. *(Third Tune.)* Rev. H. E. HODSON.

A - men.

" I, John, saw the holy city, new Jerusalem, coming down from God out of heaven, prepared
as a bride adorned for her husband."

mf BLESSÈD city, heav'nly Salem,
　　Vision dear of peace and love
f　Who of living stones art builded
　　In the height of heav'n above,
mf And, with Angel hosts encircled,
　　As a bride dost earthward move ;
cr　From celestial realms descending,
　　Bridal glory round thee shed,
p　Meet for Him Whose love espoused thee,
cr　To thy LORD shalt thou be led ;
　　All thy streets, and all thy bulwarks
　　Of pure gold are fashionèd.

mf Bright thy gates of pearl are shining,
　　They are open evermore ;
cr　And by virtue of His merits
　　Thither faithful souls do soar ,
p　Who for CHRIST'S dear Name in this world
　　Pain and tribulation bore.

　　Many a blow and biting sculpture
　　Polish'd well those stones elect,
cr　In their places now compacted
　　By the heavenly Architect,
　　Who therewith hath will'd for ever
　　That His Palace should be deck'd.

(328)

Festival of the Dedication of a Church.

PART 2.

f   CHRIST is made the sure Foundation,
    CHRIST the Head and Corner-stone,
mf Chosen of the LORD, and precious,
    Binding all the Church in one,
f   Holy Sion's help for ever,
    And her confidence alone.

mf All that dedicated city,
    Dearly loved of GOD on high,
f   In exultant jubilation
    Pours perpetual melody,
p   GOD the ONE in THREE adoring
cr   In glad hymns eternally.

mf To this Temple, where we call Thee,
    Come, O LORD of hosts, to-day ;
    With Thy wonted loving-kindness

    Hear Thy servants, as they pray ;
cr   And Thy fullest benediction
    Shed within its walls alway.

p   Here vouchsafe to all Thy servants
    What they ask of Thee to gain,
cr   What they gain from Thee for ever
    With the Blessèd to retain,
f   And hereafter in Thy glory
    Evermore with Thee to reign.

The following may be sung at the end of each Part :

f   Laud and honour to the FATHER,
    Laud and honour to the SON,
    Laud and honour to the SPIRIT,
    Ever THREE, and ever ONE,
    Consubstantial, Co-eternal,
    While unending ages run.

J. M. NEALE and Compilers:
from the Latin.

The following Hymns are suitable :

215 The Church's one corner-stone.
228 Jerusalem the golden.
237 O GOD of hosts, the mighty LORD.
242 We love the place, O GOD.
239 CHRIST is our corner-stone.
240 Pleasant are Thy courts above.
241 Hosanna to the living LORD.

The Restoration of a Church.

Hymn 397.   REX GLORIÆ.—8 7 8 7.8 7 8 7.   H. SMART.

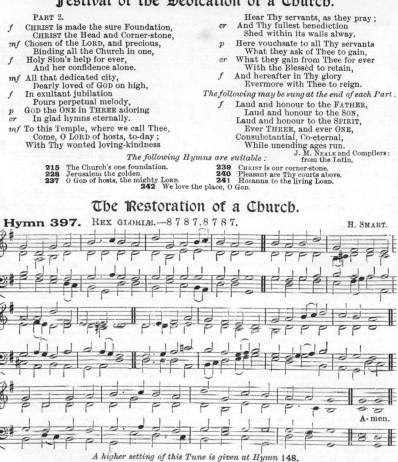

A - men.

A higher setting of this Tune is given at Hymn 148.

"*We are the servants of the God of Heaven and earth, and build the house that was builded these many years ago.*"

f   LIFT the strain of high thanksgiving !
    Tread with songs the hallow'd way !
Praise our fathers' GOD for mercies
    New to us their sons to-day :
mf Here they built for Him a dwelling,
cr   Served Him here in ages past,
f   Fix'd it for His sure possession,
    Holy ground, while time shall last.

mf When the years had wrought their changes,
    He, our own unchanging GOD,
    Thought on this His Habitation,
    Look'd on His decay'd abode ;
    Heard our prayers, and help'd our counsels,
    Bless'd the silver and the gold,
cr   Till once more His House is standing
f   Firm and stately as of old.

mf Entering then Thy gates with praises,
    LORD, be ours Thine Israel's prayer ;
cr   "Rise into Thy place of resting,
    Show Thy promised Presence there !"

p   Let the gracious Word be spoken
cr   Here, as once on Sion's height,
    "This shall be My rest for ever,
    This My dwelling of delight."

f   Fill this latter house with glory
    Greater than the former knew ;
mf Clothe with righteousness its Priesthood,
    Guide its Choir to reverence true ;
    Let Thy Holy One's anointing
    Here its sevenfold blessings shed ;
    Spread for us the heavenly Banquet,
    Satisfy Thy poor with Bread.

f   Praise to Thee, Almighty FATHER,
    Praise to Thee, Eternal SON,
    Praise to Thee, all-quickening SPIRIT,
    Ever-blessèd THREE in ONE ;
p   Threefold Power and Grace and Wisdom,
cr   Moulding out of sinful clay
f   Living stones for that true Temple
    Which shall never know decay.

J ELLERTON
M 2

Burial of the Dead.

Hymn 398. Dies Iræ.—Irregular. (*First Tune.*)

"He cometh to judge the earth."

Rev. J. B. Dykes.

Day of Wrath! O day of mourn-ing! See ful-fill'd the pro-phets' warn-ing!

Heav'n and earth in ash-es burn-ing! Oh, what fear man's bo-som rend-eth

When from Heav'n the Judge de-scend-eth, On Whose sen-tence all de-pend--eth!

ff Wondrous sound the trumpet flingeth,
Through earth's sepulchres it ringeth,
All before the Throne it bringeth.
Death is struck, and nature quaking,
All creation is awaking,
To its Judge an answer making.

mf Lo! the Book exactly worded,
Wherein all hath been recorded;
Thence shall judgment be awarded.
When the Judge His seat attaineth,
And each hidden deed arraigneth,
Nothing unavenged remaineth.

p What shall I, frail man, be pleading,
Who for me be interceding,
When the just are mercy needing?
ff King of Majesty tremendous,
mf Who dost free salvation send us,
Fount of pity, (*p*) then befriend us!

Think, good Jesu, my salvation
Caused Thy wondrous Incarnation;
Leave me not to reprobation.
Faint and weary Thou hast sought me,
On the Cross of suffering bought me;
Shall such grace be vainly brought me?

mf Righteous Judge! for sin's pollution
Grant Thy gift of absolution,
Ere that day of retribution.
Guilty, now I pour my moaning,
All my shame with anguish owning;
Spare, O God, Thy suppliant groaning.

Thou the sinful woman savedst;
Thou the dying thief forgavest;
cr And to me a hope vouchsafest.
p Worthless are my prayers and sighing;
Yet, good Lord, in grace complying,
Rescue me from fires undying.

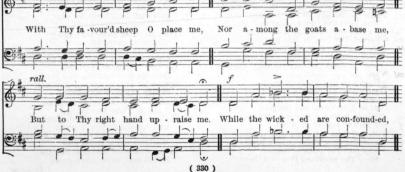

With Thy fa-vour'd sheep O place me, Nor a-mong the goats a-base me,

But to Thy right hand up-raise me. While the wick-ed are con-found-ed,

Burial of the Dead.

Doom'd to flames of woe un-bounded, Call me with Thy Saints sur-round ed.

Low I kneel, with heart sub-mis-sion, See, like ash-es, my con-tri-tion;

Help me in my last con-di-tion. Ah! that day of tears and mourn-ing!

From the dust of earth re-turn-ing Man for judg-ment must pre-pare him;

Spare, O GOD, in mer-cy spare him! LORD, all-pity-ing,

JE-SU Blest, Grant them Thine e-ter-nal rest. A-men.

W. J. IRONS and Compilers: from the Latin of Thomas of Celano.

Burial of the Dead.

Hymn 398. Dies Iræ.—Irregular. *(Second Tune.)*

" He cometh to judge the earth."

Proper Melody.

mf Day of Wrath! O day of mourn-ing! See ful-fill'd... the pro-phets' warn-ing!

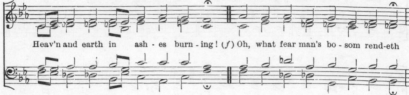

Heav'n and earth in ash-es burn-ing! *(f)* Oh, what fear man's bo-som rend-eth

(p) When from Heav'n the Judge de-scend-eth,*(f)* On Whose sentence*(dim)*all de-pend-eth!

(f) Won-drous sound the trum - - pet fling-eth, Through earth's se - pul -

- chres it ring-eth, All be-fore... the Throne it bring-eth.

For Alternative Version of this Tune, see page 338.

(332)

Burial of the Dead.

Death is struck, and na - ture quak - ing, All cre - a - tion is a - wak - ing,

To its Judge .. an an - swer mak - ing. (*mf*) Lo! the Book ex -

- act - ly word - ed, Where - in all hath been re - cord - ed;

Thence shall judgment be a - ward - ed. When the Judge His seat at - tain - eth,

And each hid - den deed ar - raign - eth, No - thing un - a - venged re - main - eth.

(*p*) What shall I, frail man, be plead - ing, Who for me be in - ter - ced - ing,

Burial of the Dead.

When the just are mer - cy need - ing? (f) King of Ma - jes - ty tre - men-dous,

(mf) Who dost free sal - va - tion send us, Fount of pi - ty, (p) then be-friend us!

Think, good JE - - SU, my . . sal - va - tion Caused Thy won - drous

In - car - na - tion; Leave me not . . to re - pro - ba - tion.

Faint and wea - ry Thou . . hast sought me, On the Cross of suff'-ring bought me;

Shall such grace . . be vain - ly brought me? (mf) Right-eous Judge! for

Burial of the Dead.

sin's pol - lu - tion Grant Thy gift of ab - so - lu - tion,

Ere that day of re - tri - bu - tion. Guil - ty now I pour my moan - ing,

All my shame with an - guish own - ing; Spare, O GOD, Thy sup-pliant groan - ing.

Thou the sin - ful wo - man sav - edst; Thou the dy - ing thief for - gav - est;

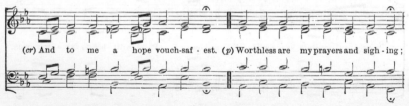

(cr) And to me a hope vouch-saf - est. (p) Worthless are my prayers and sigh - ing;

(335)

Burial of the Dead.

Yet, good LORD, in grace com-ply-ing, Res-cue me from fires un-dy-ing.

(p) With Thy fa-vour'd sheep .. O place me, (cr) Nor a-mong the goats a-base me,

But to Thy right .... hand up-raise me. (f) While the wick-ed

dim. & rit.

are ... con-found-ed, Doom'd to flames of woe un-bound-ed, Call me with

Slower.

Thy ... Saints sur-round-ed. (p) Low I kneel, with heart sub-mis-sion,

Burial of the Dead.

See, like ash - es, my con - tri - tion; Help me in my last con - di - tion.

(p) Ah! that day of tears and mourn - ing! From the dust of earth . . .

re - turn - ing (f) Man for (ff) judg - ment must . . pre - pare him; Spare,

O GOD, in mer - cy spare him! (pp) LORD, all pity - ing, JE - SU Blest,

(cr) Grant them Thine (dim) e - ter - nal rest. (pp) A - - - - men.

W. J. Irons and Compilers: from the Latin of Thomas of Celano.

Burial of the Dead.

Hymn 398. Dies Iræ.—Irregular. (*Second Tune.*) (*Alternative Version.*)

Proper Melody.

Burial of the Dead.

" He cometh to judge the earth.'

mf DAY of Wrath ! O day of mourning !
 See fulfill'd the prophets' warning !
 Heav'n and earth in ashes burning !
f Oh, what fear man's bosom rendeth
p When from Heav'n the Judge descendeth,
f On Whose sentence (*dim*) all dependeth !
ff Wondrous sound the trumpet flingeth,
 Through earth's sepulchres it ringeth,
 All before the Throne it bringeth.
 Death is struck, and nature quaking,
 All creation is awaking,
 To its Judge an answer making.
mf Lo ! the Book exactly worded,
 Wherein all hath been recorded ;
 Thence shall judgment be awarded.
 When the Judge His seat attaineth,
 And each hidden deed arraigneth,
 Nothing unavenged remaineth.

p What shall I, frail man, be pleading,
 Who for me be interceding,
 When the just are mercy needing ?
ff King of Majesty tremendous,
mf Who dost free salvation send us,
 Fount of pity, (p) then befriend us !
 Think, good JESU, my salvation

 Caused Thy wondrous Incarnation ;
 Leave me not to reprobation.
 Faint and weary Thou hast sought me,
 On the Cross of suffering bought me ;
 Shall such grace be vainly brought me ?
mf Righteous Judge ! for sin's pollution
 Grant Thy gift of absolution,
 Ere that day of retribution.
 Guilty, now I pour my moaning,
 All my shame with anguish owning ;
 Spare, O GOD, Thy suppliant groaning.

 Thou the sinful woman savedst ;
 Thou the dying thief forgavest ;
cr And to me a hope vouchsafest.
p Worthless are my prayers and sighing ;
 Yet, good LORD, in grace complying,
 Rescue me from fires undying.
 With Thy favour'd sheep O place me,
cr Nor among the goats abase me,
rall But to Thy right hand upraise me.
f While the wicked are confounded,
ff Doom'd to flames of woe unbounded,
pp rit Call me with Thy Saints surrounded.
p Low I kneel, with heart submission,
 See, like ashes, my contrition ;
 Help me in my last condition.

Ah ! that day of tears and mourning ! From the dust of earth . . re - turn - ing
Man for judg - ment must pre - pare him ; Spare, O GOD, in mer - - cy spare him !

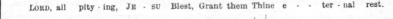

LORD, all pity - ing, JE - SU Blest, Grant them Thine e - - ter - nal rest.

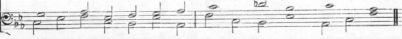

W. J. IRONS and Compilers : from the Latin of Thomas of Celano.

(339)

Burial of the Dead.

Hymn 399. St. Prisca.—7 7 7 7.

R. Redhead.

A - men.

"Surely He hath borne our griefs and carried our sorrows."

p WHEN our heads are bow'd with woe,
   When our bitter tears o'erflow,
When we mourn the lost, the dear,
Jesu, Son of Mary, hear.

mf Thou our throbbing flesh hast worn,
Thou our mortal griefs hast borne,
Thou hast shed the human tear;
Jesu, Son of Mary, hear.

p When the solemn death-bell tolls
For our own departed souls,
When our final doom is near,
Jesu, Son of Mary, hear.

mf Thou hast bow'd the dying head,
Thou the blood of life hast shed,
Thou hast fill'd a mortal bier;
Jesu, Son of Mary, hear.

p When the heart is sad within
With the thought of all its sin,
When the spirit shrinks with fear,
Jesu, Son of Mary, hear.

mf Thou the shame, the grief, hast known,
Though the sins were not Thine own;
cr Thou hast deign'd their load to bear;
Jesu, Son of Mary, hear.

H. H. Milman, 1827.

Hymn 400. Heinlein.—7 7 7 7.

Nürnbergisches, Gesangbuch, 1676.

A - men.

"Where I am there shall also My servant be."

p CHRIST will gather in His own
   To the place where He is gone,
mf Where their heart and treasure lie,
Where our life is hid on high.

p Day by day the voice saith, "Come,
Enter thine eternal home;"
Asking not if we can spare
This dear soul it summons there.

Had He ask'd us, well we know
We should cry, "O spare this blow!"

Yes, with streaming tears should pray,
"Lord, we love *him*, let *him* stay."

mf But the Lord doth nought amiss,
And, since He hath order'd this,
We have nought to do but still
pp Rest in silence on His Will.

mf Many a heart no longer here,
Ah! was all too inly dear;
cr Yet, O Love, 'tis Thou dost call,
f Thou wilt be our All in all.

Catherine Winkworth: from the
German of Count Zinzendorf.

Hymn 401. Requiescat.—7 7 7 7. 8 8. (*First Tune.*)

Rev. J. B. Dykes.

Burial of the Dead.

* If there is no accompaniment, the small notes may be sung.

Hymn 401. LUARD.—7 7 7 7.8 8. *(Second Tune.)* Sir C. V. STANFORD.

[For copyright, see p. lv.]

"The souls of the righteous are in the hand of God, and there shall no torment touch them."

p   NOW the labourer's task is o'er ;
     Now the battle day is past ;
cr   Now upon the farther shore
     Lands the voyager at last.
p   FATHER, in Thy gracious keeping
     Leave we now Thy servant sleeping.

There the tears of earth are dried ;
     There its hidden things are clear ;
cr   There the work of life is tried
     By a juster Judge than here.
p   FATHER, in Thy gracious keeping
     Leave we now Thy servant sleeping.

There the sinful souls, that turn
     To the Cross their dying eyes,
cr   All the love of CHRIST shall learn
     At His Feet in Paradise.
p   FATHER, in Thy gracious keeping
     Leave we now Thy servant sleeping.

mf There no more the powers of hell
     Can prevail to mar their peace ;
cr   CHRIST the LORD shall guard them well,
     He Who died for their release.
p   FATHER, in Thy gracious keeping
     Leave we now Thy servant sleeping.

"Earth to earth, and dust to dust,"
     Calmly now the words we say,
     Leaving *him* to sleep in trust
cr   Till the Resurrection-day.
p   FATHER, in Thy gracious keeping
     Leave we now Thy servant sleeping.

J. ELLERTON.

(341)

Burial of the Dead.

Hymn 402. MEINHOLD.—7 8 7 8. 7 7.   *Gesangbuch* (Lüneburg, 1686).

A men.

FOR A CHILD.   *" They are in peace."*

p   TENDER Shepherd, Thou hast still'd
     Now Thy little lamb's brief weeping ;
Oh, how peaceful, pale, and mild,
     In its narrow bed 'tis sleeping.
     cr   And no sigh of anguish sore
     p   Heaves that little bosom more,

mf In a world of pain and care,
     LORD, Thou wouldst no longer leave it ;
To Thy meadows bright and fair

Lovingly Thou dost receive it ;
     cr   Clothed in robes of spotless white
     Now it dwells with Thee in light.

p   Ah, LORD JESU, grant that we
     There may live where it is living,
     cr   And the blissful pastures see
     That its heavenly food are giving ;
     p   Lost awhile our treasured love,
     cr   Gain'd for ever, safe above.

CATHERINE WINKWORTH : from the
German of J. W. Meinhold.

The following Hymns are suitable :

St. Andrew the Apostle.

Hymn 403. ST. ANDREW.—8 7 8 7.   E. H. THORNE.

A - men.

" One of the two which . . . followed Him was Andrew."

mf   JESUS calls us ; (*cr*) o'er the tumult
     Of our life's wild restless sea
Day by day His sweet voice soundeth,
     Saying, (*p*) "Christian, follow Me :"

mf As of old Saint Andrew heard it
     By the Galilean lake,
Turn'd from home, and toil, and kindred,
     Leaving all for His dear sake.

p   JESUS calls us (*cr*) from the worship
     Of the vain world's golden store,

From each idol that would keep us,
     Saying, (*p*) "Christian, love Me more."

mf In our joys and in our sorrows,
     Days of toil and hours of ease,
Still He calls, in cares and pleasures,
     That we love Him more than these.

p   JESUS calls us : (*cr*) by Thy mercies,
     SAVIOUR, make us hear Thy call,
Give our hearts to Thine obedience,
     Serve and love Thee best of all.

MRS. ALEXANDER.

St. Thomas the Apostle.

Hymn 404. HOLLAND.—L.M.   B. TOURS.

" Be not faithless, but believing."

mf HOW oft, O LORD, Thy Face hath shone
   On doubting souls whose wills were
Thou CHRIST of Cephas and of John, [true !
Thou art the CHRIST of Thomas too.

He loved Thee well, and calmly said,
dim " Come, let us go, and die with Him : "
cr Yet when Thine Easter-news was spread,
'Mid all its light (*p*) his eyes were dim.

mf His brethren's word he would not take,
But craved to touch those Hands of Thine :
p The bruisèd reed Thou didst not break ;
cr He saw, and hail'd his LORD Divine.

f He saw Thee risen ; at once he rose
To full belief's unclouded height ;
And still through his confession flows
To Christian souls Thy life and light.

mf O Saviour, make Thy Presence known
To all who doubt Thy Word and Thee ;
And teach them in that Word alone
To find the truth that sets them free.

And we who know how true Thou art,
And Thee as GOD and LORD adore,
Give us, we pray, a loyal heart,
cr To trust and love Thee more and more.
              W. BRIGHT.

ALTERNATIVE TUNE, HYMN 449.

The following Hymn is suitable :   **612** We have not seen, we cannot see.

The Conversion of St. Paul.

Hymn 405. VULPIUS.—7 6 7 6.   M. VULPIUS, 1609.

" The voice of the Lord breaketh the cedar trees ; yea, the Lord breaketh the cedars of Libanus."

mf THE Shepherd now was smitten ;
   The wolf was ravening near ;
The scatter'd flock he threaten'd,
But knew not Whose they were.

cr In zealous fury seeking
To bind and crucify,
A sudden voice withheld him,
A loud and startling cry :

mf " Saul ! Saul ! why blindly daring
To persecute thy LORD ?
p 'Tis JESUS Whom thou hatest,
cr Rebel not at My Word."

mf Then forth in prayer he stretcheth
Those hands prepared to slay ;
" What wouldst Thou with Thy servant ?
My LORD and Master, say."

CHRIST'S foe becomes His soldier,
   The wolf destroys no more,
p A gentle lamb he enters
The sheepfold by the door.

f O voice of GOD Almighty,
What wonders hath it wrought !
It rends the lofty cedars,
It bends the haughty thought.

p JESU, our Shepherd, cease not
Thy flock from harm to free,
And, when Thy sheep are wandering,
O lead them back to Thee.

f To FATHER, SON, and SPIRIT
All glory, praise, and might,
mf Who call'd us out of darkness
f To His own glorious light.

              F. POTT and Compilers : from the
              Latin of G. de la Brunetière.

(343)

The Conversion of St. Paul.

Hymn 406.   JERUSALEM.—7 6 7 6. 7 6 7 6.   Sir J. STAINER.

A - men.

" He which persecuted us in times past now preacheth the faith which once he destroyed."

f   WE sing the glorious conquest
      Before Damascus' gate,
mf When Saul, the Church's spoiler,
      Came breathing threats and hate ;
      The ravening wolf rush'd forward
      Full early to the prey ;
f   But lo ! the Shepherd met him,
      And bound him fast to-day.

Oh, glory most excelling
      That smote across his path !
Oh, light that pierced and blinded
      The zealot in his wrath !
p   Oh, voice that spake within him
      The calm reproving word !
cr Oh, love that sought and held him
      The bondman of his LORD !

mf O Wisdom, ordering all things
      In order strong and sweet,
cr What nobler spoil was ever
      Cast at the Victor's feet ?
mf What wiser master-builder
      E'er wrought at Thine employ
      Than he, till now so furious
      Thy building to destroy ?

p   LORD, teach Thy Church the lesson,
      Still in her darkest hour
      Of weakness and of danger,
      To trust Thy hidden power :
cr Thy Grace by ways mysterious
      The wrath of man can bind,
      And in Thy boldest foeman
      Thy chosen Saint can find.

J. ELLERTON.

ALTERNATIVE TUNE, HYMN 542 (SECOND TUNE).

Presentation of Christ in the Temple,
COMMONLY CALLED
The Purification of St. Mary the Virgin.

Hymn 407.   BRISTOL.—C.M.   RAVENSCROFT, *Psalmes*, 1621.

A - men.

A setting with additional harmonies is given at Hymn 53.

Presentation of Christ in the Temple.

" The Lord, Whom ye seek, shall suddenly come to His temple."

mf O SION, open wide thy gates,
    Let figures disappear ;
A Priest and Victim, both in one,
    The Truth Himself, is here.

    No more the simple flock shall bleed ;
cr   Behold, the FATHER'S SON
    Himself to His own Altar comes,
dim For sinners to atone.

p Conscious of hidden Deity,
    The lowly Virgin brings
Her new-born Babe, with two young doves,
    Her tender offerings.

mf The aged Simeon sees at last
    His LORD so long desired,
cr And Anna welcomes Israel's Hope
    With holy rapture fired.

p But silent knelt the Mother blest
    Of the yet silent WORD,
And, pondering all things in her heart,
    With speechless praise adored.

f All glory to the FATHER be,
    All glory to the SON,
All glory, HOLY GHOST, to Thee,
    While endless ages run.

E. CASWALL and Compilers : from the
Latin of J. B. de Santeuil.

The following Hymns are suitable :

449 The GOD, Whom earth, and sea, and sky.   **450** Shall we not love thee, Mother dear.
611 Hail to the LORD Who comes.

St. Matthias the Apostle.

Hymn 408.   SHERBORNE.—7 7 7 7. 7 7.   W. H. MONK.

A-men.

" And they gave forth their lots ; and the lot fell upon Matthias ; and he was numbered with
the eleven Apostles."

mf B ISHOP of the souls of men,
p   When the foeman's step is nigh,
When the wolf lays wait by night
    For the lambs continually,
cr Watch, O LORD, about us keep,
    Guard us, Shepherd of the sheep.

p When the hireling flees away,
    Caring only for his gold,
And the gate unguarded stands
    At the entrance to the fold,
f Stand, O LORD, Thy flock before,
    Thou the Guardian, Thou the Door.

mf LORD, Whose guiding finger ruled
    In the casting of the lot,
That Thy Church might fill the throne
    Of the lost Iscariot,
p In our trouble ever thus
f Stand, good Master, nigh to us.

mf When the Saints their order take
    In the New Jerusalem,
f And Matthias stands elect,
p Give us part and lot with him,
cr Where in Thine own dwelling-place
    We may witness face to face.

G. MOULTRIE.

ALTERNATIVE TUNE, HYMN 7.

The following Hymn is suitable :
613 Praise to the Heavenly Wisdom.

(345)

The Annunciation of the Blessed Virgin Mary.

Hymn 409. ANNUNCIATION.—S.M.

C. A. BARRY.

A-men.

" Behold, a Virgin shall be with child, and shall bring forth a Son, and they shall call His Name Emmanuel, which being interpreted is, God with us."

f PRAISE we the LORD this day,
　　This day so long foretold,
Whose promise shone with cheering ray
On waiting saints of old.

mf The Prophet gave the sign
　　For faithful men to read ;
A Virgin, born of David's line,
Shall bear the promised Seed.

　　Ask not how this should be,
p But worship and adore ;
Like her, whom Heaven's Majesty
Came down to shadow o'er.

Meekly she bow'd her head
　　To hear the gracious word,
mf Mary, the pure and lowly maid,
　　The favour'd of the LORD.

Blessèd shall be her name
　　In all the Church on earth,
Through whom that wondrous mercy came,
The Incarnate SAVIOUR'S birth.

f JESU, the Virgin's SON,
　　We praise Thee and adore,
Who art with GOD the FATHER ONE
And SPIRIT evermore.

From FALLOW, *Selection of Hymns,* 1847.

The following Hymns are suitable :

449 The GOD, Whom earth, and sea, and sky.　　**450** Shall we not love thee, Mother dear.

St. Mark the Evangelist.

Hymn 410. ST. PETROX.—L.M.

Rev. R. F. DALE.

A-men.

" The face of a lion on the right side."

mf FROM out the cloud of amber light,
　　Borne on the whirlwind from the north,
Four living creatures wing'd and bright
Before the Prophet's eye came forth.

f The voice of GOD was in the Four
p Beneath that awful crystal mist,
cr And every wondrous form they wore
Foreshadow'd an Evangelist.

f The lion-faced, he told abroad
The strength of love, the strength of faith ;

He show'd the Almighty SON of GOD,
The Man Divine Who won by death.

O Lion of the Royal Tribe,
Strong SON of GOD, and strong to save,
All power and honour we ascribe
To Thee Who only makest brave.

mf For strength to love, for will to speak,
f For fiery crowns by Martyrs won,
p For suffering patience, strong and meek,
f We praise Thee, LORD, and Thee alone.

MRS. ALEXANDER.

ALTERNATIVE TUNE, HYMN 449.

St. Philip and St. James the Apostles.

Hymn 411. St. Philip and St. James.—L.M.　　J. Langran.

A-men.

" Philip saith unto Him, Lord, shew us the Father and it sufficeth us."
" James, a servant of God."

mf THERE is one Way, and only one,
　　Out of our gloom, and sin, and care,
To that far land where shines no sun
Because the Face of GOD is there.

There is one Truth, the Truth of GOD,
That CHRIST came down from Heav'n to show,
One Life that His redeeming Blood
Has won for all His saints below.

The lore from Philip once conceal'd,
We know its fulness now in CHRIST;

In Him the FATHER is reveal'd,
And all our longing is sufficed.

And still unwavering faith holds sure
The words that James wrote sternly down;
Except we labour and endure,
We cannot win the heavenly crown.

f O Way Divine, through gloom and strife,
Bring us Thy FATHER'S Face to see;
O heavenly Truth, O precious Life,
p At last, at last, we rest in Thee.

Mrs. Alexander.

Alternative Tune, Hymn 754 (First Tune).

St. Barnabas the Apostle.

Hymn 412. Vienna.—7 7 7 7.　　J. H. Knecht, 1799.

A-men.

*" He was a good man, and full of the Holy Ghost, and of faith; and much people was added
unto the Lord."*

mf BRIGHTLY did the light Divine
　　From his words and actions shine,
Whom the Twelve, with love unblamed,
" Son of consolation " named.

Full of peace and lively joy
Sped he on his high employ,
By his mild exhorting word
Adding many to the LORD.

p Blessed SPIRIT, Who didst call
Barnabas and holy Paul,
cr And didst them with gifts endue,
Mighty words and wisdom true,

mf Grant us, LORD of life, to be
By their pattern full of Thee;
cr That beside them we may stand
In that day on CHRIST'S right Hand.

H. Alford

(347)

St. Barnabas the Apostle.

Hymn 413. ST. BARNABAS.—11 10 11 10.   H. J. GAUNTLETT.

A - men.

" Joses, who by the Apostles was surnamed Barnabas, which is, being interpreted, The son of consolation."

mf O SON of GOD, our Captain of Salvation,
Thyself by suffering school'd to human grief,
cr We bless Thee for Thy sons of consolation,
Who follow in the steps of Thee their Chief ;

mf Those whom Thy SPIRIT'S dread vocation severs
To lead the vanguard of Thy conquering host ;
Whose toilsome years are spent in brave endeavours
To bear Thy saving Name from coast to coast ;

f Those whose bright faith makes feeble hearts grow stronger,
And sends fresh warriors to the great campaign,
p Bids the lone convert feel estranged no longer,
cr And wins the sunder'd to be one again ;

mf And all true helpers, patient, kind, and skilful,
Who shed Thy light across our darken'd earth,
Counsel the doubting, and restrain the wilful,
dim e cr Soothe the sick bed, and share the children's mirth.

f Such was Thy Levite, strong in self-oblation
To cast his all at Thine Apostles' feet ;
He whose new name, through every Christian nation,
From age to age our thankful strains repeat.

mf Thus, LORD, Thy Barnabas in memory keeping,
Still be Thy Church's watchword, " Comfort ye ;"
Till in our FATHER'S House shall end our weeping,
cr And all our wants be satisfied in Thee.

                                                    J. ELLERTON.

ALTERNATIVE TUNE, HYMN 12.

The Nativity of St. John Baptist.

Hymn 414. CROFT'S 148TH.—6 6 6 6. 4 4 4 4.   W. CROFT, 1678–1727.

The Nativity of St. John Baptist.

" Repent ye, for the kingdom of heaven is at hand."

mf LO! from the desert homes,
 Where he hath hid so long,
The new Elias comes,
 In sternest wisdom strong ;
cr The voice that cries
  Of CHRIST from high,
dim And judgment nigh
 From opening skies.

mf Your GOD e'en now doth stand
 At heaven's opening door ;
His fan is in His hand,
 And He will purge His floor :
f The wheat he claims
  And with Him stows,
p The chaff He throws
 To quenchless flames.

f Ye haughty mountains, bow
 Your sky-aspiring heads ;
p Ye valleys, hiding low,
cr Lift up your gentle meads ;

Make His way plain
 Your King before,
f For evermore
He comes to reign.

mf May thy dread voice around,
 Thou harbinger of Light,
On our dull ears still sound,
dim Lest here we sleep in night,
  Till judgment come,
 And on our path
 Shall burst the wrath,
 And deathless doom.

mf O GOD, with love's sweet might,
 Who dost anoint and arm
CHRIST'S soldier for the fight
 With grace that shields from harm,
f Thrice Blessèd THREE,
  Heav'n's endless days
 Shall sing Thy praise
 Eternally.

    I. WILLIAMS : from the Latin
     of C. Coffin.

Hymn 415. BECCLES.—L.M.
                    C. GALL, 1625.

" Behold I will send My messenger, and he shall prepare the way before Me."

mf THE great forerunner of the morn,
 The herald of the WORD, is born :
And faithful hearts shall never fail
With thanks and praise his light to hail.

With heavenly message Gabriel came,
That John should be that herald's name,
And with prophetic utterance told
His actions great and manifold.

John, still unborn, yet gave aright
His witness to the coming Light ;
cr And CHRIST, the Sun of all the earth,
Fulfill'd that witness at His Birth.

f Of woman-born shall never be
A greater Prophet than was he,

Whose mighty deeds exalt his fame
To greater than a Prophet's name.

mf But why should mortal accents raise
The hymn of John the Baptist's praise ?
Of whom, or e'er his course was run,
Thus spake the FATHER to the SON :

p " Behold My herald, who shall go
Before Thy Face Thy way to show,
And shine, as with the day-star's gleam,
Before Thine own eternal beam."

f All praise to GOD the FATHER be,
All praise, Eternal SON, to Thee,
Whom with the SPIRIT we adore
For ever and for evermore.

    J. M. NEALE : from Venerable Bede.

ALTERNATIVE TUNE, HYMN 50.

St. Peter the Apostle.

Hymn 416. DERRY.—8 8 8 6.   Rev. J. B. DYKES.

A-men.

" Lovest thou Me ? "

p FORSAKEN once, and thrice denied,
cr The risen LORD gave pardon free,
Stood once again at Peter's side,
  And ask'd him, (*p*) " Lov'st thou Me ? "

How many times with faithless word
Have we denied His holy Name,
How oft forsaken our dear LORD,
  And shrunk when trial came !

mf Saint Peter, when the cock crew clear,
  Went out, and wept his broken faith ;
f Strong as a rock through strife and fear,
  He served his LORD till death.

p How oft his cowardice of heart
We have without his love sincere,
The sin without the sorrow's smart,
  The shame without the tear !

mf O oft forsaken, oft denied,
  Forgive our shame, wash out our sin ;
Look on us from Thy FATHER'S side
p And let that sweet look win.

mf Hear when we call Thee from the deep,
  Still walk beside us on the shore,
Give hands to work, (*p*) and eyes to weep,
cr And hearts to love Thee more.

MRS. ALEXANDER.

Hymn 417. CEPHAS.—6 6 6 6.8 8.   W. H. MONK.

St. Peter the Apostle.

" Simon Peter answered and said, Thou art the Christ, the Son of the living God."

f   "THOU art the CHRIST, O LORD,
      The SON of GOD most high ! "
   For ever be adored
   That Name in earth and sky,
dim In which, though mortal strength may fail,
cr   The Saints of GOD at last prevail !

mf   Oh, surely he was blest
   With blessedness unpriced,
   Who, taught of GOD, confess'd
   The GODHEAD in the CHRIST !
   For of Thy Church, LORD, Thou didst own
   Thy Saint a true foundation-stone.

p   Thrice was he put to shame,
   Thrice did the dauntless fall ;
   But, oh, that look that came

cr   From out the judgment-hall !
   It pierced and broke the spell-bound heart,
f   And foil'd the tempter's sifting art.

p   Thrice fallen, thrice restored !
   The bitter lesson learnt,
cr   That heart for Thee, O LORD,
   With triple ardour burnt.
   The cross he took he laid not down
   Until he grasp'd the Martyr's crown.

f   Oh, bright triumphant faith !
   Oh, courage void of fears !
   Oh, love most strong in death !
p   Oh, penitential tears !
mf By these, LORD, keep us lest we fall,
   And make us go where Thou shalt call.

Bishop W. WALSHAM HOW.

ALTERNATIVE TUNE, HYMN 414.

St. James the Apostle.

Hymn 418.   ST. JAMES —C.M.   R. COURTEVILLE, 1697.

" He killed James, the brother of John, with the sword."

mf FOR all Thy Saints, a noble throng,
     Who fell by fire and sword,
  Who soon were call'd, or waited long,
  We praise Thy Name, O LORD ;

  For him who left his father's side,
     Nor linger'd by the shore,
p   When, softer than the weltering tide,
   Thy summons glided o'er ;

  Who stood beside the maiden dead,
cr   Who climb'd the mount with Thee,
  And saw the glory round Thy Head,
   One of Thy chosen three ;

p   Who knelt beneath the olive shade,
     Who drank Thy cup of pain,
  And pass'd from Herod's flashing blade
cr   To see Thy Face again.

mf LORD, give us grace, and give us love,
     Like him to leave behind
  Earth's cares and joys, and look above
   With true and earnest mind.

  So shall we learn to drink Thy cup,
     So meek and firm be found,
cr   When Thou shalt come to take us up
   Where Thine elect are crown'd.

MRS. ALEXANDER.

The following Hymn is suitable :
751 Two brothers freely cast their lot.

St. Bartholomew the Apostle.

Hymn 419. Everton.—8 7 8 7. 8 7 8 7.

H. Smart.

A-men.

"The Lord knoweth them that are His."

mf KING of Saints, to Whom the number
 Of Thy starry host is known,
Many a name, by man forgotten,
 Lives for ever round Thy Throne ;
Lights, which earth-born mists have darken'd,
cr There are shining full and clear,
Princes in the court of Heaven,
dim Nameless, unremember'd here.

mf In the roll of Thine Apostles
 One there stands, Bartholomew,
He for whom to-day we offer,
 Year by year, our praises due ;
p How he toil'd for Thee and suffer'd
 None on earth can now record ;
cr All his saintly life is hidden
 In the knowledge of his LORD.

mf Was it he, beneath the fig-tree
 Seen of Thee, and guileless found ;
He who saw the good he long'd for
 Rise from Nazareth's barren ground ;
He who met his risen Master
 On the shore of Galilee ;
He to whom the Word was spoken,
 "Greater things thou yet shall see"?

p None can tell us ; *(cr)* all is written
 In the LAMB's great book of life,
All the faith, and prayer, and patience,
 All the toiling, and the strife ;
f There are told Thy hidden treasures ;
p Number us, O LORD, with them,
cr When Thou makest up the jewels
f Of Thy living Diadem.

J Ellerton.

(352)

St. Matthew the Apostle.

Hymn 420. St. Bernard.—L.M.

W. H. Monk.

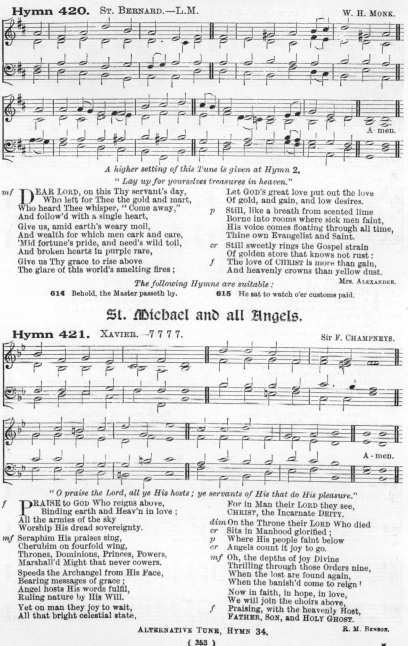

A - men.

A higher setting of this Tune is given at Hymn 2.

" Lay up for yourselves treasures in heaven."

mf DEAR LORD, on this Thy servant's day,
Who left for Thee the gold and mart,
Who heard Thee whisper, "Come away,"
And follow'd with a single heart,

Give us, amid earth's weary moil,
And wealth for which men cark and care,
'Mid fortune's pride, and need's wild toil,
And broken hearts in purple rare,

Give us Thy grace to rise above
The glare of this world's smelting fires ;

Let GOD'S great love put out the love
Of gold, and gain, and low desires.

p Still, like a breath from scented lime
Borne into rooms where sick men faint,
His voice comes floating through all time,
Thine own Evangelist and Saint.

cr Still sweetly rings the Gospel strain
Of golden store that knows not rust :
f The love of CHRIST is more than gain,
And heavenly crowns than yellow dust.

Mrs. Alexander.

The following Hymns are suitable :

614 Behold, the Master passeth by.

615 He sat to watch o'er customs paid.

St. Michael and all Angels.

Hymn 421. Xavier. —7 7 7 7.

Sir F. Champneys.

A - men.

" O praise the Lord, all ye His hosts ; ye servants of His that do His pleasure."

f PRAISE to GOD Who reigns above,
Binding earth and Heav'n in love ;
All the armies of the sky
Worship His dread sovereignty.

mf Seraphim His praises sing,
Cherubim on fourfold wing,
Thrones, Dominions, Princes, Powers,
Marshall'd Might that never cowers.

Speeds the Archangel from His Face,
Bearing messages of grace ;
Angel hosts His words fulfil,
Ruling nature by His Will.

Yet on man they joy to wait,
All that bright celestial state,

For in Man their LORD they see,
CHRIST, the Incarnate DEITY.

dim On the Throne their LORD Who died
cr Sits in Manhood glorified ;
p Where His people faint below
cr Angels count it joy to go.

mf Oh, the depths of joy Divine
Thrilling through those Orders nine,
When the lost are found again,
When the banish'd come to reign !

Now in faith, in hope, in love,
We will join the choirs above,
f Praising, with the heavenly Host,
FATHER, SON, and HOLY GHOST.

Alternative Tune, Hymn 34.

R. M. Benson.

(353)

N

St. Michael and all Angels.

Hymn 422. LAMBORNE.—8 7 8 7. 7 7.

Sir G. C. MARTIN.

A - men.

"There was war in heaven ; Michael and his angels fought against the dragon ; and the dragon fought and his angels."

f CHRIST, in highest Heav'n enthronèd,
 Equal of the FATHER'S Might,
By pure spirits, trembling, ownèd,
 GOD of GOD, and LIGHT of LIGHT,
Thee 'mid Angel hosts we sing,
Thee their Maker and their King.

mf All who circling round adore Thee,
 All who bow before Thy Throne,
Burn with flaming zeal before Thee,
 Thy behests to carry down ;
To and fro, 'twixt earth and Heav'n,
Speed they each on errands given.

f First of all those legions glorious,
 Michael waves his sword of flame,
Who of old in war victorious

Did the Dragon's fierceness tame ;
Who with might invincible
Thrust the rebel down to hell.

mf Strong to aid the sick and dying,
 Call'd from Heav'n they swiftly fly,
 Grace Divine and strength supplying
p In their mortal agony :
Souls released from bondage here
Safe to Paradise they bear.

f To the FATHER praise be given
 By the un allen Angel-host,
Who in His great war have striven
 With the legions of the lost ;
Equal praise in highest Heav'n
To the SON and HOLY GHOST.

W. PALMER and Compilers : from
the Latin of J. B. de Santeuil.

Hymn 423. TRISAGION.—10 10 10 10.

H. SMART.

A - men.

ORG.

St. Michael and all Angels.

" When the morning stars sang together, and all the sons of God shouted for joy."

f STARS of the morning, so gloriously bright,
    Fill'd with celestial virtue and light,
These that, where night never followeth day,
p   Raise the " Trisagion " * ever and aye :

mf These are Thy ministers, these dost Thou own,
LORD GOD of Sabaoth, nearest Thy Throne ;
These are Thy messengers, these dost Thou send,
Help of the helpless ones ! man to defend.

These keep the guard amidst Salem's dear bowers,
Thrones, Principalities, Virtues, and Powers,
Where, with the Living Ones, mystical Four,
Cherubim, Seraphim (*p*) bow and adore.

mf Then, when the earth was first poised in mid space,
Then, when the planets first sped on their race,
Then, when were ended the six days' employ,
f   Then all the Sons of GOD shouted for joy.

mf Still let them succour us ; still let them fight,
LORD of Angelic hosts, battling for right ;
Till where their anthems they ceaselessly pour
We with the Angels may (*p*) bow and adore.

J. M. NEALE: from the Greek of St. Joseph.

* *In Greek, from which this Hymn is translated, " Trisagion " is the same as the Latin
" Tersanctus " and the English " Thrice-Holy."*

Hymn 424. WOOLMER'S.—L.M.
Rev. Sir F. A. G. OUSELEY.

A - men.

*" Are they not all ministering spirits, sent forth to minister for them who shall be heirs
of salvation ? "*

mf THEY come, GOD'S messengers of love,
    They come from realms of peace
From homes of never-fading light, [above,
From blissful mansions ever bright.

They come to watch around us here,
To soothe our sorrow, calm our fear :
Ye heavenly guides, speed not away,
GOD willeth you with us to stay.

p But chiefly at its journey's end
'Tis yours the spirit to befriend,
And whisper to the faithful heart,
rall pp " O Christian soul, in peace depart."

p Blest JESU, Thou Whose groans and tears
Have sanctified frail nature's fears,
To earth in bitter sorrow weigh'd,
Thou didst not scorn Thine Angel's aid ;

cr An Angel guard to us supply,
When on the bed of death we lie ;
And by Thine own Almighty power
p O shield us in the last dread hour.

f To GOD the FATHER, GOD the SON,
And GOD the SPIRIT, THREE in ONE,
From all above and all below
Let joyful praise unceasing flow.

R. CAMPBELL, 1850.

These Hymns on the ministry of Angels may be sung, if desired, at other times.

ALTERNATIVE TUNE, HYMN 146.

The following Hymns are suitable :

St. Luke the Evangelist.

Hymn 425. ELY.—L.M.   Bishop TURTON, 1844.

A - men.

A higher setting of this Tune is given at Hymn 75.

" The brother, whose praise is in the gospel."

f   WHAT thanks and praise to Thee we owe,
        O Priest and Sacrifice Divine,
    For Thy dear Saint through whom we know
    So many a gracious Word of Thine ;

mf Whom Thou didst choose to tell the tale
    Of all Thy Manhood's toils and tears,
    And for a moment lift the veil
    That hides Thy Boyhood's spotless years.

p   How many a soul with guilt oppress'd
cr Has learn'd to hear the joyful sound
    In that sweet tale of sin confess'd,
    The FATHER'S love, the lost and found !

p   How many a child of sin and shame
cr Has refuge found from guilty fears
    Through her, who to the Saviour came
    With costly ointments and with tears !

mf What countless worshippers have sung,
    In lowly fane or lofty choir,
    The song that loosed the silent tongue
    Of him who was the Baptist's sire !

cr And still the Church through all her days
    Uplifts the strains that never cease,
    The Blessèd Virgin's hymn of praise,
p   The aged Simeon's words of peace.

f   O happy Saint ! whose sacred page,
    So rich in words of truth and love,
    Pours on the Church from age to age
mf This healing unction from above ;

    The witness of the Saviour's life,
    The great Apostle's chosen friend
p   Through weary years of toil and strife,
cr And still found faithful to the end.

mf So grant us, LORD, like him to live,
    Beloved by man, approved by Thee,
    Till Thou at last the summons give,
    And we, with him, Thy Face shall see.

Archbishop MACLAGAN.

St. Simon and St. Jude, Apostles.

Hymn 426. NUKAPU.—8 7 8 7 8 7.

E. J. HOPKINS.

A - men.

" Just and true are Thy ways, Thou King of Saints."

mf THOU Who sentest Thine Apostles
  Two and two before Thy Face,
Partners in the night of toiling,
  Heirs together of Thy grace,
Throned at length, their labours ended,
  Each in his appointed place ;

f Praise to Thee for those Thy champions
  Whom our hymns to-day proclaim ;
mf One, whose zeal by Thee enlighten'd
  Burn'd anew with nobler flame ;
One, the kinsman of Thy Childhood,
  Brought at last to know Thy Name.

f Praise to Thee ! Thy fire within them
  Spake in love, and wrought in power ;
Seen in mighty signs and wonders
  In Thy Church's morning hour ;
Heard in tones of sternest warning
  When the storms began to lower.

p Once again those storms are breaking ;
  Hearts are failing, love grows cold ;
Faith is darken'd, sin abounding ;
  Grievous wolves assail Thy fold :
cr Save us, LORD, our One Salvation ;
  Save the Faith reveal'd of old.

mf Call the erring by Thy pity ;
  Warn the tempted by Thy fear ;
Keep us true to Thine allegiance,
  Counting life itself less dear,
cr Standing firmer, holding faster,
dim As we see the end draw near.

mf Till, with holy Jude and Simon
  And the thousand faithful more,
We, the good confession witness'd
  And the lifelong conflict o'er,
cr On the sea of fire and crystal
  Stand, and wonder, (*p*) and adore.

f GOD the FATHER, great and wondrous
  In Thy works, to Thee be praise ;
KING of Saints, to Thee be glory,
  Just and true in all Thy ways ;
Praise to Thee, from Both proceeding,
  HOLY GHOST, through endless days.

J. ELLERTON.

ALTERNATIVE TUNE, HYMN 281.

All Saints' Day.

Hymn 427. ALL SAINTS.—8 7 8 7. 7 7.

Geistreiches Gesangbuch (Darmstadt, 1698).

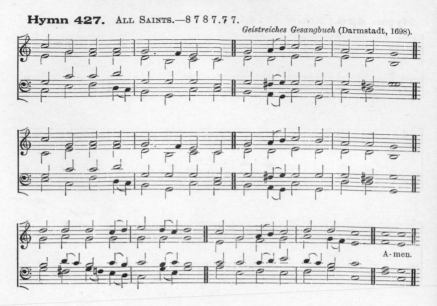

A-men.

" What are these which are arrayed in white robes? and whence came they?"

mf WHO are these like stars appearing,
These, before GOD's Throne who stand?
Each a golden crown is wearing,
Who are all this glorious band?
Alleluia, hark! they sing,
f Praising loud their heavenly King.

mf Who are these in dazzling brightness,
Clothed in GOD's own righteousness,
These, whose robes of purest whiteness
Shall their lustre still possess,
Still untouch'd by time's rude hand?
Whence came all this glorious band?

f These are they who have contended
For their SAVIOUR's honour long,
Wrestling on till life was ended,
Following not the sinful throng;
These, who well the fight sustain'd,
Triumph by the LAMB have gain'd.

p These are they whose hearts were riven,
Sore with woe and anguish tried,
Who in prayer full oft have striven
With the GOD they glorified;
cr Now, their painful conflict o'er,
GOD has bid them weep no more.

mf These, the ALMIGHTY contemplating,
Did as priests before Him stand,
Soul and body always waiting
Day and night at His command:
f Now in GOD's most holy place
Blest they stand before His Face.

FRANCES E. COX: from the
German of H. T. Schenk.

All Saints' Day.

Hymn 428. REST.—8 8.8 8.8 8.

Sir J. STAINER.

Voices in Unison. Harmony. A-men.

A lower setting of this Tune is given at Hymn 600.

"*That they may rest from their labours.*"

mf THE Saints of GOD! their conflict past,
And life's long battle won at last,
No more they need the shield or sword,
They cast them down before their LORD:
cr   O happy Saints! for ever blest,
p   At JESUS' feet how safe your rest!

mf The Saints of GOD! their wanderings done,
No more their weary course they run,
No more they faint, no more they fall,
No foes oppress, no fears appal:
cr   O happy Saints! for ever blest,
p   In that dear home how sweet your rest!

mf The Saints of GOD! life's voyage o'er,
Safe landed on that blissful shore,
No stormy tempests now they dread,
No roaring billows lift their head:
cr   O happy Saints! for ever blest,
p   In that calm haven of your rest!

    The Saints of GOD their vigil keep
While yet their mortal bodies sleep,
cr Till from the dust they too shall rise
And soar triumphant to the skies:
f   O happy Saints! rejoice and sing;
He quickly comes, your LORD and King.

mf O GOD of Saints, to Thee we cry;
O SAVIOUR, plead for us on high;
O HOLY GHOST, our Guide and Friend,
p Grant us Thy grace till life shall end;
cr That with all Saints our rest may be
f In that bright Paradise with Thee.

Archbishop MACLAGAN.

ALTERNATIVE TUNE, HYMN **345** (SECOND TUNE).

All Saints' Day.

Hymn 429. St. Alphege.—7 6 7 6.   H. J. Gauntlett.

A-men.

A lower setting of this Tune is given at Hymn 225.

"And the city had no need of the sun, neither of the moon, to shine in it; for the glory of God did lighten it, and the Lamb is the Light thereof."

mf   O HEAVENLY Jerusalem,
     Of everlasting halls,
cr   Thrice blessèd are the people
dim   Thou storest in thy walls.

f   Thou art the golden mansion,
     Where Saints for ever sing,
The seat of God's own chosen,
     The palace of the King.

p   There God for ever sitteth,
cr   Himself of all the Crown;
The Lamb, the Light that shineth,
     And never goeth down.

p   Nought to this seat approacheth
     Their sweet peace to molest;
f   They sing their God for ever,
     Nor day nor night they rest.

mf   Sure hope doth thither lead us;
     Our longings thither tend;
cr   May short-lived toil ne'er daunt us
     For joys that cannot end.

f   To Christ the Sun that lightens
     His Church above, below,
To Father, and to Spirit,
     All things created bow.

Alternative Tune, Hymn 405.   I. Williams: from the Latin.

The Hymns for this Festival may be used on other days.

The following Hymns are suitable for this Festival:

222 Ten thousand times ten thousand.
228 Jerusalem the golden.
233 Jerusalem on high.
235 Oh, what the joy and the glory must be.
435 Lo! round the Throne, a glorious band.

436 Hark! the sound of holy voices.
438 How bright those glorious spirits shine.
447 Soldiers, who are Christ's below.
618 Bride of Christ, whose glorious warfare.
619 Who the multitudes can number.

Festivals of Apostles.

Hymn 430. Æterna Christi munera.—L.M. *(First Tune.)* *(First Version.)*
To be sung in Unison.   Proper Melody.

A-men.

Festivals of Apostles.

Hymn 430. Æterna Christi munera.—L.M. *(First Tune.)*
(Alternative Version.)

Proper Melody.

The'e-ter - nal gifts of CHRIST the King, Th' A - pos - tles' glo - ry, . . let us sing;

And all, with hearts of glad-ness, raise . Due hymns of thankful love . . and praise. A - men.

Hymn 430. Affection.—L.M. *(Second Tune.)* GREENWOOD, *Psalmody*, 1838.

A - men.

"And the wall of the city had twelve foundations, and in them the names of the twelve Apostles of the Lamb."

f   TH' eternal gifts of CHRIST the King,
       The Apostles' glory, let us sing ;
And all, with hearts of gladness, raise
Due hymns of thankful love and praise.

For they the Church's Princes are,
Triumphant Leaders in the war,
In heav'nly courts a warrior band,
True lights to lighten every land.

mf Theirs is the steadfast faith of Saints,
And hope that never yields nor faints,
And love of CHRIST in perfect glow
That lays the prince of this world low.

In them the FATHER'S glory shone,
In them the Will of GOD the SON,
In them exults the HOLY GHOST,
cr Through them rejoice the heav'nly Host.

p   To Thee, Redeemer, now we cry,
      That Thou wouldst join to them on high
      Thy servants, who this grace implore,
mf For ever and for evermore.

J. M. NEALE and Compilers:
from St. Ambrose.

N 2

Festivals of Apostles.

Hymn 431. HANOVER.—5 5 5 5.6 5 6 5.   *Supplement to the New Version,* 1708.

" Their sound went into all the earth, and their words unto the ends of the world."

mf **D**ISPOSER Supreme,
　　And Judge of the earth,
Who choosest for Thine
　The weak and the poor ;
To frail earthen vessels
　And things of no worth
Entrusting Thy riches
　Which aye shall endure ;

p　Those vessels soon fail,
　Though full of Thy light,
And at Thy decree
　Are broken and gone ;
cr　Thence brightly appeareth
Thy truth in its might,
As through the clouds riven
　The lightnings have shone.

f　Like clouds are they borne
　To do Thy great Will,
And swift as the winds
　About the world go ;
The WORD with His wisdom
　Their spirits doth fill,
They thunder, they lighten,
　The waters o'erflow.

Their sound goeth forth,
　"CHRIST JESUS the LORD ;"
Then Satan doth fear,
　His citadels fall :
As when the dread trumpets
　Went forth at Thy Word,
And one long blast shatter'd
　The Canaanite's wall.

O loud be their trump,
　And stirring their sound,
mf To rouse us, O LORD,
　From slumber of sin ;
The lights Thou hast kindled
　In darkness around,
O may they illumine
　Our spirits within.

f　All honour and praise,
　Dominion and might,
To GOD, THREE in ONE,
　Eternally be,
Who round us hath shed
　His own marvellous light,
And call'd us from darkness
　His glory to see.

I. WILLIAMS: from the Latin
of J. B. de Santeuil.

ALTERNATIVE TUNE, HYMN **167.**

Hymn 432. UNIVERSITY COLLEGE.—7 7 7 7. (*First Tune.*)   H. J. GAUNTLETT.

Festivals of Apostles.

Hymn 432. ALL SAINTS.—7 7 7 7. *(Second Tune.)* R. REDHEAD, 1860.

A - men.

" Ye also shall sit upon twelve thrones, judging the twelve tribes of Israel."

mf CAPTAINS of the saintly band,
Lights who lighten every land,
Princes who with JESUS dwell,
Judges of His Israel,

On the nations sunk in night
Ye have shed the Gospel light ;
cr Sin and error flee away,
Truth reveals the promised day.

mf Not by warrior's spear and sword,
Not by art of human word,
p Preaching but the Cross of shame,
cr Rebel hearts for CHRIST ye tame.

p Earth, that long in sin and pain
Groan'd in Satan's deadly chain,
f Now to serve its GOD is free
In the law of liberty.

mf Distant lands with one acclaim
Tell the honour of your name,
Who, wherever man has trod,
Teach the mysteries of GOD.

f Glory to the THREE in ONE
While eternal ages run,
Who from deepest shades of night
Call'd us to His glorious light.

Sir H. W. BAKER : from the
Latin of J. B. de Santeuil.

The following Hymns are suitable :
620 In royal robes of splendour. **754** Let all on earth their voices raise.

Festivals of Evangelists.

Hymn 433. CLIFTON.—C.M. *(First Tune.)* E. H. TURPIN.

A - men.

" Behold upon the mountains the feet of him that bringeth good tidings, that publisheth peace."

mf BEHOLD the messengers of CHRIST,
Who bear to every place
The unveil'd mysteries of GOD,
The Gospel of His grace.

p The things through mists and shadows dim
By holy prophets seen,
cr In the full light of day they saw
With not a cloud between.

p What CHRIST, True Man, divinely wrought,
What GOD in Manhood bore,

mf They wrote, as GOD inspired, in words
That live for evermore.

Although in space and time apart,
One SPIRIT ruled them all ;
And in their sacred pages still
We hear that SPIRIT'S call.

f To GOD, the Blessèd THREE in ONE,
Be glory, praise, and might,
Who call'd us from the shades of death
To His own glorious light.

I. WILLIAMS and Compilers: from
the Latin of J. B. de Santeuil.

(363)

Festivals of Evangelists.

Hymn 433. TIVERTON.—C.M. *(Second Tune.)* Rev. J. GRIGG, c. 1791.

A-men.

"Behold upon the mountains the feet of him that bringeth good tidings, that publisheth peace."

mf BEHOLD the messengers of CHRIST,
Who bear to every place
The unveil'd mysteries of GOD,
The Gospel of His grace.

p The things through mists and shadows dim
By holy prophets seen,
cr In the full light of day they saw
With not a cloud between.

p What CHRIST, True Man, divinely wrought,
What GOD in Manhood bore,

mf They wrote, as GOD inspired, in words
That live for evermore.

Although in space and time apart,
One SPIRIT ruled them all ;
And in their sacred pages still
We hear that SPIRIT'S call.

f To GOD, the Blessèd THREE in ONE,
Be glory, praise, and might,
Who call'd us from the shades of death
To His own glorious light.

I. WILLIAMS and Compilers: from
the Latin of J. B. de Santeuil.

Hymn 434. EVANGELISTS.—8 8 7. 8 8 7. J. B. KÖNIG (?), 1691–1758.

A-men.

Festivals of Evangelists.

"And a river went out of Eden to water the garden; and from thence it was parted, and became into four heads."

mf **C**OME, pure hearts, in sweetest measures
 Sing of those who spread the treasures
 In the holy Gospels shrined;
 Blessèd tidings of salvation,
p Peace on earth, their proclamation,
cr Love from GOD to lost mankind.

mf See the Rivers four that gladden
 With their streams the better Eden
 Planted by our LORD most dear;

f CHRIST the Fountain, (mf) these the waters
f Drink, O Sion's sons and daughters,
 Drink and find salvation here.

mf O that we Thy truth confessing,
 And Thy holy Word possessing,
 JESU, may Thy love adore;
 Unto Thee our voices raising,
cr Thee with all Thy ransom'd praising
 Ever and for evermore.

R. CAMPBELL and Compilers: from
the Latin of Adam of St. Victor.

The Hymn No. 126, Parts 2 and 3, may be used on the Festivals of Apostles or Evangelists between Easter Day and Trinity Sunday.

The following Hymns are suitable:
621 Come sing, ye choirs exultant. **755** How beauteous are their feet.

Festivals of Martyrs and other Holy Days.

Hymn 435. OLD 100TH.—L.M. (*First Tune.*) L. BOURGEOIS, 1551.

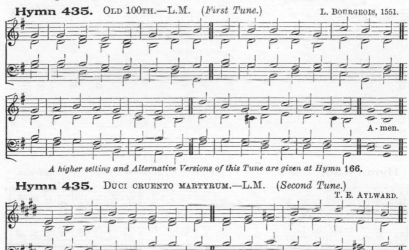

A higher setting and Alternative Versions of this Tune are given at Hymn **166.**

Hymn 435. DUCI CRUENTO MARTYRUM.—L.M. (*Second Tune.*)
T. E. AYLWARD.

[*For copyright, see p. lv.*]

" Therefore are they before the throne of God, and serve Him day and night in His temple."

f **L**O! round the Throne, a glorious band,
 The Saints in countless myriads stand,
 Of every tongue redeem'd to GOD,
dim Array'd in garments wash'd in Blood.

p Through tribulation great they came;
cr They bore the cross, despised the shame;
 From all their labours now they rest,
 In GOD's eternal glory blest.

mf They see their Saviour face to face,
 And sing the triumphs of His grace;

f Him day and night they ceaseless praise,
 To Him the loud thanksgiving raise:
ff " Worthy the LAMB, for sinners slain,
 Through endless years to live and reign;
p Thou hast redeem'd us by Thy Blood,
f And made us kings and priests to GOD."

mf O may we tread the sacred road
cr That Saints and holy Martyrs trod;
 Wage to the end the glorious strife,
f And win, like them, a crown of life.

R. HILL and others.

Festivals of Martyrs and other Holy Days.

Hymn 436. GLORIA.—8 7 8 7 . 8 7 8 7 . *(First Tune.)* H. SMART.

A - men.

Hymn 436. DEERHURST.—8 7 8 7 . 8 7 8 7 . *(Second Tune.)* J. LANGRAN.

A - men.

Festivals of Martyrs and other Holy Days.

Hymn 436. SANCTUARY.—8 7 8 7. 8 7 8 7. *(Third Tune.)* REV. J. B. DYKES.

A- men.

"After this I beheld, and lo, a great multitude, which no man could number, of all nations and kindreds and people and tongues, stood before the throne and before the Lamb, clothed with white robes, and palms in their hands."

f HARK ! the sound of holy voices, chanting at the crystal sea
    (*p*) A'leluia, (*f*) Alleluia, (*ff*) Alleluia, LORD, to Thee :
p Multitude, which none can number, (*cr*) like the stars in glory stands,
f Clothed in white apparel, holding palms of victory in their hands.

mf Patriarch, and holy Prophet, who prepared the way of CHRIST,
  King, Apostle, Saint, Confessor, Martyr, and Evangelist,
p Saintly Maiden, godly Matron, (*cr*) widows who have watch'd to prayer,
f Join'd in holy concert, singing to the LORD of all, are there.

p They have come from tribulation, and have wash'd their robes in Blood,
  Wash'd them in the Blood of JESUS ; (*cr*) tried they were, and firm they stood ;
p Mock'd, imprison'd, stoned, tormented, sawn asunder, slain with sword,
cr They have conquer'd death and Satan (*f*) by the might of CHRIST the LORD.

f Unis. Marching with Thy Cross their banner, they have triumph'd following
   Thee, the Captain of salvation, Thee their Saviour and their King ;
dim Harm. Gladly, LORD, with Thee they suffer'd ; gladly, LORD, with Thee they died,
   And by death (*cr*) to life immortal they were born, and glorified.

ff Unis. Now they reign in heavenly glory, now they walk in golden light,
   Now they drink, as from a river, holy bliss and infinite ;
p Harm. Love and peace they taste for ever, (*cr*) and all truth and knowledge see
   In the Beatific Vision of the Blessèd TRINITY.

f GOD of GOD, the One-begotten, LIGHT of LIGHT, Emmanuel,
  In Whose Body join'd together all the Saints for ever dwell ;
p Pour upon us of Thy fulness, (*cr*) that we may for evermore
  GOD the FATHER, GOD the SON, and GOD the HOLY GHOST adore.
            Bishop C. WORDSWORTH.

(367)

Festivals of Martyrs and other Holy Days.

Hymn 437. TROYTE'S CHANT No. 2.—Irregular. (*First Tune.*)

A. H. DYKE TROYTE.

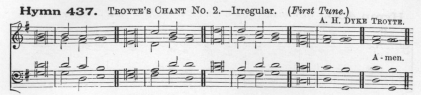

A - men.

" Compassed about with so great a cloud of witnesses."

f FOR all the Saints who from their lábours rest,
    Who Thee by faith before the wórld confess'd,
Thy Name, O JESU, be for éver blest.
              Alleluia !

Thou wast their Rock, their Fortress, ánd their Might ;
Thou, LORD, their Captain in the wéll-fought fight ;
Thou in the darkness drear their óne true Light.
              Alleluia !

O may Thy soldiers, faithful, trúe, and bold,
Fight as the Saints who nobly fóught of old,
And win, with them, the victor's crówn of gold.
              Alleluia !

mf O blest communion ! fellowship Divine !
    We feebly struggle, they in glóry shine ;
cr Yet all are one in Thee, for áll are Thine.
              Alleluia !

p And when the strife is fierce, the wárfare long,
    Steals on the ear the distant tríumph-song,
cr And hearts are brave again, and árms are strong.
              Alleluia !

mf The golden evening brightens ín the west ;
    Soon, soon to faithful warriors cómes their rest ;
p Sweet is the calm of Paradíse the blest.
              Alleluia !

f But lo ! there breaks a yet more glórious day ;
    The Saints triumphant rise in bright array :
    The King of glory passes ón His way.
              Alleluia !

ff From earth's wide bounds, from ocean's fárthest coast,
    Through gates of pearl streams in the cóuntless host,
    Singing to FATHER, SON, and HÓLY GHOST.
              Alleluia !

Bishop W. WALSHAM HOW.

Hymn 437. FOR ALL THE SAINTS.—10 10 10 4. (*Second Tune.*)

In Unison. 1st v. :8: vv. 2, 7, 8.

E. HULTON.

ORGAN.

Festivals of Martyrs and other Holy Days.

Harmony.   A - men.

"Compassed about with so great a cloud of witnesses."

VERSES 1, 2.

f FOR all the Saints who from their labours
   rest,
Who Thee by faith before the world confess'd,
Thy Name, O JESU, be for ever blest.
                                    Alleluia !

Thou wast their Rock, their Fortress, and
   their Might ;
Thou, LORD, their Captain in the well-fought
   fight ;
Thou in the darkness drear their one true
   Light.   Alleluia !

VERSES 7, 8.

f But lo ! there breaks a yet more glorious
   day ;
The Saints triumphant rise in bright array :
The King of glory passes on His way.
                                    Alleluia !

ff From earth's wide bounds, from ocean's
   farthest coast,
Through gates of pearl streams in the
   countless host,
Singing to FATHER, SON, and HOLY GHOST.
                                    Alleluia !

Verses 3, 4, 5, 6 rather faster than verses 1 and 2.
Harmony.

p   *cres.*   *f*   *dim.*

vv. 3, 4, 5.   v. 6.   *rall.*   vv. 7, 8 *(opposite.)*

Unison.   Unison.   Tempo 1mo.   *ff*

VERSES 3, 4.

f O may Thy soldiers, faithful, true, and
   bold,
Fight as the Saints who nobly fought of
   old,
And win, with them, the victor's crown of
   gold.   Alleluia !

mf O blest communion ! fellowship Divine !
We feebly struggle, they in glory shine ;
cr Yet all are one in Thee, for all are Thine.
                                    Alleluia !

VERSES 5, 6.

p And when the strife is fierce, the warfare
   long,
Steals on the ear the distant triumph-song,
cr And hearts are brave again, and arms are
   strong.   Alleluia !

mf The golden evening brightens in the west ;
Soon, soon to faithful warriors comes
   their rest ;
p Sweet is the calm of Paradise the blest.
                                    Alleluia !

Hymn 437. FOR ALL THE SAINTS.—10 10 10 4. (*Third Tune.*)

Sir J. BARNBY.

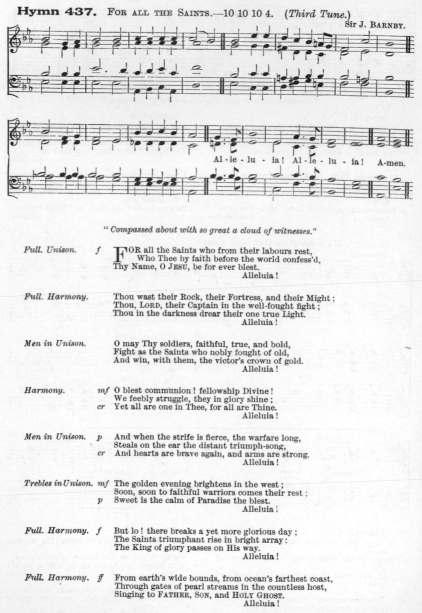

Al - le - lu - ia! Al - le - lu - ia! A - men.

" Compassed about with so great a cloud of witnesses."

Full. Unison.   *f*   FOR all the Saints who from their labours rest,
Who Thee by faith before the world confess'd,
Thy Name, O JESU, be for ever blest.
Alleluia !

Full. Harmony.   Thou wast their Rock, their Fortress, and their Might :
Thou, LORD, their Captain in the well-fought fight ;
Thou in the darkness drear their one true Light.
Alleluia !

Men in Unison.   O may Thy soldiers, faithful, true, and bold,
Fight as the Saints who nobly fought of old,
And win, with them, the victor's crown of gold.
Alleluia !

Harmony.   *mf*   O blest communion ! fellowship Divine !
We feebly struggle, they in glory shine ;
cr   Yet all are one in Thee, for all are Thine.
Alleluia !

Men in Unison.   *p*   And when the strife is fierce, the warfare long,
Steals on the ear the distant triumph-song,
cr   And hearts are brave again, and arms are strong.
Alleluia !

Trebles in Unison.   *mf*   The golden evening brightens in the west ;
Soon, soon to faithful warriors comes their rest ;
p   Sweet is the calm of Paradise the blest.
Alleluia !

Full. Harmony.   *f*   But lo ! there breaks a yet more glorious day ;
The Saints triumphant rise in bright array :
The King of glory passes on His way.
Alleluia !

Full. Harmony.   *ff*   From earth's wide bounds, from ocean's farthest coast,
Through gates of pearl streams in the countless host,
Singing to FATHER, SON, and HOLY GHOST.
Alleluia !

Bishop W. WALSHAM HOW.

Hymn 437. ENGELBERG.—10 10 10 4. (*Fourth Tune.*)

"Compassed about with so great a cloud of witnesses."

Sir C. V. STANFORD.

In Unison.

1. FOR all the Saints who from their la-bours rest, . .
2. Thou wast their Rock, their Fort-ress, and their Might; . .
3. O may Thy sol-diers, faith-ful, true, and bold, . .

. . . Who Thee by faith be-fore the world con-fess'd, . . Thy Name, O
. . Thou, LORD, their Cap-tain in the well-fought fight; . . Thou in the
. . Fight as the Saints who no-bly fought of old, . . . And win, with

JE-SU, be for ev-er bless'd. . . Al-le-lu-ia!
dark-ness drear their one true Light. . . Al-le-lu-ia!
them, the vic-tor's crown of gold. . . Al-le-lu-ia!

In Harmony.

mf

4. O blest com-mu-nion! fel-low-ship Di-vine! . .

cres.

. . We fee-bly strug-gle, they in glo-ry shine; . . Yet all are

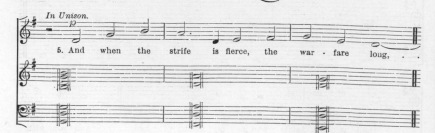

one in Thee, for all are Thine. . . Al - le - lu - - ia! . .

In Unison.

5. And when the strife is fierce, the war - fare long, . .

. . Steals on the ear the dis - tant tri - umph - song, . . And hearts are

cres.

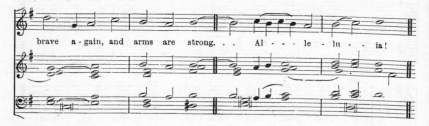

brave a - gain, and arms are strong. . . Al - - le - lu - - ia!

Sopranos only.
mf

6. The gold - en eve - ning bright - ens in the west; . . .

p

Without Pedals.

Festivals of Martyrs and other Holy Days.

p

... Soon, soon to faith - ful war - riors comes their rest; ... Sweet is the

calm of Par - a - dise the blest. ... Al - - le - lu - - ia!

Tenors and Basses only.
f

cres.

7. But lo! there breaks a yet more glo - rious day; ...

Ped.

... The Saints tri - um - phant rise in bright ar - ray: ... The King of

(373)

Festivals of Martyrs and other Holy Days.

glo - ry pass - es on His way.... Al - - le - lu - ia!

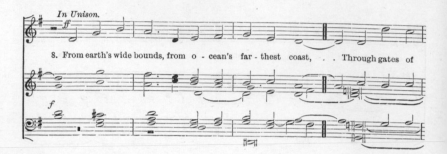

In Unison.

ff

8. From earth's wide bounds, from o - cean's far - thest coast, . . . Through gates of

f

pearl streams in the count - less host, . . . Sing - ing to FA - THER, SON, and

HO - LY GHOST. . . . Al - - le - lu - - ia!

Harmony.

A - men.

Bishop W. WALSHAM HOW.

Festivals of Martyrs and other Holy Days.

Hymn 438. BEATITUDO.—C.M. (*First Tune.*) Rev. J. B. DYKES.

A-men.

Hymn 438. BROMSGROVE.—C.M. (*Second Tune.*) — COLLINS, 1789.

A-men.

"*These are they which came out of great tribulation, and have washed their robes, and made them white in the Blood of the Lamb.*"

f **H**OW bright these glorious spirits shine !
mf Whence all their white array?
How came they to the blissful seats
Of everlasting day?

p Lo ! these are they from sufferings great
Who came to realms of light ;
cr And in the Blood of CHRIST have wash'd
Those robes that shine so bright.

f Now with triumphal palms they stand
Before the Throne on high,
And serve the GOD they love amidst
The glories of the sky.

mf Hunger and thirst are felt no more,
Nor suns with scorching ray ;
cr GOD is their Sun, Whose cheering beams
Diffuse eternal day.

mf The LAMB, Which dwells amidst the Throne,
Shall o'er them still preside,
p Feed them with nourishment Divine,
cr And all their footsteps guide.

p 'Midst pastures green He'll lead His flock,
Where living streams appea ;
cr And GOD the LORD from every eye
Shall wipe off every tear.

f To FATHER, SON, and HOLY GHOST,
The GOD Whom we adore,
Be glory, as it was, is now,
And shall be evermore.

I. WATTS and W. CAMERON, 1707.

Hymn 439. OLD 81ST.—D.C.M. *(First Tune.)* Psalmes, 1562.

This Tune may also be sung in Common Time if preferred, by making the Semibreves, throughout, into Minims. A Version in Common Time is given at Hymn 557.

Hymn 439. ST. ANNE.—C.M. *(Second Tune.)* W. CROFT, 1708.

" Fight the good fight of faith, lay hold on eternal life."

f THE SON of GOD goes forth to war,
  A Kingly crown to gain ;
His blood-red banner streams afar !
  Who follows in His train?

mf Who best can drink his cup of woe,
f   Triumphant over pain,
p Who patient bears his cross below,
f   He follows in His train.

mf The Martyr first, whose eagle eye
  Could pierce beyond the grave ;
Who saw his Master in the sky,
cr And call'd on Him to save.

dim Like Him, with pardon on his tongue
  In midst of mortal pain,
mf He pray'd for them that did the wrong ;
f   Who follows in his train?

A glorious band, the chosen few
  On whom the SPIRIT came,
Twelve valiant Saints, their hope they knew,
  And mock'd the cross and flame.

They met the tyrant's brandish'd steel,
  The lion's gory mane,
p They bow'd their necks, the death to feel:
f   Who follows in their train?

A noble army, men and boys,
  The matron and the maid,
Around the SAVIOUR'S Throne rejoice
  In robes of light array'd.

They climb'd the steep ascent of Heav'n
mf Through peril, toil, and pain ;
p O GOD, to us may grace be given
  To follow in their train.

Bishop HEBER. 1827.

Festivals of Martyrs and other Holy Days.

Hymn 440. LANGDALE.—8 7 8 7. *(First Tune.)* R. REDHEAD.

Hymn 440. ALTA TRINITÀ BEATA.—8 7 8 7. 8 7 8 7. *(Second Tune.)*
Medieval Italian Melody.

*" They were stoned, they were sawn asunder, were tempted, were slain with the sword ; . . .
being destitute, afflicted, tormented ; of whom the world was not worthy."*

mf BLESSED feasts of blessèd Martyrs,
　　Holy days of holy men,
With affection's recollections
　Greet we your return again.

f　Worthy deeds they wrought and wonders,
　Worthy of the Name they bore ;
We with meetest praise and sweetest
　Honour them for evermore.

mf Faith prevailing, hope unfailing,
　JESUS loved with single heart—
f　Thus they glorious and victorious
　Bravely bore the Martyr's part.

mf Rack'd with torture, haled to slaughter,
　Fire, and axe, and murderous sword,
f　Chains and prison, foes' derision
　They endured for CHRIST the LORD.

p　So they pass'd through pain and sorrow,
　Till they sank in death to rest ;
cr Earth's rejected, GOD'S elected,
　Gain'd a portion with the blest.

mf By contempt of worldly pleasures,
　And by deeds of valour done,
f　They have reach'd the land of Angels,
　And with them are knit in one.

Made co-heirs with CHRIST in glory,
　His celestial bliss they share :
p　May they now before Him bending
　Help us onward by their prayer ;

That, this weary life completed,
　And its fleeting trials past,
f　We may win eternal glory
　In our FATHER'S home at last.

J. M. NEALE and Compilers :
from the Latin.

(377)

Festivals of Martyrs and other Holy Days.

Hymn 441.   St. Joseph of the Studium.—7 6 7 6. 7 6 7 6.   Sir J. Barnby.

" Blessed are they which are persecuted for righteousness' sake ; for theirs is the kingdom of heaven."

f   LET our Choir new anthems raise,
      Wake the song of gladness ;
   GOD Himself to joy and praise
      Turns the Martyrs' sadness :
   Bright the day that won their crown,
      Open'd Heav'n's bright portal,
dim As they laid the mortal down
cr   To put on the immortal.

mf Never flinch'd they from the flame,
      From the torture never ;
   Vain the foeman's sharpest aim,
      Satan's best endeavour :
cr For by faith they saw the land
      Deck'd in all its glory,
f   Where triumphant now they stand
      With the victor's story.

   Up and follow, Christian men !
      Press through toil and sorrow ;
   Spurn the night of fear, and then,
      Oh, the glorious morrow !
mf Who will venture on the strife ?
f   Blest who first begin it ;
mf Who will grasp the land of life ?
ff   Warriors, up and win it !

                    J. M. Neale: from the Greek
                       of St. Joseph, *c.* 846.

ALTERNATIVE TUNE, HYMN 679.

(378)

Festivals of Martyrs and other Holy Days.

Hymn 442. BAVARIA.—L.M.

German.

A-men.

" Blessed is the man that endureth temptation, for when he is tried he shall receive the crown of life."

mf O GOD, Thy soldiers' great Reward,
　Their Portion, Crown, and faithful LORD,
From all transgressions set us free
Who sing Thy Martyr's victory.

By wisdom taught he learn'd to know
The vanity of all below,
The fleeting joys of earth disdain'd,
And everlasting glory gain'd.

Right manfully his cross he bore,
And ran his race of torments sore ;

dim For Thee he pour'd his life away,
cr With Thee he lives in endless day.

p We therefore pray Thee, LORD of Love,
　Regard us from Thy Throne above ;
cr On this Thy Martyr's triumph-day
p Wash every stain of sin away.

f All praise to GOD the FATHER be,
　All praise, Eternal SON, to Thee,
Whom with the SPIRIT we adore
For ever and for evermore.

J. M. NEALE: from the Latin

ALTERNATIVE TUNE, HYMN 760.

Hymn 443. ABERYSTWYTH. S.M.

REV. F. A. G. OUSELEY.

A-men.

" Be thou faithful unto death, and I will give thee a crown of life."

p FOR man the Saviour shed
　His all-atoning Blood,
cr And oh, shall ransom'd man refuse
　To suffer for his GOD ?

mf Ashamed who now can be
　To own the Crucified ?
cr Nay, rather be our glory this,
　To die for Him Who died.

mf So felt Thy Martyr, LORD ;
　By Thy right hand sustain'd,
He waged for Thee the battle's strife,
And threaten'd death disdain'd.

Upon the golden crown
Gazing with eager breath,

He fought as one who fain would die,
　And, dying, conquer death.

Alone he stood unmoved
　Amid his cruel foes ;
f Oh, wondrous was the might that then
　Above his torturers rose !

p LORD, give us grace to bear
　Like him our cross of shame,
To do and suffer what Thou wilt,
For love of Thy dear Name.

f JESU, the King of Saints,
　We praise Thee and adore,
Who art with GOD the FATHER ONE
And SPIRIT evermore.

Compilers : from the Latin
of J. B. de Santeuil.

Festivals of Martyrs and other Holy Days.

Hymn 444. CONSTANCE.—L.M.

H. J. GAUNTLETT.

A - men.

" Of whom the world was not worthy."

f   YE servants of our glorious King,
      To Him your thankful praises bring ;
  And tell the deeds that grace has done,
  The triumphs by His Martyrs won.

mf Since they were faithful to the last,
  Their holy struggles now are past ;
  The bitterness of death is o'er,
f   And theirs is bliss for evermore.

p   The flame might scorch, the knife lay bare,
  And cruel beasts their members tear ;

cr   No powers of earth, no powers of hell
  The souls that loved their LORD could quell.

f   For ever broken is the chain
  That sought to bind them, but in vain :
mf O let us strive like them to win
  Our freedom from the bonds of sin.

p   O Saviour, may our portion be
  With those who gave themselves to Thee,
f   Through all eternity to sing
  All praise to Thee the Martyrs' King.

R. CAMPBELL and Compilers :
from St. Ambrose.

ALTERNATIVE TUNE, HYMN 719.

Hymn 445. PALMS OF GLORY.—7 7 7 7.

Archbishop MACLAGAN.

A - men.

" Clothed with white robes, and palms in their hands."

f   PALMS of glory, raiment bright,
      Crowns that never fade away,
  Gird and deck the Saints in light,
  Priests, and kings, and conquerors they.

mf Yet the conquerors bring their palms
  To the LAMB amidst the Throne,
cr   And proclaim in joyful psalms
  Victory through His Cross alone.

mf Kings their crowns for harps resign,
  Crying, **as** they strike the chords,

cr   " Take the Kingdom, it is Thine,
  King of kings, and LORD of lords."

p   Round the Altar Priests confess,
  If their robes are white as snow,
  'Twas the Saviour's Righteousness,
  And His Blood, that made them so.

mf They were mortal too like us :
  O, when we like them must die,
cr   May our souls translated thus
  Triumph, reign, and shine on high.

J. MONTGOMERY, 1829.

Hymn 446. St. Michael.—S.M. *Psalmes, 1561.*

A - men.

A higher setting of this Tune is given at Hymn 152.

" I reckon that the sufferings of this present time are not worthy to be compared with the glory which shall be revealed in us."

mf   OH! what, if we are CHRIST'S,
    Is earthly shame or loss?
cr   Bright shall the crown of glory be
dim   When we have borne the cross.

p   Keen was the trial once,
   Bitter the cup of woe,
When martyr'd Saints, baptized in blood,
CHRIST'S sufferings shared below:

f   Bright is their glory now,
   Boundless their joy above,
Where, on the bosom of their GOD,
They rest in perfect love.

mf   LORD, may that grace be ours,
   Like them in faith to bear
p   All that of sorrow, grief, or pain
   May be our portion here ;

mf   Enough if Thou at last
   The word of blessing give,
And let us rest beneath Thy feet,
Where Saints and Angels live.

f   All glory, LORD, to Thee,
   Whom Heav'n and earth adore ;
To FATHER, SON, and HOLY GHOST,
ONE GOD for evermore

Sir H. W. Baker

Hymn 447. Orientis partibus.—7 7 7 7.   Medieval French Melody.

A - men.

" To him that overcometh."

f   SOLDIERS, who are CHRIST'S below,
   Strong in faith resist the foe :
Boundless is the pledged reward
Unto them who serve the LORD.

mf   'Tis no palm of fading leaves
That the conqueror's hand receives ;
Joys are his, serene and pure,
Light that ever shall endure.

For the souls that overcome
Waits the beauteous heavenly home,

cr   Where the Blessèd evermore
Tread, on high, the starry floor.

p   Passing soon and little worth
Are the things that tempt on earth ;
mf   Heavenward lift thy soul's regard ;
GOD Himself is thy Reward.

f   FATHER, Who the crown dost give,
SAVIOUR, by Whose Death we live,
SPIRIT, Who our hearts dost raise,
THREE in ONE, Thy Name we praise.

J. H. Clark: from the Latin.

Festivals of Martyrs and other Holy Days.

Hymn 448. ST. HELENA.—S.M.   B. MILGROVE (Mount Ephraim), 1769.

A lower setting of this Tune is given at Hymn 344.

"And they glorified God in me."

mf FOR Thy dear Saint, O LORD,
　　Who strove in Thee to live,
Who follow'd Thee, obey'd, adored,
　　Our grateful hymn receive.

p　For Thy dear Saint, O LORD,
　　Who strove in Thee to die,
cr And found in Thee a full reward,
　　Accept our thankful cry.

mf　Thine earthly members fit
　　To join Thy Saints above,

In one communion ever knit,
　　One fellowship of love.

　　JESU, Thy Name we bless,
　　And humbly pray that we
May follow them in holiness,
　　Who lived and died for Thee.

f　　All might, all praise, be Thine,
　　FATHER, co-equal SON,
And SPIRIT, Bond of love Divine,
　　While endless ages run.

Bishop MANT, 1837.

Hymn 449. ST. AMBROSE.—L.M. *(First Tune.)*   LA FEILLÉE, *Méthode*, 1808.

Hymn 449. INNOCENCE.—L.M. *(Second Tune.)*   B. LUARD SELBY.

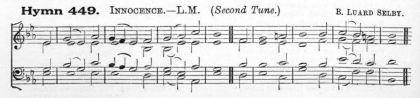

Festivals of Martyrs and other Holy Days.

A - men.

"Hail, thou that art highly favoured, the Lord is with thee; blessed art thou among women."

FOR THE B.V. MARY.

mf THE GOD, Whom earth, and sea, and sky
  Adore, and laud, and magnify,
Whose might they own, Whose praise they
  swell,
p In Mary's womb vouchsafed to dwell.

mf The LORD, Whom sun and moon obey,
  Whom all things serve from day to day,
p Was by the HOLY GHOST conceived
  Of her who through His grace believed.

mf How blest that Mother, in whose shrine
  The world's Creator, LORD Divine,

Whose Hand contains the earth and sky,
p Once deign'd, as in His ark, to lie;

f Blest in the message Gabriel brought,
  Blest by the work the SPIRIT wrought;
From whom the great Desire of earth
p Took human flesh and human birth.

f O LORD, the Virgin-born, to Thee
  Eternal praise and glory be,
Whom with the FATHER we adore
And HOLY GHOST for evermore.

J. M. NEALE and Compilers: from
Venantius Fortunatus.

Hymn 450. ST. AGNES.—C.M.

Rev. J. B. DYKES.

A - men.

"Mary, the Mother of Jesus."

FOR THE B.V. MARY.

mf SHALL we not love thee, Mother dear,
  Whom JESUS loves so well?
And, to His glory, year by year,
  Thy joy and honour tell?

p Bound with the curse of sin and shame
cr We helpless sinners lay,
Until in tender love He came
  To bear the curse away.

mf And thee He chose from whom to take
  True flesh His Flesh to be;
p In It to suffer for our sake,
f By It to make us free.

p Thy Babe He lay upon thy breast,
  To thee He cried for food;
Thy gentle nursing sooth'd to rest
  Th' Incarnate SON of GOD.

mf O wondrous depth of grace Divine
  That He should bend so low!
cr And, Mary, oh, what joy 'twas thine
  In His dear love to know;

f Joy to be Mother of the LORD,
  And thine the truer bliss,
In every thought, and deed, and word
  To be for ever His.

mf And as He loves thee, Mother dear,
  We too will love thee well;
cr And, to His glory, year by year,
  Thy joy and honour tell.

f JESU, the Virgin's Holy Son,
  We praise Thee and adore,
WHO art with GOD the FATHER ONE
  And SPIRIT evermore.

Sir H. W. BAKER.

ALTERNATIVE TUNES, HYMN 705 (FIRST TUNE) OR HYMN 675 (SECOND TUNE).

Festivals of Martyrs and other Holy Days.

Hymn 451. WELLS.—L.M.

W. H. MONK.

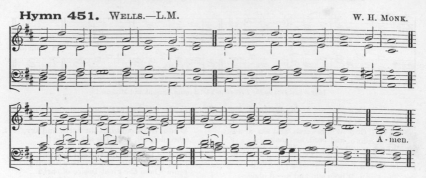

A - men.

" Whosoever therefore shall confess Me before men, him will I confess also before My Father Which is in heaven."

FOR A CONFESSOR.

mf NOT by the Martyr's death alone
The Saint his crown in Heav'n has won,
There is a triumph robe on high
For bloodless fields of victory.

What though he was not call'd to feel
The cross, or flame, or torturing wheel,
cr Yet daily to the world he died ;
His flesh, through grace, he crucified.

p What though nor chains, nor scourges sore,
Nor cruel beasts his members tore,

cr Enough if perfect love arise
To CHRIST a grateful sacrifice.

p LORD grant us so to Thee to turn
That we through life to die may learn,
cr And thus, when life's brief day is o'er,
May live with Thee for evermore.

mf O Fount of sanctity and love,
O perfect Rest of Saints above,
f All praise, all glory be to Thee
Both now and through eternity.

I. WILLIAMS and Compilers : from
the Latin of J. B. de Santeuil.

ALTERNATIVE TUNE, HYMN 709 (FIRST TUNE).

Hymn 452. LEIPSIC (EISENACH).—L.M.

J. H. SCHEIN, 1628.

A - men.

" If a man desire the office of a bishop, he desireth a good work."

FOR A BISHOP.

mf O THOU Whose all-redeeming might
Crowns every Chief in faith's true fight,
On this commemoration day
Hear us, good JESU, while we pray.

In faithful strife for Thy dear Name
Thy servant earn'd the saintly fame,
Which pious hearts with praise revere
In constant memory year by year.

p Earth's fleeting joys he counted nought,
cr For higher, truer joys he sought,

f And now, with Angels round Thy Throne,
Unfading treasures are his own.

p O grant that we, most gracious GOD,
May follow in the steps he trod ;
cr And, freed from every stain of sin,
As he hath won may also win.

f To Thee, O CHRIST, our loving King,
All glory, praise, and thanks we bring ;
Whom with the FATHER we adore
And HOLY GHOST for evermore.

R. M. BENSON and Compilers :
from the Latin.

ALTERNATIVE TUNE, HYMN 719.

Festivals of Martyrs and other Holy Days.

Hymn 453. Swabia.—S.M.

J. M. Spiess, 1745.

A-men.

For a Bishop.

"The memory of the just is blessed."

mf   O SHEPHERD of the sheep,
     High Priest of things to come,
Who didst in grace Thy servant keep,
p   And take him safely home ;

f   Accept our song of praise
    For all his holy care,
His zeal unquench'd through length of days,
    The trials that he bare.

mf   Chief of Thy faithful band,
    He held himself the least,
Though Thy dread keys were in his hand,
    O everlasting Priest.

f   So, trusting in Thy might,
    He won a fair renown ;

So, waxing valiant in the fight,
    He trod the lion down.

p   Then render'd up to Thee
    The charge Thy love had given,
And pass'd away (*cr*) Thy Face to see
    Reveal'd in highest Heav'n.

mf   On all our Bishops pour
    The Spirit of Thy grace ;
That, as he won the palm of yore,
    So they may run their race ;

    That, when this life is done,
    They may with him adore
cr The ever Blessèd Three in One,
    In bliss for evermore.

V. S. S. Coles.

Hymn 454. Culford.—7 7 7 7.7 7 7 7.

E. J. Hopkins.

A-men.

For a Doctor.

"He gave some . . . Pastors and Teachers."

mf JESU, for the beacon-light
    By Thy holy Doctors given,
p   When the mists of error's night
    Gather'd o'er the path to Heav'n ;
mf For the witness that they bare
cr   To the truth they learn'd of Thee,
f   For the glory that they share,
    Let our praise accepted be.

mf In Jerusalem below
    They were workmen at Thy call,
cr Each with one hand met the foe,
    With the other built the wall ;

f   Watchmen on the mountain set,
    Scribes instructed in Thy Word,
dim Fishers with the Gospel net
cr   Drawing souls to Thee their Lord.

mf Like Thy learnèd sons of yore,
    Jesu, may Thy Pastors still
cr Know and teach Thy sacred lore
    With brave heart and patient skill ;
p   In these latter days of strife
cr Keep, O keep them true to Thee,
f   Till beside the well of life
    Light in Thine own Light they see.

Sir H. W. Baker.

O

Festivals of Martyrs and other Holy Days.

Hymn 455. Jesu dulcis memoria.—L.M. (*First Tune.*) Proper Sarum Melody.

An Alternative Version of this Tune is given at Hymn 177.

Hymn 455. St. Bernard.—L.M. (*Second Tune.*) W. H. Monk.

A lower setting of this Tune is given at Hymn 420.

"Thy Name is as ointment poured forth, therefore do the virgins love Thee."

FOR A VIRGIN.

mf JESU, the Virgins' Crown, do Thou
　　　Accept us as in prayer we bow,
Born of that Virgin whom alone
The Mother and the Maid we own.

Amongst the lilies Thou dost feed,
And thither choirs of Virgins lead;
Adorning all Thy chosen brides
With glorious gifts Thy love provides.

And whither, LORD, Thy footsteps wend,
The Virgins still with praise attend;

For Thee they pour their sweetest song,
And after Thee rejoicing throng.

p O gracious LORD, we Thee implore
Thy grace on every sense to pour;
From all pollution keep us free,
And make us pure in heart for Thee.

f All praise to GOD the FATHER be,
All praise, Eternal SON, to Thee,
Whom with the SPIRIT we adore
For ever and for evermore.

J. M. NEALE: from St. Ambrose.

ALTERNATIVE TUNE, HYMN 44.

Festivals of Martyrs and other Holy Days.

Hymn 456. Intercession.—L.M.   *Easy Music for Church Choirs, 1853.*

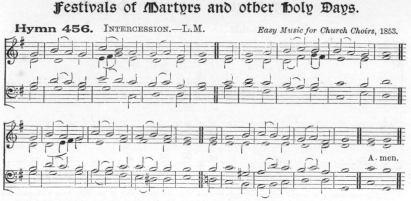

A-men.

"My Beloved is mine, and I am His."

FOR A VIRGIN.

p O LAMB of GOD, Whose love Divine
      Draws Virgin-souls to follow Thee ;
cr And bids them earthly joys resign
     If so they may Thy beauty see ;

mf The Saint of whom we sing to-day
     Was faithful to Thy loving call,
     And, casting other hopes away,
     Took Thee to be her GOD, her All.

     To Thee she yielded up her will,
     Her heart was drawn to Thine above ;
     Content if Thou wouldst deign to fill
     Thine handmaid with Thy perfect love.

p Beneath Thy Cross she loved to stand,
     Like Mary in Thy dying hour,

cr That blessings from Thy piercèd Hand
     Might clothe her with undying power ;

mf With power to win the crown of light
     For Virgin-souls laid up on high,
     And ready keep her lamp at night
     To hail the Bridegroom drawing nigh.

p And surely Thou at last didst come
     To end the sorrows of Thy bride,
pp And bear her to Thy peaceful home
cr With Thee for ever to abide.

f All glory, JESU, for the grace
     That drew Thy Saint to follow Thee ;
p Grant us too in Thy love a place
     Both now and through eternity.

                            V. S. S. COLES.

Hymn 457. ST. PATRICK.—L.M.   REV. F. W. HOGAN.

A-men.

"Who can find a virtuous woman? for her price is far above rubies : the heart of her husband doth safely trust in her."

FOR A HOLY MATRON.

mf HOW blest the matron, who, endued
      With holy zeal and fortitude,
     Has won through grace a saintly fame,
     And owns a dear and honour'd name.

     Such holy love inflamed her breast
     She would not seek on earth her rest,
     But, strong in faith and patience, trod
     The narrow way that leads to GOD.

p She learn'd, through fasting, to control
     The flesh that weigheth down the soul,

cr And then, by prayer's sweet food sustain'd,
     To seek the joys she now has gain'd.

mf O CHRIST, from Whom all virtue springs,
     Who only doest wondrous things,
     To Thee, the King of Saints, we pray,
     Accept and bless Thy flock to-day.

f All praise to GOD the FATHER be,
     All praise, Eternal SON, to Thee,
     Whom with the SPIRIT we adore
     For ever and for evermore.

ALTERNATIVE TUNE, HYMN 449.

Compilers : from the Latin of Cardinal S. Antoniano.

Festivals of Martyrs and other Holy Days.

Hymn 458. UTRECHT.—S.M. B. TOURS.

A - men.

"*I.John, who also am your brother and companion in tribulation, and in the kingdom and patience of Jesus Christ, was in the isle that is called Patmos, for the Word of God and for the testimony of Jesus Christ.*"

ST. JOHN BEFORE THE LATIN GATE.

mf   AN exile for the faith
      Of his Incarnate LORD,
   Beyond the stars, beyond all space,
cr   His soul in vision soar'd :

mf   There saw in glory Him
      Who liveth, and was dead,
   There Judah's Lion, and the LAMB
p   That for our ransom bled :

mf   There of the Kingdom learn'd
      The mysteries sublime :

p   How, sown in Martyrs' blood, the faith
cr   Should spread from clime to clime.

p   LORD, give us grace, like him,
      In Thee to live and die ;
cr   To spurn the fleeting things of earth,
      And seek for joys on high.

f   JESU, our risen LORD,
      We praise Thee and adore,
   Who art with GOD the FATHER ONE
      And SPIRIT evermore.

E. CASWALL : from the Latin of N. Le Tourneaux.

ALTERNATIVE TUNE, HYMN 58.

Hymn 459. ST. MARY MAGDALENE.—C.M. J. CRÜGER, 1653.

A - men.

"*Mary Magdalene, out of whom He had cast seven devils.*"

ST. MARY MAGDALENE.

mf   SON of the Highest, deign to cast
      On us a pitying eye,
   Thou Who repentant Magdalene
cr   Didst call to joys on high.

mf   Thy long-lost coin is stored at length
      In treasure-house Divine,
   The jewel from pollution cleansed
      Doth now the stars outshine.

   JESU, the balm of every wound,
      The sinner's only stay,

p   Grant us, like Magdalene, to weep
      In this Thy mercy's day ;
cr   Absolve us by Thy gracious Word,
      Fulfil us with Thy love,
   And guide us through the storms of life
      To perfect rest above.

f   All praise, all glory be to Thee,
      O everlasting LORD,
   Whose mercy doth our souls forgive,
      Whose bounty doth reward.

E. CASWALL and Compilers : from the Latin of St. Odo of Cluny (?).

ALTERNATIVE TUNE, HYMN 433 (SECOND TUNE).

Festivals of Martyrs and other Holy Days.

Hymn 460. AURELIA.—7 6 7 6.7 6 7 6.

S. S. WESLEY, 1864.

A - men.

" His Face did shine as the sun, and His raiment was white as the light."

THE TRANSFIGURATION OF OUR LORD.

f   IN days of old on Sinai
     The LORD Almighty came
cr In majesty of terror,
    In thunder-cloud and flame :
mf On Tabor, with the glory
    Of sunniest light for vest,
The excellence of beauty
    In JESUS was express'd.

p All light created paled there,
    And did Him worship meet ;
The sun itself adored Him,
    And bow'd before His Feet ;
cr While Moses and Elias,
    Upon the Holy Mount,
The co-eternal glory
    Of CHRIST our GOD recount.

p O holy, wondrous vision !
cr   But what when, this life past,
The beauty of Mount Tabor
    Shall end in Heav'n at last?
f But what when all the glory
    Of uncreated light
Shall be the promised guerdon
    Of them that win the fight ?

J. M. NEALE : partly from the
Greek of St. Cosmas, c. 760.

(389)

Festivals of Martyrs and other Holy Days.

Hymn 461. SEMPER ASPECTEMUS.—C.M.   J. H. CASSON.

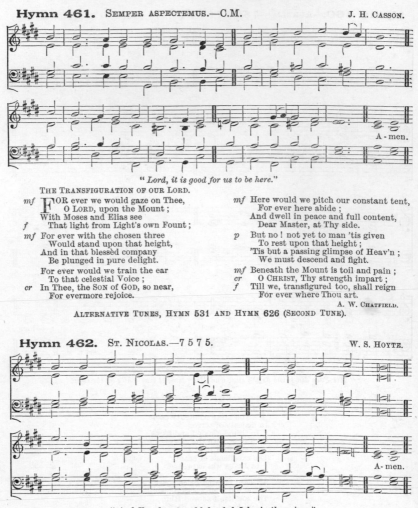

A-men.

" Lord, it is good for us to be here."

THE TRANSFIGURATION OF OUR LORD.

mf FOR ever we would gaze on Thee,
  O LORD, upon the Mount ;
With Moses and Elias see
f   That light from Light's own Fount ;

mf For ever with the chosen three
  Would stand upon that height,
And in that blessèd company
  Be plunged in pure delight.

For ever would we train the ear
  To that celestial Voice ;
cr In Thee, the SON of GOD, so near,
  For evermore rejoice.

mf Here would we pitch our constant tent,
  For ever here abide ;
And dwell in peace and full content,
  Dear Master, at Thy side.

p But no ! not yet to man 'tis given
  To rest upon that height ;
'Tis but a passing glimpse of Heav'n ;
  We must descend and fight.

mf Beneath the Mount is toil and pain ;
cr   O CHRIST, Thy strength impart ;
f Till we, transfigured too, shall reign
  For ever where Thou art.

         A. W. CHATFIELD.

ALTERNATIVE TUNES, HYMN 531 AND HYMN 626 (SECOND TUNE).

Hymn 462. ST. NICOLAS.—7 5 7 5.   W. S. HOYTE.

A-men.

" And Herod sent and beheaded John in the prison."

THE BEHEADING OF ST. JOHN BAPTIST.

mf HERALD, in the wilderness
  Breaking up the road,
Sinking mountains, raising plains,
For the path of GOD ;

Prophet, to the multitudes
  Calling to repent,
In the way of righteousness
  Unto Israel sent ;

Messenger, GOD'S chosen One
  Foremost to proclaim,
Proffer'd titles passing by,
  Pointing to the LAMB ;

Captive, for the word of truth
  Boldly witnessing ;
dim Then in Herod's dungeon-cave
  Faint and languishing ;

p Martyr, sacrificed to sin
  At that feast of shame ;
cr As his life foreshow'd the LORD,
  In his death the same—

p Holy JESUS, When He heard,
  Went apart to pray :
cr Thus may we our lesson take
  From His Saint to-day.

         H. ALFORD.

Litany of the Four Last Things.

Hymn 463.

W. H. MONK.

mf GOD the FATHER, GOD the SON,
   GOD the SPIRIT, THREE in ONE,
Hear us from Thy heavenly Throne,
   p   Spare us, Holy TRINITY.

mf JESU, Life of those who die,
Advocate with GOD on high,
Hope of immortality,
      Hear us, Holy JESU.

Thou Whose Death to mortals gave
Power to triumph o'er the grave,
Living now from death to save,
      Hear us, Holy JESU.

p Thou before Whose great white Throne
All our doings must be shown,
Pleading now for us Thine own,
      Hear us, Holy JESU.

Thou Whose Death was borne that we,
From the power of Satan free,
Might not die eternally,
      Hear us, Holy JESU.

mf Thou Who dost a place prepare,
That in heavenly mansions fair
Sinners may Thy glory share,
      Hear us, Holy JESU.

DEATH.
ORG.

DEATH.

p We are dying day by day ;
Soon from earth we pass away ;
LORD of life, to Thee we pray :
      Hear us, Holy JESU.

Ere we hear the Angel's call,
And the shadows round us fall,
cr Be our SAVIOUR, be our All ;
      Hear us, Holy JESU.

mf Wean our hearts from things below,
Make us all Thy love to know,
Guard us from our ghostly foe :
      Hear us, Holy JESU.

p Shelter us with Angel's wing,
To our souls Thy pardon bring ;
So shall death have lost its sting :
      Hear us, Holy JESU.

In the gloom Thy light provide ;
Safely through the valley guide ;
Thee we trust, for Thou hast died :
      Hear us, Holy JESU.

Litany of the Four Last Things.

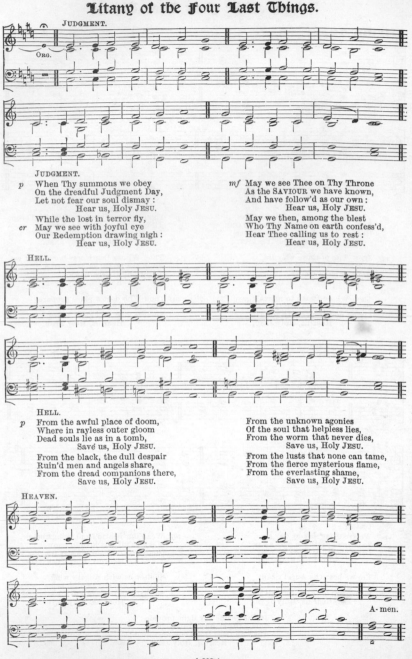

JUDGMENT.

p When Thy summons we obey
On the dreadful Judgment Day,
Let not fear our soul dismay :
    Hear us, Holy Jesu.

While the lost in terror fly,
cr May we see with joyful eye
Our Redemption drawing nigh :
    Hear us, Holy Jesu.

mf May we see Thee on Thy Throne
As the Saviour we have known,
And have follow'd as our own :
    Hear us, Holy Jesu.

May we then, among the blest
Who Thy Name on earth confess'd,
Hear Thee calling us to rest :
    Hear us, Holy Jesu.

HELL.

p From the awful place of doom,
Where in rayless outer gloom
Dead souls lie as in a tomb,
    Save us, Holy Jesu.

From the black, the dull despair
Ruin'd men and angels share,
From the dread companions there,
    Save us, Holy Jesu.

From the unknown agonies
Of the soul that helpless lies,
From the worm that never dies,
    Save us, Holy Jesu.

From the lusts that none can tame,
From the fierce mysterious flame,
From the everlasting shame,
    Save us, Holy Jesu.

Litany of the Four Last Things.

HEAVEN.

f   Where Thy Saints in glory reign,
Free from sorrow, free from pain,
Pure from every guilty stain,
    Bring us, Holy JESU.

mf Where the captives find release,
Where all foes from troubling cease,
Where the weary rest in peace,
    Bring us, Holy JESU.

cr Where the pleasures never cloy,
Where in Angels' holy joy

Thy redeem'd their powers employ,
    Bring us, Holy JESU.

Where in wondrous light are shown
All Thy dealings with Thine own,
Who shall know as they are known,
    Bring us, Holy JESU.

f   Where, with loved ones gone before,
We may love Thee and adore
In Thy Presence evermore,
    Bring us, Holy JESU.

                  Compilers.

Litany of the Incarnate Word.

Hymn 464. *(First Tune.)*   REV. J. B. DYKES.

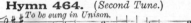

A-men.

Hymn 464. *(Second Tune.)*   REV. F. A. J. HERVEY.

To be sung in Unison.

A-men.

mf GOD the FATHER, GOD the SON,
    GOD the SPIRIT, THREE in ONE,
Hear us from Thy heavenly Throne,
    p   Spare us, Holy TRINITY.

mf SON of GOD, for man decreed
To be born the woman's Seed,
Very GOD and Man indeed,
    Hear us, Holy JESU.

Thou Whose Wisdom all things plann'd,
Held by Whose Almighty Hand
All things in their order stand,
    Hear us, Holy JESU.

GOD with us, Emmanuel,
Coming here as Man to dwell,
Saving us when Adam fell,
    Hear us, Holy JESU.

SAVIOUR, full of truth and grace,
Leaving Thine eternal place
To restore our fallen race,
    Hear us, Holy JESU.

Image of the GOD unseen,
Still what Thou hadst ever been,
Though in form of Infant mean,
    Hear us, Holy JESU.

WORD, by Whom the worlds were made,
In a lowly manger laid,
Taught on earth an humble trade,
    Hear us, Holy JESU.

p JESU, led by love to share
All the forms of grief and care,

That we sinful mortals bear,
    Hear us, Holy JESU.

mf Good Physician, come to cure
All the ills that men endure,
And to make our nature pure,
    Hear us, Holy JESU.

p Man of Sorrows, weak and worn
With Thy woes for sinners borne,
Lest we should for ever mourn,
    Hear us, Holy JESU.

mf Shepherd, Who Thy watch dost keep,
Guarding still Thy chosen sheep
From the spoiler's malice deep,
    Hear us, Holy JESU.

p LAMB, from earth's foundation slain,
By Whose bitter stripes of pain
We are freed from guilty stain,
    Hear us, Holy JESU.

mf Only Victim we can plead,
Our High Priest to intercede,
Advocate in all our need,
    Hear us, Holy JESU.

Standing now before the Throne,
Pleading that which can alone
For the sin of man atone,
    Hear us, Holy JESU.

Only Hope of those who pray,
Only Help while here we stay,
Life of those who pass away,
    Hear us, Holy JESU

                  T. B. POLLOCK.

                  O 2

Litanies of Penitence.

Hymn 465. (*First Tune.*) PARTS 1 and 3.

SIR J STAINER.

A-men.

Hymn 465. (*Second Tune.*) PARTS 1 and 3.

E. H. TURPIN.

A-men.

NO. 1.   PART 1.

mf GOD the FATHER, GOD the SON,
GOD the SPIRIT, THREE in ONE,
Hear us from Thy heavenly Throne,
p   Spare us, Holy TRINITY.

FATHER, hear Thy children's call :
Humbly at Thy feet we fall,
Prodigals, confessing all :
    We beseech Thee, hear us.

CHRIST, beneath Thy Cross we blame
All our life of sin and shame,
Penitent we breathe Thy Name :
    We beseech Thee, hear us.

HOLY SPIRIT, grieved and tried,
Oft forgotten and defiled,
Now we mourn our stubborn pride :
    We beseech Thee, hear us.

mf LOVE, that caused us first to be,
p   LOVE, that bled upon the Tree,
cr LOVE, that draws us lovingly :
    We beseech Thee, hear us

p We Thy call have disobey'd,
Into paths of sin have stray'd,
And repentance have delay'd :
    We beseech Thee, hear us.

Sick, we come to Thee for cure,
Guilty, seek Thy mercy sure,
Evil, long to be made pure :
    We beseech Thee, hear us.

Blind, we pray that we may see,
Bound, we pray to be made free,
Stain'd, we pray for sanctity :
    We beseech Thee, hear us.

mf Thou Who hear'st each contrite sigh,
Bidding sinful souls draw nigh,
Willing not that one should die,
    We beseech Thee, hear us

PART 3.

p Teach us what Thy love has borne,
That with loving sorrow torn
Truly contrite we may mourn :
    We beseech Thee, hear us.

mf Gifts of light and grace bestow,
Help us to resist the foe,
Fearing what alone is woe :
    We beseech Thee, hear us.

Let not sin within us reign,
May we gladly suffer pain,
If it purge away our stain :
    We beseech Thee, hear us.

Litanies of Penitence.

May we to all evil die,
Fleshly longings crucify,
Fix our hearts and thoughts on high :
    We beseech Thee, hear us.

Grant us faith to know Thee near,
Hail Thy grace, Thy judgment fear,
And through trial persevere :
    We beseech Thee, hear us.

Grant us hope from earth to rise,
And to strain with eager eyes
Towards the promised heavenly prize :
    We beseech Thee, hear us.

Grant us love Thy love to own,
Love to live for Thee alone,
And the power of grace make known :
    We beseech Thee, hear us.

All our weak endeavours bless,
As we ever onward press,
Till we perfect holiness :
    We beseech Thee, hear us.

cr Lead us daily nearer Thee,
Till at last Thy Face we see,
Crown'd with Thine own purity :
    We beseech Thee, hear us.

Hymn 465. (*First Tune.*) PART 2.

Sir J. STAINER.

Hymn 465. (*Second Tune.*) PART 2.

E. H. TURPIN.

PART 2.

mf By the gracious saving call
Spoken tenderly to all
Who have shared in Adam's fall,
    We beseech Thee, hear us.

p By the nature JESUS wore,
By the Stripes and Death He bore,
cr By His Life for evermore,
    We beseech Thee, hear us.

mf By the love that longs to bless,
Pitying our sore distress,
Leading us to holiness,
    We beseech Thee, hear us.

By the love so calm and strong,
Patient still to suffer wrong
And our day of grace prolong,
    We beseech Thee, hear us.

By the love that speaks within,
Calling us to flee from sin
And the joy of goodness win,
    We beseech Thee, hear us.

By the love that bids Thee spare,
cr By the Heav'n Thou dost prepare,
By Thy promises to prayer,
    We beseech Thee, hear us.

T. B. POLLOCK.

Litanies of Penitence.

Hymn 466. (*First Tune.*) Harmonised by C. BUCKNALL.

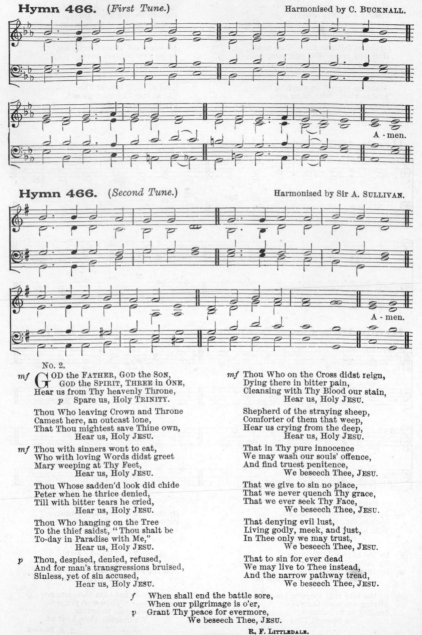

A - men.

Hymn 466. (*Second Tune.*) Harmonised by Sir A. SULLIVAN.

A - men.

NO. 2.

mf GOD the FATHER, GOD the SON,
  GOD the SPIRIT, THREE in ONE,
Hear us from Thy heavenly Throne,
  p Spare us, Holy TRINITY.

Thou Who leaving Crown and Throne
Camest here, an outcast lone,
That Thou mightest save Thine own,
  Hear us, Holy JESU.

mf Thou with sinners wont to eat,
Who with loving Words didst greet
Mary weeping at Thy Feet,
  Hear us, Holy JESU.

Thou Whose sadden'd look did chide
Peter when he thrice denied,
Till with bitter tears he cried,
  Hear us, Holy JESU.

Thou Who hanging on the Tree
To the thief saidst, "Thou shalt be
To-day in Paradise with Me,"
  Hear us, Holy JESU.

p Thou, despised, denied, refused,
And for man's transgressions bruised,
Sinless, yet of sin accused,
  Hear us, Holy JESU.

mf Thou Who on the Cross didst reign,
Dying there in bitter pain,
Cleansing with Thy Blood our stain,
  Hear us, Holy JESU.

Shepherd of the straying sheep,
Comforter of them that weep,
Hear us crying from the deep,
  Hear us, Holy JESU.

That in Thy pure innocence
We may wash our souls' offence,
And find truest penitence,
  We beseech Thee, JESU.

That we give to sin no place,
That we never quench Thy grace,
That we ever seek Thy Face,
  We beseech Thee, JESU.

That denying evil lust,
Living godly, meek, and just,
In Thee only we may trust,
  We beseech Thee, JESU.

That to sin for ever dead
We may live to Thee instead,
And the narrow pathway tread,
  We beseech Thee, JESU.

f When shall end the battle sore,
  When our pilgrimage is o'er,
p Grant Thy peace for evermore,
  We beseech Thee, JESU.

R. F. LITTLEDALE.

Litany of the Passion.

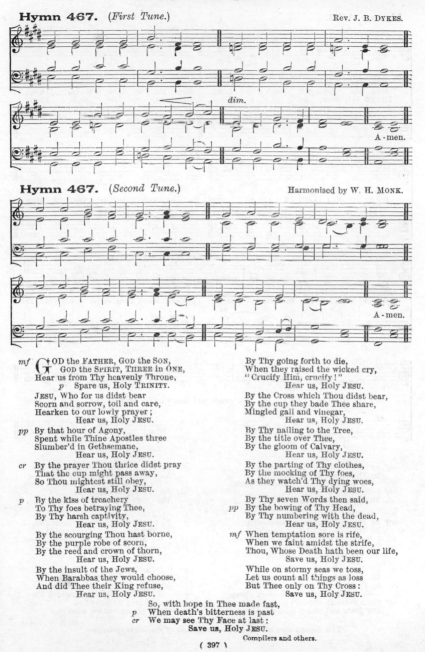

A - men.

A - men.

mf GOD the FATHER, GOD the SON,
  GOD the SPIRIT, THREE in ONE,
Hear us from Thy heavenly Throne,
  p   Spare us, Holy TRINITY.

JESU, Who for us didst bear
Scorn and sorrow, toil and care,
Hearken to our lowly prayer ;
  Hear us, Holy JESU.

pp By that hour of Agony,
Spent while Thine Apostles three
Slumber'd in Gethsemane,
  Hear us, Holy JESU.

cr By the prayer Thou thrice didst pray
That the cup might pass away,
So Thou mightest still obey,
  Hear us, Holy JESU.

p   By the kiss of treachery
To Thy foes betraying Thee,
By Thy harsh captivity,
  Hear us, Holy JESU.

By the scourging Thou hast borne,
By the purple robe of scorn,
By the reed and crown of thorn,
  Hear us, Holy JESU.

By the insult of the Jews,
When Barabbas they would choose,
And did Thee their King refuse,
  Hear us, Holy JESU.

By Thy going forth to die,
When they raised the wicked cry,
" Crucify Him, crucify ! "
  Hear us, Holy JESU.

By the Cross which Thou didst bear,
By the cup they bade Thee share,
Mingled gall and vinegar,
  Hear us, Holy JESU.

By Thy nailing to the Tree,
By the title over Thee,
By the gloom of Calvary,
  Hear us, Holy JESU.

By the parting of Thy clothes,
By the mocking of Thy foes,
As they watch'd Thy dying woes,
  Hear us, Holy JESU.

By Thy seven Words then said,
pp By the bowing of Thy Head,
By Thy numbering with the dead,
  Hear us, Holy JESU.

mf When temptation sore is rife,
When we faint amidst the strife,
Thou, Whose Death hath been our life,
  Save us, Holy JESU.

While on stormy seas we toss,
Let us count all things as loss
But Thee only on Thy Cross :
  Save us, Holy JESU.

So, with hope in Thee made fast,
  p   When death's bitterness is past
  cr We may see Thy Face at last :
  Save us, Holy JESU.

Compilers and others.

Litany for the Rogation Days.

Hymn 468.

Semi-Chorus.   *Chorus.*   German.

mf GOD the FA-THER, from Thy Throne, Hear us, we be-seech Thee;
GOD the co-e-ter-nal SON, Hear us, we be-seech Thee;
GOD the SPI-RIT, migh-ty LORD, Hear us, we be-seech Thee;
THREE in ONE, by all a-dored, Hear us, we be-seech Thee;

Semi-Chorus.   *In Unison.*

p JE - SU! (*cr*) JE - SU! (*mf*) By Thy won-drous In - car - na - tion,

Chorus.
In Harmony.   *cres.*   *mf*

By Thy Birth for our sal-va - - tion, . . (*p*)We be-seech Thee, we be-seech Thee, From

ev'-ry ill de - fend us, Thy grace and mer-cy send . us. A - men.

---

p   JESU! JESU!
mf By Thy Fasting and Temptation,
By Thy nights of supplication,
p   We beseech Thee, we beseech Thee,
mf From every ill defend us,
Thy grace and mercy send us.

p   JESU! JESU!
mf By Thy works of sweet compassion,
By Thy Cross and bitter Passion,
p   We beseech Thee, we beseech Thee,
mf From every ill defend us,
Thy grace and mercy send us.

p   JESU! JESU!
By Thy Blood for sinners flowing,
cr By Thy Death true life bestowing,
p   We beseech Thee, we beseech Thee,
mf From every ill defend us,
Thy grace and mercy send us.

p   JESU! JESU!
f By Thy glorious Resurrection,
Earnest of our own perfection,
p   We beseech Thee, we beseech Thee,
mf From every ill defend us,
Thy grace and mercy send us.

p   JESU! JESU!
f To the FATHER'S Throne ascended,
All Thy pain and sorrows ended,
p   We beseech Thee, we beseech Thee,
mf From every ill defend us,
Thy grace and mercy send us.

p   JESU! JESU!
mf Advocate for sinners pleading,
With the FATHER interceding,
p   We beseech Thee, we beseech Thee,
mf From every ill defend us,
Thy grace and mercy send us.

Sir H. W. BAKER.

This Litany may also be sung in any time of special supplication.

Litany of Jesus Glorified.

Hymn 469. *(First Tune.)*

E. H. TURPIN.

A - men.

<table>
<tr><td>

mf G OD the FATHER, throned on high,
    SAVIOUR, Who didst come to die,
SPIRIT, Who dost sanctify,
  p Save us, Holy TRINITY.

mf JESU, Prince of life and light,
Dwelling now in glory bright,
Ruling all things by Thy might,
  p Hear us, Holy JESU.

    Thou Whose Death did death destroy,
cr Who through pain didst pass to joy
Endless and without alloy,
    Hear us, Holy JESU.

f Thou Who didst to Heav'n ascend
Still to be the sinner's Friend,
Still Thy people to defend,
    Hear us, Holy JESU.

JESU, raised to GOD'S right hand,
Round Whose Throne the Angel band
Waits Thy Word of dread command,
    Hear us, Holy JESU.

Thou Who dost the Sceptre bear,
And in Heav'n a place prepare
That we may be with Thee there,
    Hear us, Holy JESU.

Thou Who must in glory reign,
Conqueror of sin and pain,
Till no enemy remain,
    Hear us, Holy JESU.

mf JESU, Who art glorified
In the very Flesh that died,
p With the piercèd Hands and Side,
    Hear us, Holy JESU.

mf JESU, though enthroned on high,
Still for our infirmity
Touch'd with human sympathy,
    Hear us, Holy JESU.

JESU, in our time of need
Our High Priest to intercede,
Living still Thy Death to plead,
    Hear us, Holy JESU.

</td><td>

JESU, able to bestow
On Thy struggling Church below
More than we can ask or know,
    Hear us, Holy JESU.

JESU, Who to Heav'n upborne
Didst not leave Thy Church to mourn,
p Orphan'd, comfortless, forlorn,
    Hear us, Holy JESU.

mf Thou Who, still our Saviour Friend,
Didst the HOLY SPIRIT send
To be with us to the end,
    Hear us, Holy JESU.

p JESU, Who Thy Flesh and Blood,
Offer'd once upon the Rood,
Givest for Thy children's Food,
    Hear us, Holy JESU.

mf Only Balm for souls distress'd,
Happiness of all the bless'd,
Peace of those who long for rest,
    Hear us, Holy JESU.

f Thou Who, as Thou once didst rise,
Shalt be seen by human eyes
Coming through the parted skies,
    Hear us, Holy JESU.

p Thou Who then on quick and dead,
All for whom Thy Blood was shed,
Shalt pronounce the judgment dread,
    Hear us, Holy JESU.

mf JESU, GOD'S Incarnate SON,
By Thy work for sinners done,
By the gifts for sinners won,
    Hear us, Holy JESU.

That while pilgrims toiling here
We Thy Name may love and fear,
And to death may persevere,
    Hear us, Holy JESU.

cr That when earthly toil is o'er
We, in rest for evermore,
May behold Thee and adore,
    Hear us, Holy JESU.

</td></tr>
</table>

T. B. POLLOCK.

Litany of Jesus Glorified.

Hymn 469. *(Second Tune.)*

Rev. F. A. J. Hervey.

A - men.

mf GOD the FATHER, throned on high,
SAVIOUR, Who didst come to die,
SPIRIT, Who dost sanctify,
   p Save us, Holy TRINITY.

mf JESU, Prince of life and light,
Dwelling now in glory bright,
Ruling all things by Thy might,
   p Hear us, Holy JESU.

Thou Whose Death did death destroy.
cr Who through pain didst pass to joy
Endless and without alloy,
   Hear us, Holy JESU.

f Thou Who didst to Heav'n ascend
Still to be the sinner's Friend,
Still Thy people to defend,
   Hear us, Holy JESU.

JESU, raised to GOD'S right hand,
Round Whose Throne the Angel band
Waits Thy Word of dread command,
   Hear us, Holy JESU.

Thou Who dost the Sceptre bear,
And in Heav'n a place prepare
That we may be with Thee there,
   Hear us, Holy JESU.

Thou Who must in glory reign,
Conqueror of sin and pain,
Till no enemy remain,
   Hear us, Holy JESU.

mf JESU, Who art glorified
In the very Flesh that died,
p With the piercèd Hands and Side,
   Hear us, Holy JESU.

mf JESU, though enthroned on high,
Still for our infirmity
Touch'd with human sympathy,
   Hear us, Holy JESU.

JESU, in our time of need
Our High Priest to intercede,
Living still Thy Death to plead,
   Hear us, Holy JESU.

JESU, able to bestow
On Thy struggling Church below
More than we can ask or know,
   Hear us, Holy JESU.

JESU, Who to Heav'n upborne
Didst not leave Thy Church to mourn,
p Orphan'd, comfortless, forlorn,
   Hear us, Holy JESU.

mf Thou Who, still our Saviour Friend,
Didst the HOLY SPIRIT send
To be with us to the end,
   Hear us, Holy JESU.

p JESU, Who Thy Flesh and Blood,
Offer'd once upon the Rood,
Givest for Thy children's Food,
   Hear us, Holy JESU.

mf Only Balm for souls distress'd,
Happiness of all the bless'd,
Peace of those who long for rest,
   Hear us, Holy JESU.

f Thou Who, as Thou once didst rise,
Shalt be seen by human eyes
Coming through the parted skies,
   Hear us, Holy JESU.

p Thou Who then on quick and dead,
All for whom Thy Blood was shed,
Shalt pronounce the judgment dread,
   Hear us, Holy JESU.

mf JESU, GOD'S Incarnate SON,
By Thy work for sinners done,
By the gifts for sinners won,
   Hear us, Holy JESU.

That while pilgrims toiling here
We Thy Name may love and fear,
And to death may persevere,
   Hear us, Holy JESU.

cr That when earthly toil is o'er
We, in rest for evermore,
May behold Thee and adore,
   Hear us, Holy JESU.

T. B. POLLOCK.

Litany of the Holy Ghost.

Hymn 470. *(First Tune.)* J. W. ELLIOTT.

A - men.

Hymn 470. *(Second Tune.)* E. H. TURPIN.

A - men.

mf G OD the FATHER, GOD the SON,
GOD the SPIRIT, THREE in ONE,
Hear us from Thy heavenly Throne,
p Spare us, Holy TRINITY.

mf HOLY SPIRIT, heavenly Dove,
Dew descending from above,
Breath of life, and Fire of love,
p Hear us, Holy SPIRIT.

Source of strength, of knowledge clear,
Wisdom, godliness sincere,
Understanding, counsel, fear,
Hear us, Holy SPIRIT.

Source of meekness, love, and peace,
Patience, pureness, faith's increase,
Hope and joy that cannot cease,
Hear us, Holy SPIRIT.

SPIRIT guiding us aright,
SPIRIT making darkness light,
cr SPIRIT of resistless might,
Hear us, Holy SPIRIT.

p Thou by Whom the Virgin bore
Him Whom heaven and earth adore,
Sent our nature to restore,
Hear us, Holy SPIRIT.

mf Thou Whom JESUS from His Throne
Gave to cheer and help His own,
That they might not be alone,
Hear us, Holy SPIRIT.

COMFORTER, to Whom we owe
All that we rejoice to know
Of our Saviour's work below,
Hear us, Holy SPIRIT.

Thou Whose sound Apostles heard,
Thou Whose power their spirit stirr'd,

Giving them the living Word,
Hear us, Holy SPIRIT.

Thou Whose grace the Church doth fill,
Showing her GOD'S perfect Will,
Making JESUS present still,
Hear us, Holy SPIRIT.

Coming with Thy power to save,
Moving on Baptismal wave,
Raising us from sin's dark grave,
Hear us, Holy SPIRIT.

p All our evil passions kill,
Bend aright our stubborn will,
Though we grieve Thee, patient still ;
Hear us, Holy SPIRIT.

mf Come to raise us when we fall,
And, when snares our souls enthral,
Lead us back with gentle call ;
Hear us, Holy SPIRIT.

Come to strengthen all the weak,
Give Thy courage to the meek,
Teach our faltering tongues to speak :
Hear us, Holy SPIRIT.

Come to aid the souls who yearn
More of truth Divine to learn,
And with deeper love to burn ;
Hear us, Holy SPIRIT.

Keep us in the narrow way,
Warn us when we go astray,
Plead within us when we pray ;
Hear us, Holy SPIRIT.

cr Holy, loving, as Thou art,
All Thy sevenfold gifts impart,
Never more from us depart ;
Hear us, Holy SPIRIT.

Compilers and others.

(401)

Litany of the Church.

Hymn 471. *(First Tune.)*

E. H. TURPIN.

Hymn 471. *(Second Tune.)*

(?)

mf GOD the FATHER, GÓD the SON,
GOD the SPIRIT, THRÉE in ÓNE,
Hear us from Thy héavenly Throne,
p   Spare us, Holy TRÍNITY.

mf JESU, with Thy Chúrch abide,
Be her SAVIOUR, LÓRD, and Guide,
While on earth her fáith is tried :
      We beseech Thee, héar us.

Arms of love aróund her throw,
Shield her safe from évery foe,
dim Comfort her in time of woe :
      We beseech Thee, héar us.

mf Keep her life and dóctrine pure,
Grant her patience tó endure,
Trusting in Thy prómise sure :
      We beseech Thee, héar us.

May her voice be éver clear,
Warning of a júdgment near,
Telling of a Sáviour dear :
      We beseech Thee, héar us.

All her fetter'd pówers release,
Bid our strife and énvy cease,
Grant the heavenly gíft of peace :
      We beseech Thee, héar us.

All that she has lóst restore,
May her strength and zéal be more
Than in brightest dáys of yore :
      We beseech Thee, héar us.

May she one in dóctrine be,
One in truth and chárity,
Winning all to fáith in Thee :
      We beseech Thee, héar us.

May she guide the póor and blind,
Seek the lost untíl she find,
And the broken-héarted bind :
      We beseech Thee, héar us.

Save her love from grówing cold,
Make her watchmen stróng and bold,
Fence her round, Thy péaceful fold :
      We beseech Thee, héar us.

May her Priests Thy péople feed,
Shepherds of the flóck indeed,
Ready, where Thou cáll'st, to lead ;
      We beseech Thee, héar us.

p Judge her not for wórk undone,
Judge her not for fíelds unwon,
cr Bless her works in Thée begun :
      We beseech Thee, héar us.

p For the past give déeper shame,
cr Make her jealous fór Thy Name,
Kindle zeal's most hóly flame :
      We beseech Thee, héar us.

f Raise her to her cálling high,
Let the nations fár and nigh
Hear Thy heralds' wárning cry :
      We beseech Thee, héar us.

May her lamp of trúth be bright,
Bid her bear alóft its light
Through the realms of héathen night :
      We beseech Thee, héar us.

mf May her scatter'd chíldren be
From reproach of évil free,
Blameless witnessés for Thee :
      We beseech Thee, héar us.

Arm her soldiers with the Cross,
Brave to suffer tóil or loss,
Counting earthly gáin but dross :
      We beseech Thee, héar us.

cr May she holy tríumphs win,
Overthrow the hósts of sin,
Gather all the nátions in :
      We beseech Thee, héar us.

f May she soon all glórious be,
Spotless and from wrínkle free,
Pure, and bright, and wórthy Thee :
      We beseech Thee, héar us.

Fit her all Thy jóy to share
In the home Thou dóst prepare,
And be ever bléssèd there :
      We beseech Thee, héar us.

T. B. POLLOCK.

Litany of the Blessed Sacrament
of the Body and Blood of Christ.

Hymn 472. *(First Tune.)* PARTS 1 and 3. W. H. MONK.

A-men.

PART 2.

Hymn 472. *(Second Tune.)* Rev. Sir H. W. BAKER.

A - men.

mf GOD the FATHER, GÓD the SON,
GOD the SPIRIT, THREE in ONE,
p Spare us, Holy TRINITY.

f GOD of GOD, and Light of Light,
King of glory, LÓRD of might,
Hear us, Holy JESU.

p Very Man, Who fór our sake
Didst true Flesh of Máry take,
Hear us, Holy JESU.

mf Shepherd, Whom the FÁTHER gave
His lost sheep to find and save,
Hear us, Holy JESU.

Priest and Victim, Whóm of old
Type and prophecý foretold,
Hear us, Holy JESU.

King of Salem, Príest Divine,
Bringing forth Thy Bréad and Wine,
Hear us, Holy JESU.

Paschal Lamb, Whose sprinkled Blood
Saves the Israél of GOD,
Hear us, Holy JESU.

Manna, found at dáwn of day,
Pilgrim's Food in désert-way,
Hear us, Holy JESU.

Offering pure, in évery place
Pledge and means of héavenly grace,
Hear us, Holy JESU.

PART 2.

p By the mercy, thát of yore
Shadow'd forth Thy gifts in store,
Save us, Holy JESU.

cr By the love, on thát last night
That ordain'd the bétter rite,
Save us, Holy JESU.

p By the Death, that cóuld alone
For the whole world's sin atone,
Save us, Holy JESU.

By the Wounds, that éver plead
For our help in time of need,
Save us Holy JESU.

PART 3.

That we may remémber still
Kedron's brook and Cálvary's hill,
Grant us, Holy JESU.

mf That our thankful héarts may glow
As Thy precious Déath we show,
Grant us, Holy JESU.

That, with humble cóntrite fear,
We may joy to féel Thee near,
Grant us, Holy JESU.

cr That in faith we máy adore,
Praise, and love Thee móre and more,
Grant us, Holy JESU.

p That Thy Sacred Flésh and Blood
Be our true life-giving Food,
Grant us, Holy JESU.

mf That in all our wórds and ways
We may daily shów Thy praise,
Grant us, Holy JESU.

cr That, as death's dark vále we tread,
Thou mayst be our stréngthening Bread,
Grant us, Holy JESU.

mf That, unworthy thóugh we be,
We may ever dwéll with Thee,
Grant us, Holy JESU.

Sir H. W. BAKER.

(403)

Litany for Children.

Hymn 473. *(First Tune.)*

Rev. J. B. DYKES.

PART 1.

PART 2.

PART 3.

A - men.

Litany for Children.

mf GOD the FATHER, GOD the SON,
   GOD the SPIRIT, THREE in ONE,
Hear us from Thy heavenly Throne,
   p   Spare us, Holy TRINITY.

p   From all pride and vain conceit,
From all spite and angry heat,
From all lying and deceit,
   Save us, Holy JESU.

p   JESU, Saviour ever mild,
Born for us a little Child
Of the Virgin undefiled,
   Hear us, Holy JESU.

From all sloth and idleness,
From not caring for distress,
From all lust and greediness,
   Save us, Holy JESU.

JESU, by the Mother-Maid
In Thy swaddling-clothes array'd,
And within a manger laid,
   Hear us, Holy JESU.

From refusing to obey,
From the love of our own way,
From forgetfulness to pray,
   Save us, Holy JESU.

JESU, at Whose Infant Feet
Shepherds, coming Thee to greet,
Knelt to pay their worship meet,
   Hear us, Holy JESU.

PART 3.

mf By Thy Birth and early years,
By Thine Infant wants and fears,
By Thy sorrows and Thy tears,
   Save us, Holy JESU.

mf JESU, unto Whom of yore
Wise men, hastening to adore,
Gold and myrrh and incense bore,
   Hear us, Holy JESU.

By Thy Pattern bright and pure,
By the pains Thou didst endure
Our salvation to procure,
   Save us, Holy JESU.

JESU, to Thy Temple brought,
Whom, by Thy good SPIRIT taught,
Simeon and Anna sought,
   Hear us, Holy JESU.

p   By Thy Wounds and thorn-crown'd Head
By Thy Blood for sinners shed,
mf By Thy Rising from the dead,
   Save us, Holy JESU.

p   JESU, Who didst deign to flee
From King Herod's cruelty
In Thy earliest Infancy,
   Hear us, Holy JESU.

By the Name we bow before,
Human Name, which evermore
All the hosts of Heav'n adore,
   Save us, Holy JESU.

cr JESU, Whom Thy Mother found
'Midst the doctors sitting round,
Marvelling at Thy Words profound,
   Hear us, Holy JESU.

f   By Thine own unconquer'd might,
By Thy glory in the height,
By Thy mercies infinite,
   Save us, Holy JESU.

Committee of Clergy (chiefly)

Litany for Children.

Hymn 473. *(Second Tune.)*

Rev. F. A. J. Hervey.

A - men.

mf G OD the FATHER, GOD the SON,
    GOD the SPIRIT, THREE in ONE,
Hear us from Thy heavenly Throne,
   p Spare us, Holy TRINITY.

p JESU, Saviour ever mild,
Born for us a little Child
Of the Virgin undefiled,
   Hear us, Holy JESU.

JESU, by the Mother-Maid
In Thy swaddling-clothes array'd,
And within a manger laid,
   Hear us, Holy JESU.

JESU, at Whose Infant Feet
Shepherds, coming Thee to greet,
Knelt to pay their worship meet,
   Hear us, Holy JESU.

mf JESU, unto Whom of yore
Wise men, hastening to adore,
Gold and myrrh and incense bore,
   Hear us, Holy JESU.

JESU, to Thy Temple brought,
Whom, by Thy good SPIRIT taught,
Simeon and Anna sought,
   Hear us, Holy JESU.

p JESU, Who didst deign to flee
From King Herod's cruelty
In Thy earliest Infancy,
   Hear us, Holy JESU.

cr JESU, Whom Thy Mother found
'Midst the doctors sitting round,
Marvelling at Thy Words profound,
   Hear us, Holy JESU.

PART 2.

p From all pride and vain conceit,
From all spite and angry heat,
From all lying and deceit,
   Save us, Holy JESU.

From all sloth and idleness,
From not caring for distress,
From all lust and greediness,
   Save us, Holy JESU.

From refusing to obey,
From the love of our own way,
From forgetfulness to pray,
   Save us, Holy JESU.

PART 3.

mf By Thy Birth and early years,
By Thine Infant wants and fears,
By Thy sorrows and Thy tears,
   Save us, Holy JESU.

By Thy Pattern bright and pure,
By the pains Thou didst endure
Our salvation to procure,
   Save us, Holy JESU.

p By Thy Wounds and thorn-crown'd Head,
By Thy Blood for sinners shed,
mf By Thy Rising from the dead,
   Save us, Holy JESU.

By the Name we bow before,
Human Name, which evermore
All the hosts of Heav'n adore,
   Save us, Holy JESU.

f By Thine own unconquer'd might,
By Thy glory in the height,
By Thy mercies infinite,
   Save us, Holy JESU.

Committee of Clergy (chiefly).

FIRST SUPPLEMENT.

Morning.

Hymn 474. GERRANS.—6 6 8 6.11 11.

A. H. BROWN.

A - men.

" I laid me down and slept, and rose up again, for the Lord sustained me."

mf   A WAKED from sleep we fall
      Before Thee, GOD of love,
  And chant the praise the Angels raise,
    O GOD of might, above ;
  Holy, Holy, Holy ! Thou art GOD adored !
p In Thy pitying mercy show us mercy, LORD.

mf Thou wakedst me from sleep ;
    Shine on this mind and heart,
  And touch my tongue, that I among
    Thy choir may take my part ;
  Holy, Holy, Holy ! TRINITY adored !
p In Thy pitying mercy show me mercy, LORD.

mf The Judge will come with speed,
    And each man's deeds be known ;
dim Our trembling cry shall rise on high
    At midnight to Thy Throne ;
  Holy, Holy, Holy ! King of Saints adored !
p In the hour of judgment show us mercy, LORD.

R. M. MOORSOM · from the Greek.

(407)

Mid=day—for a City Church.

Hymn 475. ELM.—C.M. *(First Tune.)*

J. V. ROBERTS.

A-men.

Hymn 475. BYZANTIUM.—C.M. *(Second Tune.)*

T. JACKSON, 1780.

A-men.

" A House of rest."

mf BEHOLD us, LORD, a little space
  From daily tasks set free,
And met within Thy holy place
  To rest awhile with Thee.

Around us rolls the ceaseless tide
  Of business, toil, and care ;
p And scarcely can we turn aside
  For one brief hour of prayer.

Yet these are not the only walls
  Wherein Thou may'st be sought ;
cr On homeliest work Thy blessing falls
  In truth and patience wrought.

Thine is the loom, the forge, the mart,
  The wealth of land and sea ;
The worlds of science and of art,
  Reveal'd and ruled by Thee.

mf Then let us prove our heavenly birth
  In all we do and know ;
And claim the kingdom of the earth
  For Thee, and not Thy foe.

Work shall be prayer, if all be wrought
  As Thou wouldst have it done ;
And prayer, by Thee inspired and taught,
  Itself with work be one.

J. ELLERTON.

(408)

Evening.

Hymn 476. BRIGHTNESS.—D.C.M.   Rev. Sir F. A. G. OUSELEY.

A-men.

" The Lord shall be thine everlasting light."

mf BEHOLD the sun, that seem'd but now
    Enthronèd overhead,
Beginneth to decline below
    The globe whereon we tread;
And he, whom yet we look upon
    With comfort and delight,
dim Will quite depart from hence anon,
p   And leave us to the night.

Thus time, unheeded, steals away
    The life which nature gave;
Thus are our bodies every day
    Declining to the grave;
Thus from us all our pleasures fly
    Whereon we set our heart;
And when the night of death draws nigh,
    Thus will they all depart.

cr LORD! though the sun forsake our sight,
    And mortal hopes are vain;
mf Let still Thine everlasting light
    Within our souls remain;
And in the nights of our distress
    Vouchsafe those rays Divine,
cr Which from the Sun of Righteousness
    For ever brightly shine.

G. WITHER, 1623.

ALTERNATIVE TUNES, HYMN 216 OR HYMN 168 (SECOND TUNE)

(409)

Evening.

Hymn 477. St. Clement.—9 8 9 8.   Rev. C. C. Scholefield.

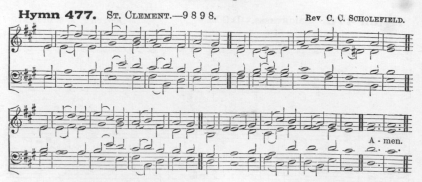

A - men.

" The Lord's Name is praised from the rising up of the sun unto the going down of the same."

mf THE day Thou gavest, LORD, is ended,
    The darkness falls at Thy behest ;
To Thee our morning hymns ascended,
cr   Thy praise shall sanctify our rest.

mf We thank Thee that Thy Church unsleeping,
    While earth rolls onward into light,
Through all the world her watch is keeping,
    And rests not now by day or night.

As o'er each continent and island
    The dawn leads on another day,

The voice of prayer is never silent,
    Nor dies the strain of praise away.

The sun that bids us rest is waking
    Our brethren 'neath the western sky,
And hour by hour fresh lips are making
    Thy wondrous doings heard on high.

cr So be it, LORD ; Thy Throne shall never,
    Like earth's proud empires, pass away ;
f   Thy Kingdom stands, and grows for ever,
    Till all Thy creatures own Thy sway.

J. Ellerton.

Sunday.

Hymn 478. Nativity.—C.M. *(First Tune.)*   H. Lahee, 1855.

A - men.

Hymn 478. Bishopthorpe.--C.M. *(Second Tune.)*   J. Clarke, 1669–1707.

Sunday.

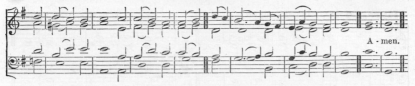

"A good day."

mf THIS is the day the LORD hath made,
  He calls the hours His own ;
Let Heav'n rejoice, let earth be glad,
  And praise surround the Throne.

*To-day He rose and left the dead,
  And Satan's empire fell ;
To-day the saints His triumphs spread,
  And all His wonders tell.

*Hosanna to th' anointed King,
  To David's Holy SON !

dim Make haste to help us, LORD, and bring
cr Salvation from Thy Throne.

  *Bless'd be the LORD, Who comes to men
    With messages of grace ;
  Who comes, in GOD His Father's Name,
dim To save our sinful race.

f *Hosanna in the highest strains
    The Church on earth can raise ;
  The highest Heav'ns in which He reigns
    Shall give Him nobler praise.

I. WATTS, 1719.

* *For First Tune verses 2, 3, 4, 5 must begin thus :*

Hymn 479. EISENACH.—L.M.

J. H. SCHEIN, 1628.

A - men.

A simpler form of this Tune is given at Hymn 173.

" There shall be no night there."

EVENING.

mf GREAT GOD, Who, hid from mortal sight,
  Dost dwell in unapproachèd light,
Before Whose Throne with veilèd brow,
Thy sinless Angels trembling bow.

dim Awhile in darkness here below
  We lie oppress'd with sin and woe ;
cr But soon the everlasting day
  Shall chase the night of gloom away ;—

  The day prepared for us by Thee ;
  Tho day reserved for us to see ;—
  A day but faintly imaged here
  By brightest sun at noontide clear.

p Too long, alas ! it still delays,
  It lingers yet, that day of days ;
  The flesh, with all its load of sin,
  Must perish, ere its joy we win.

cr Then from these earthy bonds set free
  The soul shall fly, O GOD, to Thee ;
  To see Thee, love Thee, and adore,
  Her blissful task for evermore.

mf All bounteous TRINITY ! prepare
  Our souls Thy hidden joy to share,
  That our brief daytime, used aright,
  May issue in eternal light.

J. CHANDLER : from the
Latin of C. Coffin.

(411)

Friday.

Hymn 480. INTERCESSION.—L.M.

Easy Music for Church Choirs, 1853.

A-men.

"The marks of the Lord Jesus."

<table>
<tr><td>

p O JESU, crucified for man,
    O Lamb, all glorious on Thy Throne,
cr Teach Thou our wond'ring souls to scan
    The mystery of Thy love unknown.

We pray Thee, grant us strength to take
    Our daily cross, whate'er it be,
mf And gladly, for Thine own dear sake,
p   In paths of pain to follow Thee.

mf As on our daily way we go,
    Through light or shade, in calm or strife,

</td><td>

Oh ! may we bear Thy marks below
    In conquer'd sin and chasten'd life.

And week by week this day we ask
    That holy memories of Thy Cross
May sanctify each common task,
    And turn to gain each earthly loss.

Grant us, dear LORD, our cross to bear
    Till at Thy Feet we lay it down,
cr Win through Thy Blood our pardon there,
    And through the Cross attain the crown.

</td></tr>
</table>

Bishop W. Walsham How.

ALTERNATIVE TUNE, HYMN 108.

Saturday.

Hymn 481. ST. CLEMENT.—7 7. 7 7. 7 7.

C. STEGGALL.

A-men.

EVENING.   *"There remaineth a rest to the people of God."*

<table>
<tr><td>

mf NOW the busy week is done,
    Now the rest-time is begun ;
Thou hast brought us on our way,
Kept and led us day by day ;
cr Now there comes the first and best,
Day of worship, light and rest.

p Hallow, LORD, the coming day !
When we meet to praise and pray,
cr Hear Thy Word, Thy Feast attend,
Hours of happy service spend ;
To our hearts be manifest,
LORD of labour and of rest !

</td><td>

For Thy children gone before
We can trust Thee and adore ;
p All their earthly week is past,
Sabbath-time is theirs at last ;
Fold them, FATHER, to Thy breast,
*dim*Give them everlasting rest.

mf Guide us all the days to come,
Till Thy mercy call us home :
All our powers do Thou employ,
Be Thy work our chiefest joy ;
Then, the promised land possest,
p Bid us enter into rest.

</td></tr>
</table>

S. J. JONES.

Christmas.

Hymn 482. ST. OSMUND.—8 7 8 7. 4 7. *(First Tune.)* H. S. IRONS.

A - men.

Hymn 482. LEWES.—8 7 8 7. 8 7. *(Second Tune.)* J. RANDALL, 1715–1799.

A - men.

" We are come to worship Him."

mf ANGELS, from the realms of glory,
  Wing your flight o'er all the earth ;
Ye who sang creation's story,
  Now proclaim Messiah's birth ;
cr   Come and worship,
  Worship CHRIST, the new-born King.

mf Shepherds, in the field abiding,
  Watching o'er your flocks by night,
God with man is now residing,
  Yonder shines the Infant Light ;
cr   Come and worship,
  Worship CHRIST, the new-born King.

mf Sages, leave your contemplations,
  Brighter visions beam afar ;
Seek the great Desire of nations,
  Ye have seen His natal star ;
cr   Come and worship,
  Worship CHRIST, the new-born King.

mf All creation, join in praising
  GOD the FATHER, SPIRIT, SON—
Evermore your voices raising
  To th' Eternal THREE in ONE ;
cr   Come and worship,
f   Worship CHRIST, the new-born King.

J. MONTGOMERY, 1816.

(413)

Christmas.

Hymn 483. A Patre unigenitus.—L.M. *(First Tune.)* *(First Version.)*

Proper Sarum Melody.

To be sung in Unison.

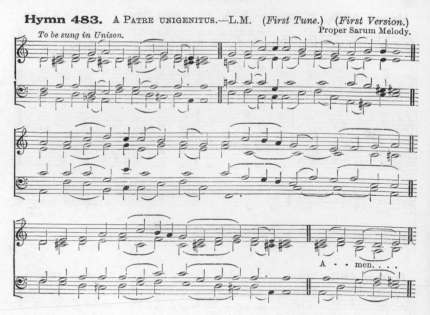

A - - men. . . .

"*Who being in the form of God . . . made Himself of no reputation, and took upon Him the form of a servant, and was made in the likeness of men.*"

f FROM east to west, from shore to shore,
  Let every heart awake and sing
dim The HOLY CHILD Whom Mary bore,
f   The CHRIST, the everlasting King.

mf Behold! the world's Creator wears
  The form and fashion of a slave ;
  Our very flesh our Maker shares,
  His fallen creature, man, to save.

  For this how wondrously He wrought !
dim A maiden, in her lowly place,
  Became, in ways beyond all thought,
  The chosen vessel of His grace.

  She bow'd her to the Angel's word
  Declaring what the FATHER will'd,
  And suddenly the promised LORD
  That pure and hallow'd temple fill'd.

p He shrank not from the oxen's stall,
  He lay within the manger bed,
  And He Whose bounty feedeth all
  At Mary's breast Himself was fed.

cr And while the Angels in the sky
  Sang praise above the silent field,
mf To shepherds poor the LORD Most High,
  The one great Shepherd, was reveal'd.

f All glory for this blessèd morn
  To GOD the FATHER ever be ;
  All praise to Thee, O Virgin-born,
  All praise, O HOLY GHOST, to Thee.

J. ELLERTON and Compilers:
from Sedulius.

(414)

Christmas.

Hymn 483. A Patre unigenitus.—L.M. (*First Tune.*) (*Alternative Version.*)

" Who being in the form of God . . . made Himself of no reputation, and took upon Him the form of a servant, and was made in the likeness of men."

Proper Sarum Melody.

From east to west, from shore to shore, Let ev - 'ry heart
Be - hold! the world's Cre - a - - tor wears The form and fash -
For this how won - drous - ly . . He wrought! A mai - den, in
She bow'd her to the An - - gel's word De - clar - ing what
He shrank not from the ox - - en's stall, He lay with - in
And while the An - gels in - the sky Sang praise a - bove
All glo - ry for this bless - - ed morn To God the Fa -

a - wake and sing The Ho - ly Child Whom Ma - ry bore, . .
- ion of a slave; Our ve - ry flesh our Ma - ker shares, . .
her low - ly place, Be - came, . in ways be - yond . all thought .
the Fa - ther will'd, And sud - den - ly the prom - ised Lord . .
the man - ger bed, And He . . whose boun - ty feed - eth all . . .
the si - lent field, To shep - herds poor the Lord . Most High, . .
- ther ev - er be; All praise to Thee, O Vir - gin - born, . .

The Christ, the ev - er - - last - - ing King.
His fal - len crea - ture, man, . . to save.
The chos - en ves - sel - of . . His grace.
That pure and hal - low'd . tem - - ple fill'd.
At Ma - ry's breast Him - - self . . was fed.
The one great Shep - herd, . was - re - veal'd.
All praise, O Ho - ly . . Ghost, . to Thee. A - men. .

Christmas.

Hymn 483. TRINITY COLLEGE.—L.M. *(Second Tune.)* Rev. J. B. DYKES.

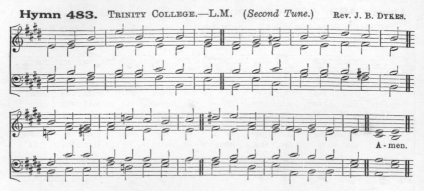

A - men.

A lower setting of this Tune is given at Hymn 486.

Hymn 483. SEDULIUS.—L.M. *(Third Tune.)* *Nürnbergisches Gesangbuch,* 1676.

A - men.

" Who being in the form of God . . . made Himself of no reputation, and took upon Him the form of a servant, and was made in the likeness of men."

f F ROM east to west, from shore to shore,
     Let every heart awake and sing
dim The HOLY CHILD Whom Mary bore,
 f   The CHRIST, the everlasting King.

mf Behold ! the world's Creator wears
    The form and fashion of a slave ;
    Our very flesh our Maker shares,
    His fallen creature, man, to save.

    For this how wondrously He wrought !
dim A maiden, in her lowly place,
    Became, in ways beyond all thought,
    The chosen vessel of His grace.

    She bow'd her to the Angel's word
    Declaring what the FATHER will'd,
    And suddenly the promised LORD
    That pure and hallow'd temple fill'd.

p He shrank not from the oxen's stall,
    He lay within the manger bed,
    And He Whose bounty feedeth all
    At Mary's breast Himself was fed.

cr And while the Angels in the sky
    Sang praise above the silent field,
mf To shepherds poor the LORD Most High,
    The one great Shepherd, was reveal'd.

f All glory for this blessèd morn
    To GOD the FATHER ever be ;
    All praise to Thee, O Virgin-born,
    All praise, O HOLY GHOST, to Thee.

J. ELLERTON and Compilers :
from Sedulius.

(416)

Christmas.

Hymn 484. GENEVAN PSALM CXVIII.—9 8 9 8.9 8 9 8. (*First Tune.*)

L. BOURGEOIS, 1544.

A-men.

" Jesus Christ is come in the flesh."

f CHRISTIANS, sing out with exultation,
And praise your Benefactor's Name !
To-day the Author of Salvation,
The FATHER'S Well-belovèd came.
mf Of undefilèd Virgin Mother
An Infant, all Divine, was born,
cr And GOD Himself became your Brother
Upon this happy Christmas morn.

mf In Him eternal might and power
To human weakness hath inclined ;
And this poor Child brings richest dower
Of gifts and graces to mankind.
dim While here His Majesty disguising,
A servant's form the Master wears,
cr Behold the beams of glory rising
E'en from His poverty and tears.

p A stable serves Him for a dwelling,
And for a bed a manger mean ;
cr Yet o'er His Head, His Advent telling,
A new and wondrous star is seen.
Angels rehearse to men the story,
The joyful story of His birth ;
To Him they raise the anthem—(*f*) " Glory
To GOD on high, and peace on earth ! "

For through this holy Incarnation
The primal curse is done away ;
dim And blessèd peace o'er all creation
Hath shed its pure and gentle ray.
cr Then, in that heavenly concert joining,
O Christian men, with one accord,
f Your voices tunefully combining,
Salute the Birthday of your LORD !

Bishop JENNER : from the
French of B. Pictet.

(417)

P

Christmas.

Hymn 484. St. Martin Orgar.—9 8 9 8. 9 8 9 8. (*Second Tune.*)

C. W. Pearce.

cres - - - cen - - - - do.

dim - - - in - - u - en - do.

f   A - men.

* *This note must be used for all verses except the first.*

" Jesus Christ is come in the flesh."

f   CHRISTIANS, sing out with exultation,
        And praise your Benefactor's Name!
    To-day the Author of Salvation,
       The FATHER'S Well-belovèd came.

mf Of undefilèd Virgin Mother
       An Infant, all Divine, was born,
cr   And GOD Himself became your Brother
       Upon this happy Christmas morn.

mf In Him eternal might and power
       To human weakness hath inclined ;
    And this poor Child brings richest dower
       Of gifts and graces to mankind.
dim While here His Majesty disguising,
       A servant's form the Master wears,
cr   Behold the beams of glory rising
       E'en from His poverty and tears.

p   A stable serves Him for a dwelling,
       And for a bed a manger mean ;
cr   Yet o'er His Head, His Advent telling,
       A new and wondrous star is seen.
    Angels rehearse to men the story,
       The joyful story of His birth ;
    To Him they raise the anthem—(*f*) " Glory
       To GOD on high, and peace on earth ! "

    For through this holy Incarnation
       The primal curse is done away ;
dim And blessèd peace o'er all creation
       Hath shed its pure and gentle ray.
cr   Then, in that heavenly concert joining,
       O Christian men, with one accord,
f   Your voices tunefully combining,
       Salute the Birthday of your LORD !

Bishop JENNER : from the
French of B. Pictet.

(**418**)

New Year's Day

Hymn 485. St. Columb.—7 6 7 6. 7 6 8 6. W S. Hoyte.

" They will go from strength to strength."

f FROM glory unto glory ! Be this our joyous song,
    As on the King's own highway, we bravely march along !
    From glory unto glory ' O word of stirring cheer,
mf As dawns the solemn brightness of another glad New Year.

f From glory unto glory ! What great things He hath done,
    What wonders He hath shown us, what triumphs He hath won !
    From glory unto glory ! What mighty blessings crown
    The lives for which our LORD hath laid His own so freely down !

    The fulness of His blessing encompasseth our way ;
    The fulness of His promises crowns every bright'ning day ;
    The fulness of His glory is beaming from above,
    While more and more we learn to know the fulness of His love.

    And closer yet and closer the golden bonds shall be,
    Uniting all who love our LORD in pure sincerity ;
    And wider yet and wider shall the circling glory glow,
    As more and more are taught of GOD that mighty Love to know.

mf O let our adoration for all that He hath done,
    Peal out beyond the stars of GOD, while voice and life are one ;
dim And let our consecration be real, deep, and true ;
    Oh, even now our hearts shall bow, and joyful vows renew.

f Now onward, ever onward, from strength to strength we go,
    While grace for grace abundantly shall from His fulness flow,
    To glory's full fruition, from glory's foretaste here,
ff Until His very presence crown our happiest New Year.

FRANCES R. HAVERGAL.

(419)

Epiphany.

Hymn 486. A Patre unigenitus.—L.M. *(First Tune.)* *(First Version.)*

Proper Sarum Melody.

" The kindness and love of God our Saviour toward man appeared."

mf   THE FATHER'S sole-begotten Son
dim   Was born, the Virgin's Child, on earth ;
 His Cross for us adoption won,—
mf   The life and grace of second birth.

 Forth from the height of Heav'n He came,
dim In form of man with man abode ;
mf   Redeem'd His world from death and shame,
 The joys of endless life bestow'd.

p   Redeemer, come with power benign,
 Dwell in the souls that look for Thee ;
 O let Thy light within us shine
 That we may Thy salvation see.

 Abide with us, O Lord, we pray,
 Dispel the gloom of doubt and woe ;
 Wash every stain of guilt away,
 Thy tender healing grace bestow.

mf   Lord, Thou hast come, and well we know
 That Thou wilt likewise come again ;
 Thy Kingdom shield from every foe,
 Thy honour and Thy rule maintain.

f   Eternal glory, Lord, to Thee,
 Whom, now reveal'd, our hearts adore ;
 To God the Father glory be,
 And Holy Spirit evermore.

Compilers : from the Latin.

Hymn 486. A Patre unigenitus.—L.M. *(First Tune.)* *(Alternative Version.)*

" The kindness and love of God our Saviour toward man appeared."

Proper Sarum Melody.

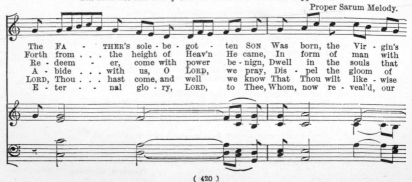

The FA - THER'S sole - be - got - ten Son Was born, the Vir - gin's
Forth from . . . the height of Heav'n He came, In form of man with
Re - deem - er, come with power be - nign, Dwell in the souls that
A - bide . . . with us, O Lord, we pray, Dis - pel the gloom of
Lord, Thou . . . hast come, and well we know That Thou wilt like - wise
E - ter - - nal glo - ry, Lord, to Thee, Whom, now re - veal'd, our

Epiphany.

Child, on earth; His Cross . . for us a - dop - - tion won,— . .
man a - bode; Re - deem'd His world from death . . and shame, . .
look for Thee; O let . . Thy light with . in . . . us shine . . .
doubt and woe; Wash ev - - 'ry stain of guilt . . a - way, . . .
come a - gain; Thy King - - dom shield from ev - - 'ry foe, ...
hearts a - dore; To GOD . . the FA - THER glo - - ry be, ...

The life and grace of . . . se - - cond birth.
The joys of end - less . life - - be - stow'd.
That we may Thy sal - - va - - tion see.
Thy ten - der heal - ing . grace . . be - stow.
Thy hon - our and Thy rule . . main - tain.
And HO - LY SPI - RIT . . . ev - - er - more. A - men.

Hymn 486. TRINITY COLLEGE.—L.M. *(Second Tune.)* Rev. J. B. DYKES.

A - men.

A higher setting of this Tune is given at Hymn 483.

" The kindness and love of God our Saviour toward man appeared."

mf THE FATHER'S sole-begotten SON
dim　Was born, the Virgin's Child, on earth ;
　His Cross for us adoption won,—
mf The life and grace of second birth.

　Forth from the height of Heav'n He came,
dim In form of man with man abode ;
mf Redeem'd His world from death and shame,
　The joys of endless life bestow'd.

p Redeemer, come with power benign,
　Dwell in the souls that look for Thee ;
　O let Thy light within us shine
　That we may Thy salvation see.

　Abide with us, O LORD, we pray,
　Dispel the gloom of doubt and woe ;
　Wash every stain of guilt away,
　Thy tender healing grace bestow.

mf LORD, Thou hast come, and well we know
　That Thou wilt likewise come again ;
　Thy Kingdom shield from every foe,
　Thy honour and Thy rule maintain.

f Eternal glory, LORD, to Thee,
　Whom, now reveal'd, our hearts adore ;
　To GOD the FATHER glory be,
　And HOLY SPIRIT evermore.

Compilers : from the Latin.

Epiphany.

Hymn 487. IRISH.—C.M.   *Hymns and Sacred Poems* (Dublin, 1749).

A-men.

A lower setting of this Tune is given at Hymn 320.

" He was baptized."

mf THE Son of Man from Jordan rose,
　　And pray'd to GOD above ;
When lo, the op'ning Heav'ns disclose
　　A swift-descending Dove.

The SPIRIT, lighting on His Brow,
　　Anoints the Holy One ;—
The FATHER'S voice declaring—" Thou
　　Art My Belovèd SON."

So when, through His Baptizing bless'd
　　The Font new birth conveys,
Man kneels a son of GOD confess'd,
　　Heav'n opens as he prays.

This Hymn is suitable for an Adult Baptism.

p Fair innocency, like the dove's,
　　Invests him, purged from sin ;
For GOD the brooding SPIRIT moves,
　　Directs and rules within.

mf O CHRIST, Whose mercy cleansed our stain
　　With streams of grace Divine ;
Let us not soil the robes again
　　Made white in Blood of Thine.

Redeemer of a world undone,
　　We praise Thee and adore ;—
JESU, with GOD the FATHER ONE,
　　And SPIRIT evermore.

J. MASON and Compilers : from
the Latin of N. le Tourneaux.

ALTERNATIVE TUNE, HYMN 373.

Hymn 488. FRANCONIA.—S.M.   *Harmonischer Liederschatz*, 1738.

A - men.

A lower setting of this Tune is given at Hymns 48, 261.

" The Lord shall suddenly come to His temple."

mf WITHIN the FATHER'S house
　　The SON hath found His home ;
cr And to His temple suddenly
f 　　The LORD of life hath come.

mf The doctors of the law
　　Gaze on the wondrous Child,
And marvel at His gracious words
　　Of wisdom undefiled.

p Yet not to them is giv'n
　　The mighty truth to know,
To lift the fleshly veil which hides
　　Incarnate GOD below.

The secret of the LORD
Escapes each human eye,

cr And faithful pond'ring hearts await
　　The full Epiphany.

p LORD, visit Thou our souls,
　　And teach us by Thy grace
Each dim revealing of Thyself
　　With loving awe to trace ;

cr Till from our darken'd sight
　　The cloud shall pass away,
And on the cleansèd soul shall burst
mf 　　The everlasting day ;

Till we behold Thy Face,
　　And know, as we are known,
f Thee, FATHER, SON, and HOLY GHOST,
　　Co-equal THREE in ONE.

Bishop WOODFORD.

(422)

Septuagesima.

Hymn 489. STYALL.—L.M.　　　　　　　Rev. W. STATHAM.

A-men.

A lower setting of this Tune is given at Hymn 529.

"God Who created all things by Jesus Christ."

mf O GOD, the joy of Heav'n above,
　　Thou didst not need Thy creatures' love,
When from Thy secret place of rest
Thy Word the earth's foundations blest.

Thou spakest :—worlds began to be ;
They bow before Thy Majesty ;
And all to their Creator raise
A wondrous harmony of praise.

But ere, O LORD, this lovely earth
From Thy creative will had birth,
Thou in Thy counsels didst unfold
Another world of fairer mould.

cr That realm shall our Redeemer frame,
And build upon His mighty Name ;
His Hand the word of power shall sow,
That all the earth His truth may know.

When time itself has pass'd away,
His Church, secure in Heav'n for aye,
Shall share His Table and His Throne,
And GOD the FATHER reign alone.

f O FATHER, SON, and SPIRIT BLEST,
One GOD in Heav'n and earth confest,
Preserve, direct, and fill with love
Thy realm on earth, Thy realm above.

Compilers: from the Latin of C. Coffin.

The following Hymn is suitable for this season:
533 Oh how fair that morning broke.

Lent.

Hymn 490. SHOTTERY.—8 8 8 8.8 8.　　　　　E. HULTON.

Rather slower.

p　　*pp*　　A-men.

"Hear my crying, O God : give ear unto my prayer."

mf SWEET SAVIOUR ! in Thy pitying grace
　　Thy sweetness to our souls impart ;
Thou only Lover of our race
　Give healing to the wounded heart ;
p Oh ! hear Thy contrite servants' cry,
pp And save us, JESU ! lest we die.

p Long-suffering JESU ! hear our prayer
　　Who weep before Thee in our shame ;
We have no hope but Thee ; O spare,
　LORD, spare us from th' undying flame ;
Oh ! hear Thy contrite servants' cry,
pp And save us, JESU ! lest we die.

p All we have broken Thy command ;
　LORD, help us for Thy mercies' sake ;
Deliver us from Satan's hand,
　And safely to Thy Kingdom take ;
Oh ! hear Thy contrite servants' cry,
pp And save us, JESU ! lest we die.

p We flee for refuge to Thy love,
cr　Salvation of the helpless soul ;
Pour down Thy radiance from above,
　And make these sin-worn spirits whole :
p Good LORD, in mercy hear our cry,
pp And save us, JESU ! lest we die.

R. M. MOORSOM : from the Greek
of Theoktistus, c. 890.

(423)

Lent.

Hymn 491. St. Omer.—S.M.

C. S. Jekyll.

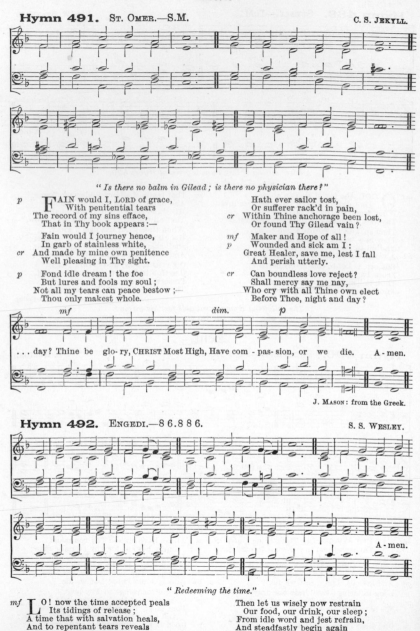

" Is there no balm in Gilead ; is there no physician there ? "

p   Fain would I, Lord of grace,
     With penitential tears
The record of my sins efface,
     That in Thy book appears :—

Fain would I journey hence,
     In garb of stainless white,
cr   And made by mine own penitence
     Well pleasing in Thy sight.

p   Fond idle dream ! the foe
     But lures and fools my soul ;
Not all my tears can peace bestow ;—
     Thou only makest whole.

Hath ever sailor tost,
     Or sufferer rack'd in pain,
cr   Within Thine anchorage been lost,
     Or found Thy Gilead vain ?

mf   Maker and Hope of all !
p   Wounded and sick am I :
Great Healer, save me, lest I fall
     And perish utterly.

cr   Can boundless love reject ?
     Shall mercy say me nay,
Who cry with all Thine own elect
     Before Thee, night and day ?

... day ? Thine be glo-ry, Christ Most High, Have com-pas-sion, or we die. A-men.

J. Mason : from the Greek.

Hymn 492. Engedi.—8 6.8 8 6.

S. S. Wesley.

A-men.

" Redeeming the time."

mf   Lo ! now the time accepted peals
     Its tidings of release ;
A time that with salvation heals,
And to repentant tears reveals
p   The mercy-seat of peace.

Then let us wisely now restrain
     Our food, our drink, our sleep ;
From idle word and jest refrain,
And steadfastly begin again
     A stricter watch to keep.

Lent.

cr Now heaven-taught love will haste to rise
And seek the cheerless bed,
Where cold and wan the sufferer lies,
And CHRIST Himself to heedful eyes
Is hungering for bread.

'Tis now that zealous charity
Her goods more largely spends,
Lays up her treasure in the sky,
And freely yields, ere death draw nigh,
To GOD the wealth He lends.

p Then consecrate us, LORD, anew,
And fire our hearts with love;
That all we think, and all we do,
Within, without, be pure and true,
Rekindled from above.

mf Now fuller praise and glory be
To Thee, the First and Last;
And make us, Blessed TRINITY,
More faithful soldiers, worthier Thee,
Through this our chastening fast.

R. M. MOORSOM: from the Latin.

Hymn 493. MINSTER.—7 7 7 7.7 7 7 7. (*First Tune.*) Sir R. STEWART.

A-men.

"*Resist the devil, and he will flee from you; draw nigh to God, and He will draw nigh to you.*"
FOR A LATE EVENING SERVICE.

mf FATHER, Most High, be with us,*
Unseen, Thy goodness showing,
And CHRIST the WORD Incarnate,
And SPIRIT grace bestowing.
cr O Trinity, O Oneness
Of light and power exceeding;
O GOD of GOD Eternal,
O GOD, from Both proceeding!

mf While daylight hours are passing,
We live and work before Thee;
dim Now, ere we rest in slumber,
We gather to adore Thee.
Our Christian name and calling
Of our new birth remind us;
The SPIRIT'S gifts and sealing
To firm obedience bind us.

mf Begone, ye powers of evil
With snares and wiles unholy!
Disturb not with your temptings
The spirits of the lowly.
Depart! for CHRIST is present,
Beside us, yea, within us;
Away! His sign, ye know it,
The victory shall win us.

p Awhile the body resteth;
The spirit, wakeful ever,
cr Abideth in communion
With CHRIST, Who sleepeth never.
f To GOD, th' Eternal FATHER,
To CHRIST, our sure salvation,
To GOD, the HOLY SPIRIT,
Be endless adoration.

Compilers: from the Latin of Prudentius.

* *Verse 1 only must begin thus:*

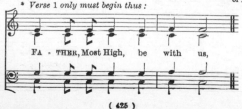

FA - THER, Most High, be with us,

(425)

P 2

Lent.

Hymn 493. ADES PATER SUPREME.—7 7 7 7. (*Second Tune.*)

Melodiæ Prudentianæ, 1533.

A - men.

" Resist the devil, and he will flee from you ; draw nigh to God, and He will draw nigh to you."

FOR A LATE EVENING SERVICE.

mf FATHER, Most High, be with us,
　　Unseen, Thy goodness showing,
And CHRIST the WORD Incarnate,
And SPIRIT grace bestowing.

cr O Trinity, O Oneness
　Of light and power exceeding ;
O GOD of GOD Eternal,
O GOD, from Both proceeding !

mf While daylight hours are passing,
　We live and work before Thee ;
dim Now, ere we rest in slumber,
　We gather to adore Thee.

Our Christian name and calling
Of our new birth remind us ;
The SPIRIT'S gifts and sealing
To firm obedience bind us.

mf Begone, ye powers of evil
With snares and wiles unholy !
Disturb not with your temptings
The spirits of the lowly.

Depart ! for CHRIST is present,
Beside us, yea, within us ;
Away ! His sign, ye know it,
The victory shall win us.

p Awhile the body resteth ;
　The spirit, wakeful ever,
cr Abideth in communion
　With CHRIST, Who sleepeth never.

f To GOD, th' Eternal FATHER,
To CHRIST, our sure salvation,
To GOD, the HOLY SPIRIT,
Be endless adoration.

　　　　Compilers : from the Latin of Prudentius.

The following Hymns are suitable for this season :

528 Not for our sins alone.　　　　**638** O GOD, to know that Thou art just.

Hymns on the Passion.

Hymn 494. WOODLYNN.—11 10 11 10. (*First Tune.*)　　Sir J. STAINER.

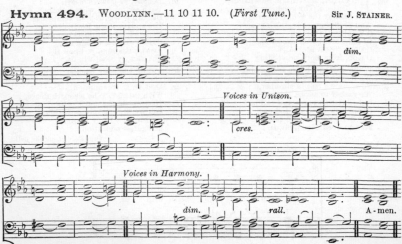

dim.

Voices in Unison.

cres.

Voices in Harmony.

dim.　　*rall.*　　A - men.

Hymns on the Passion.

Hymn 494. CHANT.—11 10 11 10. *(Second Tune.)* W. H. MONK.

Hymn 494. GENEVAN PSALM XII.—11.10.11.10. *(Third Tune.)*
L. BOURGEOIS, 1551.

A - men.

" Forasmuch then as Christ hath suffered in the flesh, arm yourselves likewise with the same mind."

mf MY LORD, my Master, at Thy Feet adóring,
　　　　I see Thee bow'd beneath Thy lóad of woe ;
　　　For me, a sinner, is Thy Life-Blood póuring ;
dim　For Thee, my SAVIOUR, scarce my téars will flow.

mf Thine own disciple to the Jews has sóld Thee,
　　　With friendship's kiss and loyal wórd he came ;
　　　How oft of faithful love my lips have tóld Thee,
dim　While Thou hast seen my falsehood ánd my shame !

mf With taunts and scoffs they mock what seems Thy wéakness,
　　　With blows and outrage adding páin to pain ;
　　　Thou art unmoved and steadfast in Thy méekness ;
dim　When I am wrong'd how quickly Í complain !

p　My LORD, my SAVIOUR, when I see Thee wéaring
　　　Upon Thy bleeding brow the crówn of thorn,
cr　Shall I for pleasure live, or shrink from béaring
　　　Whate'er my lot may be of páin or scorn ?

mf O Victim of Thy love ! O pangs most héaling !
dim O saving Death ! O wounds that Í adore !
mf O shame most glorious ! CHRIST, before Thee knéeling,
p　　I pray Thee keep me Thine for évermore.

　　　　　　　　　T. B. POLLOCK : from the French of J. Bridaine.

Hymns on the Passion.

Hymn 495. OLD MARTYRS.—C.M.
Psalms (Edinburgh, 1615).

" Weep not for Me, but weep for yourselves."

p WEEP not for Him Who onward bears
　　　His Cross to Calvary ;
He does not ask man's pitying tears,
　Who wills for man to die.

The awful sorrow of His Face,
　The bowing of His Frame,
Come not from torture or disgrace ;
　He fears not Cross or shame.

There is a deeper pang of grief,
　An agony unknown,
In which His Love finds no relief ;
　He bears it all alone.

He thinks of all for whom His Life
　Of lowliness and pain,

And weariness and care and strife,
　Will be alas ! in vain.

He sees the souls for whom He dies
　Yet clinging to their sin,
And heirs of mansions in the skies
　Who will not enter in.

cr Ah ! this, my SAVIOUR, was the shame
　That bow'd Thy Head so low !
These were the wounds that rack'd Thy Frame,
　And made Thy Tears to flow.

p Oh ! may I in Thy sorrow share,
　And mourn that sins of mine
Should ever wound with grief or care
　That loving Heart of Thine.

T. B. POLLOCK.

ALTERNATIVE TUNE, HYMN 693.

Hymn 496. ST. ALBAN.—8 7 8 7.
C. STEGGALL.

" A very scorn of men, and the outcast of the people."

mf O SCORN'D and outcast LORD, beneath
　　　Thy burden meekly bending,
Thou, our true Isaac, to Thy death
　Art wearily ascending.

dim And soon, with nail-pierced Feet and Hands
　Upon the Cross they raise Thee ;
The Cross, which there uplifted stands,
　To all the earth displays Thee.

mf Oh ! wondrous love of GOD on high,
　The sinful thus to cherish !
He gave His guiltless SON to die,
dim　Lest guilty man should perish.

p Our sin's pollution to remove
　His Blood was freely given ;
cr So mighty was the SAVIOUR'S love,
　So just the wrath of Heaven.

Yes ! 'tis the Cross that breaks the rod
　And chain of condemnation,
cr And makes a league 'twixt man and GOD
　For our entire salvation.

f O praise the FATHER, praise the SON,
　The Lamb for sinners given,
And HOLY GHOST, through Whom alone
　Our hearts are raised to Heaven.

J. CHANDLER and Compilers :
from the Latin of C. Coffin.

Easter.

Hymn 497. SALVE FESTA DIES.—11 11 11 11 11.

Sir J. BARNBY.

A - men.

" Let us keep the Feast."

mf " WELCOME, happy morning ! " age to age shall say ;
　　　　Hell to-day is vanquish'd ! Heav'n is won to-day !
f　Lo ! the Dead is living, GOD for evermore !
　　Him, their true Creator, all His works adore :
　　" Welcome, happy morning ! " age to age shall say.

　　Earth with joy confesses, clothing her for Spring,
　　All good gifts return with her returning King ;
　　Bloom in every meadow, leaves on every bough,
　　Speak His sorrows ended, hail His triumph now :
　　Hell to-day is vanquish'd ! Heav'n is won to-day !

mf Months in due succession, days of length'ning light,
　　Hours and passing moments praise Thee in their flight ;
　　Brightness of the morning, sky and fields and sea,
　　Vanquisher of darkness, bring their praise to Thee :
　　" Welcome, happy morning ! " age to age shall say.

　　Maker and Redeemer, Life and Health of all,
　　Thou from Heav'n beholding man's abasing fall,
　　Of th' Eternal FATHER true and only SON,
　　Manhood to deliver, manhood didst put on :
　　Hell to-day is vanquish'd ! Heav'n is won to-day !

　　Thou, of life the Author, (*dim*) death didst undergo,
　　Tread the path of darkness, (*cr*) saving strength to show ;
mf Come then, True and Faithful, now fulfil Thy word ;
　　'Tis Thine own Third Morning ! rise, O buried LORD !
f　" Welcome, happy morning ! " age to age shall say.

　　Loose the souls long prison'd, bound with Satan's chain ;
　　All that now is fallen raise to life again ;
　　Show Thy Face in brightness, bid the nations see !
　　Bring again our daylight : day returns with Thee ;
ff Hell to-day is vanquish'd ! Heav'n is won to-day !

J. ELLERTON : from Venantius Fortunatus.

(429)

Easter.

Hymn 498. THE FOE.—IRREGULAR. *(First Tune.)*

" Sing ye to the Lord, for He hath triumphed gloriously."

Sir J. BARNBY

The foe be-hind, the deep be-fore, Our hosts have dared and past the sea; And Pha-raoh's war-riors strew the shore, And Is-rael's ran-som'd tribes are free. Lift up, lift up your voi-ces now! The whole wide world re-joi-ces now; The LORD hath tri-umph'd glo-rious-ly! The LORD shall reign vic-to-rious-ly! Hap-py mor-row, Turn-ing sor-row In-to peace and mirth!

Easter.

HARM.—TRE. & TEN.

Bond - age end - ing, Love de - scend - ing O'er the earth.

TENORS ONLY.

Seals as - sur - ing, Guards se - cur - ing, Watch His earth - ly prison:

HARMONY.

Seals are shat - ter'd, Guards are scat - ter'd; CHRIST is risen!

TREBLES ONLY.

No long - er must the mourn - ers weep, Nor call de - part - ed Christ-ians dead; For

dim.   HARMONY.
                                                                           cres.

death is hal-low'd in - to sleep, And ev' - ry grave be - comes a bed. Now once more

cres.

E - den's door O - pen stands to mor - tal eyes; For CHRIST hath risen, and

Easter.

man shall rise. Now at last, Old things past, Hope, and joy, and peace be - gin; For

cres.   TREBLES ONLY. *dim.*

CHRIST hath won, and man shall win. It is not ex - ile, rest on high ; It

is not sad - ness, peace from strife ; To fall a - sleep is not to die ; To

HARMONY.

dwell with CHRIST is bet - ter life. Where our ban - ner leads us We may safe - ly go ;

Where our Chief pre - cedes us, We may face the foe. His right arm is o'er us,

He our Guide will be : CHRIST hath gone be - fore us, Christians, fol - low ye ! A - men.

J. M. NEALE.

Easter.

Hymn 498. AUCTOR HUMANI GENERIS.—Irregular. *(Second Tune.)*

" Sing ye to the Lord, for He hath triumphed gloriously."

NYLAND, *Piæ Cantiones*, 1582.

Unison.

1. THE foe be-hind, the deep be-fore, Our hosts have dared and pass'd the sea; And
2. Lift up, lift up your voi-ces now! The whole wide world re-joi-ces now; The

Pha-raoh's war-riors strew the shore, And Is-rael's ran-som'd tribes are free.
LORD hath tri-umph'd glo-rious-ly! The LORD shall reign vic-to-rious-ly!

Harmony.

3. Hap-py mor-row, Turn-ing sor-row In-to peace and mirth!
4. Seals as-sur-ing, Guards se-cur-ing, Watch His earth-ly prison:

Bond-age end-ing, Love de-scend-ing O'er .. the earth. ..
Seals are shat-ter'd, Guards are scat-ter'd;—CHRIST is risen! ..

Unison.

5. No long-er must the mourn-ers weep, Nor call de-part-ed Chris-tians dead; For

(433)

Easter.

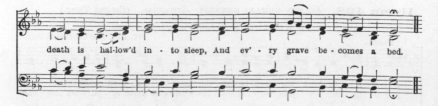

death is hal-low'd in - to sleep, And ev' - ry grave be - comes a bed.

Harmony.

6. Now once more E - den's door O - pen stands to
7. Now at last, Old things past, Hope, and joy, and

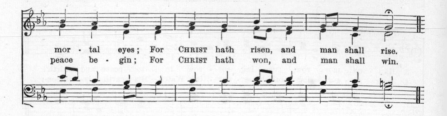

mor - tal eyes; For CHRIST hath risen, and man shall rise.
peace be - gin; For CHRIST hath won, and man shall win.

Unison.

8. It is not ex - ile, rest on high; It is not sad-ness, peace from strife; To

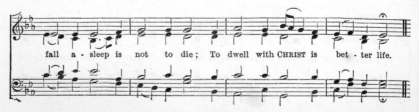

fall a - sleep is not to die; To dwell with CHRIST is bet - ter life.

Easter.

Harmony.

9. Where our ban - ner leads us We may safe . . . ly go;
10. His right arm is o'er us, He our Guide . . . will be:

Where our Chief pro - cedes us We may face the foe.
CHRIST hath gone be - fore us, Chris-tians, fol - low ye!

Unison.

Lift up, lift up . . . your voi - ces now! The whole wide world re -

joi - ces now; The LORD hath tri - umph'd glo - rious-ly! The

LORD shall reign . . vic - to - - rious - ly! A - - men.

J. M. NEALE.

Easter.

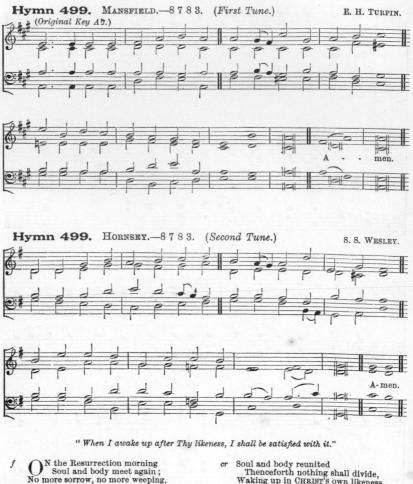

Hymn 499. MANSFIELD.—8 7 8 3. *(First Tune.)*   E. H. TURPIN.

(Original Key A♭.)

A - - men.

Hymn 499. HORNSEY.—8 7 8 3. *(Second Tune.)*   S. S. WESLEY.

A - men.

" When I awake up after Thy likeness, I shall be satisfied with it."

f   ON the Resurrection morning
      Soul and body meet again ;
  No more sorrow, no more weeping,
      no more pain !

p   Here awhile they must be parted,
      And the flesh its Sabbath keep,
  Waiting in a holy stillness,
      wrapt in sleep.

  For a while the tirèd body
      Lies with feet toward the morn ;
cr Till the last and brightest Easter
      day be born.

  But the soul in contemplation
      Utters earnest prayer and strong,
mf Bursting at the Resurrection
      into song.

cr Soul and body reunited
      Thenceforth nothing shall divide,
  Waking up in CHRIST'S own likeness,
      satisfied.

f   Oh ! the beauty, Oh ! the gladness
      Of that Resurrection day,
  Which shall not through endless ages
      pass away !

mf On that happy Easter morning
      All the graves their dead restore ;
  Father, sister, child, and mother,
      meet once more.

  To that brightest of all meetings
dim Bring us, JESU CHRIST, at last ;
  By Thy Cross, through death (*cr*) and
      judgment,   holding fast.

S. BARING-GOULD.

Easter.

Hymn 500. O Voice.—7 6 7 6. 7 6 7 6. (*First Tune.*)   Sir J. BARNBY.

A·men.

"*My Beloved spoke and said unto me, Rise up, My love, My fair one, and come away. For the winter is past; the rain is over and gone; the flowers appear upon the earth; the time of the singing of birds is come, and the voice of the turtle is heard in our land.*"

mf O VOICE of the Belovèd!
Thy Bride hath heard Thee say,—
"Rise up, My love, My fair one,
Arise and come away.
For lo, 'tis past, the winter,
The winter of thy year;
The rain is past and over,
The flowers on earth appear.

"And now the time of singing
Is come for every bird;
And over all the country
The turtle dove is heard:
The fig her green fruit ripens,
The vines are in their bloom;
Arise and smell their fragrance,
My love, My fair one, come!"

p Yea, LORD! Thy Passion over,
We know this life of ours
cr Hath pass'd from death and winter
To leaves and budding flowers:
No more Thy rain of weeping
In drear Gethsemane;
No more the clouds and darkness,
p That veil'd Thy bitter Tree.

mf Our Easter Sun is risen!
dim And yet we slumber long,
And need Thy Dove's sweet pleading
To waken prayer and song.
p Oh breathe upon our deadness,
Oh shine upon our gloom;
cr LORD, let us feel Thy Presence,
f And rise and live and bloom.

J. MASON.

{ 437 }

Easter.

Hymn 500. WERDE MUNTER.—7 6 7 6. 7 6 7 6. *(Second Tune.)*

J. SCHOP, 1641.

A-men.

" My Beloved spoke and said unto me, Rise up, My love, My fair one, and come away. For the winter is past ; the rain is over and gone ; the flowers appear upon the earth ; the time of the singing of birds is come, and the voice of the turtle is heard in our land."

mf O VOICE of the Belovèd !
    Thy Bride hath heard Thee say,—
"Rise up, My love, My fair one,
    Arise and come away.
For lo, 'tis past, the winter,
    The winter of thy year ;
The rain is past and over,
    The flowers on earth appear.

" And now the time of singing
    Is come for every bird ;
And over all the country
    The turtle dove is heard ;
The fig her green fruit ripens,
    The vines are in their bloom ;
Arise and smell their fragrance,
    My love, My fair one, come !"

p Yea, LORD ! Thy Passion over,
    We know this life of ours
cr Hath pass'd from death and winter
    To leaves and budding flowers :
No more Thy rain of weeping
    In drear Gethsemane ;
No more the clouds and darkness,
p   That veil'd Thy bitter Tree.

mf Our Easter Sun is risen !
dim And yet we slumber long,
    And need Thy Dove's sweet pleading
    To waken prayer and song.
p Oh breathe upon our deadness,
    Oh shine upon our gloom ;
cr LORD, let us feel Thy Presence,
f   And rise and live and bloom.

J. MASON.

(438)

Easter.

Hymn 501. VICTORY.—8 8 7 7. 8 8 7. *(First Tune.)* Rev. S. J. ROWTON.

A-men.

Hymn 501. EXODUS.—8 8 7 7. 8 8 7. *(Second Tune.)* J. F. RÖTSCHER, 1790.

A-men.

" Thanks be to God, Who giveth us the victory."

mf FAR be sorrow, tears, and sighing!
   Waves are calming, storms are dying;
    Moses hath o'erpass'd the sea,
    Israel's captive hosts are free ;
Life by death slew death and saved us,
In His Blood the Lamb hath laved us,
    Clothing us with victory.

f JESUS CHRIST from death hath risen,
   Lo ! His Godhead bursts the prison,
    While His Manhood passes free,
    Vanquishing our misery.

mf Rise we free from condemnation ;
dim Through our GOD's humiliation,
   f Ours is now the victory.

mf Vain the foe's despair and madness !
   See the dayspring of our gladness !
    Slaves no more of Satan we ;
    Children, by the SON set free ;
f Rise, for Life with death hath striven,
   All the snares of hell are riven,
    Rise and claim the victory.

Compilers : from the Latin.

Easter.

Hymn 502. MIDSOMER NORTON.—D.C.M.

C. W. PEARCE.

A - men.

"Who is this that cometh from Edom, with dyed garments from Bozrah? this that is glorious in His apparel, travelling in the greatness of His strength?"

mf TO Thee and to Thy CHRIST, O GOD,
　　We sing—we ever sing;
　For He the lonely winepress trod,
　　Our cup of joy to bring.
cr　His glorious Arm the strife maintain'd,
　　He march'd in might from far;
　His robes were with the vintage stain'd,
　　Red with the wine of war.

　To Thee and to Thy CHRIST, O GOD,
　　We sing—we ever sing;
dim　For He invaded Death's abode,
cr　　And robb'd him of his sting.
　The house of dust enthrals no more,
　　For He, the Strong to save,
　Himself doth guard that silent door,
　　Great Keeper of the grave.

mf　To Thee and to Thy CHRIST, O GOD,
　　We sing—we ever sing;
　For He hath crush'd beneath His rod
　　The world's proud rebel king.
　He plunged in His imperial strength
　　To gulfs of darkness down;
　He brought His trophy up at length,
　　The foil'd usurper's crown.

　To Thee and to Thy CHRIST, O GOD,
　　We sing—we ever sing;
dim　For He redeem'd us with His Blood
　　From every evil thing.
mf　Thy saving strength His Arm upbore,
　　The Arm that set us free;
f　Glory, O GOD, for evermore
　　Be to Thy CHRIST and Thee.

MRS. COUSIN.

(440)

Easter.

Hymn 503. CONFIDENCE.—7 7 7 7.   Rev. Sir F. A. G. OUSELEY.

A - men.

" Being seen of them forty days."

mf FORTY days Thy seer of old
     Communed with Thee, O Most High;
Fain Thy goings to behold
And Thy glory passing by.

p In the rocky cleft he bow'd;
     Thou, as mortal gaze might bear,
Part reveal'd and part in cloud,
cr   Didst Thy secret Name declare.

mf Forty days of Easter-tide
     Thou didst commune with Thine own;
Now by glimpses, LORD, descried,
Handled now and proved and known;—

p Known, most Merciful, yet veil'd;
     Else before the awful sight
Surely heart and flesh had fail'd,
Smitten with exceeding light.

mf Risen Master, fain would we,
     Sharing those uncarthly days,
Morn and eve, on shore and sea,
Watch Thy movements, mark Thy ways;—

Catch by faith each glad surprise
     Of Thy footstep drawing nigh,
Hear Thy sudden greeting rise—
dim   " Peace be to you! It is I;"—

mf Secrets of Thy Kingdom learn,
     Read the vision open spread,
Feel Thy Word within us burn,
Know Thee in the broken Bread.

So Thy glory's skirts beside
     Gently led from grace to grace,
We Thy coming may abide,
dim   And adore Thee face to face.

                                                 J. MASON

ALTERNATIVE TUNE, HYMN 127.

Hymn 504. NARENZA.—S.M.   LEISENTRIT, *Catholicum Hymnologium*, 1587.

A - men.

A lower setting of this Tune is given at Hymn 268.

" Risen with Him."

f THE LORD is risen indeed;
     Now is His work perform'd;
Now is the mighty Captive freed,
And death's strong castle storm'd.

The LORD is risen indeed;
     Then Hell has lost his prey;
With Him is risen the ransom'd seed
To reign in endless day.

The LORD is risen indeed;
     He lives, to die no more;

He lives, the sinner's cause to plead,
dim   Whose curse and shame He bore.

f The LORD is risen indeed;
     Attending Angels, hear!
Up to the Courts of Heav'n with speed
The joyful tidings bear.

Then take your golden lyres,
     And strike each cheerful chord;
Join, all ye bright celestial choirs,
To sing our risen LORD.

                                                 T. KELLY, 1802.

ALTERNATIVE TUNE, HYMN 706.

Rogation Days.

Hymn 505. SUNNINGHILL.—D.C.M.

Sir G. ELVEY.

A - men.

" The earth is the Lord's, and the fulness thereof."

mf O THRONED, O crown'd with all renown,
Since Thou the earth hast trod,
Thou reignest, and by Thee come down
Henceforth the gifts of GOD.
[By Thee the suns of space, that burn
Unspent, their watches hold ;
The hosts that turn, and still return,
Are sway'd, and poised, and roll'd.

The powers of earth, for all her ills,
An endless treasure yield ;
The precious things of the ancient hills,
Forest, and fruitful field.]
Thine is the health, and Thine the wealth
That in our halls abound ;
And Thine the beauty and the joy
With which the years are crown'd.

dim[And as, when ebbed the flood, our sires
Kneel'd on the mountain sod,
While o'er the new world's altar fires
Shone out the bow of GOD ;
And sweetly fell the peaceful spell—
Word that shall aye avail—
"Summer and winter shall not cease,
Seed time nor harvest fail ;"]

cr Thus in their change let frost and heat
And winds and dews be given ;
All fostering power, all influence sweet,
Breathe from the bounteous heaven.
Attemper fair with gentle air
The sunshine and the rain,
That kindly earth with timely birth
May yield her fruits again ;

mf That we may feed Thy poor aright,
And, gath'ring round Thy Throne,
Here in the holy Angels' sight
Repay Thee of Thine own.
For so our sires in olden time
Spared neither gold nor gear,
Nor precious wood, nor hewen stone,
Thy sacred shrines to rear.

cr For there to give the second birth
In mysteries and signs,
The Face of CHRIST o'er all the earth
On kneeling myriads shines.
mf And if so fair beyond compare
Thine earthly houses be,
cr In how great grace shall we Thy Face
In Thine own Palace see?

Archbishop BENSON.

The parts within [brackets] may be omitted if the Hymn be thought too long.

Ascension.

Hymn 506. TRIUMPH.—8 8.7 7.7 7 4. *(First Tune.)*

W. H. MONK.

Know ye the LORD hath borne a - way Your Mas - ter from your head to - day?
Men only.*

* If there are no men in the Choir, the 1st and 2nd lines must be sung by the Choir Trebles, and
the accompaniment played an octave higher.

(442)

Ascension.

Hymn 506. MINSTER COURT.—8 8.7 7.7 7 4. *(Second Tune.)*

Unison, or Men only.

E. C. BAIRSTOW.

Full, Harmony.

Quietly.

Al - le - lu - ia! A - men.

" Knowest thou that the Lord will take away thy Master from thy head to-day?"

mf KNOW ye the LORD hath borne away
Your Master from your head to-day?
Yea, we know it; yet we raise
Joyous strains of hope and praise!
He is gone, but not before
All His earthly work is o'er.
Alleluia!

Know ye the LORD hath borne away
Your Master from your head to-day?
Yea, we know it; stand afar;
Mark His bright triumphal car,
Mighty end of mighty deeds,
Clouds His chariot, winds His steeds!
Alleluia!

Know ye the LORD hath borne away
Your Master from your head to-day?
Yea, we know it; ere He left,
Jordan's stream in twain was cleft:
With that glorious act in view,
We shall one day cleave it too!
Alleluia!

Know ye the LORD hath borne away
Your Master from your head to-day?
Yea, we know it; wondrous love
Bids Him seek His Home above:
dim He hath said 'tis better so;
See His mantle dropt below!
Alleluia!

mf Know ye the LORD hath borne away
Your Master from your head to-day?
Yea, we know it; lo! we trace
Plenteous portions of His grace,
Sent to all whose hearts can soar
Whither He has gone before.
Alleluia!

Know ye the LORD hath borne away
Your Master from your head to-day?
Yea, we know it; search would fail,
cr If ye pass'd through mount and vale:
Earth contains Him not, though wide:
ff Seek Him at His Father's side!
Alleluia!

H. TWELLS.

(443)

Whitsuntide.

Hymn 507. BARMOUTH.—8 5 8 8 5.7 7 7 7.

C. J. FROST.

A-men.

" The Spirit of the Lord filleth the world."

mf BOUNTEOUS SPIRIT, ever shedding
　　Life the world to fill !
Swarms the fruitful globe o'erspreading,
Shoals their ocean pathway threading,
cr　　Own Thy quick'ning thrill :
Author of each creature's birth,
Life of life beneath the earth,
Everywhere, O SPIRIT Blest,
f　Thou art motion, (*p*) Thou art rest.

mf *Come, Creator ! grace bestowing,—
　　All Thy sevenfold dower !
Come, Thy peace and bounty strowing,
Earth's Renewer ! Thine the sowing,
　　Thine the gladd'ning shower.
Comforter ! what joy Thou art
To the blest and faithful heart ;
But to man's primeval foe
Uttermost despair and woe.

O'er the waters of creation
　　Moved Thy Wings Divine ;
When the world, to animation
Waking 'neath Thy visitation,
　　Teem'd with powers benign :
Thou didst man to being call,
Didst restore him from his fall ;
Pouring, like the latter rain,
Grace to quicken him again.

cr　Thine the Gospel voices, crying
　　As with trumpet sound ;
Till the world, in darkness lying,
Rose from deathly sleep, descrying
　　Heavenly light around.

Man, to reach that prize reveal'd,
Arm'd with Thee as with a shield,
Nerved and girt his fight to win,
Quells the prince of death and sin.

mf *Lowliest homage now before Thee
　　Let the ransom'd pay ;
For Thy wondrous gifts adore Thee,
By Thy holiness implore Thee,
　　While in love they pray :
dim Holy ! Holy ! we repeat,
Kneeling at Thy mercy-seat ;
There unbosom every woe,
Groanings Thou alone canst know.

mf Fount of grace for every nation,
　　Refuge of the soul !
Strengthen Thou each new creation,
With the waters of salvation
　　Make the guilty whole :
Rule on earth the powers that be ;
Give us priests inspired of Thee ;
Through Thy Holy Church increase
Purest unity and peace.

*Purge and sanctify us wholly
　　From the leaven of ill ;
Save from Satan's grasp unholy ;
To a living faith and lowly
　　Mould the upright will ;
Till the olden zeal return,
And with mutual love we burn ;
Till in peace, no more to roam,
All the flock be gather'd home.

J. MASON.

* These verses may be omitted, if the Hymn be thought too long.

(444)

Whitsuntide.

Hymn 508. Tallis.—C.M. (*First Tune.*) T. Tallis, 1567.

A lower setting of this Tune is given at Hymn 78.

Hymn 508. St. Flavian.—C.M. (*Second Tune.*) Psalmes, 1562.

A setting with additional Harmonies is given at Hymn 320.

" The Comforter, which is the Holy Ghost."

mf COME, Holy Ghost, Eternal God,
Proceeding from above,
Both from the Father and the Son,
The God of peace and love ;

Visit our minds, into our hearts
Thy heavenly grace inspire ;
That truth and godliness we may
Pursue with full desire.

Thou in Thy gifts art manifold ;
By them Christ's Church doth stand ;
In faithful hearts Thou writ'st Thy law,
The Finger of God's hand.

According to Thy promise, Lord,
Thou givest speech with grace,
cr That through Thy help God's praises may
Resound in every place.

dim O Holy Ghost, into our minds
Send down Thy Heavenly Light ;
or Kindle our hearts with fervent zeal
To serve God day and night.

Our weakness strengthen and confirm,
For, Lord, Thou know'st us frail ;

That neither devil, world, nor flesh
dim Against us may prevail.

mf Put back our enemy from us,
And help us to obtain
Peace in our hearts with God and man,—
The best, the truest gain ;

Of strife and of dissension
Dissolve, O Lord, the bands,
And knit the knots of peace and love
Throughout all Christian lands.

Grant us the grace that we may know
The Father of all might,
That we of His belovèd Son
May gain the blissful sight ;

And that we may with perfect faith
Ever acknowledge Thee,
The Spirit of Father, and of Son,
One God in Persons Three.

f To God the Father laud and praise,
And to His Blessèd Son,
And to the Holy Spirit of grace,
Co-equal Three in One.

Part of 2nd Translation of the
Veni Creator in the Ordinal.

Trinity Sunday.

Hymn 509. ADESTO, SANCTA TRINITAS.—L.M. *(First Tune.)* *(First Version.)*

In Unison.   Proper Sarum Melody.

A - men . . .

Hymn 509. ADESTO, SANCTA TRINITAS.—L.M. *(First Tune.)*

(Alternative Version.)   Proper Sarum Melody.

Be near us, Ho - ly TRIN - I - TY, One Light, one on - ly De - i - ty!

All things are Thine, on Thee de - pend, Who art Be - gin - ning with - out end. A - men.

Hymn 509. SHARON.—L.M. *(Second Tune.)*   Rev. Sir F. A. G. OUSELEY.

(446)

Trinity Sunday.

" I am Alpha and Omega, the beginning and the end, the first and the last."

mf BE near us, Holy TRINITY,
     One Light, one only Deity !
cr All things are Thine, on Thee depend,
f Who art Beginning without end.

The myriad armies of the sky
Praise, bless, adore Thy Majesty :
Earth's triple frame—land, air, and sea—
Upraise their canticle to Thee.

f   Praise to the FATHER, made of none,
    Praise to His sole-begotten SON,
    Praise to the HOLY SPIRIT be,—
    Mysterious Godhead, ONE in THREE !

dim We too, Thy suppliant servants all,
Before Thy feet adoring fall :
To Thee our vows and prayers we bring,
With hymns that Saints and Angels sing.

cr One we believe Thee, Light Divine,
And worship in a glorious Trine :
mf O First and Last, we humbly cry,
And all things having breath reply.

                     Compilers : from the Latin.

General Hymns.

Hymn 510.   SEMPER ASPECTEMUS.—C.M.   J. H. CASSON.

" Lo, these are parts of His ways."

mf HAIL, FATHER, Whose creating call
     Unnumber'd worlds attend ;
Who art in all and over all,
    Thyself both Source and End :

In light unsearchable enthroned,
    Whom Angels dimly see,
The Fountain of the GODHEAD own'd,
    First-named among the THREE.

From Thee, through an eternal Now,
    Springs Thy co-equal SON ;
An everlasting FATHER Thou,
    Ere time began to run.

p Not quite display'd to worlds above,
    Nor quite on earth conceal'd,
cr By wondrous, unexhausted love
    To mortal man reveal'd ;

When Nature's outworn robe shall be
    Exchanged for new attire ;
And earth, which rose at Thy decree,
    Dissolve before Thy fire ;

f Thy Name, O GOD, be still adored
    Through ages without end,
Whom none but Thine essential WORD
    And SPIRIT comprehend.

                     S. WESLEY, 1736.

General Hymns.

Hymn 511. GLORIA.—7 7.7 7.7 7.

C. BUCKNALL.

A-men.

"This glorious and fearful Name, the Lord thy God."

f G LORIOUS is Thy Name, O LORD!
Heav'n and earth with one accord
Tell Thy greatness, part reveal'd,
But the larger part conceal'd.
dim How shall we poor sinners dare
Seek Thy face in praise and prayer?

f Fearful is Thy Name, O LORD!
Dread Thy voice, and sharp Thy sword;
Thunders roll around Thy path:
None can stand before Thy wrath!
dim How shall trembling sinners dare
Lift their voice in praise and prayer?

mf Yet with all Thy wondrous might
Far beyond our mortal sight,
Perfect wisdom, boundless powers,
cr Thou, O glorious GOD! art ours.
dim So, though fill'd with awe, we dare
Name Thy Name in praise and prayer.

p Since, to save a world undone,
Thou didst give Thine only SON,
cr All Thy greatness, LORD Most High,
Brings Thee to our hearts more nigh.
Thus in faith and hope we dare
f Claim Thy love in praise and prayer.

H. TWELLS.

ALTERNATIVE TUNE, HYMN 6 (SECOND TUNE).

Hymn 512. MARTYRDOM.—C.M. (*First Tune.*)

H. WILSON, 1766–1824.

A-men.

A lower setting of this Tune is given at Hymn 630.

(448)

General Hymns.

Hymn 512. CREDITON.—C.M. (*Second Tune.*)   T. CLARK, 1807.

A - men.

"*Jacob vowed a vow, saying, If God will be with me, and will keep me in this way that I go, and will give me bread to eat, and raiment to put on, so that I come again to my father's house in peace; then shall the Lord be my God.*"

mf O GOD of Jacob, by Whose hand
     Thy people still are fed,
Who through this weary pilgrimage
     Hast all our fathers led;

Our vows, our prayers, we now present
     Before Thy Throne of grace;
GOD of our fathers, be the GOD
     Of their succeeding race.

p   Through each perplexing path of life
     Our wandering footsteps guide;
Give us each day our daily bread,
     And raiment fit provide.

cr   O spread Thy covering wings around,
     Till all our wanderings cease,
And at our FATHER'S loved abode
     Our souls arrive in peace.

                       P. DODDRIDGE, 1737.

Hymn 513. ST. LUKE.—C.M.   J. HEYWOOD.

A - men.

"*Strive for the truth to the death, and the Lord shall fight for thee.—Thou requirest truth in the inward parts.*"

mf O GOD of Truth, Whose living word
     Upholds whate'er hath breath,
dim Look down on Thy creation, LORD,
     Enslaved by sin and death.

mf Set up Thy standard, LORD, that they
     Who claim a heavenly birth
May march with Thee to smite the lies
     That vex Thy ransom'd earth.

dim Ah! would we join that blest array,
     And follow in the might

Of Him, the Faithful and the True,
     In raiment clean and white?

cr Then, GOD of Truth, for Whom we long—
     Thou Who wilt hear our prayer—
Do Thine own battle in our hearts,
     And slay the falsehood there.

Yea, come! then, tried as in the fire,
     From every lie set free,
Thy perfect truth shall dwell in us,
mf   And we shall live in Thee.

                       T. HUGHES

                                                   Q

General Hymns.

Hymn 514. VIA PACIS.—6 6 6 6. 8 8.

Sir J. BARNBY.

A - men.

" Our Father, which art in Heaven.'

mf FATHER of all, to Thee
With loving hearts we pray,
Through Him, in mercy given,
The Life, the Truth, the Way ;
cr From Heav'n, Thy Throne, in mercy shed
Thy blessings on each bended head.

FATHER of all, to Thee
Our contrite hearts we raise,
Unstrung by sin and pain,
Long voiceless in Thy praise ;
Breathe Thou the silent chords along,
Until they tremble into song.

FATHER of all, to Thee
We breathe unutter'd fears,
Deep-hidden in our souls,
That have no voice but tears ;
Take Thou our hand, and through the wild
Lead gently on each trustful child.

mf FATHER of all, may we
In praise our tongues employ,
When gladness fills the soul
With deep and hallow'd joy ;
In storm and calm give us to see
The path of peace which leads to Thee.

J. JULIAN.

ALTERNATIVE TUNE, HYMN 727.

Hymn 515. ST. COLUMBA.—C.M.

J. A. MacMEIKAN.

A - men.

*" Jabez called on the God of Israel, saying, Oh that Thou wouldest bless me indeed . . . and
that Thine hand might be with me, and that Thou wouldest keep me from evil . . . And
God granted him that which he requested."*

p FATHER, whate'er of earthly bliss
Thy sovereign will denies,
Accepted at Thy Throne of grace
Let this petition rise :—

Give me a calm and thankful heart,
From every murmur free ;

The blessings of Thy grace impart,
And let me live to Thee.

cr Let the sweet hope that Thou art mine
My path of life attend ;
Thy presence through my journey shine,
mf And crown my journey's end.

ANNE STEELE, 1760.

General Hymns.

Hymn 516. Old Hundredth.—L.M. *(First Tune.)* L. Bourgeois, 1551.

A lower setting of this Tune is given at Hymn 435.

Hymn 516. Penshurst.—L.M. *(Second Tune.)* V. Novello, 1836.

"O be joyful in the Lord, all ye lands."

mf B EFORE JEHOVAH'S awful Throne,
Ye nations, bow with sacred joy ;
f Know that the LORD is GOD alone ;
mf He can create, and He destroy.

His sov'reign power, without our aid,
dim Made us of clay, and form'd us men ;
And when like wand'ring sheep we stray'd
He brought us to His fold again.

f We'll crowd Thy gates with thankful songs ;
High as the heav'ns our voices raise ;
And earth, with her ten thousand tongues,
Shall fill Thy courts with sounding praise.

Wide as the world is Thy command ;
Vast as eternity Thy love ;
Firm as a rock Thy truth shall stand,
When rolling years shall cease to move.

I. WATTS, 1719.

General Hymns.

Hymn 517. CONTEMPLATION.—C.M.

Rev. Sir F. A. G. OUSELEY.

A-men.

" The multitude of His mercies."

mf WHEN all Thy mercies, O my GOD,
  My rising soul surveys,
Transported with the view, I'm lost
In wonder, love, and praise.

Unnumber'd comforts to my soul
Thy tender care bestow'd,
Before my infant heart conceived
From Whom those comforts flow'd.

p When in the slippery paths of youth
With heedless steps I ran,

cr Thine arm unseen convey'd me safe,
  And led me up to man.

Through every period of my life
Thy goodness I'll pursue,
cr And after death in distant worlds
The glorious theme renew.

f Through all eternity to Thee
A joyful song I'll raise ;
But oh ! eternity's too short
To utter all Thy praise.

J. ADDISON, 1712.

ALTERNATIVE TUNE, HYMN 267 (SECOND TUNE).

Hymn 518. WESTBOURNE.—8 8 8 8. 8 8.

C. E. STEPHENS.

A-men.

" I have gone astray like a sheep that is lost ; O seek Thy servant."

mf WE have not known Thee as we ought,
  Nor learn'd Thy wisdom, grace, and
    power ;
The things of earth have fill'd our thought,
And trifles of the passing hour.
p LORD, give us light Thy truth to see,
And make us wise in knowing Thee.

mf We have not fear'd Thee as we ought,
Nor bow'd beneath Thine awful eye,
Nor guarded deed, and word, and thought,
Remembering that GOD was nigh.
p LORD, give us faith to know Thee
  near,
And grant the grace of holy fear.

(452)

General Hymns.

mf We have not loved Thee as we ought,
Nor cared that we are loved by Thee ;
Thy presence we have coldly sought,
And feebly long'd Thy Face to see.
p LORD, give a pure and loving heart
To feel and own the love Thou art.

mf We have not served Thee as we ought,
Alas ! the duties left undone,—
dim The work with little fervour wrought,—

The battles lost, or scarcely won !
LORD, give the zeal, and give the might,
For Thee to toil, for Thee to fight.
mf When shall we know Thee as we ought,
And fear, and love, and serve aright !
When shall we out of trial brought
cr Be perfect in the land of light !
LORD, may we day by day prepare
To see Thy Face, and serve Thee there.

T. B. POLLOCK.

Hymn 519. NUTBOURNE.—7 7.7 7.7 7.

T. E. AYLWARD.

A-men.

" Yea, Lord, I believe that Thou art the Christ, the Son of God."

mf GOD the FATHER'S only SON,
And with Him in glory ONE,
ONE in wisdom, ONE in might,
Absolute and Infinite ;
f JESU, I believe in Thee,
Thou art LORD and GOD to me.

mf Preacher of eternal peace,
CHRIST Anointed to release,
Setting wide the dungeon door
Unto sinners chain'd before ;
f JESU, I believe in Thee,
CHRIST the Prophet sent to me.

p Low in deep Gethsemane,
cr High on dreadful Calvary,
In the Garden, on the Cross,
Making good our utter loss ;
f JESU, I believe in Thee,
Priest and Sacrifice for me.

mf Ruler of Thy ransom'd race,
And Protector by Thy grace,
Leader in the way we wend,
And Rewarder at the end ;
f JESU, I believe in Thee,
CHRIST, the King of kings to me.

S. J. STONE.

Hymn 520. LOVE DIVINE. —8 7 8 7. (*First Tune.*)

Sir J. STAINER.

A-men.

" Visit me with Thy salvation."

mf LOVE Divine, all loves excelling,
Joy of Heav'n, to earth come down,
Fix in us Thy humble dwelling,
All Thy faithful mercies crown.

p JESU, Thou art all compassion,
Pure unbounded love Thou art ;
or Visit us with Thy salvation,
Enter every trembling heart.

Come, Almighty to deliver,
Let us all Thy grace receive ;
Suddenly return, and never,
Never more Thy temples leave.

Thee we would be always blessing,
Serve Thee as Thy Hosts above ;
p Pray, and (*cr*) praise Thee, without ceasing,
Glory in Thy perfect love.

mf Finish then Thy new creation,
Pure and spotless let us be ;
Let us see Thy great salvation,
Perfectly restored in Thee.

cr Changed from glory into glory,
Till in Heav'n we take our place,
Till we cast our crowns before Thee,
Lost in wonder, love, and praise.

(453)

C. WESLEY, 1747.

General Hymns.

Hymn 520. Airedale.—8 7 8 7. 8 7 8 7. *(Second Tune.)* Sir C. V. STANFORD.

A · men.

" Visit me with Thy salvation."

mf   LOVE Divine, all loves excelling,
     Joy of Heav'n, to earth come down,
    Fix in us Thy humble dwelling,
     All Thy faithful mercies crown.
p   JESU, Thou art all compassion,
     Pure unbounded love Thou art ;
cr Visit us with Thy salvation,
     Enter every trembling heart.

Come, Almighty to deliver,
   Let us all Thy grace receive ;
Suddenly return, and never,
   Never more Thy temples leave.
Thee we would be always blessing,
   Serve Thee as Thy Hosts above ;
p Pray, and (*cr*) praise Thee, without ceasing,
   Glory in Thy perfect love.

mf Finish then Thy new creation,
   Pure and spotless let us be ;
Let us see Thy great salvation,
   Perfectly restored in Thee.
cr Changed from glory into glory,
   Till in Heav'n we take our place,
Till we cast our crowns before Thee,
   Lost in wonder, love, and praise.

C. WESLEY, 1747.

(454)

General Hymns.

Hymn 521. NOMEN TERSANCTUM.—8 8 8 8.8 8 8 8.88. Sir J. BARNBY.

cres - - cen - - - - do.

p

cres.

p

A - men.

"The Name of the Lord Jesus."

mf ⌠THRICE-HOLY Name! that sweeter sounds
 Than streams which down the valley run,
And tells of more than human love,
 And more than human power, in one :
First from the gracious herald heard,
cr Heard since through all the choirs on high ;
O Child of Mary, SON of GOD,
 Eternal, hear Thy children's cry !
 p While at the blessèd Name we bow,
  LORD JESUS, be among us now !

mf Within our dim-eyed souls call up
 The vision of Thine earthly years ;
The Mount of the transfigured Form ;
 p The Garden of the bitter Tears ;
The Cross uprear'd in darkening skies ;

The thorn-wreath'd Head, the bleeding Side ;
 And whisper in the heart, " For you,
For you, I left the Heav'ns, and died,"
 While at the blessèd Name we bow,
 LORD JESUS, be among us now !

mf Ah ! with faith's inward piercing eye
 The riven rock-hewn bed we see,
Whence Thou in triumph hast gone forth
 By death from death to make us free !
And when on earth's last awful day
 The Judgment-seat of GOD shall shine,
Lift Thou our trembling eyes to read
 In Thy dear Face the mercy-sign.
 p While at the blessèd Name we bow,
  LORD JESUS, be among us now.

          F. T. PALGRAVE.

General Hymns.

Hymn 522. SELBY.—C.M. *(First Tune.)* A. J. EYRE.

A - men.

Hymn 522. OXFORD NEW.—C.M. *(Second Tune.)* J. H. COOMBES, 1784.

A - men.

"When ye glorify the Lord, exalt Him as much as ye can: for even yet will He far exceed: and when ye exalt Him, put forth all your strength, and be not weary: for ye can never go far enough."

f   O FOR a thousand tongues to sing
     My blest Redeemer's praise,
The glories of my GOD and King,
     The triumphs of His grace !

dim JESUS—the Name that charms our fears,
     That bids our sorrows cease ;
'Tis music in the sinner's ears,
     'Tis life, and health, and peace.

mf *He speaks ;—and, list'ning to His Voice,
     New life the dead receive,

The mournful broken hearts rejoice,
     The humble poor believe.

Hear Him, ye deaf ; His praise, ye dumb,
     Your loosen'd tongues employ ;
Ye blind, behold your SAVIOUR come ;
     And leap, ye lame, for joy !

*My gracious Master and my GOD,
     Assist me to proclaim
And spread through all the earth abroad
f   The honours of Thy Name.

C. WESLEY, 1738.

* *First Tune, verses 3 and 5 to begin thus:*

General Hymns.

Hymn 523. CROSS AND CROWN.—8 7 8 7.8 7 8 7.   J. W. ELLIOTT

* *The small notes for the Organ to be used in second verse only.*

"*Who is this ?*"

p   WHO is this so weak and helpless,
     Child of lowly Hebrew maid,
Rudely in a stable shelter'd,
     Coldly in a manger laid?
f   'Tis the LORD of all creation,
     Who this wondrous path hath trod ;
He is GOD from everlasting,
     And to everlasting GOD.

p   Who is this—a Man of Sorrows,
     Walking sadly life's hard way,
Homeless, weary, sighing, weeping
     Over sin and Satan's sway?
f   'Tis our GOD, our glorious SAVIOUR,
     Who above the starry sky
Now for us a place prepareth,
     Where no tear can dim the eye.

p   Who is this—behold Him shedding
     Drops of Blood upon the ground?
Who is this—despised, rejected,
     Mock'd, insulted, beaten, bound?
f   'Tis our GOD, Who gifts and graces
     On His Church now poureth down ;
Who shall smite in righteous judgment
     All His foes beneath His Throne.

p   Who is this that hangeth dying,
     While the rude world scoffs and scorns ;
Number'd with the malefactors,
     Torn with nails, and crown'd with thorns?
f   'Tis the GOD Who ever liveth
     'Mid the shining ones on high,
cr   In the glorious golden city
     Reigning everlastingly.

Bishop W. WALSHAM HOW

ALTERNATIVE TUNE, HYMN **677.**

General Hymns.

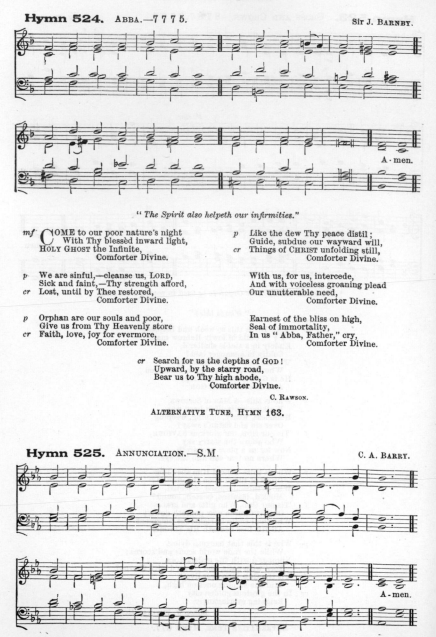

Hymn 524. ABBA.—7 7 7 5.

Sir J. BARNBY.

A-men.

" The Spirit also helpeth our infirmities."

mf COME to our poor nature's night
 With Thy blessèd inward light,
HOLY GHOST the Infinite,
  Comforter Divine.

p We are sinful,—cleanse us, LORD,
 Sick and faint,—Thy strength afford,
cr Lost, until by Thee restored,
  Comforter Divine.

p Orphan are our souls and poor,
 Give us from Thy Heavenly store
cr Faith, love, joy for evermore,
  Comforter Divine.

p Like the dew Thy peace distil;
 Guide, subdue our wayward will,
cr Things of CHRIST unfolding still,
  Comforter Divine.

With us, for us, intercede,
 And with voiceless groaning plead
Our unutterable need,
  Comforter Divine.

Earnest of the bliss on high,
 Seal of immortality,
In us " Abba, Father," cry,
  Comforter Divine.

cr Search for us the depths of GOD!
 Upward, by the starry road,
 Bear us to Thy high abode,
  Comforter Divine.

C. RAWSON.

ALTERNATIVE TUNE, HYMN 163.

Hymn 525. ANNUNCIATION.—S.M.

C. A. BARRY.

A-men.

General Hymns.

" When they had prayed, the place was shaken where they were assembled together, and they were all filled with the Holy Ghost."

mp   L ORD GOD the HOLY GHOST,
     In this accepted hour,
As on the day of Pentecost,
   Descend in all Thy power.

We meet with one accord
   In our appointed place,
And wait the promise of our LORD,
   The SPIRIT of all grace.

cr   Like mighty rushing wind
     Upon the waves beneath,
Move with one impulse every mind,
   One soul, one feeling breathe :

mf   The young, the old inspire
     With wisdom from above ;
And give us hearts and tongues of fire,
   To pray and praise and love.

SPIRIT of light, explore,
   And chase our gloom away,
With lustre shining more and more
   Unto the perfect day.

SPIRIT of truth, be Thou
   In life and death our Guide ;
O SPIRIT of adoption, now
   May we be sanctified.

J. MONTGOMERY, 1819.

Hymn 526.   ST. JEROME.—8 8 8 8. 8 8.   Sir F. CHAMPNEYS.

A-men.

" The Lord is in this place . . . how dreadful is this place."

mf   L O ! GOD is here ! let us adore,
     And own how dreadful is this place !
Let all within us feel His power,
   And silent bow before His face ;
dim Who know His power, His grace who prove,
p   Serve Him with awe, with reverence love.

mf Lo ! GOD is here ! Him day and night
   The united choirs of Angels sing ;
To Him, enthroned above all height,
   The hosts of Heav'n their praises bring ;
dim Disdain not, LORD, our meaner song,
   Who praise Thee with a falt'ring tongue.

mf Being of beings ! may our praise
   Thy courts with grateful fragrance fill ;
Still may we stand before Thy face,
   Still hear and do Thy sovereign will ;
To Thee may all our thoughts arise
A true and ceaseless sacrifice.

J. WESLEY : from the German
of G. Tersteegen.

General Hymns.

Hymn 527. RICHMOND.—7 7 7 7.

C. E. STEPHENS.

A - men.

" Ask what I shall give thee."

mp COME, my soul, thy suit prepare,
Jesus loves to answer prayer ;
cr He Himself has bid thee pray,
Therefore will not say thee nay.

cr Thou art coming to a King,
Large petitions with thee bring ;
For His grace and power are such,
None can ever ask too much.

p With my burden I begin ;
Lord, remove this load of sin ;

Let Thy Blood, for sinners spilt,
Set my conscience free from guilt.

Lord, I come to Thee for rest ;
Take possession of my breast ;
There Thy blood-bought right maintain,
And without a rival reign.

While I am a pilgrim here,
Let Thy love my spirit cheer ;
cr Be my Guide, my Guard, my Friend,
Lead me to my journey's end.

J. Newton, 1779.

ALTERNATIVE TUNE, HYMN 372.

Hymn 528. WALTHAM.—6 6 6 6 6 6.

W. H. MONK.

A-men.

" All our righteousnesses are as filthy rags."

mf NOT for our sins alone
Thy mercy, Lord, we sue ;
dim Let fall Thy pitying glance
On our devotions too,
What we have done for Thee,
And what we think to do.

mf The holiest hours we spend
In prayer upon our knees,
The times when most we deem
Our songs of praise will please,
Thou Searcher of all hearts,
p Forgiveness pour on these.

mf And all the gifts we bring,
And all the vows we make,
And all the acts of love

We plan for Thy dear sake,
p Into Thy pard'ning thought,
O God of mercy, take.

mp And most, when we, Thy flock,
Before Thine Altar bend,
And strange, bewild'ring thoughts
With those sweet moments blend,
pp By Him Whose death we plead,
Good Lord, Thy help extend.

p Bow down Thine ear and hear !
cr Open Thine eyes and see !
Our very love is shame,
And we must come to Thee
mf To make it of Thy grace
What Thou would'st have it be.

H. Twells.

(460)

General Hymns.

Hymn 529. Styall.—L.M. (*First Tune.*)   Rev. W. Statham.

A - men.

A higher setting of this Tune is given at Hymn 489.

Hymn 529. Wareham.—L.M. (*Second Tune.*)   W. Knapp, 1738.

A - men.

" In all places where I record My Name, I will come unto thee, and I will bless thee."

> *mp*   JESUS, where'er Thy people meet,
>   There they behold Thy mercy-seat ;
> Where'er they seek Thee Thou art found,
> And every place is hallow'd ground.
>
> For Thou within no walls confined,
> Inhabitest the humble mind ;
> Such ever bring Thee when they come,
> And going, take Thee to their home.
>
> *cr*   Great Shepherd of Thy chosen few,
> Thy former mercies here renew ;
> Here to our waiting hearts proclaim
> The sweetness of Thy saving Name.
>
> Here may we prove the power of prayer,
> To strengthen faith and sweeten care,
> To teach our faint desires to rise,
> And bring all Heav'n before our eyes.
>
> *p*   LORD, we are few, but Thou art near,
>   Nor short Thine arm, nor deaf Thine ear ;
> *cr*   O rend the Heav'ns, come quickly down,
> And make a thousand hearts Thine own.
>
>   W. Cowper, 1769.

ALTERNATIVE TUNE, HYMN 682 (SECOND TUNE).

(461)

Hymn 530. Melton Mowbray.—9 6 9 6. 3. 9 6 9 6.

W. H. Monk.

"The entrance of Thy word giveth light."

mf THE Voice of God's Creation found me
dim   Perplex'd midst hope and fear,
mf For though His sunshine flash'd around me,
dim His storms at times drew near :
    And I said—
  mf Oh ! that I knew where He abideth !
    For doubts beset our lot,
dim And lo ! His glorious face He hideth,
    And men ⋁ perceive it not !

mf The Voice of God's Protection told me
    He loveth all He made ;
    I seem'd to feel His arms enfold me,
p   And yet was half afraid :
    And I said—
  mf Oh ! that I knew where I might find Him !
    His eye would guide me right :
    He leaveth countless tracks behind Him,
p   Yet passeth ⋁ out of sight.

mf The Voice of Conscience sounded nearer,
    It stirr'd my inmost breast ;
    But though its tones were firmer, clearer,
dim 'Twas not the voice of rest :
    And I said—
    Oh ! that I knew if He forgiveth !
    My soul is faint within,
    Because in grievous fear it liveth
    Of wages ⋁ due to sin.

mf It was the Voice of Revelation
    That met my utmost need ;
    The wondrous message of salvation
cr   Was joy and peace indeed :
    And I said—
    Oh ! how I love the sacred pages
    From which such tidings flow,
    As monarchs, patriarchs, poets, sages,
dim Have long'd ⋁ in vain to know !

    f   For now is life a lucid story,
        And death (*dim*) a rest in Him,
  cr   And all is bathed in light and glory
        That once was dark or dim :
        And I said—
  mf O Thou Who dost my soul deliver,
        And all its hopes uplift ;
        Give me a tongue to praise the Giver,
    f   A heart ⋁ to prize the gift.

H. Twells.

 No pause in verses 2 and 3.

Breath to be taken at ⋁.

General Hymns.

Hymn 531. SOUTHWELL.—C.M. (*First Tune.*)   H. S. IRONS.

Hymn 531. SOUTHWELL.—C.M. (*First Tune.*)   H. S. IRONS.

A-men.

Hymn 531. ST. JOHN BAPTIST.—C.M. (*Second Tune.*)   J. B. CALKIN.

A-men.

[*For copyright, see p.* lv.]

"*O how sweet are Thy words.*"

mf FATHER of mercies, in Thy Word
What endless glory shines !
For ever be Thy Name adored
For these celestial lines.

Here may the blind and hungry come,
And light and food receive ;
Here shall the lowliest guest have room,
And taste and see and live.

Here springs of consolation rise
To cheer the fainting mind,
And thirsting souls receive supplies,
And sweet refreshment find.

Here the Redeemer's welcome Voice
Spreads heav'nly peace around,
And life and everlasting joys
Attend the blissful sound.

Oh, may these heav'nly pages be
My ever dear delight,
And still new beauties may I see,
And still increasing light.

Divine Instructor, gracious LORD,
Be Thou for ever near ;
Teach me to love Thy sacred Word,
And view my SAVIOUR here.

ANNE STEELE, 1760.

(463)

General Hymns.

Hymn 532. Dominica.—S.M.　　　　　　　　Sir H. Oakeley.

A-men.

A higher setting of this Tune is given at Hymn 37.

" Thy word is tried to the uttermost ; and Thy servant loveth it."

mf CHURCH of the Living God,
　　Pillar and ground of truth,
Keep the old paths the fathers trod
　　In thy illumined youth.

Lo, in thy bosom lies
　　The touchstone for the age ;
Seducing error shrinks and dies
　　At light from yonder page.

Woe to the hands that dare,
　　By lust of power enticed,
To mingle with the doctrine there
　　The frauds of Antichrist.

Once to the saints was given
　　All blessèd gospel lore ;
There, written down in words from Heav'n,
　　Thou hast it evermore.

Fear not, though doubts abound,
　　And scoffing tongues deride ;
Love of GOD'S Word finds surer ground
　　When to the utmost tried.

Toil at thy sacred text ;
　　More fruitful grows the field ;
Each generation for the next
　　Prepares a richer yield.

GOD'S SPIRIT in the Church
　　Still lives unspent, untired,
Inspiring hearts that fain would search
　　The truths Himself inspired.

cr Move, HOLY GHOST, with might
　　Amongst us as of old ;
Dispel the falsehood, and unite
　　In true faith the true fold.

　　　　　　　　　　　A. J. Mason.

Hymn 533. Morning.—7 7 7 7.7 7.　　　　　W. H. Monk.

A-men.

" He that sat on the Throne said, Behold I make all things new."

mf OH how fair that morning broke,
　　When in Eden man awoke !
Beast and bird and insect bright
Revell'd in the gladsome light ;
cr GOD look'd down from Heav'n above,
All was life and joy and love.

p Ah ! the doleful change when sin
Darkly, subtly enter'd in !
War and pestilence and dearth
Mar and sadden GOD'S fair earth ;
Human sorrow fills the air ;
Death is reigning everywhere.

mf Yet rejoice ; for GOD on high
f Hath not left His world to die !
GOD'S dear SON, with dying breath,
Broke the power of sin and death ;
CHRIST the Tempter overthrew,
CHRIST is making all things new.

p LORD, in me be sin subdued,
So may I with heart renew'd,
cr Fight the fight and run the race,
Work in my appointed place,
mf Waiting for the glad new birth
Of Thy perfect Heav'n and earth.

　　　　　　　　　　　J. Ellerton.

(464)

General Hymns.

Hymn 534. Hammersmith.—S.M. W. C. Filby.

A - men.

" Verily when we were with you, we told you before that we should suffer tribulation.'

mf
FAR down the ages now,
Her journey well-nigh done,
The pilgrim Church pursues her way,
And longs to reach her crown.

mp
No wider is the gate,
No broader is the way,
No smoother is the ancient path
That leads to light and day.

mf
No feebler is the foe,
No slacker grows the fight,

Nor less the need of armour tried,
Of shield and helmet bright.

cr
Thus onward still we press,
Through evil and through good,
Through pain, or poverty, or want,
Through peril or through blood.

Still faithful to our God,
And to our Captain true,

cr
We follow where He leads the way,
The Kingdom still in view.

H. Bonar.

Hymn 535. St. Hugh.—C.M. *(First Tune.)* E. J. Hopkins.

A - men.

"To me to live is Christ, and to die is gain."

p
LORD, it belongs not to my care
Whether I die or live ;
cr
To love and serve Thee is my share,
And this Thy grace must give.

If life be long, oh make me glad
The longer to obey ;
If short, no labourer is sad
To end his toilsome day.

p
CHRIST leads me through no darker rooms
Than He went through before ;
He that unto GOD's kingdom comes
Must enter by this door.

Come, LORD, when grace hath made me meet
Thy blessèd Face to see :
cr
For if Thy work on earth be sweet,
What will Thy glory be !

Then I shall end my sad complaints
And weary sinful days,
mf
And join with the triumphant Saints
That sing my SAVIOUR's praise.

p
My knowledge of that life is small,
The eye of faith is dim ;
But 'tis enough that CHRIST knows all,
cr
And I shall be with Him.

R. Baxter, 1681.

General Hymns.

Hymn 535. WACHUSETT.—C.M. (Second Tune.)

Slow.

CLARK, *Congregational Harmonist*, 1828.

A · men.

"To me to live is Christ, and to die is gain."

  p LORD, it belongs not to my care
        Whether I die or live ;
  cr To love and serve Thee is my share,
        And this Thy grace must give.

      If life be long, oh make me glad
        The longer to obey ;
      If short, no labourer is sad
        To end his toilsome day.

  p CHRIST leads me through no darker rooms
        Than He went through before ;
      He that unto GOD's kingdom comes
        Must enter by this door.

      Come, LORD, when grace hath made me meet
        Thy blessèd Face to see :
  cr For if Thy work on earth be sweet,
        What will Thy glory be !

      Then I shall end my sad complaints
        And weary sinful days,
  mf And join with the triumphant Saints
        That sing my SAVIOUR's praise.

  p My knowledge of that life is small,
        The eye of faith is dim ;
      But 'tis enough that CHRIST knows all,
  cr And I shall be with Him.

R. BAXTER, 1681.

Hymn 536. BEULAH.—C.M.

G. M. GARRETT.

A-men.

General Ibymns.

" For now they desire a better country, that is a heavenly."

mf THERE is a land of pure delight,
　　Where Saints immortal reign ;
Infinite day excludes the night,
　　And pleasures banish pain.

There everlasting spring abides,
　　And never-withering flowers ;
dim Death, like a narrow sea, divides
　　That heav'nly land from ours.

cr Sweet fields beyond the swelling flood
　　Stand dress'd in living green ;
So to the Jews old Canaan stood,
　　While Jordan roll'd between.

p But timorous mortals start and shrink
　　To cross the narrow sea,
And linger shivering on the brink,
　　And fear to launch away.

mf Oh, could we make our doubts remove,
　　Those gloomy doubts that rise,
And see the Canaan that we love
　　With unbeclouded eyes :

cr Could we but climb where Moses stood,
　　And view the landscape o'er ;
Not Jordan's stream, nor death's cold flood,
　　Should fright us from the shore.

I. WATTS, 1707.

ALTERNATIVE TUNE, HYMN 531 (SECOND TUNE).

Hymn 537. PAX TECUM.—10 10. *(First Tune.)*　　G. T. CALDBECK.

A-men.

Hymn 537. ELBERTON.—10 10. *(Second Tune.)*　　B. HARWOOD.

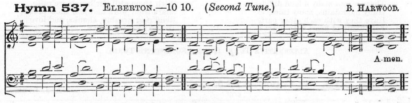

A-men.

" Thou wilt keep him in perfect peace, whose mind is stayed on Thee."

mf PEACE, perfect peace, in this dark world of sin ?
p 　　The Blood of JESUS whispers peace within.

mf Peace, perfect peace, by thronging duties press'd ?
p 　　To do the will of JESUS, this is rest.

mf Peace, perfect peace, with sorrows surging round ?
p 　　On JESUS' Bosom nought but calm is found.

mf Peace, perfect peace, with loved ones far away ?
p 　　In JESUS' keeping we are safe and they.

mp Peace, perfect peace, our future all unknown ?
f 　　JESUS we know, and He is on the Throne.

mp Peace, perfect peace, death shadowing us and ours ?
f 　　JESUS has vanquish'd death and all its powers.

p 　It is enough : (mf) earth's struggles soon shall cease,
　　And JESUS call us to Heav'n's perfect peace.

Bishop E. H. BICKERSTETH.

(467)

General Hymns.

Hymn 538. WARNBOROUGH.—7 7 7 7.

(Original Key—A♭.)

F. ILIFFE.

A - men.

" That whether we wake or sleep we should live together with Him."

p THEY whose course on earth is o'er,
　　Think they of their brethren more?
They before the Throne who bow,
Feel they for their brethren now?

We, by enemies distrest—
They in Paradise at rest ;
We the captives—they the freed—
We and they are one indeed.

One in all we seek or shun,
One—because our LORD is one ;
One in heart and one in love—
We below, and they above.

Those whom many a land divides,
Many mountains, many tides,
Have they with each other part,
Fellowship of heart with heart?

Each to each may be unknown,
Wide apart their lots be thrown ;
Diff'ring tongues their lips may speak,
One be strong, and one be weak ;—

cr Yet in Sacrament and prayer
　　Each with other hath a share ;
dim Hath a share in tear and sigh,
　　Watch, and Fast and Litany.

mf Saints departed even thus
　　Hold communion still with us ;
Still with us, beyond the veil
Praising, pleading without fail.

cr With them still our hearts we raise,
　　Share their work and join their praise,
Rend'ring worship, thanks, and love
To the TRINITY above.

J. M. NEALE.

ALTERNATIVE TUNE, HYMN 280 (SECOND TUNE).

Hymn 539. ST. CLARE.—8 7 8 5.

cres.

A. J. EYRE.

A - men.

*" Seek ye first the kingdom of God and His righteousness, and all these things shall
be added unto you."*

mp TAKE not thought for food or raiment,
　　Careful one, so anxiously ;
cr For the King Himself provideth
　　Food and clothes for thee.

He Who daily feeds the sparrows,
He Who clothes the lilies bright,
More than birds and flowers holds thee
Precious in His sight.

General Hymns.

dim Would'st thou give a stone, a serpent
   To thy pleading child for food?
cr And shall not thy Heavenly FATHER
   Give thee what is good?

mf On the heart that careth for thee
   Rest thou then from sorrow free ;
   For of all most tender fathers
   None so good as He.

Seek thou first His gracious promise,
   Treasure stored in Heav'n above ;
So thou may'st entrust all other
   Safely to His love.

f Unto Thee, O bounteous FATHER,
   Glory, honour, praise be done ;
With the SON and HOLY SPIRIT,
   GOD for ever ONE.

Compilers : from the Latin.

Hymn 540. PENTECOST.—L.M. (*First Tune.*)   REV. W. BOYD.

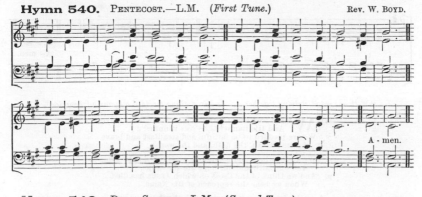

A - men.

Hymn 540. DUKE STREET. —L.M. (*Second Tune.*)   J. HATTON, 1793.

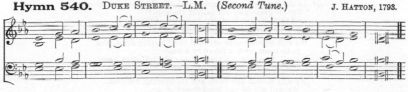

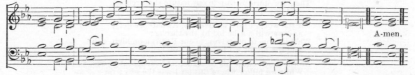

A-men.

" Fight the good fight."

mf FIGHT the good fight with all thy might,
   CHRIST is thy Strength, and CHRIST thy Right ;
Lay hold on life, and it shall be
Thy joy and crown eternally.

Run the straight race through GOD'S good grace,
Lift up thine eyes, and seek His Face ;
Life with its way before us lies,
cr CHRIST is the path, and CHRIST the prize.

mf Cast care aside, lean on thy Guide ;
His boundless mercy will provide ;
Trust, and thy trusting soul shall prove
cr CHRIST is its life, and CHRIST its love.

mf Faint not nor fear, His Arms are near,
He changeth not, and thou art dear ;
cr Only believe, and thou shalt see
That CHRIST is all in all to thee.

J. S. B. MONSELL.

General Hymns.

Hymn 541.   MILITES.—12 9 12 9.   W. H. MONK.

A - men.

" With one mind striving together . . . and in nothing terrified by your adversaries."

mf WE are soldiers of CHRIST, Who is mighty to save,
     And His Banner the Cross is unfurl'd ;
  We are pledged to be faithful and steadfast and brave
     Against Satan, the flesh, and the world.

  We are brothers and comrades, we stand side by side,
     And our faith and our hope are the same ;
p   And we think of the Cross on which JESUS has died,
     When we bear the reproach of His Name.

mf At the font we were mark'd with the Cross on our brow,
     Of our grace and our calling the sign :
  And the weakest is strong to be true to his vow,
     For the armour we wear is Divine.

  We will watch ready arm'd if the Tempter draw near,
     If he come with a frown or a smile :
  We will heed not his threats, nor his flatteries hear,
     Nor be taken by storm or by wile.

  We will master the flesh, and its longings restrain,
     We will not be the bond-slaves of sin,
  The pure Spirit of GOD in our nature shall reign,
     And our spirits their freedom shall win.

  For the world's love we live not, its hate we defy,
     And we will not be led by the throng ;
  We'll be true to ourselves, to our FATHER on high,
     And the bright world to which we belong.

  Now let each cheer his comrade, let hearts beat as one,
     While we follow where CHRIST leads the way ;
  'Twere dishonour to yield, or the battle to shun,
     We will fight, and will watch, and will pray.

dim Though the warfare be weary, the trial be sore,
cr   In the might of our GOD we will stand ;
mf Oh ! what joy to be crown'd and be pure evermore,
     In the peace of our own Fatherland.

                         T. B. POLLOCK.

Hymn 542.   STAND UP.—7 6 7 6. 7 6 7 6. *(First Tune.)*   Sir J. BARNBY.

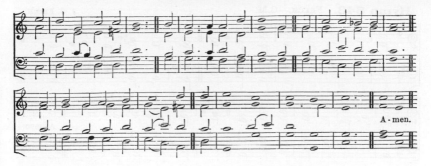

A - men.

Hymn 542. MORNING LIGHT.—7 6 7 6. 7 6 7 6. *(Second Tune.)*

G. J. WEBB, 1837.

A - men.

" Quit you like men ; be strong."

mf STAND up !—stand up for JESUS !
 Ye soldiers of the Cross ;
 Lift high His royal banner,
  It must not suffer loss.
cr From victory unto victory
  His army He shall lead,
 Till every foe is vanquish'd,
f And CHRIST is LORD indeed.

mf Stand up !—stand up for JESUS !
dim The solemn watchword hear ;
 If while ye sleep He suffers,
cr Away with shame and fear ;
 Where'er ye meet with evil,
  Within you or without,
 Charge for the GOD of battles,
  And put the foe to rout.

mf Stand up !—stand up for JESUS !
 The trumpet call obey ;
 Forth to the mighty conflict
  In this His glorious day.

Ye that are men now serve Him
 Against unnumber'd foes ;
 Let courage rise with danger
  And strength to strength oppose.

Stand up !—stand up for JESUS !
 Stand in His strength alone ;
dim The arm of flesh will fail you,
  Ye dare not trust your own.
cr Put on the Gospel armour,
  Each piece put on with prayer ;
 When duty calls or danger
  Be never wanting there !

mf Stand up !—stand up for JESUS !
 The strife will not be long ;
 This day the noise of battle,
  The next the victor's song.
cr To him that overcometh,
  A crown of life shall be ;
f He with the King of Glory
  Shall reign eternally.

G. DUFFIELD.

ALTERNATIVE TUNE, HYMN 271 (SECOND TUNE).

General Hymns.

Hymn 543. FRECH.—C.M.

J. G. FRECH.

A - men.

" When the enemy shall come in like a flood, the Spirit of the Lord shall lift up a standard against him."

p   THERE'S peace and rest in Paradise,
     In weary hours we say ;
  And oh that we had wings like doves
     That we might flee away !

mp For here so strong the evil seems,
     So weak appears the good,
  Our standard wavers in the rush
     Of evil, like a flood.

At times, through the long lonely watch,
    Nor sun nor moon appears ;
Without, incessant fightings are,
    Within, incessant fears.

Then for the quiet land we long,
    And the abode of Peace ;
And for the word, (*cr*) "Come, weary soul,
    From war and vigil cease !"

cr But in our stronger hours we grasp
     The warrior's sword again,
  And burn the good fight yet to fight,
     The faithful watch maintain.

mf We fain would tread the famous way
     Martyrs and saints have trod ;
  The hours ebb fast of this one day
     Of noblest war for GOD !

The LORD Himself hath need of us ;
cr   On ! till the fight be won ;
f   And the King's words shall thrill the heart:
    "Servant of GOD, well done !"

J. R. VERNON.

Hymn 544. ETHELBERT.—7 7 7 7. 7 7 7 7. (*First Tune.*)

Rev. Sir F. A. G. OUSELEY.

General Hymns.

A - men.

Hymn 544. St. Hilary.—7 7 7 7.7 7 7 7. (*Second Tune.*) Sir J. Goss.

A - men.

"*O praise God.*"

f PRAISE the Lord, His glories show,
    Saints within His courts below,
Angels round His Throne above,
All that see and share His love.
Earth to Heav'n, and Heav'n to earth,
Tell His wonders, sing His worth;
Age to age, and shore to shore,
Praise Him, praise Him, evermore.

Praise the Lord, His mercies trace;
Praise His providence and grace,
All that He for man hath done,
All He sends us through His Son:
Strings and voices, hands and hearts,
In the concert bear your parts;
All that breathe, your Lord adore,
ff Praise Him, praise Him, evermore.

H. F. Lyte, 1834.

(473)

General Hymns.

Hymn 545. AUSTRIA.—8 7 8 7. 8 7 8 7.

J. HAYDN, 1797.

A higher setting of this Tune is given at Hymn 292.

" Glorious things are spoken of thee, O thou city of God."

f GLORIOUS things of thee are spoken,
　　Zion, city of our GOD;
He Whose word cannot be broken
　　Form'd thee for His own abode.
On the Rock of ages founded,
　　What can shake thy sure repose?
With salvation's walls surrounded,
　　Thou may'st smile at all thy foes.

mf See, the streams of living waters,
　　Springing from eternal love,
Well supply thy sons and daughters,
　　And all fear of want remove.
Who can faint while such a river
　　Ever flows their thirst to assuage;
Grace, which like the LORD the Giver,
　　Never fails from age to age?

Round each habitation hov'ring,
　　See the cloud and fire appear,
For a glory and a cov'ring—
　　Showing that the LORD is near.
Thus they march, the pillar leading,
　　Light by night and shade by day;
Daily on the manna feeding
　　Which He gives them when they pray.

p SAVIOUR, since of Zion's city
　　I, through grace, a member am,
Let the world deride or pity,
　　I will glory in Thy Name.
Fading is the world's best pleasure,
　　All its boasted pomp and show;
f Solid joys and lasting treasure
　　None but Zion's children know.

J. NEWTON, 1779.

Hymn 546. DARWALL'S 148TH.—6 6 6 6. 4 4 4 4.

J. DARWALL, 1731-1789.

(474)

General Hymns.

A-men.

"*Praise the Lord from the heavens. Praise the Lord from the earth.*"

f   YE holy Angels bright,
    Who wait at GOD'S right hand,
Or through the realms of light
Fly at your LORD'S command,
    Assist our song,
    Or else the theme
    Too high doth seem
    For mortal tongue.

mf Ye blessèd souls at rest,
    Who ran this earthly race,
And now, from sin released,
Behold the SAVIOUR'S Face,
    His praises sound,
    As in His light
    With sweet delight
    Ye do abound.

Ye saints, who toil below,
    Adore your heavenly King,
And onward as ye go
Some joyful anthem sing ;
    Take what He gives
    And praise Him still,
    Through good and ill,
    Who ever lives !

My soul, bear thou thy part,
    Triumph in GOD above,
And with a well-tuned heart
Sing thou the songs of love !
    Let all thy days
f   Till life shall end,
    Whate'er He send,
    Be fill'd with praise.

R. BAXTER, 1681.

Hymn 547.   BEWDLEY.—7 7 7 7.

Rev. Sir F. A. G. OUSELEY.

A-men.

"*The ransomed of the Lord shall return and come to Zion with songs.*"

mf CHILDREN of the Heav'nly King,
    As ye journey, sweetly sing ;
Sing your SAVIOUR'S worthy praise,
Glorious in His works and ways.

p   We are travelling home to GOD
    In the way the fathers trod ;
cr They are happy now, and we
    Soon their happiness shall see.

mf Lift your eyes, ye sons of light,
    Sion's city is in sight ;

There our endless home shall be,
There our LORD we soon shall see.

Fear not, brethren, joyful stand
On the borders of your land ;
JESUS CHRIST, your FATHER'S SON,
Bids you undismay'd go on.

p   LORD, obedient we would go,
    Gladly leaving all below ;
cr Only Thou our Leader be,
f   And we still will follow Thee.

J. CENNICK, 1742.

ALTERNATIVE TUNE, HYMN 33.

(475)

General Hymns.

Hymn 548. Herbert.—10 4.6 6.6 6.10 4. *(First Tune.)* W. H. Monk.

A - men.

Hymn 548. Luckington.—10 4.6 6.6 6.10 4. *(Second Tune.)* B. Harwood.

Cheerfully.

Full.

Dec.

Can.

Dec.

Can.

Full.

A - men.

General Hymns.

" His name only is excellent, and His praise above Heaven and earth."

f LET all the world in every corner sing,
    My GOD and King!
  The heav'ns are not too high,
    His praise may thither fly;
dim The earth is not too low,
cr His praises there may grow.
f Let all the world in every corner sing,
    My GOD and King!

Let all the world in every corner sing,
    My GOD and King!
The Church with psalms must shout,
    No door can keep them out;
But above all the heart
    Must bear the longest part.
Let all the world in every corner sing,
    My GOD and King!

G. HERBERT, 1593–1632.

Hymn 549. STOCKTON.—C.M. (*First Tune.*)   T. WRIGHT, 1763–1829.

A - men.

A lower setting of this Tune is given at Hymn 213.

Hymn 549. ST. MATTHIAS.—C.M. (*Second Tune.*)   O. GIBBONS, 1623.

A - men.

" A perfect heart."

mf O FOR a heart to praise my GOD,
    A heart from sin set free;
  A heart that's sprinkled with the Blood
    So freely shed for me:

A heart resign'd, submissive, meek,
    My great Redeemer's Throne;
Where only CHRIST is heard to speak,
    Where JESUS reigns alone:

A humble, lowly, contrite heart,
    Believing, true, and clean,

Which neither life nor death can part
    From Him that dwells within:

A heart in every thought renew'd,
    And full of love Divine;
Perfect, and right, and pure, and good,
    A copy, LORD, of Thine.

Thy nature, gracious LORD, impart,
    Come quickly from above;
Write Thy new Name upon my heart,
    Thy new best Name of Love.

C. WESLEY, 1742.

(477)

General Hymns.

Hymn 550. ANGEL-VOICES.—8 5 8 5. 8 4 3. (*First Tune.*)   E. G. MONK.

Hymn 550. SERAPHIM.—8 5 8 5. 8 4 3. (*Second Tune.*)   S. S. WESLEY.

[*For copyright, see p. lv.*]

" The Lord hath given me a tongue . . . and I will praise Him therewith."

mf **A**NGEL-VOICES, ever singing,
   Round Thy Throne of light,
Angel-harps for ever ringing,
   Rest not day nor night ;
Thousands only live to bless Thee
cr   And confess Thee
f   LORD of might !

mf Thou, Who art beyond the farthest
   Mortal eye can scan,—
Can it be that Thou regardest
   Songs of sinful man ?
Can we know that Thou art near us,
cr   And wilt hear us ?
f   Yea, we can !

(478)

General Hymns.

mf Yea, we know that Thou rejoicest
 O'er each work of Thine ;
Thou didst ears and hands and voices
 For Thy praise design ;
Craftsman's art and music's measure
 For Thy pleasure
 All combine.

In Thy House, Great GOD, we offer
 Of Thine own to Thee ;
And for Thine acceptance proffer
 All unworthily
Hearts and minds and hands and voices,
 In our choicest
 Psalmody.

f Honour, glory, might, and merit
 Thine shall ever be,
FATHER, SON, and HOLY SPIRIT,
 Blessèd TRINITY !
Of the best that Thou hast given,
 Earth and Heaven
 Render Thee.

F. POTT.

Hymn 551.   WALTHAM.—8 7 8 7.   H. ALBERT, 1642.

" The grace of our Lord Jesus Christ, and the love of God, and the communion of the Holy Ghost be with you all."

mf MAY the grace of CHRIST our SAVIOUR,
 And the FATHER'S boundless love,
With the HOLY SPIRIT'S favour,
Rest upon us from above.

Thus may we abide in union
 With each other and the LORD,
And possess, in sweet communion,
Joys which earth cannot afford.

J. NEWTON, 1779.

Holy Communion.

Hymn 552.   GLOUCESTER.—L.M.   E. HODGES.

" It is the Spirit that quickeneth."

p LOOK down upon us, GOD of grace,
 And send from Thy most holy place
The quickening SPIRIT all Divine
On us and on this bread and wine.

O may His overshadowing
Make now for us this bread we bring
The Body of Thy SON our LORD,
This cup His Blood for sinners pour'd.

A. J. MASON.

Holy Communion.

Hymn 553. SACRAMENTUM UNITATIS.—10 10 10 10.10 10.

C. H. LLOYD.

Unison.

pp   cres.   dim.   A - men.

" We being many are one bread, and one body, for we are all partakers of that one bread."

mf O THOU, Who at Thy Eucharist didst pray
        That all Thy Church might be for ever one,
p   Grant us at every Eucharist to say
        With longing heart and soul, "Thy will be done."
        Oh, may we all one Bread, one Body be,
pp Through this blest Sacrament of Unity.

mp For all Thy Church, O LORD, we intercede ;
        Make Thou our sad divisions soon to cease ;
cr   Draw us the nearer each to each, we plead,
        By drawing all to Thee, O Prince of peace ;
        Thus may we all one Bread, one Body be,
pp Through this blest Sacrament of Unity.

p   We pray Thee too for wanderers from Thy Fold ;
        O bring them back, Good Shepherd of the sheep,
        Back to the Faith which Saints believed of old,
        Back to the Church which still that Faith doth keep ;
        Soon may we all one Bread, one Body be,
pp Through this blest Sacrament of Unity.

mp So, LORD, at length when Sacraments shall cease,
        May we be one with all Thy Church above,
        One with Thy Saints in one unbroken peace,
        One with Thy Saints in one unbounded love :
mf More blessèd still, in peace and love to be
pp One with the TRINITY in Unity.

W. H. TURTON.

Holy Communion.

Hymn 554. TROAS.—8 8.8 8.8.8 8. *(First Tune.)* Archbishop MACLAGAN.

A - men.

Hymn 554. SURREY.—8 8.8 8,8 8. *(Second Tune.)* H. CAREY, 1685–1743.

A - men.

" In the midst of the Throne . . . stood a Lamb as it had been slain."

mp O THOU, before the world began,
    Ordain'd a sacrifice for man,
And by th' Eternal SPIRIT made
An Offering in the sinner's stead ;
mf Our everlasting Priest art Thou,
dim Pleading Thy Death for sinners now.

mp Thy Offering still continues new
    Before the Righteous FATHER'S view ;
cr Thyself the Lamb for ever slain,
    Thy Priesthood doth unchanged remain ;
mf Thy years, O GOD, can never fail,
    Nor Thy blest work within the veil.

p O that our faith may never move,
    But stand unshaken as Thy love !
cr Sure evidence of things unseen,
    Now let it pass the years between,
p And view Thee bleeding on the Tree,
    MY LORD, my GOD, Who dies for me.

C. WESLEY, 1745.

R

Holy Communion.

Hymn 555. ST. HELEN.—8 7 8 7 8 7.

Sir G. C. MARTIN.

" Verily Thou art a God that hidest Thyself, O God of Israel, the Saviour."

mf LORD, enthroned in heavenly splendour,
　　First begotten from the dead,
Thou alone, our strong Defender,
　　Liftest up Thy people's head.
　　　　Alleluia,
　　JESU, True and Living Bread !

p　Here our humblest homage pay we ;
　　Here in loving reverence bow ;
Here for Faith's discernment pray we,
　　Lest we fail to know Thee now.
　　　mf Alleluia,
　　Thou art here, we ask not how.

p　Though the lowliest form doth veil Thee
　　As of old in Bethlehem,
cr　Here as there Thine Angels hail Thee,
　　Branch and Flower of Jesse's stem.
　　　mf Alleluia,
　　We in worship join with them.

Paschal LAMB, Thine Offering, finish'd
　　Once for all when Thou wast slain,
In its fulness undiminish'd
　　Shall for evermore remain,
　　　Alleluia,
　　Cleansing souls from every stain.

cr　Life-imparting Heavenly Manna,
　　Stricken Rock with streaming Side,
f　Heav'n and earth with loud Hosanna,
　　Worship Thee, the LAMB Who died,
　　　Alleluia,
　　Risen, Ascended, Glorified !

G. H. BOURNE.

(482)

Holy Communion.

Hymn 556.   VICTIM DIVINE.—8 8 8 8.8 8.   *(First Tune.)*   Sir J. BARNBY.

A - men.

"The Blood of sprinkling, which speaketh."

p   VICTIM Divine, Thy grace we claim
      While thus Thy precious Death we show ;
     Once offer'd up, a spotless Lamb,
     In Thy great temple here below,
cr   Thou didst for all mankind atone,
mf   And standest now before the Throne.

     Thou standest in the holiest place,
     As now for guilty sinners slain ;
     Thy Blood of sprinkling speaks and prays
     All-prevalent for helpless man ;
p   Thy Blood is still our ransom found,
cr   And spreads salvation all around.

     GOD still respects Thy sacrifice,
     Its savour sweet doth always please ;
     The Offering smokes through earth and skies,
     Diffusing life and joy and peace ;
     To these Thy lower courts it comes,
     And fills them with Divine perfumes.

cr   We need not now go up to Heav'n
     To bring the long-sought SAVIOUR down ;
     Thou art to all that seek Thee given,
     Thou dost e'en now Thy banquet crown :
p   To every faithful soul appear,
mf   And show Thy Real Presence here.

                        C. WESLEY, 1745.

Holy Communion.

Hymn 556. DAS NEU GEBORNE KINDELEIN.—8 8 8 8.8 8. *(Second Tune.)*

M. VULPIUS, 1609.

A - men.

" The Blood of sprinkling which speaketh."

p VICTIM Divine, Thy grace we claim
    While thus Thy precious Death we show ;
Once offer'd up, a spotless Lamb,
In Thy great temple here below,
cr Thou didst for all mankind atone,
mf And standest now before the Throne.

Thou standest in the holiest place,
As now for guilty sinners slain ;
Thy Blood of sprinkling speaks and prays
All-prevalent for helpless man ;
p Thy Blood is still our ransom found,
cr And spreads salvation all around.

GOD still respects Thy sacrifice,
Its savour sweet doth always please ;
The Offering smokes through earth and skies,
Diffusing life and joy and peace ;
To these Thy lower courts it comes,
And fills them with Divine perfumes.

cr We need not now go up to Heav'n
To bring the long-sought SAVIOUR down ;
Thou art to all that seek Thee given,
Thou dost e'en now Thy banquet crown :
p To every faithful soul appear,
mf And show Thy Real Presence here.

C. WESLEY, 1745.

(484)

Holy Communion.

Hymn 557. Ave verum Corpus.—D.C.M. *(First Tune.)* W. H. Monk.

A - men.

" The Body and Blood of the Lord."

mp   HAIL, Body true, of Mary born, and in the manger laid,
       That once with thorn and scourging torn wast on the Cross display'd,
p   That every eye might there descry th' uplifted Sacrifice,
mf   Which once for all to GOD on high paid our redemption's price!

     Hail, precious Blood, by true descent drawn from our own first sire,
     Yet innocent of that fell taint which fills our veins with fire,
     Once from the side of Him that died for love of us His kin
     Drain'd an atonement to provide and wash away our sin!

     Still Thou art there amidst us, LORD, unchangeably the same,
     When at Thy board with one accord Thy promises we claim;
     But lo! the way Thou com'st to-day is one where bread and wine
     Conceal the Presence they convey, both human and Divine.

cr   How glorious is that Body now, throned on the Throne of Heav'n,
dim   The Angels bow, and marvel how to us on earth 'tis given;
mf   Oh, to discern what splendours burn within these veils of His,—
     That faith could into vision turn, and see Him as He is!

     How mighty is the Blood that ran for sinful nature's needs!
cr   It broke the ban, it rescued man; it lives, and speaks, and pleads;
     And all who sup from this blest Cup in faith and hope and love,
f   Shall prove that death is swallow'd up in richer life above.

A. J. MASON.

(485)

Holy Communion.

Hymn 557. OLD 81ST.—D.C.M. *(Second Tune.)*   DAY, *Psalms*, 1563.

A - men.

A Version of this Tune in Triple time is given at Hymn 439 (First Tune).

"The Body and Blood of the Lord."

mp HAIL, Body true, of Mary born, and in the manger laid,
        That once with thorn and scourging torn wast on the Cross display'd,
p That every eye might there descry th' uplifted Sacrifice,
mf Which once for all to GOD on high paid our redemption's price!

Hail, precious Blood, by true descent drawn from our own first sire,
Yet innocent of that fell taint which fills our veins with fire,
Once from the side of Him that died for love of us His kin
Drain'd an atonement to provide and wash away our sin!

Still Thou art there amidst us, LORD, unchangeably the same,
When at Thy board with one accord Thy promises we claim;
But lo! the way Thou com'st to-day is one where bread and wine
Conceal the Presence they convey, both human and Divine.

cr How glorious is that Body now, throned on the Throne of Heav'n!
dim The Angels bow, and marvel how to us on earth 'tis given;
mf Oh, to discern what splendours burn within these veils of His,—
That faith could into vision turn, and see Him as He is!

How mighty is the Blood that ran for sinful nature's needs!
cr It broke the ban, it rescued man; it lives, and speaks, and pleads;
And all who sup from this blest Cup in faith and hope and love,
f Shall prove that death is swallow'd up in richer life above.

A. J. MASON.

Hymn 558. WELLS.—L.M. *(First Tune.)*   W. H. MONK.

Holy Communion.

A - men.

Hymn 558. O Jesu Christ.—L.M. *(Second Tune.)* P. Reinigius, 1587.

Slow.

A-men.

"Thanks be to God for His unspeakable gift."

mf O JESU, Blessèd LORD, to Thee
　　My heartfelt thanks for ever be,
Who hast so lovingly bestow'd
On me Thy Body and Thy Blood.

f Break forth, my soul, for joy, and say,
　　What wealth is come to me to-day!
p My SAVIOUR dwells within me now;
cr How blest am I! (*p*) how good art Thou!

A. J. Mason: from the
Danish of T. Kingo.

Hymn 559. Communio.—10 10. C. Bucknall.

A-men.

"They took knowledge of them, that they had been with Jesus."

mp O CHRIST, our GOD, Who with Thine own hast been,
　　Our spirits cleave to Thee, the Friend unseen.

Vouchsafe that all who on Thy bounty feed
May heed Thy Love, and prize Thy gifts indeed.

Make every heart that is Thy dwelling-place
A water'd garden fill'd with fruits of grace.

p Each holy purpose help us to fulfil;
Increase our faith to feed upon Thee still.

cr Illuminate our minds, that we may see
In all around us holy signs of Thee.

And may such witness in our lives appear,
That all may know Thou hast been with us here.

p O grant us peace, that by Thy peace possess'd,
Thy life within us we may manifest.

cr So shall we pass our days in holy fear,
In joyful consciousness that Thou art near.

mf So shalt Thou be for ever, loving LORD,
Our Shield and our exceeding great Reward.

C. H. Bourne.

Alternative Tunes, Hymn 313 (First and Second Tunes).

(487)

Holy Communion.

Hymn 560. St. Flavian.—C.M.

Psalmes, 1562.

A - men.

" The Lord shall give Thee rest."

FOR GATHERINGS OF CLERGY OR CHURCH-WORKERS.

mp WITH weary feet and sadden'd heart,
From toil and care we flee,
p And come, O dearest LORD, apart
To rest awhile with Thee.

The courts of Heav'n were lost to view,
The world had come between ;
cr But here the veil is rent in two ;
We see the things unseen.

p Our sins, in Thy pure light descried,
Stand out in dread array ;

cr But here in Love's absolving tide
Their guilt is wash'd away.

p With strife of tongues distraught and worn
Our troublous way we trod ;
But cast ourselves, this holy morn,
Into the peace of GOD.

mf And oh ! what depth of joy, as thus
We bend the trembling knee,
To know that Thou art one with us,
And we are one with Thee.

Bishop W. WALSHAM HOW.

The following Hymns are suitable :

520 Love Divine, all loves excelling.　　　**528** Not for our sins alone.

Holy Baptism.

Hymn 561. HEMSFORD.—C.M.

G. F. COBB.

A - men.

" Buried with Him in baptism, wherein also ye are risen with Him."

p WITH CHRIST we share a mystic grave,
With CHRIST we buried lie ;
But 'tis not in the darksome cave
By mournful Calvary.

The pure and bright baptismal flood
Entombs our nature's stain :
cr New creatures from the cleansing wave
With CHRIST we rise again.

Thrice blest, if through this world of strife,
And sin, and selfish care,
Our snow-white robe of righteousness
We undefilèd wear.

mf Thrice blest, if through the gate of death
All glorious and free
f We to our joyful rising pass,
O risen LORD, with Thee.

J. M. NEALE.

ALTERNATIVE TUNE, HYMN 189.

(488)

Holy Baptism.

Hymn 562. ST. KENELM.—7 6 7 6.7 6 7 6.   C. STEGGALL.

"Baptizing them in the Name of the Father, and of the Son, and of the Holy Ghost."

mf   O FATHER, bless the children
       Brought hither to Thy gate ;
    Lift up their fallen nature,
      Restore their lost estate ;
    Renew Thine image in them,
      And own them, by this sign,
    Thy very sons and daughters,
dim   New born of birth Divine.

mf   O JESU LORD, receive them ;
      Thy loving Arms of old
    Were open'd wide to welcome
      The children to Thy fold ;
p   Let these, baptized, and dying,
cr   Then rising from the dead,
f   Henceforth be living members
      Of Thee, their living Head.

p   O HOLY SPIRIT, keep them ;
      Dwell with them to the last,
    Till all the fight is ended,
      And all the storms are past.
cr   Renew the gift baptismal,
      From strength to strength, till each
mf   The troublous waves o'ercoming,
      The land of life shall reach.

    O FATHER, SON, and SPIRIT,
      O Wisdom, Love, and Power,
    We wait the promised blessing
      In this accepted hour !
p   We name upon the children
      The Threefold Name Divine ;
cr   Receive them, cleanse them, own them,
mf   And keep them ever Thine.

                    J. ELLERTON.

ALTERNATIVE TUNES, HYMNS 321, 341.

Holy Baptism.

Hymn 563. HOWLEY PLACE.—7 6 7 6. 7 7 7 6.   C. E. STEPHENS.

A - men.

"*If any man be in Christ, he is a new creature.*"

FOR AN ADULT.

p   FATHER, SON, and HOLY GHOST,
          In solemn power come down,
     Present with Thy heavenly host
cr   Thy Sacrament to crown :
     See a sinful child of earth ;
        Bless for *him* the cleansing flood ;
     Make *him* by a second birth
mf   One with the life of GOD.

p   Let the promised inward grace
         Accompany the sign,
      On *his* new-born soul impress
         The glorious Name Divine ;
cr FATHER, all Thy love reveal,
         JESUS, all Thy mind impart,
mf HOLY GHOST, renew, and dwell
         For ever in *his* heart.

C. WESLEY, 1749.

The following Hymn is suitable :
487 The Son of Man from Jordan rose.

For the Young.

Hymn 564. MOSELEY.—6 6 6 6.   H. SMART.

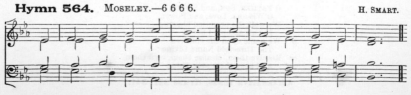

For the Young.

A - men.

"Now therefore, our God, we thank Thee, and praise Thy glorious Name."

SUNDAY EVENING.

mf AND now this holy day
Is drawing to its end,
Once more, to Thee, O LORD,
Our thanks and prayers we send.

We thank Thee for this rest
From earthly care and strife ;
We thank Thee for this help
To higher, holier life.

We thank Thee for Thy House ;
It is Thy Palace-gate
Where Thou, upon Thy Throne
Of mercy, still dost wait.

We thank Thee for Thy Word,
Thy Gospel's joyful sound ;

Oh, may its holy fruits
Within our hearts abound !

dim Yet, ere we go to rest,
FATHER, to Thee we pray,
Forgive the sins that stain
E'en this Thy holy day.

Through JESUS let the past
Be blotted from Thy sight,
And let us all now sleep

p At peace with Thee this night.

f To GOD the FATHER, SON,
And SPIRIT glory be,
From all in earth and Heav'n,
Through all eternity.

E. HARLAND.

Hymn 565. UP IN HEAVEN.—8 7 7 7 5.

FOR TREBLE VOICES ONLY. *(Not to be sung in Harmony.)*   Sir J. STAINER.

Up in Hea-ven, up in Hea-ven, In the bright place far a-way, He Whom

mf   *cres.*   *dim.*

bad men cru-ci-fied, Sit-teth at His Fa-ther's side, Till the Judg-ment Day. A-men.

cres.   *dim.*

"The Son of Man shall come in His Glory, and all the holy Angels with Him."

mf UP in Heaven, up in Heaven,
In the bright place far away,
He Whom bad men crucified,
Sitteth at His Father's side,
Till the Judgment Day.

And He loves His little children,
And He pleadeth for them there,
Asking the great GOD of Heav'n
dim That their sins may be forgiven,
And He hears their prayer.

cr Never more a helpless Baby,
Born in poverty and pain,
mf But with awful glory crown'd,
With His Angels standing round,
He shall come again.

Then the wicked souls shall tremble,
And the good souls shall rejoice ;
Parents, children, every one,
Then shall stand before His Throne,
And shall hear His voice.

cr And all faithful holy Christians,
Who their Master's work have done,
Shall appear at His right hand
And inherit the fair land
That His love has won.

MRS. ALEXANDER.

For the Young.

Hymn 566. BONAR.—D.S.M.

C. STEGGALL.

A - men.

* *If considered desirable, this Chord* * *may be omitted in Verses 1 and 2; and this* † *divided into two crotchets.*

" Partakers of the Divine nature."

mf　MEMBERS of CHRIST are we ;
　　　He is our living Head,
dim　That henceforth we should ever be
　　By His good SPIRIT led
　　In the same narrow path
　　Our LORD and SAVIOUR trod—
　　The path that leadeth by the Cross
cr　　To glory and to GOD.

mf　Children of GOD are we ;
　　Such grace to us is given,
　　To kneel and pray in CHRIST'S own words,
　　" FATHER, Which art in Heav'n ;"
　　Seeking to do His will
　　As Angels do above,
　　And walking in obedient ways
　　Of holy truth and love.

　　Of Heaven's kingdom we
　　Inheritors were made ;
　　Each at the Font in CHRIST'S own robe
　　Of spotless white array'd.
dim　Upon our forehead now
　　Is traced the suffering sign,
cr　That one day on each saintly brow
　　A glorious crown may shine.

mf　CHRIST'S little ones are we ;
　　And unto us are given
　　Angelic guards, who ever see
　　Our FATHER'S face in Heav'n.
p　　To walk in folly now
　　We may not, must not, dare,
cr　Mindful Whose seal is on our brow,
　　Whose holy Name we bear.

I. WILLIAMS.

ALTERNATIVE TUNE, HYMN 304.

For the Young.

" It shall be well with them that fear God."

mp   O MY GOD, I fear Thee \
     Thou art very high,
cr   Yet to us, Thy children,
     Thou art always nigh,
   Far removed from mortal sight,
   Dwelling in eternal light.

p   O my GOD, I fear Thee !
     Yet I come in prayer,
   For my SAVIOUR tells me
     I need not despair ;
cr   Tells me of a FATHER'S love,
   And a home prepared above.

Never earthly father
     Loveth like to Thee ;
Thou dost guide and pardon
     Guilty ones like me ;
Sending down Thy Holy SON
That all sinners might be won.

mp   O my GOD, I fear Thee,
     Holy, just, and true ;
cr   But, my Heavenly FATHER,
     I will love Thee too ;
Guide me till this life be past,
Take me to Thyself at last.

Mrs. DOBREE.

A higher setting of this Tune is given at Hymn 38.

" Looking unto Jesus."

mf   LAMB of GOD, I look to Thee,
     Thou shalt my example be :
Thou art gentle, meek, and mild,
Thou wast once a little child.

Fain I would be as Thou art ;
Give me Thy obedient heart ;
dim Thou art pitiful and kind,
   Let me have Thy loving mind.

Meek and lowly may I be ;
Thou art all humility :
Let me to my betters bow,
Subject to Thy parents Thou.

mf   Let me above all fulfil
GOD my Heavenly Father's will ;

Never His good SPIRIT grieve,
Only to His glory live.

Thou didst live to GOD alone,
Thou didst never seek Thine own,
Thou Thyself didst never please,
GOD was all Thy happiness.

p   Loving JESU, gentle Lamb,
   In Thy gracious Hands I am ;
   Make me, SAVIOUR, what Thou art ;
cr   Live Thyself within my heart.

mf   I shall then show forth Thy praise,
   Serve Thee all my happy days ;
   Then the world shall always see
   CHRIST, the Holy Child, in me.

C. WESLEY, 1742.

For the Young.

Hymn 569. GERMAN.—6 5 6 5. *(First Tune.)* German.

A-men.

Hymn 569. NEWLAND.—6 5 6 5. *(Second Tune.)* Rev. J. ARMSTRONG.

A-men.

" Cease to do evil, learn to do well."

mf DO no sinful action,
    Speak no angry word ;
Ye belong to JESUS,
    Children of the LORD.

CHRIST is kind and gentle,
    CHRIST is pure and true ;
dim And His little children
    Must be holy too.

There's a wicked spirit
    Watching round you still,
And he tries to tempt you
    To all harm and ill.

cr But ye must not hear him,
    Though 'tis hard for you

To resist the evil,
    And the good to do.

mf For ye promised truly,
    In your infant days,
To renounce him wholly,
    And forsake his ways.

Ye are new-born Christians,
    Ye must learn to fight
With the bad within you,
    And to do the right.

CHRIST is your own Master,
    He is good and true,
And His little children
    Must be holy too.

Mrs. ALEXANDER.

Hymn 570. ST. FAITH.—7 5 7 5.7 7. Sir G. C. MARTIN.

A-men.

" Thine eyes shall see the King in His beauty ; they shall behold the land that is very far off."

mf EVERY morning the red sun
    Rises warm and bright ;
dim But the evening cometh on,
    And the dark, cold night.

cr There's a bright land far away,
    Where 'tis never-ending day.

mf Every spring the sweet young flowers
    Open bright and gay,
din Till the chilly autumn hours
    Wither them away.

cr There's a land we have not seen,
    Where the trees are always green.

mf Little birds sing songs of praise
    All the summer long,
dim But in colder, shorter days

They forget their song.

cr There's a place where Angels sing
    Ceaseless praises to their King.

mf CHRIST our LORD is ever near
    Those who follow Him ;
dim But we cannot see Him here,
    For our eyes are dim ;

cr There is a most happy place,
    Where men always see His face.

p Who shall go to that bright land ?
cr All who do the right :
mf Holy children there shall stand
    In their robes of white ;
For that Heav'n, so bright and blest,
dim Is our everlasting rest.

Mrs. ALEXANDER.

For the Young.

Hymn 571. Hill Cliff.—C.M.   Rev. W. Statham.

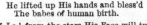

"To Him that is able to keep you from falling."

mf SING to the LORD the children's hymn,
His gentle love declare,
Who bends amid the Seraphim
To hear the children's prayer.

p He at a mother's breast was fed,
Though GOD's own SON was He ;
He learnt the first small words He said
At a meek mother's knee.

cr Close to His loving Heart He press'd
The children of the earth ;
He lifted up His hands and bless'd
The babes of human birth.

mf Lo ! from the stars His Face will turn
On us with glances mild ;
The Angels of His Presence yearn
To bless the little child.

mp Keep us, O JESUS, LORD, for Thee,
That so, by Thy dear grace,
We, children of the Font, may see
Our Heavenly FATHER's face.

R. S. Hawker.

ALTERNATIVE TUNE, HYMN 328.

Hymn 572. St. Leonard.—C.M.   H. Smart.

A higher setting of this Tune is given at Hymn 278.

" God who helpeth us, and poureth His benefits upon us."

mf LORD, I would own Thy tender care,
And all Thy love to me ;
The food I eat, the clothes I wear,
Are all bestow'd by Thee.

'Tis Thou preservest me from death
And dangers every hour ;
p I cannot draw another breath
cr Unless Thou give me power.

Kind Angels guard me every night,
As round my bed they stay :

Nor am I absent from Thy sight
In darkness or by day.

My health, and friends, and parents dear,
To me by GOD are given ;
I have not any blessing here
But what is sent from Heav'n.

mf Such goodness, LORD, and constant care
I never can repay ;
But may it be my daily prayer,
To love Thee and obey.

JANE TAYLOR, 1809.

For the Young.

Hymn 573. ALL THINGS BRIGHT AND BEAUTIFUL.—7 6 7 6.7 6 7 6.

Verse 1, and the Refrain after Verses 2, 3, 4, 5, 6, 7.

W. H. MONK.

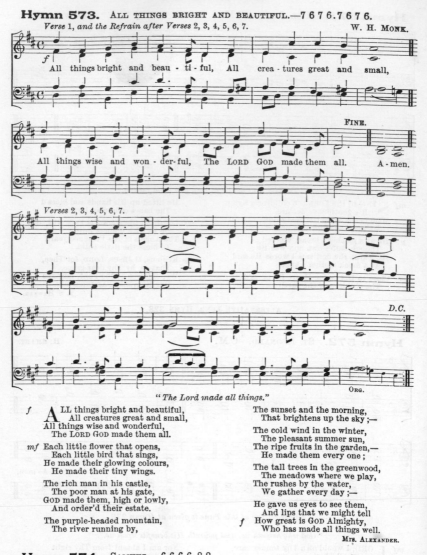

"The Lord made all things."

f ALL things bright and beautiful,
    All creatures great and small,
All things wise and wonderful,
    The LORD GOD made them all.

mf Each little flower that opens,
    Each little bird that sings,
He made their glowing colours,
    He made their tiny wings.

The rich man in his castle,
    The poor man at his gate,
GOD made them, high or lowly,
    And order'd their estate.

The purple-headed mountain,
    The river running by,

The sunset and the morning,
    That brightens up the sky ;—

The cold wind in the winter,
    The pleasant summer sun,
The ripe fruits in the garden,—
    He made them every one ;

The tall trees in the greenwood,
    The meadows where we play,
The rushes by the water,
    We gather every day ;—

He gave us eyes to see them,
    And lips that we might tell
f How great is GOD Almighty,
    Who has made all things well.

MRS. ALEXANDER.

Hymn 574. SAMUEL.—6 6 6 6.8 8.

W. H. MONK.

For the Young.

A-men.

" Speak, Lord, for Thy servant heareth."

mp HUSH'D was the evening hymn,
    The temple courts were dark;
dim The lamp was burning dim
    Before the sacred ark;
mf When suddenly a Voice Divine
    Rang through the silence of the shrine.

p The old man, meek and mild,
    The priest of Israel, slept;
    His watch the Temple child,
    The little Levite, kept;
cr And what from Eli's sense was seal'd
    The LORD to Hannah's son reveal'd.

p Oh ! give me Samuel's ear,
    The open ear, O LORD,
cr Alive and quick to hear

    Each whisper of Thy word ;
    Like him to answer at Thy call,
    And to obey Thee first of all.

p Oh ! give me Samuel's heart,
    A lowly heart, that waits
    Where in Thy house Thou art,
    Or watches at Thy gates,
cr By day and night, a heart that still
    Moves at the breathing of Thy will.

p Oh ! give me Samuel's mind,
    A sweet unmurmuring faith,
    Obedient and resign'd
    To Thee in life and death ;
cr That I may read with child-like eyes
mf Truths that are hidden from the wise.

J. D. BURNS.

Every verse after the first begins thus:

Hymn 575. ST. ETHELDREDA.—C.M.

Bishop TURTON, 1860.

A-men.

" Thy brother shall rise again."

p WITHIN the churchyard, side by side,
    Are many long low graves ;
    And some have stones set over them,
    On some the green grass waves.

Full many a little Christian child,
    Woman, and man, lies there ;
    And we pass near them every time
    When we go in to prayer.

They cannot hear our footsteps come,
    They do not see us pass ;
    They cannot feel the warm bright sun
    That shines upon the grass.

cr They do not hear when the great bell
    Is ringing overhead ;
    They cannot rise and come to Church
dim With us, for they are dead.

    But we believe a day shall come
cr When all the dead will rise,
    When they who sleep down in the grave
    Will ope again their eyes.

    For CHRIST our LORD was buried once,
mf He died and rose again,
    He conquer'd death, He left the grave ;
dim And so will Christian men.

mp So when the friends we love the best
    Lie in their churchyard bed,
    We must not cry too bitterly
    Over the happy dead ;

cr Because, for our dear SAVIOUR'S sake,
    Our sins are all forgiven ;
    And Christians only fall asleep
inf To wake again in Heav'n.

Mrs. ALEXANDER.

For School and College Use.

Hymn 576. CLIFTON COLLEGE.—8 7 8 7. 4 7.   Sir H. OAKELEY.

A-men.

"The fear of the Lord, that is wisdom; and to depart from evil is understanding."
BEGINNING OF TERM.

mf LORD, behold us with Thy blessing
        Once again assembled here;
    Onward be our footsteps pressing
        In Thy love, and faith, and fear;
dim   Still protect us
cr   By Thy Presence ever near.

mf For Thy mercy we adore Thee,
        For this rest upon our way;
p   LORD, again we bow before Thee,
        Speed our labours day by day;
cr   Mind and spirit
    With Thy choicest gifts array.

mf Keep the spell of home affection
        Still alive in every heart;
    May its power, with mild direction,
    Draw our love from self apart,
        Till Thy children
    Feel that Thou their Father art.

    Break temptation's fatal power,
        Shielding all with guardian care,
    Safe in every careless hour,
    Safe from sloth and sensual snare;
        Thou, our SAVIOUR,
    Still our failing strength repair.

H. J. BUCKOLL.

This Tune and that of Hymn 577 are interchangeable.

Hymn 577. ETON COLLEGE.—8 7 8 7. 4 7.   Sir J. BARNBY.

cres.   *dim.*

A-men.

END OF TERM.   *"Stablish the thing, O God, that Thou hast wrought in us."*

mf LORD, dismiss us with Thy blessing,
        Thanks for mercies past receive;
dim Pardon all, their faults confessing;
        Time that's lost may all retrieve;
cr   May Thy children
    Ne'er again Thy SPIRIT grieve.

mf Bless Thou all our days of leisure;
        Help us selfish lures to flee;
    Sanctify our every pleasure;
        Pure and blameless may it be;
        May our gladness
    Draw us evermore to Thee.

    By Thy kindly influence cherish
        All the good we here have gain'd;
    May all taint of evil perish
        By Thy mightier power restrain'd;
        Seek we ever
    Knowledge pure and love unfeign'd.

    Let Thy father-hand be shielding
        All who here shall meet no more;
    May their seed-time past be yielding
        Year by year a richer store;
        Those returning,
    Make more faithful than before.

H. J. BUCKOLL.

This Tune and that of Hymn 576 are interchangeable.

(498)

Holy Matrimony.

Hymn 578. LIFE AND LOVE.—11 10 11 10. W. H. MONK.

A-men.

"The Lord do so to me and more also, if ought but death part thee and me."

mf O PERFECT Love, all human thought transcending,
p Lowly we kneel in prayer before Thy Throne,
cr That theirs may be the love which knows no ending,
    Whom Thou for evermore dost join in one.

O perfect Life, be Thou their full assurance
Of tender charity and steadfast faith,
Of patient hope, and quiet brave endurance,
With childlike trust that fears nor pain nor death.

Grant them the joy which brightens earthly sorrow,
p Grant them the peace which calms all earthly strife ;
mf And to life's day the glorious unknown morrow
    That dawns upon eternal love and life.

Mrs. GURNEY.

ALTERNATIVE TUNE, HYMN 12.

Hymn 579. GENESIS.—7 6 7 6. 7 6 7 6. G. M. GARRETT.

A men.

"Except the Lord build the house, their labour is but lost that build it."

mf O FATHER all creating,
    Whose wisdom, love, and power
First bound two lives together
    In Eden's primal hour,
dim To-day, to these Thy children
    Thine earliest gifts renew,—
cr A home by Thee made happy,
    A love by Thee kept true.

mp O SAVIOUR, Guest most bounteous
    Of old in Galilee,
Vouchsafe to-day Thy presence
    With these who call on Thee ;
cr Their store of earthly gladness
    Transform to heavenly wine,
And teach them, in the tasting,
    To know the gift is Thine.

mp O SPIRIT of the FATHER,
    Breathe on them from above,
So mighty in Thy pureness,
    So tender in Thy love ;
cr That guarded by Thy presence,
    From sin and strife kept free,
Their lives may own Thy guidance,
    Their hearts be ruled by Thee.

mf Except Thou build it, FATHER,
    The house is built in vain ;
Except Thou, SAVIOUR, bless it,
    The joy will turn to pain ;
But nought can break the marriage
    Of hearts in Thee made one,
And love Thy SPIRIT hallows
    Is endless love begun.

J. ELLERTON.

ALTERNATIVE TUNE, HYMN 500 (SECOND TUNE).

For a Teachers' Meeting.

Hymn 580. LAUSANNE.—6 6 6 6.6 6 6 6.   *Lausanne Chorale Book.*

A-men.

"The word that I shall speak unto thee, that thou shalt speak."

mf SHINE Thou upon us, LORD,
　True Light of men, to-day;
And through the written word
　Thy very self display;
That so from hearts which burn
　With gazing on Thy Face,
The little ones may learn
　The wonders of Thy grace.

mp Breathe Thou upon us, LORD,
　Thy Spirit's living Flame,
cr That so with one accord
　Our lips may tell Thy Name;
Give Thou the hearing ear,
　Fix Thou the wandering thought,
That those we teach may hear
　The great things Thou hast wrought.

mf Speak Thou for us, O LORD,
　In all we say of Thee;
According to Thy Word
　Let all our teaching be;
That so Thy lambs may know
　Their own true Shepherd's voice,
Where'er He leads them go,
cr And in His love rejoice.

mf Live Thou within us, LORD;
　Thy mind and will be ours;
Be Thou beloved, adored,
　And served, with all our powers;
That so our lives may teach
　Thy children what Thou art,
dim And plead, by more than speech,
　For Thee with every heart.

J. ELLERTON.

ALTERNATIVE TUNE, HYMN 230.

For Theological Colleges.

Hymn 581. ORIEL.—8 7 8 7 8 7. ETT, *Cantica Sacra*, 1840.

A lower setting of this Tune is given at Hymn 396.

"Also I heard the voice of the Lord, saying, Whom shall I send, and who will go for us?
Then said I, Here am I; send me."

mf   L̲ORD of life, Prophetic SPIRIT,
     In sweet measure evermore
  To the holy children dealing
     Each his gift from Thy rich store ;
p   Bless Thy family, adoring
cr   As in Israel's schools of yore.

  Holy JESUS, Eye most loving
     On each young disciple bent ;
  Voice that, seeming earthly, summon'd
     Samuel to the awful tent ;
  Hand that cast Elijah's mantle ;
     Thine be all Thy Grace hath lent.

mf   As to Thine own seventy scholars
     Thou of old Thine Arm didst reach,
  Under Thy majestic shadow
     Guiding them to do and teach,
  Till their hour of solemn unction ;
dim   So be with us all and each.

mf   GOD and FATHER of all Spirits,
     Whose dread call young Joshua knew,
*dim*Forty days in darkness waiting
     With Thy servant good and true,
cr   Thence to wage Thy war descending,
     Own us, LORD, Thy champions too.

  One Thy Light, the Temple filling,
     Holy, Holy, Holy, Three :
  Meanest men and brightest Angels
     Wait alike the word from Thee ;
  Highest musings, lowliest worship,
     Must their preparation be.

p   Now Thou speakest—hear we trembling—
     From the glory comes a Voice.
  Who accepts th' Almighty's mission ?
     Who will make CHRIST'S work his choice ?
  Who for Us proclaim to sinners,
     Turn, believe, endure, rejoice?

cr   Here are we, REDEEMER, send us !
dim   But because Thy work is fire,
     And our lips, unclean and earthly,
     Breathe no breath of high desire ;
or   Send Thy Seraph from the Altar
     Veil'd, but in his bright attire.

mf   Cause him, LORD, to fly full swiftly
     With the mystic coal in hand,
  Sin-consuming, soul-transforming
dim   (Faith and love will understand);
  Touch our lips, Thou awful Mercy,
     With Thine own keen healing brand.

mf   Thou didst come that fire to kindle ;
     Fain would we Thy torches prove,
  Far and wide Thy beacons lighting
     With the undying spark of love :
*dim*Only feed our flame, we pray Thee,
     With Thy breathings from above.

f   Now to GOD, the soul's Creator,
     To His WORD and Wisdom sure,
  To His all-enlightening SPIRIT,
     Patron of the frail and poor,
  THREE in ONE, be praise and glory
     Here and while the Heav'ns endure.

J. KEBLE.

If the Hymn be thought too long, it may be divided at the end of Stanza 4.

For Theological Colleges.

Hymn 582. MACFARREN.—D.C.M.

Sir G. A. MACFARREN.

A - men.

"Make full proof of thy ministry."

mf THOU, Who didst call Thy Saints of old
  Thy chosen flock to teach,
Who mad'st the fearful-hearted bold,
  And quick the slow of speech ;
Still Thou dost ask whom Thou shalt send
  And who will go for Thee,
To feed Thy lambs, Thy sheep to tend ;
  "LORD, here am I ; send me."

 O send us—e'en as Thou, O LORD,
  Wast by the FATHER sent—
p To speak Thine own absolving word
  To sinners penitent ;
To wash Thy chosen in the flood
  Whereby new birth is given ;
cr To minister the sacred Food,
  The Bread of Life from Heav'n.

mf And Thou, Who didst by prophets deign
  To speak the will Divine,
That we may never speak in vain,
  May all our words be Thine ;
p Oh, teach us, HOLY GHOST, that we
  Thine heritage may teach ;
cr Bid us to prophesy for Thee,
  And in Thy power to preach.

mf So may we, though unworthy still,
  Most HOLY TRINITY,
Thy prophets, pastors, priests, fulfil
  Our sacred ministry :
p That, when beside the crystal sea
  We lay our office down,
cr The souls that we have train'd for Thee
f   May be our joy and crown.

E. A. WELCH.

ALTERNATIVE TUNE, HYMN 375.

(502)

For Church Workers and Guilds.

Hymn 583. St. Croix.—7 6 7 6. 7 6 7 6.

G. M. Garrett.

A-men.

" Stand fast in one spirit, striving together for the faith of the Gospel."

mf THE call to arms is sounding,
The foemen muster strong,
dim While Saints beneath the Altar
Are crying "LORD, how long?"
mf The living and the loving
CHRIST'S royal Standard raise,
And marching on to conflict
Shout forth their Captain's praise.

No time for self-indulgence,
For resting by the way ;
dim Repose will come at even,
But toil is for the day :
Work, like the blessèd JESUS,
Who from His earliest youth
Would do His FATHER'S business
And witness for the truth.

mf For the one Faith, the true Faith,
The Faith which cannot fail,
For the one Church, the true Church,
'Gainst which no foes prevail ;

Made one with GOD Incarnate,
We in His might must win
The glory of self-conquest,
Of victory over sin.

f Behold ! upon Mount Sion
A glorious people stand,
A crown on every forehead,
A palm in every hand ;
p Lo ! these are they who boldly
The Name of CHRIST confess'd,
f And now triumphant praise Him
In Heav'n's unresting rest.

p O JESU ! Who art waiting
Thy faithful ones to crown,
Vouchsafe to bless our conflict,
mf Our loving service own ;
Come in each heart for ever
cr As King adored to reign,
Till we with Saints triumphant
Uplift the victor strain.

Mrs. Hernaman.

Alternative Tune, Hymn 667.

For a Service for Working Men.

Hymn 584. Sons of Labour.—8 7 8 7. 8 7 8 7.　　　　Sir J. STAINER.

A-men.

" Do all in the Name of the Lord Jesus."

mf SONS of Labour, dear to JESUS,
　　To your homes and work again ;
cr　Go with brave hearts back to duty,
dim　Face the peril, bear the pain.
p　Be your dwellings ne'er so lowly,
cr　　Yet remember, by your bed,
mf　That the SON of GOD most Holy
dim　Had not where to lay His head.

mf Sons of Labour, think of JESUS
　　As you rest your homes within,
*dim*Think of that sweet Babe of Mary
　　In the stable of the Inn.
　　Think how in the sacred story
　　　JESUS took a humble grade,
mf　And the LORD of Life and Glory
dim　Work'd with Joseph at his trade.

mf Sons of Labour, pray to JESUS,
dim　Oh, how JESUS pray'd for you !
　　In the moonlight, on the mountain,
　　Where the shimmering olives grew.
cr　When you rise up at the dawning,
　　Ere in toil you wend your way,
　　Pray, as He pray'd, in the morning,
　　Long before the break of day.

mf Sons of Labour, be like JESUS,
　　Undefilèd, chaste, and pure ;
　　And, though Satan tempt you sorely,
　　By His grace you shall endure.

Husband, father, son, and brother,
　　Be ye gentle, just, and true,—
Be ye kind to one another,
　　As the LORD is kind to you.

Sons of Labour, seek for JESUS,
　　Where He tells you ye shall find,
*dim*In the children, 'mid the mourners,
　　In the sick, poor, lame, and blind,—
" Search the Scriptures," He entreats you,
　　" For of Me they testify ;"
Love His Altar, where He meets you,
p　　Saying, " Fear not—It is I."

mf Sons of Labour, go to JESUS,
dim　In your sorrow, shame, and loss ;
　　He is nearest, you are dearest,
cr　When you bravely bear His Cross.
　　Go to Him, Who died to save you,
　　And is still the sinner's Friend ;
　　And the great love, which forgave you,
dim　Will forgive you to the end.

mf Sons of Labour, live for JESUS,
　　Be your work your worship too ;
　　In His Name, and to His glory,
　　Do whate'er you find to do ;
　　Till this night of sin and sorrow
　　Be for ever overpast ;
f　And we see the golden morrow,
　　Home with JESUS, home at last !

S. R. HOLE.

ALTERNATIVE TUNE, HYMN 292 (FIRST TUNE).

(504)

Missions.

Hymn 585. STYALL.—L.M.   Rev. W. STATHAM.

A - men.

A lower setting of this Tune is given at Hymn 529.

" He shall testify of Me, and ye also shall bear witness."

mf O SPIRIT of the Living GOD!
In all the fulness of Thy grace,
Where'er the foot of man hath trod,
Descend on our apostate race.

Give tongues of fire and hearts of love
To preach the reconciling word;
Give power and unction from above,
Whene'er the joyful sound is heard.

Be darkness, at Thy coming, light,
Confusion order in Thy path;

Souls without strength inspire with might;
Bid mercy triumph over wrath.

mp O Spirit of the LORD! prepare
All the round earth her GOD to meet;
cr Breathe Thou abroad like morning air,
Till hearts of stone begin to beat.

mf Baptize the nations; far and nigh
The triumphs of the Cross record;
f The Name of JESUS glorify
Till every kindred call Him LORD.

J. MONTGOMERY, 1823.

ALTERNATIVE TUNE, HYMN 771.

Hymn 586. CRUCIS VICTORIA.—C.M.   M. B. FOSTER.

A - men.

" He shall set up an ensign for the nations."

mf LIFT up your heads, ye gates of brass;
Ye bars of iron, yield;
And let the King of Glory pass;
The Cross is in the field.

That banner, brighter than the star
That leads the train of night,
Shines on the march, and guides from far
His servants to the fight.

A holy war those servants wage;
In that mysterious strife,
The powers of Heav'n and hell engage
For more than death or life.

Ye armies of the living GOD,
Sworn warriors of CHRIST'S host,
Where hallow'd footsteps never trod,
Take your appointed post.

p Though few and small and weak your bands,
cr Strong in your Captain's strength,
Go to the conquest of all lands:
All must be His at length.

The spoils at His victorious Feet
You shall rejoice to lay,
And lay yourselves as trophies meet,
In His great judgment day.

mf Then fear not, faint not, halt not now;
In JESUS' Name be strong!
To Him shall all the nations bow,
And sing the triumph song:—

f Uplifted are the gates of brass,
The bars of iron yield;
Behold the King of Glory pass;
The Cross hath won the field.

J. MONTGOMERY, 1771-1854.

ALTERNATIVE TUNE, HYMN 557 (SECOND TUNE).

(505)

Thanksgiving for Missions.

Hymn 587. HARVEST.—10 10 7.

C. J. FROST.

A - men.

" Blessed be His glorious Name for ever, and let the whole earth be filled with His glory ;
Amen and Amen."

mf LORD of the harvest ! it is right and meet
　　That we should lay our first-fruits at Thy feet
　　　　With joyful Alleluia.

Sweet is the soul's thanksgiving after prayer ;
Sweet is the worship that with Heav'n we share,
　　Who sing the Alleluia !

p Lowly we prayed, *(cr)* and Thou didst hear on high—
mf Didst lift our hearts and change our suppliant cry
　　　　To festal Alleluia.

So sing we now in tune with that great song,
That all the age of ages shall prolong,
　　The endless Alleluia.

To Thee, O LORD of Harvest, Who hast heard,
And to Thy white-robed reapers given the word,
　　We sing our Alleluia.

dim O CHRIST, Who in the wide world's ghostly sea
cr Hast bid the net be cast anew, to Thee
　　　　We sing our Alleluia.

To Thee, Eternal SPIRIT, Who again
Hast moved with life upon the slumbrous main,
　　We sing our Alleluia.

cr Yea, West and East the companies go forth :
f "We come !" is sounding to the South and North :
　　　　To GOD sing Alleluia.

p The fishermen of JESUS far away
Seek in new waters an immortal prey :
　　　　mf To CHRIST sing Alleluia.

p The Holy Dove is brooding o'er the deep,
And careless hearts are waking out of sleep ;
　　　　mf To Him sing Alleluia.

Yea, for sweet hope new-born—blest work begun—
Sing Alleluia to the THREE in ONE,
　　　　Adoring Alleluia.

f Glory to GOD ! the Church in patience cries ;
Glory to GOD ! the Church at rest replies,
　　　　With endless Alleluia.

S. J. STONE.

Home Missions.

Hymn 588. CRUCIS MILITES.—7 7 7 7.

M. B. FOSTER.

Home Missions.

A-men.

"Take the sword of the Spirit, which is the word of God."

mf SOLDIERS of the Cross, arise !
 Gird you with your armour bright ;
cr Mighty are your enemies,
 Hard the battle ye must fight.

mf O'er a faithless fallen world
 Raise your banner in the sky ;
Let it float there wide unfurl'd ;
Bear it onward ; lift it high.

mp 'Mid the homes of want and woe,
 Strangers to the living word,
cr Let the SAVIOUR'S herald go,
 Let the voice of hope be heard.

p Where the shadows deepest lie,
cr Carry truth's unsullied ray ;

dim Where are crimes of blackest dye,
cr There the saving sign display.

mp To the weary and the worn
 Tell of realms where sorrows cease ;
To the outcast and forlorn
Speak of mercy and of peace.

Guard the helpless ; seek the stray'd ;
Comfort troubles, banish grief ;
In the might of GOD array'd,
Scatter sin and unbelief.

cr Be the banner still unfurl'd,
 Still unsheathed the SPIRIT'S sword,
f Till the kingdoms of the world
 Are the kingdom of the LORD.

Bishop W. WALSHAM HOW.

For a Service of Farewell to Missionaries or Emigrants.

W. H. MONK.

Hymn 589. VERBUM PACIS.—6 6 8 4.

A-men.

" The Lord of peace Himself give you peace always by all means."

p WITH the sweet word of Peace
  We bid our brethren go ;
Peace as a river to increase,
 And ceaseless flow.

 With the calm word of Prayer
 We earnestly commend
cr Our brethren to Thy watchful care,
 Eternal Friend !

mf With the dear word of Love
 We give our brief farewell ;
Our love below, and Thine above,
 With them shall dwell.

With the strong word of Faith
We stay ourselves on Thee,
That Thou, O LORD, in life and death,
 Their help shalt be ;

Then the bright word of Hope
Shall on our parting gleam,
And tell of joys beyond the scope
Of earth-born dream.

p Farewell ! in hope and love,
 In faith and peace and prayer ;
cr Till He Whose Home is ours above,
 mf Unite us there !

G. WATSON.

In verses 2, 4, 5, 6,—with a slur over the two following notes.

(507)

Missions to the Jews.

Hymn 590. SHIPLAKE.—10 10 10 10.

E. HULTON.

A-men.

" The gifts and calling of God are without repentance."

mf UNCHANGING GOD, hear from eternal Heav'n:
We plead Thy gifts of grace, for ever given,
Thy call, without repentance, calling still,
The sure election of Thy sovereign will.

Out of our faith in Thee, Who canst not lie,
Out of our heart's desire, goes up our cry,
From hope's sweet vision of the thing to be,
From love to those who still are loved by Thee.

p Bring Thy belovèd back, Thine Israel,
Thine own elect who from Thy favour fell,
But not from Thine election!—O forgive,
Speak but the word, and, lo! the dead shall live.

Father of mercies! these the long-astray,
These in soul-blindness now the far-away,
cr These are not aliens, but Thy sons of yore,
Oh, by Thy Fatherhood, restore, restore!

Breath on Thy Church, that it may greet the day,
Stir up her will to toil, and teach, and pray,
mf Till Zionward again salvation come,
And all her outcast children are at home.

Triune JEHOVAH, Thine the grace and power,
Thine all the work, its past, its future hour,
O Thou, Who failest not, Thy gifts fulfil,
And crown the calling of Thy changeless will.

S. J. STONE.

If the Hymn be thought too long, the first four stanzas may be sung.

ALTERNATIVE TUNE, HYMN 252.

Hymn 591. CULFORD.—7 7 7 7.7 7 7 7.

E. J. HOPKINS.

Missions to the Jews.

A-men.

" God is able to graft them in again."

mf THOU, The CHRIST for ever one,
Mary's Child and Israel's GOD,
Daniel's Prince and David's Son,
Jacob's Star and Jesse's Rod,
Thou of Whom the Prophets spake,
Thou in Whom their words came true,
Hear the pleading prayer we make,
Hear the Gentile for the Jew !

Knowing what the SPIRIT saith,
Sure of Thee, our CHRIST Divine,
Lo, we stand, by right of faith,
Heirs of Abraham's charter'd line ;
p Can we then his sons forget,
Branches sever'd from their tree,
Exiles from their homes, and yet
Kinsmen, LORD, in flesh to Thee ?

Though the Blood betray'd and spilt,
On the race entail'd a doom,
Let its virtue cleanse the guilt,
Melt the hardness, chase the gloom ;

cr Lift the veil from off their heart,
Make them Israelites indeed,
mf Meet once more for lot and part
With Thy household's genuine seed.

Thou that didst Thy dews outpour,
Crowning alien grafts with fruit,
Soon the native growths restore,
Making glad the parent root :
mp Ah ! but let not pride ensnare
Souls that need to mourn their sin ;
Still the boughs adopted spare,
And the outcasts—graft them in !

cr Speed the day of union sweet
When, with us in faith allied,
Israel's heart shall turn to greet
Thee, Whom Israel crucified ;
Thee, in all Thy truth and grace,
Own'd at last as Salem's King,
mf While her children find their place,
Gather'd safe beneath Thy wing.

W. BRIGHT.

ALTERNATIVE TUNE, HYMN 127.

For those at Sea.

Hymn 592. DUNDEE.—C.M.

Psalms (Edinburgh, 1615).

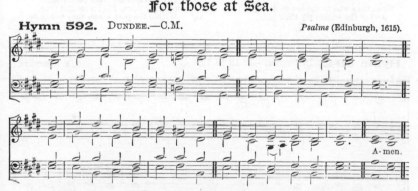

A-men.

A higher setting of this Tune is given at Hymn 80, a lower setting at Hymn 221.

" The sea is His."

p O LORD, be with us when we sail
Upon the lonely deep,
Our guard when on the silent deck
The midnight watch we keep.

We need not fear, though all around
'Mid rising winds we hear
The multitude of waters surge,
cr For Thou, O GOD, art near.

The calm, the breeze, the gale, the storm,
That pass from land to land,
All, all are Thine, are held within
The hollow of Thy hand.

mf If duty calls from threaten'd strife
To guard our native shore,
And shot and shell are answering fast
The booming cannon's roar.

dim Be Thou the mainguard of our host,
Till war and danger cease :
Defend the right, put up the sword,
And through the world make peace.

f To Thee the FATHER, Thee the SON,
Whom earth and sky adore,
And SPIRIT, moving o'er the deep,
Be praise for evermore.

E. A. DAYMAN.

For those at Sea.

Hymn 593. EISENACH.—L.M.

J. H. SCHEIN, 1628.

A - men.

A simpler form of this Tune is given at Hymn 173.

" The Lord sitteth above the waterfloods."

mf O GOD, Who metest in Thine hand
 The waters of the mighty sea,
And barrest ocean with the sand
 By Thy perpetual decree :

What time the floods lift up their voice
 And break in anger on the shore,
When deep to deep calls with the noise
 Of waterspouts and billows' roar ;

When they who to the sea go down,
 And in the waters ply their toil,

Are lifted on the surge's crown,
 And plunged where seething eddies boil ;

p Rule then, O LORD, the ocean's wrath,
 And bind the tempest with Thy will ;
Tread, as of old, the water's path,
 And speak Thy bidding, " Peace, be still."

cr So with Thy mercies ever new
 Thy servants set from peril free,
And bring them, Pilot wise and true,
mf Within the port where they would be.

R. F. LITTLEDALE.

Hymn 594. IN STORM.—12 12 12 12.

C. E. STEPHENS.

A - men.

For those at Sea.

" Save, Lord, or we perish."

IN STORMY WEATHER.

mp WHEN through the torn sail the wild tempest is streaming,
When o'er the dark wave the red lightning is gleaming,
Nor hope lends a ray the poor seaman to cherish,
We fly to our Maker, *(mf)* "Save, LORD, or we perish."

mp O JESUS, once rock'd on the breast of the billow,
Aroused by the shriek of despair from Thy pillow,
cr Now seated in glory, the mariner cherish,
Who cries in his anguish, *(mf)* "Save, LORD, or we perish."

mp And O! when the whirlwind of passion is raging,
When sin in our hearts his wild warfare is waging,
cr Then send down Thy grace Thy redeem'd to cherish,
Rebuke the destroyer ;—*(mf)* "Save, LORD, or we perish.'

Bishop HEBER, 1827.

Hymn 595. CAIRNBROOK.—8 5 8 3.

E. PROUT.

A-men.

" The Lord watch between me and thee, when we are absent one from another."

FOR ABSENT FRIENDS.

mf HOLY FATHER, in Thy mercy
Hear our anxious prayer,
Keep our loved ones, now far distant,
'Neath Thy care.

JESUS, SAVIOUR, let Thy presence
Be their light and guide ;
dim Keep, oh, keep them, in their weakness,
At Thy Side.

p When in sorrow, when in danger,
When in loneliness,
In Thy love look down and comfort
Their distress.

cr May the joy of Thy salvation
Be their strength and stay ;
May they love and may they praise Thee
Day by day.

p HOLY SPIRIT, let Thy teaching
Sanctify their life ;
cr Send Thy grace, that they may conquer
In the strife.

mf FATHER, SON, and HOLY SPIRIT,
GOD the ONE in THREE,
Bless them, guide them, save them, keep them
Near to Thee.

ISABEL S. STEVENSON.

Hymn 596. ST. PETER.—C.M.

A. R. REINAGLE, 1799–1877.

A - men.

A higher setting of this Tune is given at Hymn 176.

" Pray that ye enter not into temptation."

mf O SAVIOUR! when Thy loving Hand
Has brought us o'er the sea,
Through perils many, safe to land—
The land we long'd to see ;

Oh, help us, for Thy help we need
Each moment more and more,
dim In perils that we scarcely heed,
More deadly, on the shore.

LORD, save us ! and the Christian name
Oh, help us pure to keep,
cr On sea or land, alike the same,
p Till we in death shall sleep.

mf Then through Thy merits, wash'd and clean
From sin's polluting stain,
In raiment white may we be seen
With all Thy Saints to reign.

ELLEN M. SEWELL.

(511)

For those at Sea.

Hymn 597. MELCOMBE.—L.M.   S. WEBBE, 1782.

A - men.

A higher setting of this Tune is given at Hymn 155, a lower setting at Hymn 4.

" So He bringeth them unto the haven where they would be."

mf   A S near the wish'd-for port we draw,
         We lift our hearts in praise to Thee,
       Almighty FATHER, loving LORD,
         Our Pilot on the troubled sea.

       By Thy good care in peace we come,
         From fire and foe securely kept,
       And after tempest, at Thy word,
dim   The waves have laid them down and slept.

mf   As Thou hast given us outward calm,
         So, LORD, within us may there be
dim A peace Divine, a peace in Him,
         Through Whom alone we live to Thee.

cr   Give us more light, direct our course,
         Cleanse us from guile, our hearts renew ;
       Let not dark clouds of sin shut out
         The Star of JESUS from our view.

mf   And then, our long life voyage o'er,
         And past the perils of the sea,
       Receive us on the blissful shore,
dim   To everlasting rest with Thee.

f   To FATHER, SON, and HOLY GHOST,
         The GOD Whom Heav'n and earth adore,
       Be glory as it was of old,
         Is now, and shall be evermore.
                                    C. E. YORK.

Litany 624 may also be used.

For a Flower Service.

Hymn 598. SPRINGFIELD.—11 10 11 10.   Rev. P. MAURICE.

For a Flower Service.

" Then the people rejoiced, for that they offered willingly."

mf HERE, LORD, we offer Thee all that is fairest,
　　Flowers in their freshness from garden and field ;
　　Gifts for the stricken ones—knowing Thou carest
　　More for the love than the wealth that we yield.

p 　Speak, LORD, by these to the sick and the dying,
　　Speak to their hearts with a message of peace,
　　Comfort the sad who in weakness are lying,
　　Grant the departing a gentle release.

cr 　Raise, LORD, to health again those who have sicken'd,
　　Fair be their lives as the roses in bloom ;
　　Give of Thy grace to the souls Thou hast quicken'd,
　　Gladness for sorrow, and brightness for gloom.

p 　We, LORD, like flowers in our Autumn must wither ;
　　We, like these blossoms, must fade and must die :
cr 　Gather us, LORD, to Thy bosom for ever,
　　Grant us a place in Thy home in the sky.

A. G. W. BLUNT.

ALTERNATIVE TUNE, HYMN 643 (FIRST TUNE).

For a Bible Class.

Hymn 599. PRINCE OF PEACE.—C.M.　　　　　Archbishop MACLAGAN.

" Holy men of God spake as they were moved by the Holy Ghost."

mf COME, HOLY GHOST, our hearts inspire,
　　Let us Thy influence prove ;
　　Source of the old prophetic fire,
　　Fountain of life and love.

　　Come, HOLY GHOST, for moved by Thee
　　The prophets wrote and spoke ;
　　Unlock the Truth, Thyself the Key,
　　Unseal the Sacred Book.

　　GOD through Himself we then shall know
　　If Thou within us shine,
　　And sound, with all Thy saints below,
　　The depths of Love Divine.

C. WESLEY, 1740.

The following Hymns are suitable :

530 The Voice of GOD's Creation found me.　　**531** FATHER of mercies, in Thy Word.
　　　　532 Church of the Living GOD.

For a Retreat or Quiet Day.

Hymn 600. REST.—8 8 8 8.8 8. Sir J. STAINER.

Voices in Unison. *Harmony.* A - men.

A higher setting of this Tune is given at Hymn 428.

" I am crucified with Christ, nevertheless I live ; yet not I, but Christ liveth in me."

mf   THOU hidden love of GOD, whose height,
          Whose depth unfathom'd, no man knows ;
        I see from far Thy beauteous light,
          Inly I sigh for Thy repose ;
cr   My heart is pain'd, nor can it be
dim   At rest, till it finds rest in Thee.

mf   'Tis mercy all, that Thou hast brought
          My mind to seek her peace in Thee ;
        Yet, while I seek but find Thee not,
          No peace my wandering soul shall see ;
cr   O when shall all my wanderings end,
dim   And all my steps to Thee-ward tend ?

mf   Is there a thing beneath the sun
          That strives with Thee my heart to share ?
        Ah, tear it thence, and reign alone,
          The LORD of every motion there !
        Then shall my heart from earth be free,
dim   When it hath found repose in Thee.

mf   O hide this self from me, that I
          No more, but CHRIST in me, may live ;
        My vile affections crucify,
          Nor let one hidden lust survive !
cr   In all things nothing may I see,
dim   Nothing desire, apart from Thee.

p   Each moment draw from earth away
          My heart, that lowly waits Thy call ;
cr   Speak to my inmost soul, and say,
          "I am thy Love, thy GOD, thy All ! "
        To feel Thy power, to hear Thy voice,
        To taste Thy love, be all my choice.

                J. WESLEY : from the German of G. Tersteegen.

                ALTERNATIVE TUNE, HYMN 774.

                Hymn 560 is also suitable

                (514)

Processional.

Hymn 601. LEONI.—6684.6684. *(First Tune.)* Traditional Hebrew Melody.

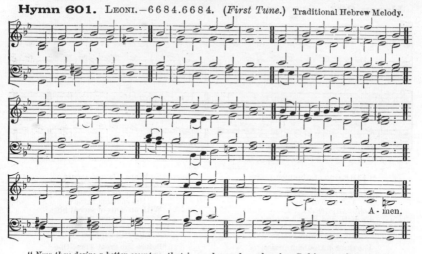

A - men.

"Now they desire a better country, that is, an heavenly: wherefore God is not ashamed to be called their God."

f   *THE GOD of Abraham praise
      Who reigns enthroned above,
  Ancient of everlasting days,
     And GOD of Love :
  JEHOVAH, Great I AM,
    By earth and Heav'n confest ;
  We bow and bless the Sacred Name
     For ever blest.

    The GOD of Abraham praise,
     At Whose supreme command
  From earth we rise, and seek the joys
    At His right Hand :
dim We all on earth forsake,
    Its wisdom, fame, and power ;
f   And Him our only Portion make,
     Our Shield and Tower.

p   Though nature's strength decay,
    And earth and hell withstand,
cr To Canaan's bounds we urge our way
    At His command.
    The watery deep we pass,
    With JESUS in our view ;
  And through the howling wilderness
     Our way pursue.

mf The goodly land we see,
    With peace and plenty blest ;
  A land of sacred liberty
p   And endless rest ;
mf There milk and honey flow,
    And oil and wine abound,
  And trees of life for ever grow,
     With mercy crown'd.

f   There dwells the LORD, our King,
    The LORD our Righteousness,
  Triumphant o'er the world of sin,
    The Prince of Peace :
  On Sion's sacred height
    His Kingdom He maintains,
  And glorious with His saints in light
     For ever reigns.

mf *He keeps His own secure,
    He guards them by His side,
  Arrays in garment white and pure
    His spotless Bride :
  With streams of sacred bliss,
    Beneath serener skies,
  With all the fruits of Paradise,
     He still supplies.

   *Before the great Three-One
    They all exulting stand,
  And tell the wonders He hath done
    Through all their land :
  The listening spheres attend,
    And swell the growing fame ;
  And sing, in songs which never end,
     The wondrous Name.

f   *The GOD Who reigns on high
    The great Archangels sing ;
dim And " Holy, Holy, Holy," cry,
f   " Almighty King !
  Who was, and is the same,
    And evermore shall be ;
  JEHOVAH, FATHER, Great I AM,
p   We worship Thee."

mf Before the SAVIOUR'S Face
    The ransom'd nations bow,
  O'erwhelm'd at His Almighty grace
    For ever new ;
p   He shows His prints of love,—
    They kindle to a flame !
cr And sound through all the worlds above
p   The slaughter'd Lamb.

f   The whole triumphant host
    Give thanks to GOD on high ;
  " Hail ! FATHER, SON, and HOLY GHOST,"
    They ever cry :
  Hail ! Abraham's GOD, and mine !
    (I join the heavenly lays),
ff All might and majesty are Thine,
    And endless praise.

                    T. OLIVERS, 1770.

* *These verses may be omitted, if the Hymn be thought too long.*

Processional.

A-men.

" Now they desire a better country, that is, an heavenly : wherefore God is not ashamed to be called their God."

f   *THE GOD of Abraham praise
    Who reigns enthroned above,
Ancient of everlasting days,
    And GOD of Love :
JEHOVAH, Great I AM,
By earth and Heav'n confest ;
We bow and bless the Sacred Name
    For ever blest.

The GOD of Abraham praise,
    At Whose supreme command
From earth we rise, and seek the joys
    At His right Hand :
dim   We all on earth forsake,
    Its wisdom, fame, and power ;
f   And Him our only Portion make,
    Our Shield and Tower.

p   Though nature's strength decay,
    And earth and hell withstand,
cr   To Canaan's bounds we urge our way
    At His command.
The watery deep we pass,
    With JESUS in our view ;
And through the howling wilderness
    Our way pursue.

mf   The goodly land we see,
    With peace and plenty blest ;
A land of sacred liberty
p   And endless rest ;
mf   There milk and honey flow,
    And oil and wine abound,
And trees of life for ever grow,
    With mercy crown'd.

f   There dwells the LORD, our King,
    The LORD our Righteousness,
Triumphant o'er the world of sin,
    The Prince of Peace :
On Sion's sacred height
His Kingdom He maintains,
And glorious with His saints in light
    For ever reigns.

mf   *He keeps His own secure,
    He guards them by His side,
Arrays in garment white and pure
    His spotless Bride :
With streams of sacred bliss,
Beneath serener skies,
With all the fruits of Paradise,
    He still supplies.

*Before the great Three-One
    They all exulting stand,
And tell the wonders He hath done
    Through all their land :
The listening spheres attend,
And swell the growing fame ;
And sing, in songs which never end,
    The wondrous Name.

f   *The GOD Who reigns on high
    The great Archangels sing,
dim And " Holy, Holy, Holy," cry,
f   "Almighty King !
Who was, and is the same,
    And evermore shall be ;
JEHOVAH, FATHER, Great I AM,
p   We worship Thee."

mf   Before the SAVIOUR'S Face
    The ransom'd nations bow,
O'erwhelm'd at His Almighty grace
    For ever new ;
p   He shows His prints of love,—
    They kindle to a flame !
cr   And sound through all the worlds above
p   The slaughter'd Lamb.

f   The whole triumphant host
    Give thanks to GOD on high ;
" Hail ! FATHER, SON, and HOLY GHOST,"
    They ever cry :
Hail ! Abraham's GOD, and mine !
    (I join the heavenly lays),
ff   All might and majesty are Thine,
    And endless praise.

T. OLIVERS, 1770.

† *Verse 1 only should be sung thus :—*

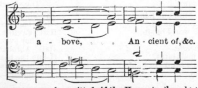

a - bove,   An - cient of, &c.

* *These verses may be omitted, if the Hymn be thought too long.*

Restoration of a Church.

Hymn 602. Blagdon.—8 7.8 7.8 7. C. E. Stephens.

A-men.

" To give us a reviving, to set up the house of our God, and to repair the desolations thereof."

f O JERUSALEM the blissful, Home of gladness yet untold;
  Thou whose countless throngs triumphal fill with joy thy street of gold;
Graven on thee, new and glorious, they the King's own Name behold!

mf Many are thy sons, O Mother, yon august and shining band!
p Gentle Peace in all thy borders makes thee glad, O happy land!
Perfect is thy Restoration, bright in holiness to stand.

cr Here, a figure of the Heavenly, shines our temple, worthier grown
By its richer restoration on the old foundation-stone,
With a majesty and beauty to the former house unknown.

mp LORD, we pray Thee, Master-Builder, Great and Holy, enter in,
Fill Thy sanctuary quickly, as our hallowing rites begin,
And Thyself its Consecrator rest for evermore therein.

  Make Thy servants, though unworthy, temples of Thy grace to be;
Let us not in flesh or spirit prove disloyal unto Thee,
But in dedicated service praise Thy Name adoringly.

mf Make, O Royal Priest, Thine Altar here henceforth a Throne of light,
Ever held in highest honour, and with many a gift made bright,
Ever blessèd, ever peaceful, ever precious in Thy sight.

  Yea, our hearts, for these Thou judgest, as Thy cleansèd Altars bless,
By Thy SPIRIT'S grace renew us unto perfect holiness,
And the sevenfold gifts from Heaven grant us ever to possess.

f Now to Thee, through endless ages, O most HOLY TRINITY,
Highest honour, power unmeasured, everlasting glory be;
GOD for ever and for ever, THREE in ONE and ONE in THREE.

J. ELLERTON: from the Latin.

ALTERNATIVE TUNES, HYMN 232 (FIRST AND SECOND TUNES).

For Church Defence.

Hymn 603. St. Frideswide.—8 7 8 7. 8 7 8 7.   C. H. Lloyd.

A-men.

" God is in the midst of her, therefore shall she not be removed ; God shall help her, and that right early."

p Round the Sacred City gather
  Egypt, Edom, Babylon ;
All the warring hosts of error,
  Sworn against her, move as one :
f Vain the leaguer ! her foundations
  Are upon the holy hills.
cr And the love of the Eternal
  All her stately temple fills

mf Get thee, watchman, to the rampart !
  Gird thee, warrior, with thy sword !
Be ye strong as ye remember
  That amidst you is the Lord :
dim Like the night mists from the valley,
  These shall vanish one by one,
Egypt's malice, Edom's envy,
  And the hate of Babylon.

mf But be true, ye sons and daughters,
  Lest the peril be within :
Watch to prayer, lest, while ye slumber,
  Stealthy foemen enter in :
cr Safe the mother and the children,
  If their will and love be strong,
While their loyal hearts go singing
  Prayer and praise for battle song.

mf Church of God ! if we forget thee
  Let His blessing fail our hand,
When our love shall not prefer thee
  Let His love forget our land :—
Nay ! to thee shall we be steadfast,
  Though the world's foundations shake,
Love of thee is love for ever,
  Love of thee for Jesus' sake.

dim Church of Christ ! upon thy banner,
  Lo, His Passion's awful sign ;
By that seal of His Redemption
  Thou art His, and He is thine :
cr From the depth of His Atonement
  Flows thy Sacramental tide :
mf From the height of His Ascension
  Flows the grace which is thy guide

God the Spirit dwells within thee,
  His Society Divine,
His the living word thou keepest,
  His thy Apostolic line.
Ancient prayer and song liturgic,
  Creeds that change not to the end,
cr As His gift we have received them,
  As His charge we will defend.

Alleluia, Alleluia,
  To the Father, Spirit, Son,
In Whose will the Church at warfare
  With the Church at rest is one ;
So to Thee we sing in union,
  God in earth and Heav'n adored,
f Alleluia, Alleluia,
dim Holy, Holy, Holy Lord.

S. J. Stone.

Alternative Tune, Hymn 274 (Second Tune).

For Church Defence.

Hymn 604. CRÜGER.—7 6 7 6. 7 6 7 6. (*First Tune.*)   J. CRÜGER, 1598–1662.

A-men.

A lower setting of this Tune is given at Hymn 219.

"One body, and one Spirit, . . . one Lord, one faith."

mf THY Hand, O GOD, has guided
    Thy flock, from age to age ;
The wondrous tale is written,
    Full clear, on every page ;
Our fathers own'd Thy goodness,
    And we their deeds record ;
And both of this bear witness,
f   One Church, one Faith, one LORD.

mf Thy heralds brought glad tidings
    To greatest, as to least ;
They bade men rise, and hasten
    To share the great King's feast ;
And this was all their teaching,
    In every deed and word,
To all alike proclaiming
f   One Church, one Faith, one LORD.

p When shadows thick were falling,
    And all seem'd sunk in night,
cr Thou, LORD, didst send Thy servants,
    Thy chosen sons of light.
mf On them and on Thy people
    Thy plenteous Grace was pour'd,
And this was still their message,
f   One Church, one Faith, one LORD.

p Through many a day of darkness,
    Through many a scene of strife,
The faithful few fought bravely,
    To guard the Nation's life.
cr Their Gospel of redemption,
    Sin pardon'd, man restored,
Was all in this enfolded,
f   One Church, one Faith, one LORD.

mf And we, shall we be faithless ?
    Shall hearts fail, hands hang down ?
Shall we evade the conflict,
    And cast away our crown ?
cr Not so : in GOD's deep counsels
    Some better thing is stored ;
We will maintain, unflinching,
f   One Church, one Faith, one LORD.

mf Thy Mercy will not fail us,
    Nor leave Thy work undone ;
cr With Thy right Hand to help us,
    The Victory shall be won ;
And then, by men and angels,
    Thy Name shall be adored,
And this shall be their anthem,
f   "One Church, one Faith, one LORD."

E. H. PLUMPTRE.

For Church Defence.

Hymn 604. THORNBURY.—7 6 7 6. 7 6 7 6. (Second Tune.)

"One body, and one Spirit, . . . one Lord, one faith."

Verses 1, 2, 4 and 6, Unison.

B. HARWOOD.

1 Thy Hand, O GOD, has guid - ed Thy flock, from age to age;
2 Thy her - alds brought glad tid - ings To great - est, as to least;
4. Thro' many a day of dark - ness, Thro' many a scene of strife,
6. Thy Mer - cy will not fail us, Nor leave Thy work un - done;

The won - drous tale is writ - ten, Full clear, on ev - 'ry page;
They bade men rise, and hast - en To share the great King's feast;
The faith - ful few fought brave - ly, To guard the Na - tion's life.
With Thy right Hand to help us, The Vic - tory shall be won;

Our fa - thers own'd Thy good - ness, And we their deeds re - cord;
And this was all their teach - ing, In ev - 'ry deed and word,
Their Gos - pel of re - demp - tion, Sin par - don'd, man re - stored,
And then, by men and an - gels, Thy Name shall be a - dored,

And both of this bear wit - ness,
To all a - like pro - claim - ing   "One Church, one
Was all in this en - fold - ed,
And this shall be their an - them,

[For copyright, see p. lv.]

(520)

For Church Defence.

In Harmony

Faith one LORD."

A · men.

Verses 3 and 5, Harmony.

mf

3. When sha · dows thick were fall · ing, And all seem'd sunk in night,
5. And we, shall we be faith · less? Shall hearts fail, hands hang down?

Thou, LORD, didst send Thy ser · vants, Thy cho · sen sons of light.
Shall we e · vade the con · flict, And cast a · way our crown?

On them and on Thy peo · ple Thy plen-teous Grace was pour'd,
Not so: in GOD'S deep coun · sels Some bet · ter thing is stored;

VOICES.

One Church, one Faith, one LORD.

ff

And this was still their mes-sage, One Church, one Faith, one LORD, one Faith, one LORD.
We will maintain, un-flinch-ing, One Church, one Faith, one LORD, one Faith, one LORD.

ff

ORGAN.

ff

(521)

E. H. PLUMPTRE.

P 2

For Temperance Meetings.

Hymn 605. STOKE.—7 6 7 6. 7 6 7 6.

Mrs. G. E. COLE.

A - men.

"He that is begotten of God keepeth himself."

mf O LORD, our strength in weakness,
　　We pray to Thee for grace ;
For power to fight the battle,
　　For speed to run the race ;
When Thy baptismal waters
　　Were pour'd upon our brow,
We then were made Thy children,
　　And pledged our earliest vow.

CHRIST with His own Blood bought us,
　　And made the purchase sure ;
His are we ; may He keep us
　　Sober, and chaste, and pure.
He, GOD in Man, has carried
　　Our nature up to Heaven ;
And thence the HOLY SPIRIT
　　To dwell in us has given.

p Conform'd to His own likeness,
　　May we so live and die,
That in the grave our bodies
　　In holy peace may lie ;

mf And at the Resurrection
　　Forth from those graves may spring
Like to the glorious Body
　　Of CHRIST, our LORD and King.

p The pure in heart are blessèd,
　　For they shall see the LORD,
For ever and for ever
　　By Seraphim adored ;

cr And they shall drink the pleasures,
　　Such as no tongue can tell,
From the clear crystal river,
　　And Life's eternal well.

mf Sing therefore to the FATHER,
　　Who sent the SON in love ;
And sing to GOD the SAVIOUR,
　　Who leads to realms above ;

f Sing we with Saints and Angels,
　　Before the Heavenly Throne,
To GOD the HOLY SPIRIT ;
　　Sing to the THREE in ONE.

Bishop C. WORDSWORTH.

ALTERNATIVE TUNE, HYMN 604 (SECOND TUNE).

Hymn 606. BICKLEY.—8 8. 8 8. 8 8.

W. H. MONK.

A-men.

(522)

For Temperance Meetings.

"This kind goeth not out but by prayer and fasting."

mp O FATHER, in Whose great design
    Our human love is made Divine,
Teach us to give our love to those
By sin beset and all its woes;
On Thee for them to cast our care,
By fasting and by lowly prayer.

p LORD JESU, grant us eyes to see
    In our poor brethren Thine and Thee—
To give ourselves where others need;
Where others sin to intercede;
And thus, by fasting and by prayer,
Our brethren's burden seek to bear.

O SPIRIT, by Whose grace alone
    The many members are made one;
cr O warm our hearts, inspire our will,
That we Thy purpose may fulfil;
And thus, by fasting and by prayer,
Through Thee "the glorious Church" prepare.

mp O GOD, All-loving THREE in ONE,
    Whom we shall see beyond the sun;
Where walk in white the blood-bought throng,
Where soars to Thee the sweet new song,
Grant that we find the brethren there
We sought by fasting and by prayer.

ALTERNATIVE TUNE, HYMN 554 (SECOND TUNE).

S. J. STONE.

Hymn 607. DAY OF REST.—7 6 7 6. 7 6 7 6.

J. W. ELLIOTT.

Voices in Unison.   *In Harmony.*

A-men.

Man.   ed.

"The Lord hath done great things for us already."

v O THOU before Whose Presence
    Nought evil may come in,
Yet Who dost look in mercy
Down on this world of sin;
cr O give us noble purpose
    To set the sin-bound free,
And CHRIST-like tender pity
To seek the lost for Thee.

Fierce is our subtle foeman:
    The forces at his hand
With woes that none can number
Despoil the pleasant land;
All they who war against them,
In strife so keen and long,
mf Must in their SAVIOUR's armour
    Be stronger than the strong.

So hast Thou wrought among us
    The great things that we see!
For things that are we thank Thee,
And for the things to be:
For bright Hope is uplifting
Faint hands and feeble knees,
To strive beneath Thy blessing
For greater things than these.

cr Lead on, O Love and Mercy,
    O Purity and Power!
Lead on till Peace Eternal
Shall close this battle-hour:
Till all who pray'd and struggled
To set their brethren free,
f In triumph meet to praise Thee,
    Most HOLY TRINITY.

S. J. STONE.

ALTERNATIVE TUNE, HYMN 500 (SECOND TUNE).

The following Hymn is suitable:
541 We are soldiers of CHRIST.

(523)

Burial of the Dead.

Hymn 608. GOD OF THE LIVING.—8 8.8 8.8 8.

E. HULTON.

To be sung in Unison.

" All live unto Him."

mp GOD of the living, in Whose eyes
  Unveil'd Thy whole creation lies :
All souls are Thine ; we must not say
That those are dead who pass away ;
From this our world of flesh set free,
cr We know them living unto Thee.

p Not spilt like water on the ground,
Not wrapp'd in dreamless sleep profound,
Not wandering in unknown despair,
Beyond Thy Voice, Thine Arm, Thy care ;
Not left to lie like fallen tree,—
cr Not dead, but living unto Thee.

mf Thy word is true, Thy will is just ;
To Thee we leave them, LORD, in trust ;
And bless Thee for the love which gave
Thy SON to fill a human grave,
That none might fear that world to see,
Where all are living unto Thee.

O Giver unto man of breath,
O Holder of the keys of death,
O Quickener of the life within,
p Save us from death, the death of sin ;
cr That body, soul, and spirit be
mf For ever living unto Thee !

J. ELLERTON.

A - men.   or   A - - - men.

Unison.

ALTERNATIVE TUNE, HYMN 556 (SECOND TUNE).

Hymn 609. AXBRIDGE.—6 6 6 6.8 8.

A. H. D. PRENDERGAST.

Burial of the Dead.

" Cry unto her, that her warfare is accomplished."

mf SAFE home, safe home in port !
    Rent cordage, shatter'd deck,
Torn sails, provision short,
    And only not a wreck :
cr But oh ! the joy upon the shore
To tell our voyage—perils o'er !

mf The prize, the prize secure !
dim The athlete nearly fell ;
Bare all he could endure,
    And bare not always well :
cr But he may smile at troubles gone
Who sets the victor-garland on.

mf No more the foe can harm ;
    No more of leaguered camp,
And cry of night alarm,

    And need of ready lamp ;
dim And yet how nearly had he fail'd—
    How nearly had that foe prevail'd !

mp The lamb is in the fold,
    In perfect safety penn'd ;
The lion once had hold,
    And thought to make an end ;
cr But One came by with wounded Side,
And for the sheep the Shepherd died.

The exile is at home !
    O nights and days of tears,
p O longings not to roam,
    O sins and doubts and fears :
cr What matters now grief's darkest day?
f The King has wiped those tears away.

J. M. NEALE.

Hymn 610. SAFELY, SAFELY.—7 7.7 7.7 7.7 7.

W. H. MONK.

A-men.

" Is it well with the child ? . . . It is well."

FOR A CHILD.

p SAFELY, safely gather'd in,
    Far from sorrow, far from sin,
No more childish griefs or fears,
No more sadness, no more tears ;
cr For the life so young and fair
    Now hath pass'd from earthly care ;
mf GOD Himself the soul will keep,
p Giving His belovèd—sleep.

Safely, safely gather'd in,
    Far from sorrow, far from sin,
cr Pass'd beyond all grief and pain,
Death for thee is truest gain ;

For our loss we must not weep,
Nor our loved one long to keep
From the home of rest and peace,
Where all sin and sorrow cease.

p Safely, safely gather'd in,
    Far from sorrow, far from sin ;
cr GOD has saved from weary strife,
    In its dawn, this fresh young life ;
Now it waits for us above,
Resting in the SAVIOUR'S love ;
p JESU, grant that we may meet
There, adoring at Thy Feet.

MRS. DOBREE

The following Hymns are also suitable :

498 The foe behind, the deep before.   499 On the Resurrection morning.

Presentation of Christ in the Temple,

COMMONLY CALLED

The Purification of St. Mary the Virgin.

Hymn 611. St. Veronica.—6 6 6 6 6 6. Sir F. Champneys.

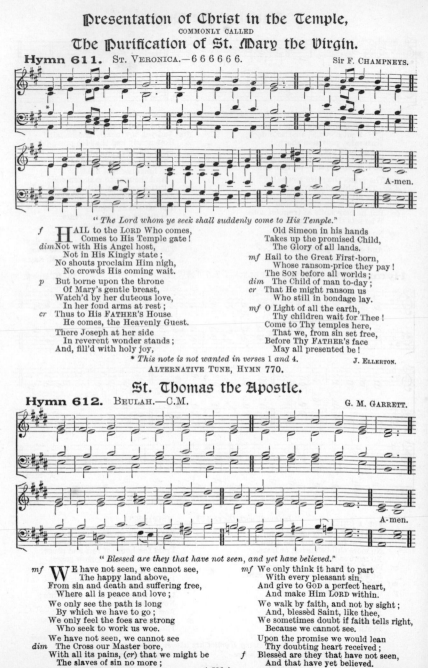

A-men.

" The Lord whom ye seek shall suddenly come to His Temple."

f HAIL to the LORD Who comes,
    Comes to His Temple gate!
dim Not with His Angel host,
    Not in His Kingly state;
    No shouts proclaim Him nigh,
    No crowds His coming wait.

p But borne upon the throne
    Of Mary's gentle breast,
    Watch'd by her duteous love,
    In her fond arms at rest;
cr Thus to His FATHER'S House
    He comes, the Heavenly Guest.

There Joseph at her side
    In reverent wonder stands;
    And, fill'd with holy joy,

Old Simeon in his hands
    Takes up the promised Child,
    The Glory of all lands.

mf Hail to the Great First-born,
    Whose ransom-price they pay!
    The SON before all worlds;
dim The Child of man to-day;
cr That He might ransom us
    Who still in bondage lay.

mf O Light of all the earth,
    Thy children wait for Thee!
    Come to Thy temples here,
    That we, from sin set free,
    Before Thy FATHER'S face
    May all presented be!

* *This note is not wanted in verses 1 and 4.*   J. Ellerton.

ALTERNATIVE TUNE, HYMN 770.

St. Thomas the Apostle.

Hymn 612. Beulah.—C.M. G. M. Garrett.

A-men.

" Blessed are they that have not seen, and yet have believed."

mf WE have not seen, we cannot see,
    The happy land above,
From sin and death and suffering free,
    Where all is peace and love;

We only see the path is long
    By which we have to go;
We only feel the foes are strong
    Who seek to work us woe.

We have not seen, we cannot see
dim The Cross our Master bore,
    With all its pains, (*cr*) that we might be
    The slaves of sin no more;

mf We only think it hard to part
    With every pleasant sin,
And give to GOD a perfect heart,
    And make Him LORD within.

We walk by faith, and not by sight;
    And, blessèd Saint, like thee,
We sometimes doubt if faith tells right,
    Because we cannot see.

Upon the promise we would lean
    Thy doubting heart received;
f Blessèd are they that have not seen,
    And that have yet believed.

J. M. Neale.

(526)

St. Matthias the Apostle.

Hymn 613. LOCHBIE.—7 6 7 6. 7 6 7 6.

W. H. MONK.

A - men.

" He was numbered with the eleven apostles."

mf PRAISE to the Heavenly Wisdom
Who knows the hearts of all—
The saintly life's beginnings,
The traitor's secret fall;
Our own ascended Master,
Who heard His Church's cry,
Made known His guiding presence,
And ruled her from on high.

Elect in His foreknowledge,
To fill the lost one's place ;
He form'd His chosen vessel
By hidden gifts of grace,
Then, by the lot's disposing,
He lifted up the poor,
cr And set him with the Princes
On high for evermore.

mf For on the golden breastplate
Of our great Priest above,
Twelve are the stones that glisten
As throbs that Heart of Love ;
And twelve the fair foundations
Of Salem's jasper wall ;
And twelve the thrones predestined
Within her judgment-hall.

No mystic gem is lacking
In that Divine array ;
No empty throne shall darken
The glory of that day :
For lo ! on Twelve the SPIRIT,
The FATHER'S Promise, came ;
And Twelve went forth together
To preach the saving Name.

Still guide Thy Church, Chief Shepherd,
Her losses still renew ;
Be Thy dread keys entrusted
To faithful hands and true ;
Apostles of Thy choosing
May all her rulers be,
That each with joy may render
His last account to Thee !

J. ELLERTON.

ALTERNATIVE TUNE, HYMN 765.

St. Matthew the Apostle.

Hymn 614. ERFURT.—L.M.

Geistliche Lieder (Leipzig, 1539).

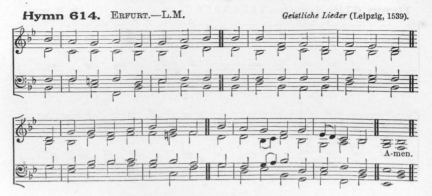

A-men.

A higher setting of this Tune is given at Hymn 57.

" And as He passed by, He saw Levi the son of Alphæus sitting at the receipt of custom, and said unto him, Follow Me."

mf BEHOLD, the Master passeth by!
dim Oh, seest thou not His pleading eye?
p With low sad voice He calleth thee ;—
cr Leave this vain world and follow Me.

p O soul, bow'd down with harrowing care,
Hast thou no thought for Heav'n to spare?
cr From earthly toils lift up thine eye ;—
mf Behold, the Master passeth by!

One heard Him calling long ago,
And straightway left all things below,
Counting his earthly gain as loss
For JESUS and His blessèd Cross.

That " Follow Me " his faithful ear
Seem'd every day afresh to hear:
Its echoes stirr'd his spirit still,
And fired his hope, and nerved his will.

p GOD sweetly calls us every day :
cr Why should we then our bliss delay?
He calls to Heav'n and endless light :
Why should we love the dreary night?

mf Praise, LORD, to Thee for Matthew's call,
At which he left his earthly all ;
cr Thou, LORD, e'en now art calling me,—
I will leave all, and follow Thee.

Bishop W. WALSHAM HOW (adapted from Bishop Ken).

Hymn 615. GLOUCESTER.—L.M.

E. HODGES.

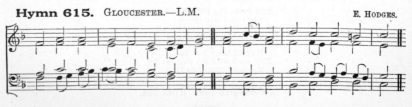

St. Matthew the Apostle.

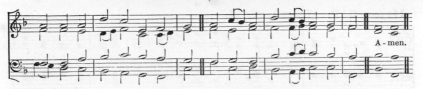

" Matthew the publican."

mf HE sat to watch o'er customs paid,
   A man of scorn'd and hard'ning trade ;
Alike the symbol and the tool
Of foreign masters' hated rule.

But grace within his breast had stirr'd ;
There needed but the timely word ;
cr It came, true LORD of souls ! from Thee,
That royal summons, " Follow Me."

Enough, when Thou wert passing by,
To hear Thy voice, to meet Thine eye :
He rose, responsive to the call,
And left his task, his gains, his all.

mf O wise exchange ! with these to part,
And lay up treasure in Thy heart ;
With twofold crown of light to shine
Amid Thy servants' foremost line !

p Come, SAVIOUR, as in days of old ;
cr Pass where the world has strongest hold,
And faithless care and selfish greed
Are thorns that choke the holy seed.

mf Who keep Thy gifts, O bid them claim
The steward's, not the owner's name ;
Who yield all up for Thy dear sake,
Let them of Matthew's wealth partake.

W. BRIGHT.

St. Michael and all Angels.

Hymn 616. HARTING.—8 7 8 7. Rev. F. A. J. HERVEY.

" I am thy fellow servant."

f LIFE and strength of all Thy servants,
   Brightness of the FATHER'S light ;
Men with Angels, earth with Heaven,
In Thy praise their songs unite.

Thousand thousand warrior princes
In Thine Angel army stand ;
Flames the victor Cross before them,
Grasp'd in Michael's dauntless hand.

mf Hurling back from Heav'n the rebels
With the lifting of his sword,

In the might of GOD he tramples
On the Dragon's head abhorr'd.

dim LORD of Angels, CHRIST, we pray Thee,
Bid them aid us in our strife,
cr Till we reach the land of life.

f GOD the FATHER, GOD Immortal,
GOD the SON, for us Who died,
GOD the Comforter, the SPIRIT,
Evermore be glorified !

Compilers : from the Latin
of Rabanus Maurus.

ALTERNATIVE TUNE, HYMN 76.

(529)

St. Michael and all Angels.

Hymn 617. WORSHIP.—D.C.M.

Sir R. STEWART.

A-men.

*" And all the Angels stood round about the throne . . . and fell before the throne on their faces,
and worshipped God."*

mf FATHER, before Thy throne of light
    The guardian Angels bend,
  And ever in Thy Presence bright
    Their psalms adoring blend ;
*dim*And casting down each golden crown,
    Beside the crystal sea,
cr With voice and lyre, in happy quire,
    Hymn glory, LORD, to Thee.

  And as the rainbow lustre falls
    Athwart their glowing wings,
  While Seraph unto Seraph calls,
    And each Thy goodness sings ;

p So may we feel, as low we kneel
    To pray Thee for Thy grace,
  That Thou art here for all who fear
    The brightness of Thy Face.

  Here, where the Angels see us come
    To worship day by day,
  Teach us to seek our Heavenly home,
    And love Thee e'en as they ;
cr Teach us to raise our notes of praise,
    With them Thy love to own,
  That childhood's flower, and manhood's
mf Be Thine, and Thine alone. [power,

F. W. FARRAR.

ALTERNATIVE TUNE, HYMN 216.

All Saints' Day.

Hymn 618. BRIDE OF CHRIST.—8 7 8 7.8 7 8 7. *(First Tune.)*

In Unison (or in G, if in Harmony).

S. NOTTINGHAM.

All Saints' Day.

A - men.

Hymn 618. SPONSA CHRISTI.—8 7 8 7. 8 7 8 7. *(Second Tune.)*

Sir H. OAKELEY.

A - men.

"The marriage of the Lamb is come."

mf BRIDE of CHRIST, whose glorious warfare
   Here on earth hath never rest ;
Lift thy voice, and tell the triumphs
   Of the holy and the blest :
Joyous be the day we hallow,
   Feast of all the Saints on high,
Earth and Heav'n together blending
   In one solemn harmony.

First the blessèd Virgin-mother,
   Reunited to her SON,
Leads the host of ransom'd people,
   Who unfading crowns have won ;
John the herald, CHRIST'S forerunner,
   More than Prophet, heads his throng,
Seer and Patriarch responsive
   Unto Psalmist in their song.

Lo, the Twelve, majestic Princes,
   In the court of JESUS sit,
Calmly watching, while the conflict
   Rages far beneath their feet :

Lo, the Martyrs, robed in crimson,
   Sign of life-blood freely spent,
Finding life, because they lost it,
   Dwell in undisturb'd content.

All the saintly host who witness'd
   Good confessions for His sake—
Priest and Deacon, world-renouncing,
   Of their Master's joy partake ;
Virgins to the Lamb devoted,
   Following with steadfast love,
Bring their lilies and their roses
   To the Marriage Feast above.

All, their happy lot fulfilling,
   GOD Omnipotent proclaim ;
dim Holy, Holy, Holy, crying,
f   Glory to His Holy Name !
mf So may GOD in mercy grant us
      Here to serve in holiness,
cr Till He call us to the portion
      Which His Saints in light possess.

J. ELLERTON : from the Latin
of J. B. Des Contes.

(531)

All Saints' Day.

Hymn 619. MODENA.—8 7 8 7 8 7.

J. V. ROBERTS.

A-men.

" A great multitude which no man can number."

mf WHO the multitudes can number
　　In the mansions of the blest,
cr He can weigh the joys eternal
　　By those ransom'd ones possess'd ;
　　Exiled now on earth no longer,
　　They have gain'd the Home of Rest.

　　Happily at last deliver'd
　　From the mournful vale of tears,
dim Sweet is now their recollection
p 　Of the sad and troubled years ;
cr While fulfill'd in all perfection
　　GOD'S eternal plan appears.

　　They behold their Tempter fallen,
　　Bound in everlasting chain ;
mf Praising CHRIST their gracious SAVIOUR,
　　All unite in joyful strain,
　　CHRIST the great reward and portion
　　Which adoring spirits gain.

p Now in shadow and in figure,
　　Mirror'd in imperfect light ;
cr Then, as we are known, our knowledge
　　Shall be clear, unveil'd, and bright ;
f For on GOD'S unclouded glory
　　We shall gaze with cleansèd sight.

　　Then the Trinity of Persons
　　We shall face to face behold,
　　And the Unity of Substance
　　Shall its mystery unfold ;
　　As the wondrous Triune Godhead
　　We adore in bliss untold.

mf Courage, man, be strong, be faithful,
　　Whatsoe'er thy burden be,
　　For unbounded are the glories
　　Which thy sorrows work for thee ;
　　Soon the light of light for ever
　　Shall thine eyes with rapture see.

f　GOD the FATHER, Fount of being,
　　Thee, most Highest, we adore ;
　　GOD the SON, our praise and homage
　　We present Thy Throne before ;
　　Glorious PARACLETE, we worship,
　　And we bless Thee evermore.

T. B. POLLOCK : from Thomas à Kempis.

ALTERNATIVE TUNES, HYMN 232 (FIRST AND SECOND TUNES).

Festivals of Apostles.

Hymn 620. STOLA REGIA.—7 6 7 6.7 6 7 6.   Sir J. STAINER.

A · men

" Ye also shall sit upon twelve thrones, judging the twelve tribes of Israel."

mf IN royal robes of splendour,
     Before the great King's feet,
The Princes of His Kingdom,
     The crown'd Apostles, meet ;
To Him their songs adoring
     With heart and tongue they bring,
Pure hearts and mighty voices—
     E'en as the Angels sing.

This Order sheds its lustre
     O'er all the human race ;
A court of righteous judgment,
     The Rock of Gospel grace ;—
Rock of His Church, for ages
     Elected and foreknown ;
Whose glorious Master-Builder
     Is Head and Corner-Stone.

These are the Nazareans,
     Famed heralds to the world,
Who, preaching CHRIST, His Banner
     Of victory unfurl'd.
Day unto day shows knowledge ;
     Night utters speech to night ;
So these to earth's four corners
     Their wondrous tale recite.

CHRIST'S burden light they proffer,
     His easy yoke proclaim ;
The seed of life they scatter,
     That all may own His Name.
The earth brought forth and budded,
     Where'er their ploughshare ran,
And fruits of increase follow'd
     The faith of GOD made Man.

These are the sure foundation
     On which the Temple stands ;
The living stones compacting
     That house not made with hands ;
The gates by which man enters
     Jerusalem the new ;
The bond which knits together
     The Gentile and the Jew.

Let error flee before them,
     Let truth extend her sway ;
Let dread of final judgment
     To faith and love give way ;
That, loosed from our offences,
     We then may number'd be
f   Among Thy Saints in glory,
     Around the Throne with Thee.

J. MASON : from the Latin of
Adam of St. Victor.

ALTERNATIVE TUNE, HYMN 271 (SECOND TUNE).

Festivals of Evangelists.

Hymn 621. COME SING.—7 6 7 6.7 6 7 6. T. L. FORBES.

A-men.

"They four had one likeness."

mf COME sing, ye choirs exultant,
  Those messengers of GOD,
Through whom the living Gospels
  Came sounding all abroad !
Whose voice proclaim'd salvation,
  That pour'd upon the night,
And drove away the shadows,
  And flush'd the world with light.

He chose them, our Good Shepherd,
  And, tending evermore
His flock through Earth's four quarters,
  In wisdom made them Four ;
True Lawgiver, He bade them
  Their healing message speed,—
One charter for all nations,
  One glorious title-deed !

In one harmonious witness
  The chosen Four combine,
While each his own commission
  Fulfils in every line ;
As in the Prophet's vision,
  From out the amber flame
In form of visage diverse
  Four Living Creatures came.

Lo, these the wingèd chariots,
  That bring Emmanuel nigh,
The golden staves, uplifting
  GOD'S very Ark on high ;
And these the fourfold river
  Of Paradise above,
Whence flow for all the nations
  New mysteries of love.

cr Four-square on this foundation
   The Church of CHRIST remains,
  A House to stand unshaken
   By floods or winds or rains.
f Oh ! glorious happy portion
   In this safe Home to be,
  By GOD, true Man, united
   With GOD eternally !

J. MASON : from the Latin of Adam of St. Victor.

ALTERNATIVE TUNE, HYMN 341.

Festivals of the Blessed Virgin Mary.

Hymn 622. BEDE.—8 8 7 7. (*First Tune.*) W. H. MONK.

A - men.

Hymn 622. QUEM PASTORES.—8 8 7 7. (*Second Tune.*) Medieval Melody.

A - men.

" Blessed is the womb that bare Thee."

mf VIRGIN-BORN, we bow before Thee ;
   Blessèd was the womb that bore Thee ;
   Mary, Maid and Mother mild,
   Blessèd was she in her Child.

Blessèd was the breast that fed Thee ;
Blessèd was the hand that led Thee ;
Blessèd was the parent's eye
That watch'd Thy slumbering infancy.

Blessèd she by all creation,
Who brought forth the world's Salvation,
dim   And blessèd they—for ever blest,
cr   Who love Thee most and serve Thee best.

mf Virgin-Born, we bow before Thee ;
   Blessèd was the womb that bore Thee ;
   Mary, Maid and Mother mild,
   Blessèd was she in her Child.

Bishop HEBER, 1827.

* *In verses 2 and 3 this note belongs to the first word of line 4.*

(535)

Commemoration of Saints.

Hymn 623. CRUCIS VICTORIA.—C.M.

M. B. FOSTER.

A - men.

" A great cloud of witnesses."

mf GIVE us the wings of faith to rise
    Within the veil, and see
The Saints above, how great their joys,
    How bright their glories be.

p   Once they were mourning here below,
    And wet their couch with tears ;
They wrestled hard, as we do now,
    With sins, and doubts, and fears.

    We ask them, whence their victory came ;
cr   They, with united breath,
mf Ascribe the conquest to the Lamb,
    Their triumph to His Death.

p   They mark'd the footsteps that He trod,
cr   His zeal inspired their breast :
    And, following their incarnate GOD,
p   They reach'd the promised rest.

f   Our glorious Leader claims our praise
    For His own pattern given ;
While the great cloud of witnesses
    Show the same path to Heav'n.

               I. WATTS, 1709.

Litany for those at Sea.

Hymn 624. PART 1.

C. E. STEPHENS.

rall.

Litany for those at Sea.

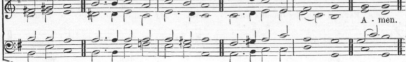

A - men.

PART 1.

p FATHER, Whose creating hand
　　Made the ocean and the land ;
All Thy creatures are Thy care,
Thou art present everywhere.
　　　　Hear us, we beseech Thee.

CHRIST, Who didst of old appear
On the waters, drawing near ;
Thou art able still to save,
Calmly ruling wind and wave.
　　　　Hear us, we beseech Thee.

HOLY GHOST, Whose presence shed
Life where all was dark and dead ;
By Thy breath we move and live,
Thou dost light and order give.
　　　　Hear us, we beseech Thee.

GOD, to Whom our life we owe,
GOD, Whose Blood for man did flow,
GOD, Who dost within us dwell,—
Keep us Thine, and all is well.
　　　　Hear us, we beseech Thee.

When the deep in slumber lies
Under bright and peaceful skies,
When the winds in fury rave,
Lifting high the rushing wave,
　　　　Hear us, we beseech Thee.

All our honest labour bless,
Give each lawful aim success ;
In our time of need draw nigh,
Saying, "Fear not, it is I."
　　　　Hear us, we beseech Thee.

Guard the loved ones left behind,
Give them peace in heart and mind ;
Keep us all in union sweet,
At our FATHER'S mercy-seat.
　　　　Hear us, we beseech Thee.

Safe from what might work our woe,
Rock and shoal, and fire and foe,
May we home and kindred see,
And the glory give to Thee.
　　　　Hear us, we beseech Thee

PART 2.

p May Thy Church our shelter be,
Ark in mercy built by Thee,
Refuge from the storms of life,
From the wearing toil and strife.
　　　　Hear us, we beseech Thee.

When temptations round us roll,
Threatening shipwreck to the soul,
Grant us faith and holy fear,
By Thy will our course to steer.
　　　　Hear us, we beseech Thee.

Through the gloom of sorrow's night,
Show Thy cheering, guiding light ;
cr Waft us homeward, LORD, we pray,
Nearer Heaven, day by day.
　　p　Hear us, we beseech Thee.

Bid the storms of passion cease,
Bid the power of love increase,
Bid each tossing doubt be still,
Bid us trust and do Thy will.
　　　　Hear us, we beseech Thee

Mark our course, and keep us true,
Till the haven fair we view,
Grant us on that peaceful shore
Home and friends for evermore.
　　　　Hear us, we beseech Thee.

Where there is no night or sea,
May we praise and worship Thee,
Glad because we are at rest
In Thy Presence with the blest.
　　　　Hear us, we beseech Thee.

T. B. POLLOCK.

Litany of the Seven Words from the Cross.

Hymn 625.

The Seven Words to be chanted in deliberate time and in Unison, thus:　　　W. H. MONK.

mp FATHER, forgive them, for they know not *(dim)* what they *(pp)* do.

mp To-day shalt thou be with Me in Pa - ra - dise.

mp Woman, be - - - - - hold thy son.

mp Be - - - - - hold thy Mo - - ther.

mp My GOD, My GOD, why hast Thou for - sa - ken Me?

mp I thirst.

mp It is fi - nish - ed.

mp FATHER, into Thy Hands I com - mend My Spi - - rit.

THE LITANY.

JE - SU, in Thy dy - ing woes, E - ven while Thy life - blood flows,

Crav - ing par - don for Thy foes, Hear us, Ho - ly JE - SU. A-men.

"FATHER, FORGIVE THEM, FOR THEY
KNOW NOT WHAT THEY DO."

p JESU, in Thy dying woes,
　Even while Thy life-blood flows,
Craving pardon for Thy foes,
　　cr Hear us, Holy JESU.

p SAVIOUR, for our pardon sue,
　When our sins Thy pangs renew,
For we know not what we do :—
　　cr Hear us, Holy JESU.

p Oh ! may we, who mercy need,
　Be like Thee in heart and deed,
When with wrong our spirits bleed.
　　cr Hear us, Holy JESU.

"TO-DAY SHALT THOU BE WITH ME IN
PARADISE."

mf JESU, pitying the sighs
　Of the thief who near Thee dies,
Promising him Paradise.
　　Hear us, Holy JESU.

May we, in our guilt and shame,
Still Thy love and mercy claim,
Calling humbly on Thy Name.
　　Hear us, Holy JESU.

Oh ! remember those who pine,
Looking from their cross to Thine ;
Cheer their souls with hope Divine.
　　Hear us, Holy JESU.

"WOMAN, BEHOLD THY SON." "BEHOLD
THY MOTHER."

mp JESU, loving to the end
　Her whose heart Thy sorrows rend,
And Thy dearest human friend,
　　cr Hear us, Holy JESU.

May we in Thy sorrows share,
For Thy sake all peril dare,
Ever know Thy tender care.
　　Hear us, Holy JESU.

Litany of the Seven Words from the Cross.

May we all Thy loved ones be,—
All one holy family,
Loving for the love of Thee.
Hear us, Holy JESU.

"MY GOD, MY GOD, WHY HAST THOU
FORSAKEN ME?"

p JESU, whelm'd in fears unknown,
With our evil left alone,
While no light from Heav'n is shown,
  cr Hear us, Holy JESU.

When we seem in vain to pray,
And our hope seems far away,
In the darkness be our stay.
Hear us, Holy JESU.

Though no Father seem to hear,
Though no light our spirits cheer,
May we know that GOD is near.
Hear us, Holy JESU.

"I THIRST."

p JESU, in Thy thirst and pain,
While Thy wounds Thy life-blood drain,
Thirsting more our love to gain ;
  cr Hear us, Holy JESU.

mp Long for us in mercy still ;
May we Thy desires fulfil,—
Satisfy Thy loving will.
  cr Hear us, Holy JESU.

May we thirst Thy love to know ;
Lead us worn with sin and woe
Where the healing waters flow.
Hear us, Holy JESU.

"IT IS FINISHED."

mp JESU,—all our ransom paid,
All Thy FATHER'S will obey'd,—
By Thy sufferings perfect made ;
Hear us, Holy JESU.

p Save us in our soul's distress,
Be our help to cheer and bless,
While we grow in holiness.
  cr Hear us, Holy JESU.

mp Brighten all our heavenward way
With an ever holier ray,
Till we pass to perfect day.
Hear us, Holy JESU.

"FATHER, INTO THY HANDS I COMMEND
MY SPIRIT."

mp JESU,—all Thy labour vast,
All Thy woe and conflict past,—
dim Yielding up Thy soul at last ;
Hear us, Holy JESU.

p When the death-shades round us lour.
Guard us from the tempter's power,
Keep us in that trial hour.
Hear us, Holy JESU.

mp May Thy life and death supply
Grace to live and grace to die,
  cr Grace to reach the Home on High.
Hear us, Holy JESU.

T. B. POLLOCK

For Mission Services and Instructions.

Hymn 626. ST. PETER.—C.M. (*First Tune.*)   A. R. REINAGLE, 1799-1877.

A - men.

A lower setting of this Tune is given at Hymn 596.

"*So shall I make answer unto my blasphemers : for my trust is in Thy word.*"

mf APPROACH, my soul, the mercy-seat,
 Where JESUS answers prayer ;
dim There humbly fall before His feet,
 For none can perish there.

p Thy promise is my only plea,
 With this I venture nigh :
Thou callest burden'd souls to Thee,
cr And such, O LORD, am I.

p Bow'd down beneath a load of sin,
 By Satan sorely press'd,

By war without, and fears within,
cr I come to Thee for rest.

p Be Thou my Shield and Hiding Place,
 That, shelter'd near Thy side,
cr I may my fierce accuser face,
 And tell him, Thou hast died.

mf Oh wondrous love, to bleed and die,
 To bear the Cross and shame,
That guilty sinners, such as I,
 Might plead Thy gracious Name !

J. NEWTON, 1779.

Hymn 626. Kent.—C.M. (*Second Tune.*)

S. Stanley, 1767–1822.

A-men.

" So shall I make answer unto my blasphemers : for my trust is in Thy word.'

mf A PPROACH, my soul, the mercy-seat,
　　Where Jesus answers prayer ;
dim There humbly fall before His feet,
　　For none can perish there.

p 　Thy promise is my only plea,
　　With this I venture nigh :
　　Thou callest burden'd souls to Thee,
cr 　And such, O Lord, am I.

p 　Bow'd down beneath a load of sin,
　　By Satan sorely press'd,

　　By war without, and fears within,
cr 　I come to Thee for rest.

p 　Be Thou my Shield and Hiding Place,
　　That, shelter'd near Thy side,
cr 　I may my fierce accuser face,
　　And tell him, Thou hast died.

mf Oh wondrous love, to bleed and die,
　　To bear the Cross and shame,
　　That guilty sinners, such as I,
　　Might plead Thy gracious Name !

J. Newton, 1779.

Hymn 627. God made me.—10 10 10 10.

Sir J. F. Bridge.

A-men.

" Thou hast destroyed thyself ; but in Me is thy help found."

mf G OD made me for Himself, to serve Him here
　　With love's pure service and in filial fear ;
　To show His praise, for Him to labour now ;
　Then see His glory where the Angels bow.

　All needful grace was mine, through His dear Son,
　Whose life and death my full salvation won ;
　The grace that would have strengthen'd me, and taught ;
　Grace that would crown me when my work was wrought.

p 　And I, poor sinner, cast it all away ;
　Lived for the toil or pleasure of each day ;
　As if no Christ had shed His precious Blood,
　As if I owed no homage to my God.

mf O Holy Spirit, with Thy fire Divine,
　Melt into tears this thankless heart of mine ;
　Teach me to love what once I seem'd to hate,
　And live to God, before it be too late.

Sir H. W. Baker.

Alternative Tune, Hymn 696.

For Mission Services and Instructions.

Hymn 628. RETURN.—8 6 8 6 4.

W. H. MONK.

A - men.

" Return unto the Lord thy God ; for thou hast fallen by thine iniquity."

mf RETURN, O wanderer, to thy home,
Thy FATHER calls for thee ;
No longer now an exile roam,
In guilt and misery :
p   Return, return !

Too long the loathsome fields of sin
Thy fruitless toil have known :
No wholesome bread ! no voice of kin !
No home to call thine own !
cr   Return, return !

Thy FATHER stands with outstretch'd hands,
He gave His SON for thee :
Poor soul, from sin's enthralling bands
He longs to set thee free.
Return, return !

mf Arise, stand up and homeward turn,
No longer dwell apart ;
His mighty love will never spurn
One humble contrite heart.
dim   Return, return !

mf Our FATHER'S house is full of bliss,
And there is room for all ;
He welcomes with forgiving kiss ;
O, hear His loving call !
dim   Return, return !

mf The feast of joys awaits thee there,
The precious robe and ring ;
O haste thy FATHER'S gifts to share,
O haste His praise to sing :
Return, return !

T. HASTINGS, 1831.

Hymn 629. SHOWERS OF BLESSING.—8 7 8 7 3. *(First Tune.)*

Archbishop MACLAGAN.

A - men.

" There shall be showers of blessing."

mf LORD, I hear of showers of blessing
Thou art scattering full and free,
Showers the thirsty land refreshing ;
Let some drops descend on me—Even me.

p Pass me not, O gracious FATHER,
Sinful though my heart may be ;
Thou might'st leave me, but the rather
Let Thy mercy light on me—Even me.

Pass me not, O gracious SAVIOUR !
Let me love and cling to Thee ;
cr I am longing for Thy favour ;
Whilst Thou'rt calling, oh call me—Even me.

Pass me not, O mighty SPIRIT !
Thou canst make the blind to see ;

Witnesser of JESU'S merit,
Speak the word of power to me—Even me.

p Have I long in sin been sleeping,
Long been slighting, grieving Thee ?
Has the world my heart been keeping ?
O forgive and rescue me—Even me.

cr Love of GOD, so pure and changeless,
Blood of CHRIST, so rich and free ;
Grace of GOD, so strong and boundless,
Magnify it all in me—Even me.

cr Pass me not ; but, pardon bringing,
Bind my heart, O LORD, to Thee ;
Whilst the streams of life are springing,
Blessing others, O bless me—Even me.

E. CODNER.

Hymn 629. ETIAM ET MIHI.—8 7 8 7 3. (*Second Tune.*) Rev. J. B. DYKES.

A-men.

[*For copyright, see p.* lv.]

" There shall be showers of blessing."

mf LORD, I hear of showers of blessing
　Thou art scattering full and free,
Showers the thirsty land refreshing ;
　Let some drops descend on me—Even me.

p Pass me not, O gracious FATHER,
　Sinful though my heart may be ;
Thou might'st leave me, but the rather
　Let Thy mercy light on me—Even me.

Pass me not, O gracious SAVIOUR !
　Let me love and cling to Thee ;
cr I am longing for Thy favour ;
　Whilst Thou'rt calling, oh call me—Even me.

Pass me not, O mighty SPIRIT !
　Thou canst make the blind to see ;

Witnesser of JESU's merit,
　Speak the word of power to me—Even me.

p Have I long in sin been sleeping,
　Long been slighting, grieving Thee ?
Has the world my heart been keeping ?
　O forgive and rescue me—Even me.

cr Love of GOD, so pure and changeless ;
　Blood of CHRIST, so rich and free ;
Grace of GOD, so strong and boundless,
　Magnify it all in me—Even me.

cr Pass me not ; but, pardon bringing,
　Bind my heart, O LORD, to Thee ;
Whilst the streams of life are springing,
　Blessing others, O bless me—Even me.

E. CODNER.

Hymn 630. MARTYRDOM.—C.M. (*First Tune.*)　　H. WILSON, 1766–1824.

A-men.

A higher setting of this Tune is given at Hymn **238.**

Hymn 630. CAITHNESS.—C.M. (*Second Tune.*)　　*Psalmes* (Edinburgh, 1635).

For Mission Services and Instructions.

A-men.

" Oh that I were as in months past."

mf O FOR a closer walk with GOD,
A calm and heav'nly frame;
A light to shine upon the road
That leads me to the LAMB!

p What peaceful hours I once enjoy'd!
How sweet their memory still!
But they have left an aching void
The world can never fill.

Return, O holy DOVE, return,
Sweet messenger of rest:

I hate the sins that made Thee mourn,
And drove Thee from my breast.

The dearest idol I have known,
Whate'er that idol be,
cr Help me to tear it from Thy Throne,
And worship only Thee.

So shall my walk be close with GOD,
Calm and serene my frame;
So purer light shall mark the road
That leads me to the LAMB.

W. COWPER, 1772.

Hymn 631. OH, THE BITTER.—8 7 8 8 7.

W. H. MONK.

A-men.

" He died for all, that they which live should not henceforth live unto themselves."

mf OH, the bitter shame and sorrow,
That a time could ever be
p When I let the SAVIOUR'S pity
Plead in vain, and proudly answer'd,
"All of self, and none of Thee."

cr Yet He found me: *(dim)* I beheld Him
Bleeding on the accursèd tree,
p Heard Him pray, "Forgive them, FATHER;"
And my wistful heart said faintly,
pp "Some of self and some of Thee."

cr Day by day His tender mercy,
Healing, helping, full and free,
Sweet and strong, and ah! so patient,
Brought me lower, while I whisper'd,
"Less of self, and more of Thee."

mf Higher than the highest heavens,
Deeper than the deepest sea,
LORD, Thy love at last hath conquer'd;
cr Grant me now my soul's desire,
f "None of self, and all of Thee."

TH. MONOD.

(543)

Hymn 632. REDEEMED.—7 6 7 6. 7 6 7 6. Sir J. STAINER.

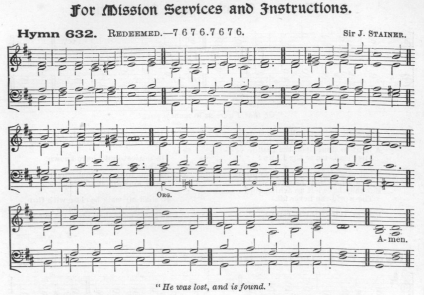

A-men.

"He was lost, and is found."

mf REDEEM'D, restored, forgiven
   Through JESUS' precious Blood,
   Heirs of His home in Heaven,
cr O praise our pardoning GOD!
   Praise Him in tuneful measures,
   Who gave His SON to die ;
f Praise Him Whose sevenfold treasures
   Enrich and sanctify !

p Once on the dreary mountain
   We wander'd far and wide,
   Far from the cleansing Fountain,
   Far from the piercèd Side ;
cr But JESUS sought and found us,
   And wash'd our guilt away ;
   With cords of love He bound us
   To be His own for aye.

   Dear Master, Thine the glory
   Of each recover'd soul ;
   Ah ! who can tell the story
p Of love that made us whole?
   Not ours, not ours the merit ;
mf Be Thine alone the praise,
cr And ours a thankful spirit
   To serve Thee all our days.

p Now keep us, Holy SAVIOUR,
   In Thy true love and fear ;
   And grant us of Thy favour
   The grace to persevere ;
cr Till, in Thy new creation,
   Earth's time-long travail o'er,
   We find our full salvation,
f And praise Thee evermore.

Sir H. W. BAKER.

ALTERNATIVE TUNE, HYMN 227 (SECOND TUNE).

Hymn 633. WILTSHIRE.—C.M. (*First Tune.*) Sir G. SMART, 1798.

A - men.

A higher setting of this Tune is given at Hymn 290.

For Mission Services and Instructions.

Hymn 633. WALSALL.—C.M. (*Second Tune.*)

Slow.

ANCHORS, *Choice Collection, c.* 1721.

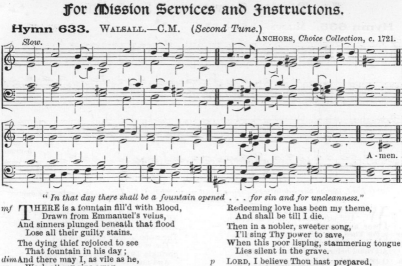

A-men.

" In that day there shall be a fountain opened . . . for sin and for uncleanness."

mf THERE is a fountain fill'd with Blood,
Drawn from Emmanuel's veins,
And sinners plunged beneath that flood
Lose all their guilty stains.

The dying thief rejoiced to see
That fountain in his day;
dim And there may I, as vile as he,
cr Wash all my sins away.

p Dear dying LAMB, Thy precious Blood
Shall never lose its power,
cr Till all the ransom'd Church of GOD
Be saved to sin no more.

E'er since by faith I saw the stream
Thy flowing Wounds supply,

Redeeming love has been my theme,
And shall be till I die.

Then in a nobler, sweeter song,
I'll sing Thy power to save,
When this poor lisping, stammering tongue
Lies silent in the grave.

p LORD, I believe Thou hast prepared,
Unworthy though I be,
For me a Blood-bought free reward,
A golden harp for me.

cr 'Tis strung and tuned for endless years,
And form'd by power Divine,
f To sound in GOD the FATHER'S ears
No other name but Thine.

W. COWPER. 1770.

Hymn 634. CLARION.—8 7 8 7.

Rev. W. S. SLOANE-EVANS.

A-men.

" I came not to judge the world, but to save the world."

mf SOULS of men! why will ye scatter
Like a crowd of frighten'd sheep?
Foolish hearts! why will ye wander
From a love so true and deep?

p Was there ever kindest shepherd
Half so gentle, half so sweet,
As the SAVIOUR Who would have us
Come and gather round His Feet?

cr There's a wideness in GOD's mercy,
Like the wideness of the sea;
There's a kindness in His justice,
Which is more than liberty.

There is no place where earth's sorrows
Are more felt than up in Heav'n;
p There is no place where earth's failings
Have such kindly judgment given.

mf There is plentiful redemption
In the Blood that has been shed;
There is joy for all the members
In the sorrows of the Head.

For the love of GOD is broader
Than the measures of man's mind;
And the Heart of the Eternal
Is most wonderfully kind.

mp Pining souls! come nearer JESUS,
And oh! come not doubting thus,
cr But with faith that trusts more bravely
His huge tenderness for us.

If our love were but more simple,
We should take Him at His word;
mf And our lives would be all sunshine
In the sweetness of our LORD.

ALTERNATIVE TUNE, HYMN 76.

F. W. FABER.

T

For Mission Services and Instructions.

Hymn 635.   MILTON.—8 8 8 8.8 8.   W. H. LONGHURST.

A-men.

"O Lord, though our iniquities testify against us, do Thou it for Thy Name's sake ; for our backslidings are many."

p   WEARY of wandering from my GOD,
     And now made willing to return,
I hear, and bow me to the rod ;
cr   For Thee, not without hope, I mourn ;
I have an Advocate above,
A Friend before the Throne of Love.

p   O JESUS, full of pardoning grace,
     More full of grace than I of sin,
Yet once again I seek Thy Face ;
cr   Open Thine Arms, and take me in,
And freely my backslidings heal,
And love the faithless sinner still.

Thou know'st the way to bring me back,
     My fallen spirit to restore ;
p   O for Thy truth and mercy's sake

Forgive, and bid me sin no more ;
The ruins of my soul repair,
And make my heart a house of prayer.

The stone to flesh again convert,
The veil of sin once more remove ;
Sprinkle Thy Blood upon my heart,
     And melt it with Thy dying love ;
cr   This rebel heart by love subdue,
And make it soft, and make it new.

Ah, give me, LORD, the tender heart
     That trembles at the approach of sin ;
A godly fear of sin impart,
Implant, and root it deep within,
That I may dread Thy gracious power,
And never dare offend Thee more.

ALTERNATIVE TUNE, HYMN 556 (SECOND TUNE).   C. WESLEY, 1749.

Hymn 636.   DULWICH.—7 7 7 7.7 7.   C. J. FROST.

A-men.

" Yield yourselves unto God . . . and your members as instruments of righteousness."

mf   FATHER, SON, and HOLY GHOST,
     ONE in THREE, and THREE in ONE,
As by the celestial host,
     Let Thy Will on earth be done ;
Praise by all to Thee be given,
Glorious LORD of earth and Heav'n.

p   If a sinner such as I
     May to Thy great glory live,
All my actions sanctify,
     All my words and thoughts receive ;
cr   Claim me for Thy service, claim
All I have, and all I am.

p   Take my soul and body's powers ;
     Take my memory, mind, and will,
All my goods, and all my hours,

All I know, and all I feel,
cr   All I think, or speak, or do ;
Take my heart ;—but make it new !
mf   O my GOD, Thine own I am,
     Let me give Thee back Thine own ;
Freedom, friends, and health, and fame,
     Consecrate to Thee alone ;
Thine to live, thrice happy I ;
Happier still if Thine I die.

FATHER, SON, and HOLY GHOST,
     ONE in THREE, and THREE in ONE,
As by the celestial host,
     Let Thy Will on earth be done ;
f   Praise by all to Thee be given,
Glorious LORD of earth and Heav'n.

(546)

C. WESLEY, 1745.

For Mission Services and Instructions.

Hymn 637. COMPASSIO.—12 11 12 11.

C. BUCKNALL

A - men

"*Be of good comfort ; rise, He calleth thee.*"

mf * OH ! come to the merciful SAVIOUR Who calls you,
    Oh ! come to the LORD Who forgives and forgets ;
dim Though dark be the fortune on earth that befalls you,
cr   There's a bright Home above, where the sun never sets.

Oh ! come then to JESUS, Whose Arms are extended
   To fold His dear children in closest embrace ;
Oh ! come, for your exile will shortly be ended,
   And JESUS will show you His beautiful Face.

mf Yes, come to the SAVIOUR, Whose mercy grows brighter
   The longer you look at the depth of His love ;
And fear not ! 'tis JESUS ! and life's cares grow lighter
   As you think of the Home and the Glory above.

p Have you sinn'd as none else in the world have before you ?
   Are you blacker than all other creatures in guilt ?
cr Oh, fear not, and doubt not ! the mother who bore you
mf   Loves you less than the SAVIOUR Whose Blood you have spilt !

Come, come to His Feet, and lay open your story
   Of suffering and sorrow, of guilt and of shame ;
For the pardon of sin is the crown of His glory,
   And the joy of our LORD to be true to His Name.

F. W. FABER.

* 1st Verse.

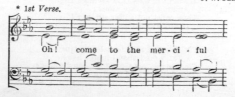

Oh!   come   to   the   mer - ci - ful

(547)

For Mission Services and Instructions.

Hymn 638. St. Francis Xavier.—C.M.

Sir J. Stainer.

A-men.

A higher setting of this Tune is given at Hymn 106.

" If we confess our sins, He is faithful and just to forgive us our sins, and to cleanse us from all unrighteousness."

p   O GOD, to know that Thou art just
    Gives hope and peace within ;
We could not in a mercy trust
  Which takes no count of sin.

I fain would open to Thy sight
  My utmost wickedness ;
Set, LORD, in Thy most searching light
  What I have done amiss.

No stern and needless law was Thine—
  Hard to be understood—
But plainly read in every line,
  Holy, and just, and good.

Though basely weak my fallen race,
  And masterful my foes,
I had th' omnipotence of grace
  To conquer, if I chose.

Well did I know the tender Heart
  I outraged by my sin,
Yet with the world I would not part,
  Nor rein my passions in.

My fault it was, O LORD Most High,
  And not my fate alone :
Thou canst not suffer sin, nor I
  In any way atone.

cr Yet there's a plea that I may trust—
    CHRIST died that I might live !
Cleanse me, my GOD, for Thou art just ;
  Be faithful, and forgive.

A. J. MASON.

(548)

SECOND SUPPLEMENT.

Noon.

Hymn 639. Bucklebury.—D.L.M.

Harmonia Perfecta, 1730.

A - men.

" In the evening, and morning, and at noonday will I pray."

f UP to the throne of GOD is borne
    The voice of praise at early morn,
And He accepts the punctual hymn,
Sung as the light of day grows dim.
Nor will He turn His ear aside
From holy off'rings at noon-tide ;
Then here to Him our souls we raise,
In songs of gratitude and praise.

mf Blest are the moments, doubly blest,
That, drawn from this one hour of rest,
Are with a ready heart bestow'd
Upon the service of our GOD.
f Look up to heav'n ; th' industrious sun
Already half his race hath run ;
He cannot halt, or go astray,
But our immortal spirits may

mf LORD, since his rising in the east
If we have falter'd or transgress'd,
Guide, from Thy love's abundant source,
What yet remains of this day's course.
Help with Thy grace, through life's short day,
Our upward and our downward way ;
cr And glorify for us the west,
When we shall sink to final rest.

W. WORDSWORTH, 1770-1850.

Advent

Hymn 640. HALTON HOLGATE.—8 7 8 7. *(First Tune.)*   W BOYCE 1775

A-men.

Hymn 640. CROSS OF JESUS.—8 7 8 7. *(Second Tune.)*   SIR J. STAINER.

A-men.

[For copyright, see p. lv.]

" Come, Lord Jesus."

mf COME, Thou long-expected JESUS,
　　Born to set Thy people free ;
From our fears and sins release us ;
　　Let us find our rest in Thee.

Israel's strength and consolation,
　　Hope of all the earth Thou art :
Dear Desire of every nation,
　　Joy of every longing heart.

f 　Born Thy people to deliver ;
　　Born a Child and yet a King :
Born to reign in us for ever ;
　　Now Thy gracious kingdom bring.

By Thy own eternal Spirit,
　　Rule in all our hearts alone :
By Thy all-sufficient merit,
　　Raise us to Thy glorious throne.

C. WESLEY. 1746.

Advent.

Hymn 641. GERONIMO.—8 8 8.8 8 6. Sir C. V. STANFORD.

[*Copyright* 1904 *by the Proprietors of* Hymns Ancient and Modern.]

"*At midnight there was a cry made, Behold the Bridegroom cometh ; go ye out to meet Him.*"

    f   "BEHOLD the Bridegroom draweth nigh :"
           Hear ye the oft-repeated cry?
        Go forth into the midnight dim ;
  mf For bless'd are they whom He shall find
        With ready heart and watchful mind ;
        Go forth, my soul, to Him.

    f   "Behold the Bridegroom cometh by,"
        The call is echo'd from the sky :
        Go forth, ye servants, watch and wait ;
  mf The slothful cannot join His train ;
        No careless one may entrance gain ;
        Awake, my soul, 'tis late.

    p   The wise will plead with one accord,
        "O Holy, Holy, Holy LORD,
        On us Thy quick'ning grace bestow,
        That none may reach the door too late,
        When Thou shalt enter at the gate
        And to Thy kingdom go."

    f   "Behold the Bridegroom draweth near,"
        The warning falls on every ear :
        That night of dread shall come to all :
        Behold, my soul, thy lamp so dim,
        Rise, rise the smoking flax to trim ;
        Soon shalt thou hear His call.

                         R. M. MOORSOM · from the Greek.

(551)

Christmas.

To be sung in Unison.

[For copyright, see p. lv.]

"Immanuel . . . God with us."

Unison.

p O LITTLE town of Bethlehem,
　How still we see thee lie!
Above thy deep and dreamless sleep
　The silent stars go by:
mf Yet in thy dark streets shineth
　The everlasting Light—
f The hopes and fears of all the years
　Are met in thee to-night.

Unison.

f For CHRIST is born of Mary;
　And, gather'd all above,
p While mortals sleep, the angels keep
　Their watch of wond'ring love.
f O morning stars, together
　Proclaim the holy birth,
And praises sing to GOD the King,
　And peace to men on earth.

(552)

Christmas.

Harmony.

p How silently, how silently,
    The wondrous gift is given !
  So GOD imparts to human hearts
    The blessings of His heaven.
  No ear may hear His coming ;
    But in this world of sin,
mp Where meek souls will receive Him, still
cr   The dear CHRIST enters in.

Unison.

f O Holy Child of Bethlehem,
    Descend to us, we pray ;
  Cast out our sin, and enter in :
    Be born in us to-day
cr We hear the Christmas angels
    The great glad tidings tell :
  O come to us, abide with us,
ff Our LORD Immanuel.

Bishop P. BROOKS.

The last line of each verse is repeated.

Epiphany.

Hymn 643. BEDE.—11 10 11 10. (*First Tune.*) Adapted by Sir J. GOSS, 1864.

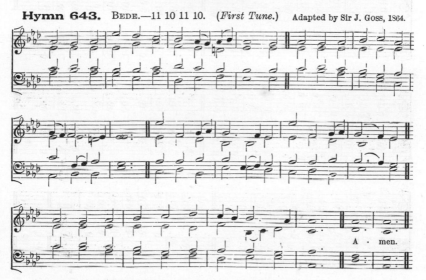

"The star which they saw in the east went before them, till it came and stood over where the young Child was."

f BRIGHTEST and best of the sons of the morning,
    Dawn on our darkness, and lend us thine aid !
  Star of the East, the horizon adorning,
    Guide where our infant Redeemer is laid !

mf Cold on His cradle the dew-drops are shining ;
    Low lies His head with the beasts of the stall ;
  Angels adore Him in slumber reclining,
    Maker and Monarch and Saviour of all.

  Say, shall we yield Him, in costly devotion,
    Odours of Edom, and offerings divine,
  Gems of the mountain, and pearls of the ocean,
    Myrrh from the forest, or gold from the mine ?

  Vainly we offer each ample oblation,
    Vainly with gifts would His favour secure :
  Richer by far is the heart's adoration,
    Dearer to GOD are the prayers of the poor.

Bishop HEBER, 1783-1826.

The first verse may be repeated at the end.

Epiphany.

Hymn 643. Epiphany.—11 10 11 10. 11 10 11 10. (*Second Tune.*)

S. S. Wesley, 1864.

A-men.

" The star which they saw in the east went before them, till it came and stood over where the young Child was."

f BRIGHTEST and best of the sons of the morning,
  Dawn on our darkness, and lend us thine aid !
 Star of the East, the horizon adorning,
  Guide where our infant Redeemer is laid !

mf Cold on His cradle the dew-drops are shining ;
  Low lies His head with the beasts of the stall ;
 Angels adore Him in slumber reclining,
  Maker and Monarch and Saviour of all.

Say, shall we yield Him, in costly devotion,
  Odours of Edom, and offerings divine,
 Gems of the mountain, and pearls of the ocean,
  Myrrh from the forest, or gold from the mine ?

Vainly we offer each ample oblation,
  Vainly with gifts would His favour secure :
 Richer by far is the heart's adoration,
  Dearer to GOD are the prayers of the poor.

        Bishop Heber, 1783–1826.

(554)

Lent.

Hymn 644. Old 112th.—8 8.8 8.8 8.

Psalmes, 1558.

A-men.

" Out of the depths have I cried unto Thee, O Lord."

mf TH' abyss of many a former sin
 Encloses me and bars me in :
Like billows my transgressions roll :
Be Thou the Pilot of my soul,
And to salvation's harbour bring,
Thou Saviour and Thou glorious King !

My FATHER'S heritage abused,
Wasted by lust, by sin misused ;
To shame and want and misery brought,
The slave to many a fruitless thought,
I cry to Thee, Who lovest men,
O pity and receive again !

p In hunger now, no more possess'd
Of that my portion bright and blest.
The exile and the alien see,
Who yet would fain return to Thee,
And save me, LORD, who seek to raise
To Thy dear love the hymn of praise !

With that blest thief my prayer I make,
" Remember " for Thy mercy's sake !
With that poor publican I cry,
" Be merciful," O GOD most high :
With that lost prodigal I fain
Back to my home would turn again :

Mourn, mourn, my soul, with earnest care,
And raise to CHRIST the contrite prayer ;
" O Thou, Who freely wast made poor,
My sorrows and my sins to cure,
Me, poor of all good works, embrace,
Enriching with Thy boundless grace ! "

J. M. NEALE : from the Greek
of St. Joseph the Studite.

(555)

Lent.

Hymn 645. TUNBRIDGE.—7 7 7 7. (*First Tune.*)   J CLARKE, 1709.

Hymn 645. ST. MARY AT HILL.—7 7 7 7. (*Second Tune.*)   G. BERG, 1775.

A men.

" God, be merciful to me a sinner."

p   SINFUL, sighing to be blest ;
      Bound, and longing to be free ;
Weary, waiting for my rest ;
    GOD, be merciful to me.

Goodness I have none to plead,
    Sinfulness in all I see,
I can only bring my need ;
    GOD, be merciful to me.

Broken heart and downcast eyes
    Dare not lift themselves to Thee ;
Yet Thou canst interpret sighs :
    GOD, be merciful to me.

From this sinful heart of mine
    To Thy bosom I would flee :
I am not my own, but Thine :
    GOD, be merciful to me.

f   There is One beside the throne,
    And my only hope and plea
Are in Him, and Him alone :
mf   GOD, be merciful to me

He my cause will undertake,
    My Interpreter will be ;
He's my all ; and for His sake,
    GOD, be merciful to me

                    J S. B. MONSELL.

ALTERNATIVE TUNE, HYMN 105.

(556)

Lent.

Hymn 646. Credo, Domine.—10 10 10. 10 10 10.

C. H. LLOYD.

[Copyright 1915 by the Proprietors of Hymns Ancient and Modern.]

" All things are possible to him that believeth."

MY sins have taken such a hold on me,
　　I am not able to look up to Thee ;
　Lord, I repent ; accept my tears and grief:
But Thou hast taken all my sin away,
And I in Thee dare now look up and pray :
　Lord, I believe ; help Thou mine unbelief.

Of nights unhallow'd, and of sinful days,
Of careless thoughts and words and works and ways,
　Lord, I repent ; accept my tears and grief :
And in the life which doth within me live,
And the forgiveness which can all forgive,
　Lord, I believe ; help Thou mine unbelief.

Of selfishness which makes the soul unjust,
Envy and strife and every sinful lust,
　Lord, I repent ; accept my tears and grief :
And in the blood, which doth my pardon plead,
The truth and love, which for me intercede,
　Lord, I believe ; help Thou mine unbelief.

Of sins that as a cloud have hid Thy face,
Of Thy care slighted, and Thy grievèd grace,
　Lord, I repent ; accept my tears and grief :
In Love, that puts sin's envious veil aside,
Rending the veil of flesh which for me died,
　Lord, I believe ; help Thou mine unbelief.

For sin I mourn, the sin that gave Thee pain ;
Thine was the burden, mine alone the stain ;
　Lord, I repent ; accept my tears and grief :
Christ is my joy ; and out of all distress
He doth deliver with His righteousness :
　Lord. I believe; help Thou mine unbelief.

J. S. B. Monsell.

Passiontide.

Hymn 647. Genevan Psalm cx.—11 10 11 10.   L. Bourgeois, 1551.

A-men.

" Let us also go that we may die with Him."

Holy Week.

mf LORD, through this Holy Week of our salvation,
    Which Thou hast won for us who went astray,
In all the conflict of Thy sore temptation
We would continue with Thee day by day.

We would not leave Thee, though our weak endurance
    Make us unworthy here to take our part ;
Yet give us strength to trust the sweet assurance
That Thou, O LORD, art greater than our heart.

Thou didst forgive Thine own who slept for sorrow,
    Thou didst have pity, O have pity now,
And let us watch through each sad eve and morrow
With Thee, in holy prayer and solemn vow.

p Along that Sacred Way where Thou art leading,
    Which Thou didst take to save our souls from loss,
Let us go also, till we see Thee pleading
In all-prevailing prayer upon Thy Cross :

mf Until Thou see Thy bitter travail's ending,
    The world redeem'd, the will of GOD complete,
And, to Thy FATHER'S hands Thy soul commending,
Thou lay the work He gave Thee at His feet.

W. H. Draper.

Hymn 648. Intercessor.—11 10 11 10.   Sir H. Parry.

A - men.

Passiontide.

" Father, forgive them, for they know not what they do."

THE FIRST WORD FROM THE CROSS.

p   O WORD of pity, for our pardon pleading,
        Breathed in the hour of loneliness and pain ;
     O voice, which through the ages interceding
cr   Calls us to fellowship with GOD again.

p   O word of comfort, through the silence stealing,
        As the dread act of sacrifice oegan ;
     O infinite compassion, still revealing
        The infinite forgiveness won for man.

mf O word of hope to raise us nearer heaven,
        When courage fails us and when faith is dim ;
     The souls for whom CHRIST prays to CHRIST are given,
        To find their pardon and their joy in Him.

     O Intercessor, Who art ever living
        To plead for dying souls that they may live,
     Teach us to know our sin which needs forgiving,
        Teach us to know the love which can forgive.

ADA R. GREENAWAY.

Hymn 649.   COVENTRY.—S.M.   *(First Tune.)*   W. DORRELL, 1853.

A - men.

Hymn 649.   WALMISLEY.—S.M.   *(Second Tune.)*   T. A. WALMISLEY, 1814–1856.

A-men.

" I thirst.'

THE FIFTH WORD FROM THE CROSS.

mf O PERFECT GOD, Thy love
        As perfect Man did share
     Here upon earth each form of ill
        Thy fellow-men must bear.

     Now from the Tree of scorn
        We hear Thy voice again ;
     Thou Who didst take our mortal flesh,
        Hast felt our mortal pain.

p   Thy Body suffers thirst,
        Parch'd are Thy lips and dry :

How poor the offering man can bring
   Thy thirst to satisfy !

mf O Saviour, by Thy thirst
        Borne on the Cross of shame,
     Grant us in all our sufferings here
        To glorify Thy Name ;

     That through each pain and grief
        Our souls may onward move
     To gain more likeness to Thy life,
        More knowledge of Thy love.

ADA R. GREENAWAY.

Easter.

SALVE FESTA DIES.—10 10.

B. LUARD SELBY.

The Refrain is first sung by Solo Voices, then repeated by Chorus in Unison.

Semi-chorus in Unison sing the Verses.

FINE.

Repeat Chorus.

[*Copyright* 1904 *by the Proprietors of* Hymns Ancient and Modern.]

A lower setting of this Tune is given at Hymn 652.

"This is the day which the Lord hath made."

f HAIL, festal day, whose glory never ends ;
Now hell is vanquish'd, CHRIST to heav'n ascends.

All nature with new births of beauty gay
Acknowledges her LORD'S return to-day.
Hail, festal day, &c.

The Crucified is King ; creation's prayer
To its Creator rises everywhere.
Hail, festal day, &c.

Let what Thou promisedst, fair Power, be done ;
The third day shines ; arise, O buried One.
Hail, festal day, &c.

It cannot be that Joseph's sepulchre
Should keep the whole world's Ransom prisoner.
Hail, festal day, &c.

No rock of stone His passage can withstand,
Who gathers all the world within His hand.
Hail, festal day, &c.

Leave to the grave Thy grave-clothes ; let them fall ;
Without Thee we have naught, and with Thee all.
Hail, festal day, &c.

Thou gavest life, and dost endure the grave ;
Thou tread'st the way of death, from death to save.
Hail, festal day, &c.

Bring back the day,—Thy dying made it night,—
That ages in Thy face may see the light.
Hail, festal day, &c.

Thy rescued are like sand beside the sea,
And where their Saviour goes, they follow free.
Hail, festal day, &c.

The law of death has ceased the world to blight,
And darkness quails before the face of light.
Hail, festal day, &c.

A. J. MASON : from Venantius Fortunatus.

Easter.

Hymn 651. GIBEON.—10 10 10 10. *(First Tune.)*   S. WESLEY, 1835.

A-men.

Hymn 651. SONG 22.—10 10 10 10. *(Second Tune.)*   O. GIBBONS, 1623.

A-men

" Behold, I make all things new."

f   GLORY to GOD! The morn appointed breaks,
And earth awakes from all the woeful past;
For, with the morn, the LORD of life awakes,
And sin and death into the grave are cast.

Glory to GOD! The cross, with all its shame,
Now sheds its glory o'er a ransom'd world;
mf For He Who bore the burden of our blame,
f With piercèd hands the foe to hell hath hurl'd.

Glory to GOD! Sing, ransom'd souls again,
And let your songs our glorious Victor laud,
Who by His might hath snapp'd the tyrant's chain,
And set us free to rise with Him to GOD.

Darkness and night, farewell! the morn is here;
Welcome! the light that ushers in the day:
Visions of joy before our sight appear,
And, like the clouds, our sorrows melt away.

Great SON of GOD, Immortal, and renown'd!
Brighter than morn the glory on Thy brow;
Crowns must be won, and Thou art nobly crown'd.
For death is dead, and sin is vanquish'd now.

J BROWNLIE.

Ascensiontide.

Hymn 652. SALVE FESTA DIES.—10 10. B. LUARD SELBY.

The Refrain is first sung by Solo Voices, then repeated by Chorus in Unison.

FINE.

Semi-chorus in Unison sing the Verses. *Repeat Chorus.*

A higher setting of this Tune is given at Hymn **650.**

" This is the day which the Lord hath made."

f HAIL, festal day, whose glory never ends ;
  Now hell is vanquish'd, CHRIST to heav'n ascends.

All nature with new births of beauty gay
Acknowledges her LORD'S return to-day.
  Hail, festal day, &c.

Fair weather brings the flow'rs, and earth is bright ;
From heaven's open door streams ampler light.
  Hail, festal day, &c.

The greenwood trees, the fields in blossom swell
The joy of CHRIST'S return from that dark hell.
  Hail, festal day. &c.

CHRIST is gone up ; no longer sin shall reign ;
Praise Him, blue sky, and sun-lit sea and plain.
  Hail, festal day, &c.

Set free the captives of the pit below ;
Call back again the things that downward go.
  Hail, festal day, &c.

Thy rescued are like sand beside the sea,
And where their Saviour goes, they follow free.
  Hail, festal day, &c.

Nurse in Thine arms Thy people cleansed from stain,
And bear to GOD a gift made pure again.
  Hail, festal day, &c.

One wreath receive for Thine own works on high,
Another for Thy people s victory.
  Hail, festal day, &c.

O SAVIOUR CHRIST, Thou art GOD'S only Son,
Creator and Redeemer both in one.
  Hail, festal day, &c.

As ancient as Thy Father and not less,
By Thee the world arose from nothingness.
  Hail, festal day, &c.

Thou, seeing all men crush'd beneath the ban,
Didst put on manhood to deliver man.
  Hail, festal day, &c.

A. J. MASON : from Venantius Fortunatus

Whitsuntide.

Hymn 653. OCKLEY.—10 10.   Sir C. V. STANFORD.

" This is the day which the Lord hath made."

Full.	*f*	HAIL, festal day, of never-dying fame, When first upon the Church the SPIRIT came.
Men.		The sun has now a higher track to keep Betwixt the eastern and the western deep. Hail, festal day, &c.
Sopranos.		Through clearer air it shoots more searching rays, And makes short nights between the length'ning days. Hail, festal day, &c.
Men.		Far depths of cloudless sky are bared to sight ; The clear stars tell their story of delight. Hail, festal day, &c.
Sopranos.		The merry country offers all her store, Now spring has brought its yearly wealth once more. Hail, festal day, &c.
Men.		White gleam the hawthorn bushes as we pass, And green and tall grows up the waving grass. Hail, festal day, &c.
Sopranos.		Day after day fresh flowers like stars arise, And all the turf breaks into laughing eyes. Hail, festal day, &c.

A. J. MASON : from Venantius Fortunatus.

Trinity Sunday.

Hymn 654. FIDES.—8 7 8 7. 8 8 7.

Rev C. C. SCHOLEFIELD.

A - men.

[For copyright, see p. lv.]

" Hallowed be Thy Name."

f SOUND aloud Jehovah's praises;
       Tell abroad the awful Name ;
Heav'n the ceaseless anthem raises,
    Let the earth her GOD proclaim,—
GOD, the hope of every nation,
GOD, the source of consolation,
    Holy, blessèd TRINITY !

This the Name from ancient ages
    Hidden in its dazzling light ;
This the Name that kings and sages
    Pray'd and strove to know aright,
Through GOD'S wondrous Incarnation
Now reveal'd the world's salvation,
    Ever blessèd TRINITY !

mf Into this great Name and holy
       We all tribes and tongues baptize ;
Thus the Highest owns the lowly,
    Homeward, heav'nward, bids them rise,
Gathers them from every nation,
Bids them join in adoration
    Of the blessèd TRINITY !

f In this Name the heart rejoices,
       Pouring forth its secret prayer ;
In this Name we lift our voices,
    And our common faith declare,
Off'ring praise and supplication,
And the thankful life's oblation,
    To the blessèd TRINITY !

Still Thy Name o'er earth and ocean
    Shall be carried, "GOD is Love,"
Whisper'd by the heart's devotion,
    Echo'd by the choirs above,
Hallow'd through all worlds for ever,
LORD, of life the only Giver,
    Blessèd, glorious TRINITY !

H. A. MARTIN.

(564)

General Hymns.

Hymn 655. ST. PATRICK'S BREASTPLATE.—Irregular.

" His faithfulness and truth shall be thy shield and buckler."

Old Irish Melodies. Arranged by Sir C. V. STANFORD.

VOICES. *Full Unison. Rather quickly, and with strong rhythm.*

1. (*f*) I bind un-to my-self to-day The strong name

of the TRIN-I-TY, By in-vo-ca-tion

of the same, The THREE in ONE, and ONE in THREE.

MEN.
2. (*mf*) I bind this day to me for ev-er, By power of
TREBLES.
*4. (*mf*) I bind un-to my-self to-day The vir-tues
FULL.
*7. A-gainst all Sa-tan's spells and wiles, A-gainst false

* *These verses may be omitted.*

General Hymns.

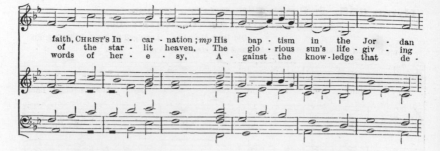

faith, CHRIST'S In - car - nation; *mp* His bap - tism in the Jor - dan
of the star - lit heaven, The glo - rious sun's life - giv - ing
words of her - e - sy, A - gainst the know - ledge that de -

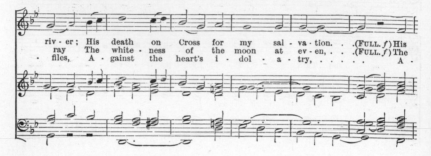

riv - er; His death on Cross for my sal - va - tion. . .(FULL. *f*)His
ray The white - ness of the moon at ev - en, . . .(FULL. *f*)The
files, A - gainst the heart's i - dol - a - try, ... A

burst - ing from the spic - ed tomb; His rid - ing
flash - ing of the light - ning free, The whirl - ing
- gainst the wiz - ard's e - vil craft, A - gainst the

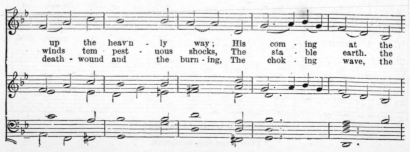

up the heav'n - ly way; His com - ing at the
winds tem - pest - uous shocks, The sta - ble earth. the
death - wound and the burn - ing, The chok - ing wave, the

General Hymns.

day of doom: I bind un - to my - self to - day.
deep salt sea, A - round the old e - ter - nal rocks.
poi - son'd shaft, Pro - tect me, CHRIST, till Thy re - turn - ing.

VOICES *in Harmony with Organ.*

*3. (*mf*) I bind un - to my - self the power . . Of the great love of
5. (*mf*) I bind un - to my - self to - day The power of GOD to
*6. (*mf*) A - gainst the de - mon snares of sin, The vice that gives temp

Cher - u - blm; The sweet "Well done" in judg - ment hour; The
hold and lead, His eye to watch, His might to stay, His
- ta - tion force, The na - tu - ral lusts that war with - in, The

ser - vice of the Ser - a - phim, (*Org.*) (*mf*) Con
ear to heark - en to my need; (*mp*) The
hos - tile men that mar my course— (*p*) Or

- fess - or's faith, A - pos - tles' word, The Pa - triarchs'
wis - dom of my GOD to teach, His hand to
few or ma - ny, far or nigh, In ev - 'ry

* These verses may be omitted.

General Hymns.

prayers, the Pro - phets' scrolls, (p) All good deeds done un -
guide, His shield to ward, The word of God to
place, and in all hours, A - gainst their fierce hos -

- to the LORD, And pu - ri - ty of vir - gin souls.
give me speech, His heaven - ly host to be my guard.
- til - i - ty, I bind to me these ho - ly powers.

In moderate time.

8. CHRIST be with me, CHRIST with - in me, CHRIST be - hind me,

CHRIST be - fore me, CHRIST be - side me, CHRIST to win me,

rall. . . . . . *tempo.*

CHRIST to com - fort and re - store me, CHRIST be - neath me,

CHRIST a - bove me, CHRIST in qui - et, CHRIST in dan - ger,

General Hymns.

CHRIST in hearts of all that love me, CHRIST in mouth of friend and stran - ger.

FULL. *A little slower.*

19. I bind un - to my - self the name, The strong name

of . . the TRIN - I - TY, By in - vo - ca - tion

of the same, The THREE in ONE, and ONE in

† *The accompaniment for verse 2 may be used.*

General Hymns.

THREE, ... Of Whom all na - ture hath cre - a - tion, E -

- ter - nal FA - THER, SPI - RIT, WORD, Praise to the LORD of

my sal - va - tion: Sal - va - tion is of CHRIST the

LORD. .... A - .... men.

MRS. ALEXANDER : from St. Patrick's *Lorica.*

General Hymns.

Hymn 656. SLEEPERS, WAKE.—8 9 8. 8 9 8. 6 6 4 8 8.   P. NICOLAI, 1599.

" Sing ye to the Lord, for He hath triumphed gloriously."

f PRAISE the LORD through every nation ;
　His holy arm hath wrought salvation ;
Exalt Him on His FATHER'S throne ;
Praise your King, ye Christian legions,
Who now prepares in heav'nly regions
　Unfailing mansions for His own :
　　With voice and minstrelsy
　　Extol His majesty :
　　　Alleluia !
His praise shall sound all nature round,
Where'er the race of man is found.

GOD with GOD dominion sharing,
And Man with man our image bearing,
　Gentile and Jew to Him are given :
Praise your Saviour, ransom'd sinners,
Of life, through Him, immortal winners ;
　No longer heirs of earth, but heaven.
　　O beatific sight
　　To view His face in light ;
　　　Alleluia !
And, while we see, transform'd to be
From bliss to bliss eternally.

JESU, LORD, our Captain glorious,
O'er sin, and death, and hell victorious,
　Wisdom and might to Thee belong :
We confess, proclaim, adore Thee,
We bow the knee, we fall before Thee,
　Thy love henceforth shall be our song :
　　The cross meanwhile we bear,
　　The crown ere long to wear.
　　　Alleluia !
Thy reign extend world without end,
Let praise from all to Thee ascend.

J. MONTGOMERY, 1828.

General Hymns.

Hymn 657. PRAXIS PIETATIS.—14 14.4 7.8.

SOHR'S edition of *Praxis Pietatis*, 1668.

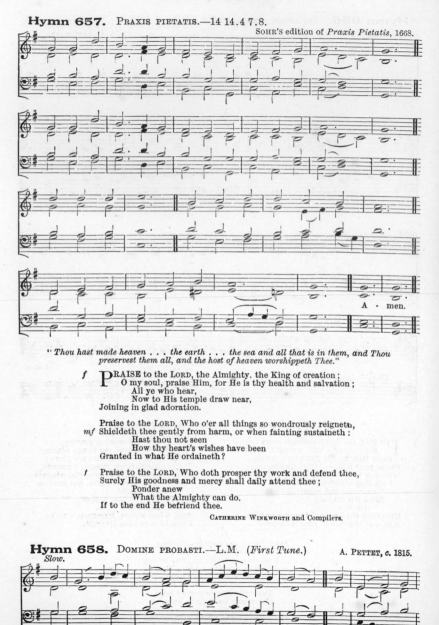

A - men.

" Thou hast made heaven . . . the earth . . . the sea and all that is in them, and Thou preservest them all, and the host of heaven worshippeth Thee."

f PRAISE to the LORD, the Almighty, the King of creation ;
O my soul, praise Him, for He is thy health and salvation ;
All ye who hear,
Now to His temple draw near,
Joining in glad adoration.

Praise to the LORD, Who o'er all things so wondrously reigneth,
mf Shieldeth thee gently from harm, or when fainting sustaineth :
Hast thou not seen
How thy heart's wishes have been
Granted in what He ordaineth?

f Praise to the LORD, Who doth prosper thy work and defend thee,
Surely His goodness and mercy shall daily attend thee ;
Ponder anew
What the Almighty can do.
If to the end He befriend thee.

CATHERINE WINKWORTH and Compilers.

Hymn 658. DOMINE PROBASTI.—L.M. (*First Tune.*)   A. PETTET, *c.* 1815.
Slow.

(572)

Hymn 658. Uffingham.—L.M. *(Second Tune.)*   J. Clarke, 1709.

"Thou art about my path, and about my bed, and spiest out all my ways."

mf   THOU, Lord, by strictest search hast known
       My rising up and lying down ;
My secret thoughts are known to Thee,
Known long before conceived by me.

Thine eye my bed and path surveys,
My public haunts and private ways ;
Thou know'st what 'tis my lips would vent,
My yet unutter'd word's intent.

f   Surrounded by Thy power I stand,
On every side I find Thy hand :
O skill, for human reach too high !
Too dazzling bright for mortal eye !

mf   Search, try, O God, my thought and heart,
If mischief lurks in any part ;
Correct me where I go astray,
cr   And guide me in Thy perfect way.

N. Tate and N. Brady, 1696.

General Hymns.

Hymn 659. IVYHATCH.—L.M.   B. LUARD SELBY.

A-men.

" The Lord reigneth ; let the earth rejoice."

f   THE LORD is King ! lift up thy voice,
      O earth, and all ye heav'ns, rejoice ;
    From world to world the joy shall ring,
    "The LORD Omnipotent is King !"

    The LORD is King ! who then shall dare
    Resist His will, distrust His care,
    Or murmur at His wise decrees,
    Or doubt His royal promises ?

    The LORD is King ! child of the dust,
    The Judge of all the earth is just ;
    Holy and true are all His ways :
    Let every creature speak His praise.

    He reigns ! ye saints, exalt your strains ;
    Your GOD is King, your FATHER reigns ;
    And He is at the FATHER'S side,
    The Man of love, the Crucified.

mf   Come, make your wants, your burdens known ;
    He will present them at the throne ;
    And angel bands are waiting there
    His messages of love to bear.

    Alike pervaded by His eye
    All parts of His dominion lie ;—
    This world of ours and worlds unseen,
    And thin the boundary between.

f   One LORD one empire all secures ;
    He reigns, and life and death are yours ;
    Through earth and heav'n one song shall ring,
    "The LORD Omnipotent is King !"

                  J. CONDER, 1824.

Hymn 660. OLD 50TH.—10 10 10 10.10 10.   *Psalmes,* 1558.

General Hymns.

A - men.

"Thou, O Lord, art our Father . . . Thy Name is from everlasting."

  f ALMIGHTY FATHER, Unoriginate,
     Whom no man hath seen ever, nor can see;
    Who reignest Bless'd and Only Potentate,
     Light unapproachable encircling Thee:
    Almighty FATHER, hallow'd be Thy Name,
    Who ever art, unchangeably the same.

mf Thou lovest us, else had we never been:
     Before we were, in ages long ago,
    Thy love had us and all our wants foreseen,
     Creating us that we Thy love might know.
    Yea, FATHER, Thou, in Whom we live and move,
    Hast loved us with an everlasting love.

    Thou madest man immortal at the first,
     An image of Thine own eternity;
  p And when he fell from life, through sin accurst,
     And lost his right to the life-giving tree,
  f Thy love, unconquer'd, would to him restore
    His life ennobled and for evermore.

mp Such was Thy love, Thou didst not even spare
     Thy Best-beloved, but gav'st Him for us all;
    To live that human life beyond compare,
     And dying, by His death retrieve our fall.
    In Him Thy love unbounded we behold,
    For, giving Him, Thou canst not aught withhold.

mf Thou knowest what we are, how frail and blind,
     Thou still rememb'rest that we are but dust:
    Like as a father pitieth, Thou art kind,
     Thy justice kindness, and Thy kindness just.
    Then hear Thy children's prayer from heav'n Thy throne,
    FATHER, Thy kingdom come; Thy will be done.

E. E. DUGMORE.

General Hymns.

Hymn 661. FESTUBERT.—6 6 10. 6 6 10. 8 12.   A. H. BREWER.

A - men.

" Of Him, and through Him, and to Him are all things : to Whom be glory
for ever.   Amen."

f LIFT up thyself, my soul,
        Above this world's control !
Spend and be spent in holy hymns of praise.
    Be arm'd with pure desire,
    Burn with celestial fire ;
Unto the King of kings our voice we raise ;
    To Him a crown we weave, and bring
A sacrifice of words, a bloodless offering.

mf Thee on the troubled deep,
    Thee o'er the islands steep,
Thee through the mighty continents of land,
    Thee in the city's throng,
    Or mountain tops along,
Or when in celebrated plains I stand,
    Thee, Thee, O blessèd One, I sing,
f Thee, Thee, O Father of the world, Eternal
    King !

    Thy praise I hymn by night,
    Thy praise at morning light,
Thy praise by day, Thy praise at eventide.
    This know the hoary stars,

    And moon with silver bars,
    And chiefly he that doth on high preside
        O'er all the host of heav'n, the sun,   [run.
    Who measuring time for holy souls his course doth

mf O Mind immutable !
        O Light inscrutable !
    Thine is the eye that guides the lightning fire,
        In Thee the ages live,
        Thou dost their limits give,
    Who can Thy praises reach, Eternal Sire ?
        Thou art beyond the dreams of men ;
    Beyond the reach of mind, or highest angel's ken

f   O'er all Thy rule is spread,
        The living and the dead ;
    To minds that be, the parent Mind Thou art ,
        All heav'n Thou dost control,
        Thou nourishest the soul,
    And dost to spirit energy impart,
        The Spring Thou art whence all things flow ,
    And from eternity the Root whence all things
        grow.

    A. W CHATFIELD : from the Greek of Synesius.

General Hymns.

Hymn 662. Addison's.—D.L.M.

J. Sheeles, c. 1720.

A - men.

" Day unto day uttereth speech, and night unto night sheweth knowledge."

f　THE spacious firmament on high,
　　With all the blue ethereal sky,
　And spangled heav'ns, a shining frame,
　Their great Original proclaim.
　The unwearied sun from day to day
　Does his Creator's power display,
　And publishes to every land
　The works of an almighty hand.

mf Soon as the evening shades prevail
　The moon takes up the wondrous tale,
　And nightly to the list'ning earth
　Repeats the story of her birth;
　Whilst all the stars that round her burn,
　And all the planets in their turn,
cr　Confirm the tidings, as they roll,
　And spread the truth from pole to pole.

p　What though in solemn silence all
　Move round the dark terrestrial ball;
　What though nor real voice nor sound
　Amid their radiant orbs be found;
f　In reason's ear they all rejoice,
　And utter forth a glorious voice,
　For ever singing as they shine,
ff　"The hand that made us is divine."

J. Addison, 1712.

The last line of each verse is repeated.

Hymn 663. WARDEN.—7 7 7 7. 7 7.

J. TURLE.

A - men.

" Every good gift and every perfect gift is from above."

mf FOR the beauty of the earth,
 For the beauty of the skies,
For the love which from our birth
 Over and around us lies,
f LORD of all, to Thee we raise
 This our grateful hymn of praise.

mf For the beauty of each hour
 Of the day and of the night,
Hill and vale, and tree and flower,
 Sun and moon and stars of light,
f LORD of all, to Thee we raise
 This our grateful hymn of praise.

mf For the joy of human love,
 Brother, sister, parent, child,
Friends on earth, and friends above,

 Pleasures pure and undefiled,
f LORD of all, to Thee we raise
 This our grateful hymn of praise.

mf For each perfect gift of Thine,
 To our race so freely given,
Graces human and divine,
 Flowers of earth and buds of heaven,
f LORD of all, to Thee we raise
 This our grateful hymn of praise.

 For Thy Church which evermore
 Lifteth holy hands above,
Off'ring up on every shore
 Her pure sacrifice of love,
 LORD of all, to Thee we raise
 This our grateful hymn of praise.

F. S. PIERPOINT.

ALTERNATIVE TUNE, HYMN 7.

Hymn 664. CHARNWOOD.—L.M.

REV. C. E. MOBERLY.

A - men.

[For copyright, see p. 1v.]

A lower setting of this Tune is given at Hymn 164.

{ 578 }

General Hymns.

"Arise, O God, and judge Thou the earth."

mf O GOD, our Maker, throned on high,
　　The earth is Thine, and Thine the sky,
Th' adoring sun obeys Thy will,
And countless stars Thy laws fulfil.

The length'ning light of summer day,
The winter frost, Thy power display,
Nature proclaims Thy sovereign skill;
Man, and man only, spurns Thy will.

The wicked sit on earth's high seat,
And tread the holy 'neath their feet;
Good goes so crookedly astray,
Bright deeds lie hidden oft away.

Great GOD! Who seest from above,
Regard us with Thy pitying love,
Perplex'd by doubts, with toil and strife,
We ask more light—we long for life.

M. TUPPER: from the Anglo-Saxon,
attributed to King Alfred.

ALTERNATIVE TUNE, HYMN 723.

Hymn 665. SALVE CORDIS GAUDIUM.—7 4 7 4.7 4 7 4.4. J. R. AHLE, 1660.

Al - - le - lu - ia. A - men.

"I will praise Thee, for Thou hast heard me, and art become my salvation."

f KING of glory, King of peace,
　　I will love Thee;
And, that love may never cease,
　　I will move Thee.
Thou hast granted my request,
　　Thou hast heard me;
Thou didst note my working breast,
　　Thou hast spared me. Alleluia.

Wherefore with my utmost art
　　I will sing Thee,
And the cream of all my heart
　　I will bring Thee.

mf Though my sins against me cried,
　　Thou didst clear me,
And alone, when they replied,
　　Thou didst hear me. Alleluia.

f Seven whole days, not one in seven,
　　I will praise Thee;
In my heart, though not in heaven,
　　I can raise Thee.

mf Small it is, in this poor sort
　　To enrol Thee;
E'en eternity's too short

cr To extol Thee. Alleluia.

GEORGE HERBERT, 1593-1632.

(579)

General Hymns.

Hymn 666. OFFERTORIUM.—7 6 7 6 7 6 7 6. M. HAYDN, 1737-1806.

A - men.

" Behold, what manner of love the Father hath bestowed upon us, that we should be called the sons of God."

f O FATHER, we would thank Thee
For all Thy love has given,
Our present joy of sonship,
Our future joy in heaven ;
The life which sin had blighted
So wondrously restored
By our mysterious union
With JESUS CHRIST our LORD.

mf Rich gifts of life and gladness,—
A new and heav'nly birth,
Baptismal waters flowing
To cleanse the sons of earth ;
The strength in which to follow
The steps that JESUS trod ;
And love beyond all knowledge
Which calls us sons of GOD.

O mercy all abundant
Bestow'd on us to-day !
O hope of future glory
Which fadeth not away !
By GOD'S great love begotten
To living hope and sure,
May we at CHRIST'S appearing
Be pure as He is pure.

f For all Thy gifts, O FATHER,
Our hymns of praise arise,—
The love which calls us children,
The hope which purifies ;
The grace by which we offer
A service glad and free ;
The earnest of perfection,
Of fuller life with Thee.

ADA R. GREENAWAY.

(580)

General Hymns.

Hymn 667.   HAMBURG.—7 6 8 6. 8 6 8 6.   J. W. FRANCK, 1681.

A-men.

" The shadow of a great rock in a weary land."

mf BENEATH the cross of JESUS
   I fain would take my stand,—
The shadow of a mighty rock
   Within a weary land ;
A home within a wilderness,
   A rest upon the way,
From the burning of the noontide heat
   And the burden of the day.

O safe and happy shelter !
   O refuge tried and sweet !
O trysting-place where heaven's love
   And heaven's justice meet !
As to the holy patriarch
   That wondrous dream was given,
So seems my Saviour's cross to me
   A ladder up to heav'n.

p There lies beneath its shadow,
   But on the farther side,
The darkness of an awful grave
   That gapes both deep and wide ;
mf And there between us stands the cross,
   Two arms outstretch'd to save,
Like a watchman set to guard the way
   From that eternal grave.

p Upon that cross of JESUS,
   Mine eye at times can see
The very dying form of One,
   Who suffer'd there for me :
And from my smitten heart, with tears,
   Two wonders I confess,—
cr The wonder of His glorious love,
p And my own worthlessness.

mf I take, O cross, thy shadow
   For my abiding-place ;
I ask no other sunshine than
   The sunshine of His face,
Content to let the world go by,
   To know no gain nor loss,—
My sinful self my only shame,
   My glory all the Cross.

ELIZABETH C. CLEPHANE.

(581)

General Hymns.

Hymn 668. St. Wulstan.—6 4 6 4. 10 10. Sir I. Atkins.

"My beloved is mine, and I am His."

mf I LIFT my heart to Thee,
　　Saviour Divine ;
For Thou art all to me,
　　And I am Thine.
Is there on earth a closer bond than this,—
That my Belovèd's mine, and I am His ?

p　Thine am I by all ties ;
　　But chiefly Thine,
That through Thy sacrifice
　　Thou, Lord, art mine.
By Thine own cords of love, so sweetly wound
Around me, I to Thee am closely bound.

To Thee, Thou bleeding Lamb,
　　I all things owe—
All that I have, and am,
　　And all I know.
All that I have is now no longer mine,
And I am not mine own ; Lord, I am Thine.

mf How can I, Lord, withhold
　　Life's brightest hour
From Thee ; or gather'd gold,
　　Or any power ?
Why should I keep one precious thing from Thee :
When Thou hast giv'n Thine own dear self for me?

p　I pray Thee, Saviour, keep
　　Me in Thy love,
Until death's holy sleep
　　Shall me remove
cr　To that fair realm where, sin and sorrow o'er,
Thou and Thine own are one for evermore.

C. E. Mudie.

Hymn 669. Thuringia.—5 5.8 8.5 5.　(*First Tune.*) A. Drese, 1698.

General Ihymns.

A - men.

Hymn 669. St. Hubert.—5 5.8 8.5 5. *(Second Tune.)* Rev. L. Darwall.

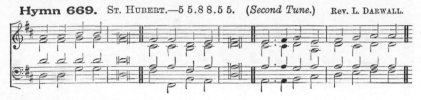

A - men.

[For copyright, see p. lv.]

Hymn 669. Bow Church.—5 5.8 8.5 5. *(Third Tune.)* G. Bullivant.

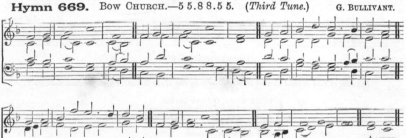

A - men.

[For copyright, see p. lv.]

" My presence shall go with thee, and I will give thee rest."

mf JESUS, still lead on,
   Till our rest be won,
And, although the way be cheerless,
cr We will follow calm and fearless;
   Guide us by Thy hand
   To our fatherland.

p If the way be drear,
   If the foe be near,
cr Let not faithless fears o'ertake us,
   Let not faith and hope forsake us;
   For, through many a foe,
   To our home we go.

p When we seek relief
   From a long-felt grief,
When oppress'd by new temptations,
   LORD, increase and perfect patience;
mf Show us that bright shore
   Where we weep no more.

f JESUS, still lead on,
   Till our rest be won;
Heav'nly Leader, still direct us,
Still support, console, protect us,
   Till we safely stand
   In our fatherland.

JANE L. BORTHWICK : from the German
of Count Zinzendorf.

General Hymns.

Hymn 670. STEPHENS.—6 6 11.6 6 11.

C. E. STEPHENS.

A-men.

[For copyright, see p. lv.]

" The love of God is shed abroad in our hearts by the Holy Ghost, Which is given unto us."

mf   COME down, O Love Divine,
        Seek Thou this soul of mine,
    And visit it with Thine own ardour glowing ;
    O Comforter, draw near,
    Within my heart appear,
cr And kindle it, Thy holy flame bestowing.

    O let it freely burn,
    Till earthly passions turn
  To dust and ashes in its heat consuming ;
f   And let Thy glorious light
    Shine ever on my sight,
  And clothe me round, the while my path illuming.

    Let holy charity
mp Mine outward vesture be,
  And lowliness become mine inner clothing ;
    True lowliness of heart,
    Which takes the humbler part,
  And o'er its own shortcomings weeps with loathing.

f   And so the yearning strong,
    With which the soul will long,
  Shall far outpass the power of human telling ;
    For none can guess its grace,
    Till he become the place
  Wherein the HOLY SPIRIT makes His dwelling.

R. F. LITTLEDALE : from the Italian of Bianco da Siena.

(584)

General Hymns.

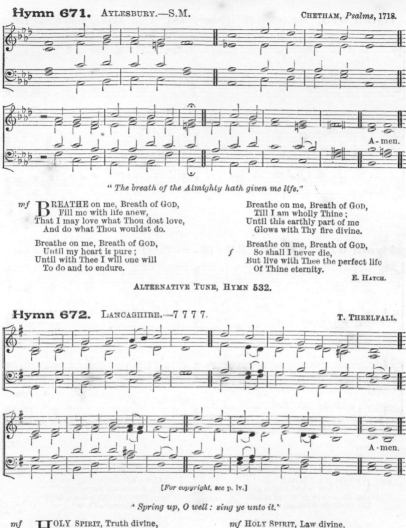

Hymn 671. AYLESBURY.—S.M.

CHETHAM, *Psalms*, 1718.

A-men.

" The breath of the Almighty hath given me life."

mf BREATHE on me, Breath of GOD,
   Fill me with life anew,
That I may love what Thou dost love,
   And do what Thou wouldst do.

Breathe on me, Breath of GOD,
   Until my heart is pure ;
Until with Thee I will one will
   To do and to endure.

Breathe on me, Breath of GOD,
   Till I am wholly Thine ;
Until this earthly part of me
   Glows with Thy fire divine.

f Breathe on me, Breath of GOD,
   So shall I never die,
But live with Thee the perfect life
   Of Thine eternity.

E. HATCH.

ALTERNATIVE TUNE, HYMN 532.

Hymn 672. LANCASHIRE.—7 7 7 7.

T. THRELFALL.

A-men.

[*For copyright, see p. lv.*]

" Spring up, O well : sing ye unto it."

mf HOLY SPIRIT, Truth divine,
   Dawn upon this soul of mine ;
Voice of GOD, and inward Light,
Wake my spirit, clear my sight.

HOLY SPIRIT, Love divine,
Glow within this heart of mine ;
Kindle every high desire ;
Perish self in Thy pure fire.

HOLY SPIRIT, Power divine,
Fill and nerve this will of mine ;
f By Thee may I strongly live,
Bravely bear, and nobly strive.

mf HOLY SPIRIT, Law divine,
Reign within this soul of mine ;
Be my law, and I shall be
Firmly bound, for ever free.

HOLY SPIRIT, Peace divine,
Still this restless heart of mine ;
Speak to calm this tossing sea,
Stay'd in Thy tranquillity.

HOLY SPIRIT, Joy divine,
f Gladden Thou this heart of mine ;
In the desert ways I sing,—
Spring, O Well, for ever spring.

S. LONGFELLOW.

U 2

General Hymns.

Hymn 673. BELLA.—S.M. (*First Tune.*)   *New and Easie Method, 1686.*

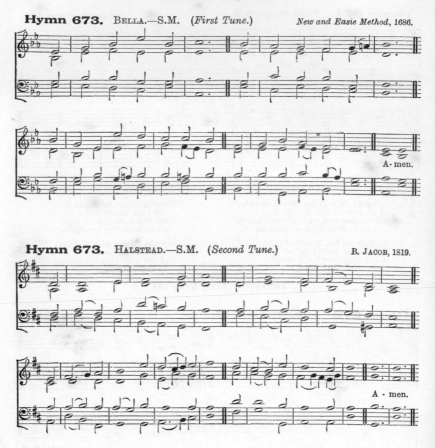

A-men.

Hymn 673. HALSTEAD.—S.M. (*Second Tune.*)   B. JACOB, 1819.

A - men.

"When He is come He will convince the world of sin."

mf COME, HOLY SPIRIT, come,
Let Thy bright beams arise ;
Dispel the sorrow from our minds,
The darkness from our eyes.

Convince us of our sin,
Then lead to JESU'S Blood ;
And to our wond'ring view reveal
The secret love of GOD.

Revive our drooping faith,
Our doubts and fears remove,
And kindle in our breasts the flame
Of never-dying love.

Cheer our desponding hearts,
Thou heav'nly Paraclete ;
Give us to lie with humble hope
At our Redeemer's feet.

'Tis Thine to cleanse the heart,
To sanctify the soul,
To pour fresh life through every part,
And new create the whole.

Dwell, therefore, in our hearts,
Our minds from bondage free ;
f Then we shall know, and praise, and love
The FATHER, SON, and Thee.

J. HART, 1759.

ALTERNATIVE TUNE, HYMN 185.

General Hymns.

Hymn 674. DYING STEPHEN.—7 7 4 4 7. 7 7 4 4 7.   J. F LAMPE, 1746.

A - men.

" If we suffer, we shall also reign with Him."

f   HEAD of Thy Church triumphant,
       We joyfully adore Thee ;
       Till Thou appear,
       Thy members here
     Shall sing like those in glory.
     We lift our hearts and voices
     With blest anticipation,
       And cry aloud,
       And give to GOD
     The praise of our salvation.

mp   While in affliction's furnace,
       And passing through the fire,
   cr   Thy love we praise,
       Which knows our days,
     And ever brings us nigher.
  f   We clap our hands exulting
     In Thine almighty favour ;
       The love divine,
       Which made us Thine,
     Shall keep us Thine for ever.

mf   Thou dost conduct Thy people
       Through torrents of temptation ;
       Nor will we fear,
       While Thou art near,
     The fire of tribulation.
     The world with sin and Satan
       In vain our march opposes ;
  f   Through Thee we shall
       Break through them all,
     And sing the song of Moses.

     By faith we see the glory
       To which Thou shalt restore us,
   mf   The cross despise
       For that high prize
     Which Thou hast set before us.
     And if Thou count us worthy,
       We each, as dying Stephen,
  f   Shall see Thee stand
       At GOD's right hand,
     To take us up to heaven.

C. WESLEY, 1746.

General Hymns.

Hymn 675. IF ANGELS SING.—C.M. (*First Tune.*)   J. CLARKE, 1709.

Slow.

A-men.

Hymn 675. UNIVERSITY.—C.M. (*Second Tune.*)   C. COLLIGNON, 1725–1785.

A-men.

" As seeing Him Who is invisible."

f   THE Church of GOD a kingdom is,
    Where CHRIST in power doth reign ;
mf Where spirits yearn till, seen in bliss,
    Their LORD shall come again.

f   Glad companies of saints possess
    This Church below, above :
    And GOD's perpetual calm doth bless
    Their paradise of love.

    An altar stands within the shrine
    Whereon, once sacrificed,
    Is set, immaculate, divine,
    The LAMB of GOD, the CHRIST.

There rich and poor, from countless lands,
    Praise GOD on mystic rood :
There nations reach forth holy hands
    To take GOD's holy food.

mf There pure life-giving streams o'erflow
    The sower's garden-ground :
    And faith and hope fair blossoms show,
    And fruits of love abound.

    O King, O CHRIST, this endless grace
    To us and all men bring,
cr To see the vision of Thy face
    In joy, O CHRIST, our King.

L. MUIRHEAD.

For First Tune the last line of each verse is repeated.

ALTERNATIVE TUNE, HYMN 352.

Hymn 676. REMEMBER, O THOU MAN.—6 5 6 5. 6 6 6 5. (*First Tune.*)

RAVENSCROFT, *Melismata*, 1611.

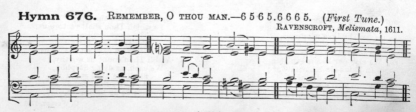

General Hymns.

A - men.

Hymn 676. BUNYAN.—6 5 6 5. 6 6 6 5. *(Second Tune.)*

Christen-schatz (Basle, 1745).

A - men.

" Whose heart is as the heart of a lion."

f WHO would true valour see
    Let him come hither ;
One here will constant be,
    Come wind, come weather ;
There's no discouragement
Shall make him once relent
His first avow'd intent
    To be a pilgrim.

Whoso beset him round
    With dismal stories,
Do but themselves confound ;
    His strength the more is.
No lion can him fright ;
He'll with a giant fight,
But he will have the right
    To be a pilgrim.

No goblin nor foul fiend
    Can daunt his spirit ;
He knows he at the end
    Shall life inherit.
Then, fancies, fly away ;
He'll not fear what men say ;
He'll labour night and day
    To be a pilgrim.

J. BUNYAN, 1684.

General Hymns.

Hymn 677. BETHANY.—8 7 8 7. 8 7 8 7.

H. SMART.

A - men.

" We are members one of another."

mf SON of GOD, Eternal Saviour,
　　Source of life and truth and grace,
Son of Man, Whose birth incarnate
　Hallows all our human race,
Thou, our Head, Who, throned in glory,
　For Thine own dost ever plead,
Fill us with Thy love and pity ;
　Heal our wrongs, and help our need.

Bind us all as one together
　In Thy Church's sacred fold,
Weak and healthy, poor and wealthy,
　Sad and joyful, young and old.
p　Is there want, or pain, or sorrow?
　Make us all the burden share.
Are there spirits crush'd and broken ?
　Teach us, LORD, to soothe their care.

mf As Thou, LORD, hast lived for others,
　So may we for others live ;
Freely have Thy gifts been granted,
　Freely may Thy servants give.
Thine the gold and Thine the silver,
　Thine the wealth of land and sea,
We but stewards of Thy bounty,
　Held in solemn trust for Thee.

Come, O CHRIST, and reign among us,
　King of love, and Prince of peace,
Hush the storm of strife and passion,
　Bid its cruel discords cease :
p　By Thy patient years of toiling,
　By Thy silent hours of pain,
Quench our fever'd thirst of pleasure,
　Shame our selfish greed of gain.

mf SON of GOD, Eternal Saviour,
　　Source of life and truth and grace,
　Son of Man, Whose birth incarnate
　　Hallows all our human race,
　Thou Who prayedst, Thou Who willest,
　　That Thy people should be one,
　Grant, O grant our hope's fruition :
　　Here on earth Thy will be done.

S. C. LOWRY.

General Hymns.

A - men.

Higher and different settings of this Tune are given at Hymn 378.

" God is our hope and strength."

f GOD is a stronghold and a tower,
        A help that never falleth,
A covering shield, a sword of power,
    When Satan's host assaileth.
    mf   In vain our crafty foe
    Still strives to work us woe,
    Still lurks and lies in wait
    With more than earthly hate ;
f We will not faint, nor tremble.

mf Frail sinners are we :—nought remains
        For hope or consolation,
f Save in His strength Whom GOD ordains
    Our Captain of salvation.
        Yes, JESUS CHRIST alone
        The LORD of hosts we own,
        GOD ere the world began,
        The Word-made-flesh for man,
    Still conquering, and to conquer.

mf Though fiercely strive the hosts of ill
        Within us, and around us,
    With fiendish strength, and fiendish skill,
    Yet ne'er may they confound us.
        Man's night of dark despair,
        When storm-clouds fill the air,
    f   Is GOD's triumphal hour,
        The noon-day of His power ;
    One word, and He prevaileth.

Our FATHER's truth abideth sure ;
    CHRIST, our Redeemer, liveth ;
For us He pleads His offering pure,
    To us His SPIRIT giveth.
    mf   Though dear ones pass away,
        Though strength and life decay,
    f   Yet loss shall be our gain,
        For GOD doth still remain
    ff Our All-in-all for ever.

ELIZABETH WORDSWORTH : from
the German of M. Luther.

(591)

General Hymns.

Hymn 679. AVE VIRGO.—7 6 7 6. 7 6 7 6. German Melody of the xvth century.

"One is your Master, even Christ; and all ye are brethren."

f   BROTHERS, joining hand to hand
In one bond united,
Pressing onward to that land
Where all wrongs are righted:
Let your words and actions be
Worthy your vocation;
Chosen of the LORD, and free,
Heirs of CHRIST'S salvation.

CHRIST, the Way, the Truth, the Life,
Who hath gone before you
Through the turmoil and the strife,
Holds His banner o'er you;
All who see the sacred sign
Press tow'rds heaven's portal,
Fired by hope that is divine,
Love that is immortal.

They who follow fear no foe,
Care not who assail them;
Where the Master leads they go,
He will never fail them;
Courage, brothers! we are one,
In the love that sought us;
Soon the warfare shall be done,
Through the grace He brought us.

J. A. WARNER.

Hymn 680. STONYPATH.—8 6 8 6. 8 6 8 6. 8 8.   C. MACPHERSON.

(592)

General Hymns.

A - men.

"We will serve the Lord."

mf BELIEVING fathers oft have told
What things by GOD were done,
When faithful men in days of old
Their lifelong battle won ;
And now when GOD calls us to life,
And Satan tempts each man,
We choose our side in th' mortal strife
To fight as best we can,—
f Like brothers true, of one accord,
To hold one faith and serve one LORD.

mf Our King has come to claim His own,
Has paid the debt we owe,
Himself has fought the fight alone,
In straits we cannot know.
Amid the world's confusèd noise,
Where we but darkly see,
The CHRIST appeals, with sweet, clear voice,
"My brothers, follow Me,"—
f Like brothers true, of one accord,
To hold one faith, to serve one LORD.

His Church our shelter, He our guide,
Our strength His healing cross,
We range ourselves upon His side,
Where none can suffer loss.
We're safe behind our Saviour's shield ;
He makes us heirs of heaven ;
We claim upon th' embattled field
The victory CHRIST has given,—
Like brothers true, of one accord,
To hold one faith and serve one LORD.

p And yet, O CHRIST, our Saviour King,
Unless Thou keep us Thine,
Our faith will soon dry at the spring,
Our love will shrink and pine.
So by Thy SPIRIT mould us, LORD ;
Inspire our hearts to pray ;
Our hungry souls feed with Thy word,
And teach our lips to say,
f "True brothers we, of one accord,
We hold one faith, we serve one LORD."

mf We fain would do our Master's part,
And help our fellow-men,
Would cheer some lonely brother's heart,
Some lost one bring again,
Would serve the Church abroad, at home,
With hearts from self set free,
Striving to make Thy kingdom come.
O GOD, so may it be,
f That, brothers true, with one accord,
We hold the faith and serve the LORD !

A. H. CHARTERIS.

(593)

General Hymns.

Hymn 681. MORNINGSIDE.—6 4 6 4. 6 7 6 4.

H. E. DIBDIN.

A · men.

" Let us not sleep, as do others ; but let us watch."

f   H ARK ! 'tis the watchman's cry,
    " Wake, brethren, wake ! "
JESUS our LORD is nigh ;
  Wake, brethren, wake !
Sleep is for sons of night ;
Ye are children of the light,
  Yours is the glory bright ;
    Wake, brethren, wake !

Call to each waking band,
  " Watch, brethren, watch ! "
Clear is our LORD'S command ;
  Watch, brethren, watch !
Be ye as men that wait
Always at the Master's gate,
  E'en though He tarry late ;
    Watch, brethren, watch !

mf Heed we the steward's call,
  " Work, brethren, work ! "
There's room enough for all ;
  Work, brethren, work !
This vineyard of the LORD
Constant labour will afford ;
  Yours is a sure reward ;
    Work, brethren, work !

f   Hear we the Shepherd's voice,
  " Pray, brethren, pray ! "
Would ye His heart rejoice ?
  Pray, brethren, pray !
Sin calls for constant fear,
Weakness needs the Strong One near
  Long as ye struggle here ;
    Pray, brethren, pray !

f   Now sound the final chord,
  " Praise, brethren, praise ! "
Thrice holy is our LORD ;
  Praise, brethren, praise !
What more befits the tongues
Soon to lead the angels' songs,
  While heav'n the note prolongs ?
    Praise, brethren, praise !

The Revival Magazine, 1859.

General Hymns.

Hymn 682. DEVONSHIRE.—L.M. (*First Tune.*)   J. F. LAMPE, 1746.

Hymn 682. ST. PETERSBURG.—L.M. (*Second Tune.*)
D. BORTNIANSKI, 1751–1825.

A - men.

"They that wait upon the Lord shall renew their strength: they shall mount up with wings as eagles."

f   AWAKE, our souls! away, our fears!
     Let every trembling thought be gone!
Awake, and run the heav'nly race,
And put a cheerful courage on.

mf   True, 'tis a strait and thorny road,
And mortal spirits tire and faint;
But they forget the mighty GOD
That feeds the strength of every saint—

f   The mighty GOD, Whose matchless power
Is ever new and ever young,
And firm endures, while endless years
Their everlasting circles run.

mf   From Thee, the ever-flowing spring,
Our souls shall drink a fresh supply;
While such as trust their native strength
Shall melt away, and droop, and die.

f   Swift as an eagle cuts the air,
cr   We'll mount aloft to Thine abode;
On wings of love our souls shall fly,
Nor tire along the heav'nly road.

I. WATTS, 1707.

(595)

General Hymns.

Hymn 683. HERMAS.—6 5. 12 lines.

Miss F. R. HAVERGAL.

A - men.

" Who is on the Lord's side ? "

f WHO is on the LORD'S side ?
　Who will serve the King ?
Who will be His helpers
　Other lives to bring ?
Who will leave the world's side ?
　Who will face the foe ?
Who is on the LORD'S side ?
　Who for Him will go ?
mf By Thy call of mercy,
　By Thy grace divine,
f We are on the LORD'S side ;
　Saviour, we are Thine.

mf JESUS, Thou hast bought us,
　Not with gold or gem,
But with Thine own life blood,
　For Thy diadem.
With Thy blessing filling
　Each who comes to Thee,
Thou hast made us willing,
　Thou hast made us free.
　By Thy great redemption,
　By Thy grace divine,
f We are on the LORD'S side ;
　Saviour, we are Thine.

mf Fierce may be the conflict,
　Strong may be the foe,
f But the King's own army
　None can overthrow.
Round His standard ranging,
　Vict'ry is secure,
For His truth unchanging
　Makes the triumph sure.
f Joyfully enlisting
　By Thy grace divine,
　We are on the LORD'S side ;
　Saviour, we are Thine.

Chosen to be soldiers
　In an alien land,
Chosen, call'd, and faithful,
　For our Captain's band ;
In the service royal
　Let us not grow cold ;
Let us be right loyal,
　Noble, true, and bold.
mf Master, Thou wilt keep us,
　By Thy grace divine,
f Always on the LORD'S side,
　Saviour, always Thine.

FRANCES R. HAVERGAL.

General Hymns.

Hymn 684. BERKELEY.—Irregular.

" Compassed about with so great a cloud of witnesses . . . looking unto Jesus."

B. HARWOOD.

1. WHAT are these that glow from a - far, These that lean o - ver the gold - en bar, Strong as the li - on, pure as the dove, With op - en arms, and hearts of love? They the bless-ed ones gone be - fore, They the bless-ed for ev - er - more; Out of great tri - bu - la - tion they went Home to their home of heav'n con - tent.

2. What are these that fly as a cloud, With flash - ing heads and fa - ces bow'd;

General Hymns.

In their mouths a vic - to - rious psalm, In their hands a robe and a palm?

Wel-com-ing An - gels these that shine, Your own An - gel, and yours, and mine;

Who have hedged us, both day and night, On the left hand and on the right.

3. Light a - bove light, and bliss be - yond bliss, Whom words can-not ut - ter, lo,

who is this? As a King with ma - ny crowns He stands, And our

names are gra - ven up - on His hands. As a Priest, with GOD - up - lift - ed eyes, He

General Hymns.

of-fers for us His Sac-ri-fice; As the Lamb of God for
sin-ners slain, That we too may live, He lives a-gain.

4. God the Fa-ther give us grace To walk in the light of Je-su's face;
God the Son give us a part In the hid-ing-place of Je-su's heart;
God the Spi-rit so hold us up That we may drink of Je-su's cup; As
our own Champion be-hold Him stand, Strong to save us at God's right hand. A-men.

Christina G. Rossetti.

General Hymns.

Hymn 635. BATTLE-CRY.—7 6 8 6. 7 6 8 6.

" Quit you like men, be strong."

A. GRAY.

To be sung in Unison.

1. RISE at the cry of bat - tle, Arm for the com - ing strife, By
2. Fie - ry and fierce the con - flict, Dar - ing and swift the foe; His
3. Strive till the strife is o - ver, Fight till the fight is won, Though

night and day you must fight your way Till you pass through death to life.
hosts are found on the bat - tle ground, Where they wait to lay you low;
sore op - prest, seek not for rest Un - til the day is done;

Rea - dy to face the dan - ger, Rea - dy to right the wrong, There is
Sharp are his darts and dead - ly, Keen is the strife and long, Then
Af - ter the well - fought bat - tle Join in the vic - tor's song, Your

ma - ny a foe on the way you go, Quit you like men, be strong!
arm for the fight in the ar - mour of light, Quit you like men, be strong!
tro - phies bring to CHRIST your King, Quit you like men, be strong! A - men.

ADA R. GREENAWAY.

General Hymns.

Hymn 686. SPLENDOR.—L.M.   B. LUARD SELBY.

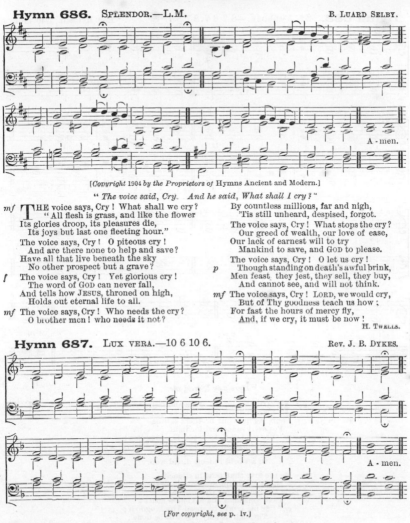

A - men.

[Copyright 1904 by the Proprietors of Hymns Ancient and Modern.]

" The voice said, Cry. And he said, What shall I cry ?"

mf THE voice says, Cry ! What shall we cry?
 " All flesh is grass, and like the flower
Its glories droop, its pleasures die,
 Its joys but last one fleeting hour."

The voice says, Cry ! O piteous cry !
 And are there none to help and save?
Have all that live beneath the sky
 No other prospect but a grave ?

f The voice says, Cry ! Yet glorious cry !
 The word of GOD can never fail,
And tells how JESUS, throned on high,
 Holds out eternal life to all.

mf The voice says, Cry ! Who needs the cry?
 O brother men ! who needs it not?

By countless millions, far and nigh,
 'Tis still unheard, despised, forgot.

The voice says, Cry ! What stops the cry?
 Our greed of wealth, our love of ease,
Our lack of earnest will to try
 Mankind to save, and GOD to please.

The voice says, Cry ! O let us cry !
p Though standing on death's awful brink,
Men feast they jest, they sell, they buy,
 And cannot see, and will not think.

mf The voice says, Cry ! LORD, we would cry,
 But of Thy goodness teach us how :
For fast the hours of mercy fly,
 And, if we cry, it must be now !

H. TWELLS.

Hymn 687. LUX VERA.—10 6 10 6.   Rev. J. B. DYKES.

A - men.

[For copyright, see p. iv.]

" All day long I have stretched forth my hands."

mf STILL throned in heav'n, to men in unbelief
 CHRIST spreads His hands all day ;
They scan His claims, give judgment cold and brief,
 And fearless turn away.

Once more, O peerless mystery of grace !
 Thy sweet appeal renew ;
Light up dark minds ; win souls to thine embrace ;
 High forts of doubt subdue.

Speak ʒill the sons of peace, with hearts unsear'd,
 Led by that voice of thine,
cr Find Him each day more glorious, more endear'd,
 CHRIST human, CHRIST divine.

W. BRIGHT.

(601)

General Hymns.

Hymn 688. St. Ambrose.—8 7 8 7. 8 7 8 7.   Rev R. Cecil, 1740–1810.

A-men.

" Here am I, send me."

mf FROM the depths of sin and failure,
      From despair as black as night,
LORD, we hear our brothers calling
      For deliv'rance and for light.
  cr Use us, LORD, to speed Thy kingdom ;
      Through us may Thy will be done ;
    Give us eyes to see the vision
      Of a world redeem'd and won.

p By the love that bore in silence
      Man's contempt and Satan's dart ;
    By the longing for the lost ones
      That consumes the Saviour's heart ;
  cr Use us, LORD, to speed Thy kingdom ;
      Through us may Thy will be done ;
    Give us eyes to see the vision
      Of a world redeem'd and won.

p By the Saviour's blood that bought us,
      By the peace His merits bring,
    By the SPIRIT that constrains us
      Now on earth to crown Him King ;
  cr Use us, LORD, to speed Thy kingdom ;
      Through us may Thy will be done ;
    Give us eyes to see the vision
      Of a world redeem'd and won.

                                    T. Rees.

ALTERNATIVE TUNE, HYMN 316.

(602)

General Hymns.

Hymn 689.   MACLURE.—15 15.15 15.15.

This Tune may be sung in Unison.

[For copyright, see p. lv.]

"Choose ye this day whom ye will serve."

mf ONCE to every man and nation comes the moment to decide,
In the strife of truth with falsehood, for the good or evil side ;
Some great cause, like CHRIST in Jewry, off'ring each the bloom or blight,
Parts the goats upon the left hand and the sheep upon the right,
And the choice goes by for ever 'twixt that darkness and that light.

We see dimly in the present what is small and what is great,
Slow of faith, how weak an arm may turn the iron helm of fate ;
But the soul is still prophetic ; list amid the market's din
To the ominous stern whisper of the oracle within,
"They enslave their children's children who make compromise with sin."

J. R. LOWELL.

(603)

General Hymns.

Hymn 690. OSWALD'S TREE.—C.M. (Original Key D♭.) Sir WALFORD DAVIES.

[For copyright, see p. lv.]

" I will give you assured peace in this place."

f GREAT Shepherd of Thy people, hear,
 Thy presence now display;
As Thou hast given a place for prayer,
 So give us hearts to pray.

mf Within these walls let holy peace,
 And love, and concord dwell;
Here give the troubled conscience ease,
 The wounded spirit heal.

May we in faith receive Thy word,
 In faith present our prayers,
And in the presence of our LORD
 Unbosom all our cares.

The hearing ear, the seeing eye,
 The contrite heart bestow;
cr And shine upon us from on high,
 That we in grace may grow.

J. NEWTON, 1769.

Hymn 691. THE GOOD SHEPHERD.—7 7 7 7. 7 7. P. HEINLEIN, 1676.

" Surely, I have behaved and quieted myself, as a child that is weaned."

mf QUIET, LORD, my froward heart;
 Make me teachable and mild,
Upright, simple, free from art;
Make me as a weanèd child,
From distrust and envy free,
Pleased with all that pleases Thee.

What Thou shalt to-day provide,
Let me as a child receive;
What to-morrow may betide,

Calmly to Thy wisdom leave;
'Tis enough that Thou wilt care:
Why should I the burden bear?

As a little child relies
On a care beyond his own,
Knows he's neither strong nor wise,
Fears to stir a step alone;
Let me thus with Thee abide,
As my Father, Guard, and Guide.

J. NEWTON, 1725–1807.

(604)

General Hymns.

Hymn 692. DONCASTER.—S.M.

S. WESLEY, 1837.

A - men.

"Put thou thy trust in the Lord, and be doing good."

f   PUT thou thy trust in GOD,
     In duty's path go on ;
Walk in His strength with faith and hope,
     So shall thy work be done.

mf   Commit thy ways to Him,
     Thy works into His hands,
And rest on His unchanging word,
     Who heav'n and earth commands.

     Though years on years roll on,
     His cov'nant shall endure ;
f Though clouds and darkness hide His path,
     The promised grace is sure.

mf   Give to the winds thy fears ;
     Hope, and be undismay'd ;
GOD hears thy sighs and counts thy tears ;
f   GOD shall lift up thy head.

mf   Through waves, and clouds, and storms,
     His power will clear thy way :
cr Wait thou His time, the darkest night
     Shall end in brightest day.

mf   Leave to His sovereign sway
     To choose and to command ;
So shalt thou, wond'ring, own His way,
     How wise, how strong His hand.

J. WESLEY and others : from the
German of P. Gerhardt.

Hymn 693. BANGOR.—C.M.

TANS'UR, *Harmony of Zion*, 1734.

A - men.

"The eternal God is thy refuge."

mf ETERNAL GOD, we look to Thee,
     To Thee for help we fly ;
Thine eye alone our wants can see,
     Thy hand alone supply.

LORD, let Thy fear within us dwell,
     Thy love our footsteps guide :
That love will all vain love expel ;
     That fear, all fear beside.

     Not what we wish, but what we want,
     O let Thy grace supply ;
     The good, unask'd, in mercy grant ;
     Tho ill, though ask'd, deny.

J. MERRICK, 1765.

ALTERNATIVE TUNE, HYMN 352.

General Hymns.

Hymn 694. FRESHWATER.—Irregular.

" When thou passeth through the waters, I will be with thee.'

Sir H. PARRY.

1. SUN - SET and eve - ning star, And one clear call for me!
2. Twi - light and eve - ning bell, And af - ter that the dark!

And may there be no moan-ing of the bar, When I put out to sea,
And may there be no sad - ness of fare - well, When I . . . em - bark;

cres.

But such a tide as mov - ing seems a - sleep, Too full for sound and foam,
For, tho' from out our bourne of time and place The flood may bear me far,

When that which drew from out the bound-less deep Turns a - gain . . home.
I hope to see my Pi - lot face to face When I have crost the bar.

ALFRED, LORD TENNYSON.

Hymn 695. POPLAR.—Irregular.

" With Thee is the fountain of life."

The Right Rev. T. B. STRONG.

mf GOD be in my head, And in my un - der - stand - ing; GOD be in my

(606)

General Hymns.

eyes, And in my look · · ing; GOD be in my mouth, And in my

speak · ing; GOD be in my heart, And in my think · ing;

dim. e rall.

GOD be at my end, And . . at my de · part · · ing. A-men.

Sarum Primer, 1514.

Hymn 696. RELIANCE.—10 10 10 10. (*First Tune.*)

Slow.   Arr. by S. S. WESLEY, 1872.

A-men.

"Turn Thou us unto Thee, O LORD, and we shall be turned; renew our days as of old."

mf AWAKE, O LORD, as in the time of old!
     Come, HOLY SPIRIT, in Thy power and might;
p   For lack of Thee our hearts are strangely cold,
     Our minds but blindly groping tow'rds the light.

Doubts are abroad: make Thou these doubts to cease!
     Fears are within: set Thou these fears at rest!
Strife is among us: melt that strife to peace!
     Change marches onward: may all change be blest!

mf Make us to be what we profess to be;
     Let prayer be prayer, and praise be heart-felt praise;
From unreality, O set us free,
     And let our words be echo'd by our ways.

Turn us, good LORD, and so shall we be turn'd:
     Let every passion grieving Thee be still'd:
f   Then shall our race be won, our guerdon earn'd,
     Our Master look'd on, and our joy fulfill'd.

H. TWELLS.

General Hymns.

Hymn 696. SAVILE.—10 10 10 10. *(Second Tune.)* C. H. LLOYD.

A-men.

" Turn Thou us unto Thee, O LORD, and we shall be turned; renew our days as of old."

mf A WAKE, O LORD, as in the time of old!
      Come, HOLY SPIRIT, in Thy power and might;
p   For lack of Thee our hearts are strangely cold,
      Our minds but blindly groping tow'rds the light.

Doubts are abroad: make Thou these doubts to cease!
Fears are within: set Thou these fears at rest!
Strife is among us: melt that strife to peace!
Change marches onward: may all change be blest!

mf Make us to be what we profess to be;
     Let prayer be prayer, and praise be heart-felt praise;
     From unreality, O set us free,
     And let our words be echo'd by our ways.

Turn us, good LORD, and so shall we be turn'd:
Let every passion grieving Thee be still'd:
f Then shall our race be won, our guerdon earn'd,
     Our Master look'd on, and our joy fulfill'd.

H. TWELLS.

Hymn 697. TOTTERIDGE.—6 6 8 4. S. H. NICHOLSON.

A - men.

" They that wait upon the Lord shall renew their strength."

f R ISE in the strength of GOD,
      And face life's uphill way,
The steps which other feet have trod
      You tread to-day.

Press onward, upward still,
      To win your way at last,

With better hope and stronger will
      Than in the past,—

Life's work more nobly wrought,
      Life's race more bravely run,
Life's daily conflict faced and fought,
      Life's duty done.

ADA R. GREENAWAY.

General hymns.

Hymn 698. HEREFORD.—L.M.

S. S. WESLEY.

A - men.

"I beseech you, brethren, by the mercies of God, that ye present your bodies a living sacrifice, holy, acceptable to God, which is your reasonable service."

mf O THOU Who camest from above
The fire celestial to impart,
Kindle a flame of sacred love
On the mean altar of my heart.

There let it for Thy glory burn
With inextinguishable blaze,
And trembling to its source return
In humble prayer, and fervent praise.

JESUS, confirm my heart's desire
To work, and speak, and think for Thee ;
Still let me guard the holy fire
And still stir up the gift in me.

Still let me prove Thy perfect will,
My acts of faith and love repeat ;
Till death Thy endless mercies seal,
And make the sacrifice complete.

ALTERNATIVE TUNE, HYMN 71.

C. WESLEY, 1762.

Hymn 699. WYKE.—8 8 8 8 6. (*First Tune.*)

L. H. HEWARD.

A-men.

"To know the love of Christ . . . that ye might be filled with all the fulness of God."

mf O LOVE that wilt not let me go,
I rest my weary soul in Thee :
I give Thee back the life I owe,
cr That in Thine ocean depths its flow
May richer, fuller be.

p O Light that followest all my way,
I yield my flick'ring torch to Thee :
My heart restores its borrow'd ray,
cr That in Thy sunshine's blaze its day
May brighter, fairer be.

p O Joy that seekest me through pain,
I cannot close my heart to Thee :
cr I trace the rainbow through the rain,
And feel the promise is not vain,
f That morn shall tearless be.

mf O Cross that liftest up my head,
I dare not ask to fly from Thee :
I lay in dust life's glory dead,
cr And from the ground there blossoms red
f Life that shall endless be.

G. MATHESON.

(609)

X

General Hymns.

Hymn 699. HAMPSTEAD.—8 8 8 8 6. (*Second Tune.*)

This Tune may be sung in Unison.

Sir WALFORD DAVIES.

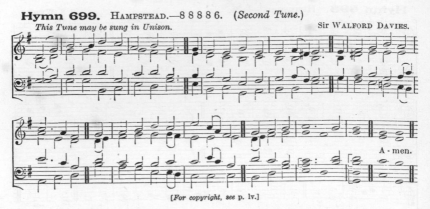

A - men.

[*For copyright, see p. lv.*]

"*To know the love of Christ . . . that ye might be filled with all the fulness of God.*"

mf O LOVE that wilt not let me go,
　　I rest my weary soul in Thee :
　　I give Thee back the life I owe,
cr　That in Thine ocean depths its flow
　　　May richer, fuller be.

p　O Light that followest all my way,
　　I yield my flick'ring torch to Thee :
　　My heart restores its borrow'd ray,
cr　That in Thy sunshine's blaze its day
　　　May brighter, fairer be.

p　O Joy that seekest me through pain,
　　I cannot close my heart to Thee :
cr　I trace the rainbow through the rain,
　　And feel the promise is not vain
f　　　That morn shall tearless be.

mf　O Cross that liftest up my head,
　　I dare not ask to fly from Thee :
　　I lay in dust life's glory dead,
cr　And from the ground there blossoms red
f　　Life that shall endless be.

G. MATHESON.

Hymn 700. ROTHLEY.—8 6 8 4.

Sir J. GOSS.

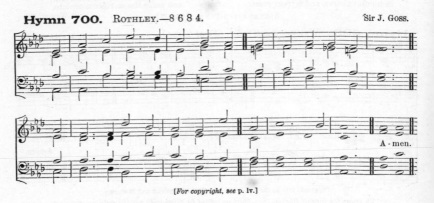

A - men.

[*For copyright, see p. lv.*]

"*O send out Thy light and Thy truth that they may lead me.*"

mf GIVE light, O LORD, that we may learn
　　The way that leads to Thee,
That where our hearts true joys discern,
　　Our life may be.

Give light, O LORD, that we may know
　　Thy one unchanging truth,
And follow, all our days below,
　　Our Guide in youth.

p　Give light, O LORD, that we may see
　　Where wisdom bids beware,
And turn our doubting minds to Thee
　　In faithful prayer.

mf　Give light, O LORD, that we may look
　　Beneath, around, above,
And learn from nature's living book
　　Thy power and love.

General Hymns.

Give light, O LORD, that we may read
All signs that Thou art near,
And, while we live, in word and deed
Thy Name revere.

p　Give light, O LORD, that we may trace
In trial, pain, and loss,

In poorest lot, and lowest place,
A Saviour's Cross.

mf　Give light, O LORD, that we may see
A home beyond the sky,
cr　Where all who live in CHRIST with Thee
Shall never die.

L. TUTTIETT.

Hymn 701. EDEN.—6 6 6 6.　　　　　Rev. O. M. FEILDEN.

A - men.

" I have set God always before me."

mf　LORD, be Thy Word my rule,
In it may I rejoice ;
Thy glory be my aim,
Thy holy will my choice ;

Thy promises my hope ;
Thy providence my guard ;
Thine arm my strong support ;
Thyself my great reward.

Bishop C. WORDSWORTH.

Hymn 702. GALWAY.—S.M.　　　　　E. MILLER, 1790.

A - men.

" Keep the charge of the Lord, that ye die not."

mf　A CHARGE to keep I have,
A GOD to glorify,
A never-dying soul to save,
And fit it for the sky ;

To serve the present age,
My calling to fulfil ;
Oh, may it all my powers engage
To do my Master's will

Arm me with jealous care,
As in Thy sight to live ;
And oh, Thy servant, LORD, prepare
A good account to give.

p　Help me to watch and pray,
cr　And on Thyself rely ;
And let me ne'er my trust betray,
But press to realms on high

C. WESLEY. 1762.

General Hymns.

Hymn 703. GLOVERNIA.—10 10.

A. H. BREWER.

A-men.

[Copyright 1915 by the Proprietors of Hymns Ancient and Modern.]

" Beloved, let us love one another : for love is of God."

mf BELOVÈD, let us love : love is of GOD ;
    In GOD alone hath love its true abode.
Belovèd, let us love : for they who love,
They only, are His sons, born from above.

p   Belovèd, let us love : for love is rest,
    And he who loveth not abides unblest.

f   Belovèd, let us love : for love is light,
    And he who loveth not dwelleth in night.

    Belovèd, let us love : for only thus
    Shall we behold that GOD Who loveth us.

H. BONAR.

Hymn 704. PADERBORN.—5 5 5 5.6 5 6 5.

Paderborn Gesangbuch, 1765.

Rather slow.

A - men.

" His Name alone is excellent."

f YE servants of GOD, your Master proclaim,
    And publish abroad His wonderful Name :
The Name all-victorious of JESUS extol ;
His Kingdom is glorious, and rules over all.

GOD ruleth on high, almighty to save ;
And still He is nigh ; His presence we have.
The great congregation His triumph shall sing,
Ascribing salvation to JESUS our King.

Salvation to GOD Who sits on the throne !
Let all cry aloud, and honour the SON.
The praises of JESUS the Angels proclaim,
Fall down on their faces, and worship the LAMB.

ff Then let us adore, and give Him His right :
All glory and power, all wisdom and might ;
And honour and blessing, with Angels above,
And thanks never-ceasing, and infinite love.

C. WESLEY, 1744.

(612)

General Hymns.

Hymn 705. RICHMOND.—C.M. (*First Tune.*)   Rev. T. HAWEIS, 1792.

A - men.

Hymn 705. ANGMERING.—C.M. (*Second Tune.*)   Sir H. PARRY.

A - men.

[*For copyright, see p. lv.*]

"*This people have I formed for Myself; they shall shew forth My praise.*"

f   FILL Thou my life, O LORD my GOD,
     In every part with praise,
That my whole being may proclaim
     Thy being and Thy ways.

Not for the lip of praise alone,
     Nor e'en the praising heart,
I ask, but for a life made up
     Of praise in every part :

Praise in the common things of life,
     Its goings out and in ;
Praise in each duty and each deed,
     However small and mean.

Fill every part of me with praise :
     Let all my being speak
Of Thee and of Thy love, O LORD,
     Poor though I be and weak.

mf   So shalt Thou, LORD, from me, e'en me,
     Receive the glory due ;
cr   And so shall I begin on earth
     The song for ever new.

So shall each fear, each fret, each care,
     Be turnèd into song ;
And ev'ry winding of the way
     The echo shall prolong.

mf   So shall no part of day or night
     From sacredness be free ;
cr   But all my life, in every step,
     Be fellowship with Thee.

H. BONAR.

(613)

General Hymns.

Hymn 706. CARLISLE.—S.M.   C. LOCKHART, 1745-1815.

A lower setting of this Tune is given at Hymn 393.

"Stand up and bless the Lord your God."

f STAND up, and bless the LORD,
        Ye people of His choice ;
Stand up, and bless the LORD your GOD
    With heart, and soul, and voice.

    Though high above all praise,
    Above all blessing high,
Who would not fear His holy Name,
    And laud and magnify ?

    Oh, for the living flame
    From His own altar brought,

To touch our lips, our mind inspire,
    And wing to heav'n our thought.

    GOD is our strength and song,
    And His salvation ours ;
Then be His love in CHRIST proclaim'd
    With all our ransom'd powers.

    Stand up, and bless the LORD,
    The LORD your GOD adore ;
Stand up, and bless His glorious Name
    Henceforth for evermore.

                          J. MONTGOMERY, 1824.

National Anthem.

Hymn 707. NATIONAL ANTHEM.—6 6 4.6 6 6 4.   *Thesaurus Musicus, c.* 1743.

" All the people shouted and said, God save the king."

mf GOD save our gracious Queen,
        Long live our noble Queen,
        GOD save the Queen.
f   Send her victorious,
    Happy and glorious,
    Long to reign over us ;
        GOD save the Queen.

 * O LORD our GOD, arise,
    Scatter our enemies,
        And make them fall ;

    Confound their politics,
    Frustrate their knavish tricks ;
    On Thee our hopes we fix ;
        GOD save us all.

mf Thy choicest gifts in store
    On her be pleased to pour,
        Long may she reign.
    May she defend our laws,
    And ever give us cause
cr To sing with heart and voice
        GOD save the Queen.

                          Anon., c. 1743.

* *May be omitted.*

(614)

National.

Hymn 708. TRAFALGAR.—8 8 8 8.8 8 8 8.88.   S. H. NICHOLSON.

" The Kingdom is the Lord's, and He is the Governor among the nations."

mf GOD of our fathers, unto Thee
　　Our fathers cried in danger's hour,
And then Thou gavest them to see
　The acts of Thine almighty power.
They cried to Thee, and Thou didst hear ;
　They call'd on Thee, and Thou didst save ;
And we their sons to-day draw near
　Thy Name to praise, Thy help to crave.
　　f　LORD GOD of Hosts, uplift Thine hand,
　　　　Protect and bless our fatherland.

f　Thine is the majesty, O LORD,
　　And Thine dominion over all ;
When Thou commandest, at Thy word
　Great kings and nations rise or fall.
For eastern realms, for western coasts,

For islands wash'd by every sea,
　The praise be given, O GOD of Hosts,
Not unto us but unto Thee.
　f　LORD GOD of Hosts, uplift Thine hand,
　　　Protect and bless our fatherland.

p　If in Thy grace Thou should'st allow
　　Our fame to wax through coming days,
Still grant us humbly, then as now,
　Thy help to crave, Thy Name to praise.
mf Not all alike in speech or birth,
　　Alike we bow before Thy throne ;
cr　One fatherland throughout the earth
　　Our Father's noble acts we own.
　f　LORD GOD of Hosts, uplift Thine hand,
　　　Protect and bless our fatherland.

A. C. AINGER.

(615)

National.

Hymn 709. HILDERSTONE.—L.M. (*First Tune.*)   P. HART, 1713.

A - men.

Hymn 709. EASTER SONG.—L.M. with Alleluias. (*Second Tune.*)

Catholische Kirchengesänge (Cologne, 1623).

Al - le - lu - ia! Al - le - lu - ia!

Al - le - lu - ia! Al - le -

- lu - ia! Al - le - lu - ia! Al - le - lu - ia! Al - le - lu - ia! A - men.

National.

'Thou shalt bless the Lord thy God for the good land which He hath given thee."

f PRAISE to our GOD, Whose bounteous hand
  Prepared of old our glorious land ;
A garden fenced with silver sea ;
A people prosp'rous, strong, and free.

Praise to our GOD ; through all our past
His mighty arm hath held us fast ;
Till wars and perils, toils and tears,
Have brought the rich and peaceful years.

Praise to our GOD ; the vine He set
Within our coasts is fruitful yet ;
On many a shore her offshoots grow ;
'Neath many a sun her clusters glow.

Praise to our GOD ; His power alone
Can keep unmoved our ancient throne,
Sustain'd by counsels wise and just,
And guarded by a people's trust.

mf Praise to our GOD ; Who still forbears,
Who still this sinful nation spares,
Who calls us still to seek His face,
And lengthens out our day of grace.

Praise to our GOD ; though chast'nings stern
Our evil dross should throughly burn,
f His rod and staff, from age to age,
Shall rule and guide His heritage !

       J. ELLERTON.

Hymn 710. SALISBURY.—L.M.   RAVENSCROFT, *Psalmes*, 1621.

"Blessed is the nation whose God is the Lord."

mf THOU Framer of the light and dark,
  Steer through the tempest Thine own ark ;
Amid the howling wintry sea,
We are in port if we have Thee.

The rulers of this Christian land,
'Twixt Thee and us ordain'd to stand,
Guide Thou their course, O LORD, aright ;
Let all do all as in Thy sight.

O GOD the FATHER, GOD the SON,
And GOD the SPIRIT, THREE in ONE,
Hear Thou in heav'n Thy children's cry,
And in our hour of need be nigh.

       J. KEBLE, 1827.

Holy Communion.

Hymn 711. Herga.—8 7 8 7. 12 lines.

P. C. Buck.

A-men.

" Forasmuch then as the children are partakers of flesh and blood, He likewise took part of the same, that through death He might destroy him that had the power of death."

For a Procession.

f CHRISTIANS, sing the Incarnation
    Of th' Eternal Son of God,
Who, to save us, took our nature,
    Soul and body, flesh and blood :
p God, He saw man's cruel bondage,
    Who in death's dark dungeon lay ;
Man, He came to fight man's battle,
    And for man He won the day.
f   Alleluia, Alleluia
        To th' Incarnate Son of God,
    Who for man as Man hath conquer'd
        In our own true flesh and blood.

mf King of kings and Lord of Angels,
    He put off His glory-crown,
Had a stable-cave for palace,
    And a manger for His throne ;
Helpless lay, to Whom creation
    All its life and being owed,
And the lowly Hebrew Maiden
    Was the Mother of her God.
f   Alleluia, Alleluia
        To th' Incarnate Son of God,
    Who conceal'd His dazzling Godhead
        'Neath the veil of flesh and blood.

(618)

Holy Communion.

mf Through a life of lowly labour
 He on earth was pleased to dwell,
All our want and sorrow sharing ;
 GOD with us, EMMANUEL :
Yet a dearer, closer union
 JESUS in His love would frame ;
He, the Passover fulfilling,
 Gave Himself as Paschal Lamb.
 f Alleluia, Alleluia
 To th' Incarnate SON of GOD,
 Who the heav'nly gifts bequeath'd us
 Of His own true Flesh and Blood.

p Then, by man refused and hated,
 GOD for man vouchsafed to die,
Love divine its depth revealing
 On the heights of Calvary ;
Through His dying the dominion
 From the tyrant death was torn,
cr When its Victim rose its Victor
 On the Resurrection morn.
 f Alleluia, Alleluia
 To th' Incarnate SON of GOD,
 Who through His eternal SPIRIT
 Offers His own Flesh and Blood.

mf Forty days of mystic converse
 Lived on earth the Risen One,
Speaking of His earthly kingdom,
 Ere He sought His heav'nly throne :
Then, His latest words a blessing,
 He ascended up on high,
cr And through rank on rank of Angels
 Captive led captivity.
 f Alleluia, Alleluia
 To th' Incarnate SON of GOD,
 Who the Holiest place hath enter'd
 In our flesh and by His Blood.

f Now upon the golden altar,
 In the midst before the throne,
Incense of His intercession
 He is offering for His own.
And on earth at all His altars
 His true Presence we adore;
And His Sacrifice is pleaded,
 Yea, till time shall be no more.
 Alleluia, Alleluia
 To th' Incarnate SON of GOD,
 Who, abiding Priest for ever,
 Still imparts His Flesh and Blood.

 f Then, adored in highest heaven,
 We shall see the Virgin's Son,
All creation bow'd before Him,
 MAN upon th' eternal throne :
Where, like sound of many waters
 In one ever rising flood,
cr Myriad voices hymn His triumph,
 Victim, Priest, Incarnate GOD.
 ff Worthy He all praise and blessing
 Who, by dying, death o'ercame :
 Glory be to GOD for ever !
 Alleluia to the LAMB !

E. E, DUGMORE.

Hymn 712. ALMONDSBURY.—L.M.

B. HARWOOD.

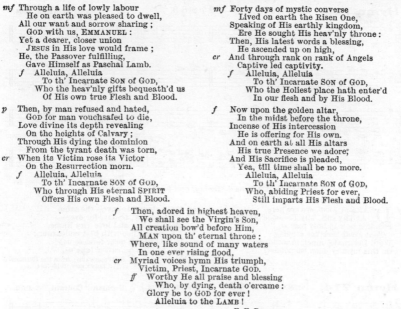

A-men.

[For copyright, see p. lv.]

AT THE OFFERTORY. *"Look upon the face of Thine anointed."*

f ALMIGHTY FATHER, LORD most High,
 Who madest all, Who fillest all,
Thy Name we praise and magnify,
For all our needs on Thee we call.

mf We offer to Thee of Thine own
Ourselves and all that we can bring,
In Bread and Cup before Thee shown,
Our universal offering.

All that we have we bring to Thee,
Yet all is naught when all is done,

Save that in it Thy love can see
The sacrifice of Thy dear SON.

By His command in Bread and Cup
His Body and His Blood we plead ;
p What on the Cross He offer'd up
Is here our Sacrifice indeed.

mf For all Thy gifts of life and grace,
Here we Thy servants humbly pray
That Thou would'st look upon the face
Of Thine anointed SON to-day.

V. S. S. COLES.

(619)

Holy Communion.

Hymn 713. LIEBSTER JESU.—7 8 7 8.88.

J. R. AHLE, 1664.

A-men.

" Jesus Christ the same yesterday, and to-day, and for ever."

AT THE COMMUNION.

mf DEAREST JESU, we are here,
 At Thy call, Thy Presence owning;
Pleading now in holy fear
 That great Sacrifice atoning:
p Word Incarnate, much in wonder
On this myst'ry deep we ponder.

mf JESU, strong to save—the same
 Yesterday, to-day, for ever—
Make us fear and love Thy Name,
 Serving Thee with best endeavour:
p In this life, O ne'er forsake us,
cr But to bliss hereafter take us.

G. R. WOODWARD: from the German
of T. Clausnitzer, 1619-1684.

Hymn 714. EMMANUEL.—9 8 9 8. (*First Tune.*)

German "Courant," *c.* 1675.

A-men.

Hymn 714. SACRAMENT.—9 8 9 8. (*Second Tune.*)

E. J. HOPKINS.

A-men.

Holy Communion.

" I am the Bread of life."

p   BREAD of the world in mercy broken,
      Wine of the soul in mercy shed,
cr By Whom the words of life were spoken,
    And in Whose death our sins are dead :

p   Look on the heart by sorrow broken,
    Look on the tears by sinners shed ;
cr And be Thy feast to us the token
    That by Thy grace our souls are fed.

Bishop Heber, 1783–1826.

Hymn 715.   Old 124th.—10 10 10 10. (*First Tune.*)   L. Bourgeois, 1561.

A-men.

Hymn 715.   Song 22.—10 10 10 10. (*Second Tune.*)   O. Gibbons, 1623.

A - men.

" I will come unto thee, and I will bless thee."

mf HERE, O my Lord, I see Thee face to face ;
     Here would I touch and handle things unseen ;
  Here grasp with firmer hand th' eternal grace,
    And all my weariness upon Thee lean.

    Here would I feed upon the Bread of God ;
    Here drink with Thee the royal Wine of heaven ;
    Here would I lay aside each earthly load ;
    Here taste afresh the calm of sin forgiven.

p   I have no help but Thine ; nor do I need
    Another arm save Thine to lean upon :
    It is enough, my Lord, enough indeed ;
    My strength is in Thy might, Thy might alone.

mf Mine is the sin, but Thine the righteousness ;
    Mine is the guilt, but Thine the cleansing Blood ;
    Here is my robe, my refuge, and my peace,—
    Thy Blood, Thy righteousness, O Lord my God.

H. Bonar.

Alternative Tunes, Hymn 761 and Hymn 31 (Second Tune).

Holy Communion.

Hymn 716. ECCLES.—6 6 6 6.

B. LUARD SELBY.

A - men.

"My soul thirsteth for Thee, my flesh also longeth after Thee."

p I HUNGER and I thirst;
JESU, my manna be;
Ye living waters, burst
Out of the rock for me.

Thou bruised and broken Bread,
My life-long wants supply;
As living souls are fed,
O feed me, or I die.

mf Thou true life-giving Vine,
Let me Thy sweetness prove;
Renew my life with Thine,
Refresh my soul with love.

p Rough paths my feet have trod
Since first their course began;
Feed me, Thou Bread of GOD;
Help me, Thou Son of Man.

For still the desert lies
My thirsting soul before;
cr O living waters, rise
Within me evermore.

J. S. B. MONSELL.

Hymn 717. GROSVENOR.—7 8 7 8, with Alleluia.

S. S. WESLEY.

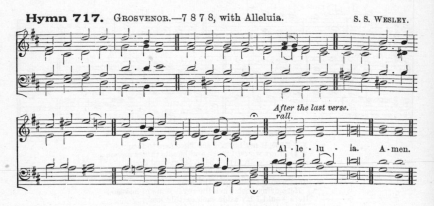

After the last verse.
rall.

Al - le - lu - ia. A - men.

"The Lord my God shall come, and all the saints with Thee."

mp NOT a thought of earthly things!
Every head in awe be bended:
cr CHRIST our GOD, the King of kings,
f Comes by angel troops attended.

mf Forth He comes, a victim He
For the wide world's need availing,
And His people's food to be,
With Himself their souls regaling.

Cherubim with watchful eyes,
Seraphim their brows concealing,
cr Powers and Principalities,
f Cry aloud, like thunder pealing,
ff Alleluia.

A. J. MASON: from the Greek.

(622)

Holy Communion.

Hymn 718. WILLINGHAM.—6 6. 7 7 7 7.   S. WESLEY, 1766–1837.

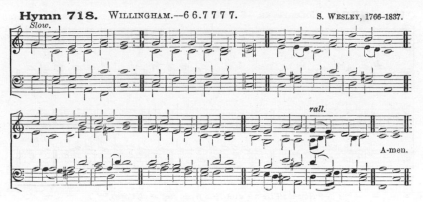

Slow.

rall.

A-men.

" Lord, I am not worthy that Thou shouldest come under my roof."

mf SAVIOUR, and can it be
 That Thou should'st dwell with me?
From Thy high and lofty throne,
Throne of everlasting bliss,
Will Thy Majesty stoop down
p To so mean a house as this?

I am not worthy, LORD,
 So foul, so self-abhorred,
Thee, my GOD, to entertain
In this poor polluted heart:
I am a frail sinful man;
All my nature cries, Depart!

Yet come, Thou heav'nly Guest,
 And purify my breast;
cr Come, Thou great and glorious King,
While before Thy Cross I bow;
With Thyself salvation bring,
Cleanse the house by entering now.

C. WESLEY, 1745.

Hymn 719. MONTGOMERY.—L.M.   J. STANLEY, 1762.

A - men.

" Jesus Himself drew near."

mp BE still, my soul! for GOD is near!
 The great High Priest is with thee now;
The LORD of life Himself is near,
Before Whose face the angels bow.

To make thy heart His lowly throne
 Thy Saviour GOD in love draws nigh;
He gives Himself unto His own,
For whom He once came down to die.

p He pleads before the mercy-seat;
 He pleads with GOD; He pleads for thee;
He gives thee bread from heav'n to eat,
His Flesh and Blood in mystery.

mf I come, O LORD! for Thou dost call—
 To blend my pleading prayer with Thine;
To Thee I give myself—my all,
And feed on Thee and make Thee mine.

Archbishop MACLAGAN

(623)

Holy Communion.

Hymn 720. COLCHESTER.—8 8 8 8.8 8.

S. S. WESLEY.

A-men.

"How shall He not with Him freely give us all things."

mf WITH solemn faith we offer up
　　And spread, O GOD, before Thine eyes
That only ground of all our hope,
That precious, once-made Sacrifice,
Which brings Thy grace on sinners down,
And perfects all our souls in one.

Acceptance through His only Name,
Forgiveness in His Blood we have;
But more abundant life we claim

Through Him Who died our souls to save,
To sanctify us by His Blood
And fill with all the life of GOD.

As it were slain behold Thy SON,
And hear His Blood that speaks above;
On us let all Thy grace be shown,
Peace, righteousness, and joy, and love:
Thy Kingdom come to every heart,
And all Thou hast, and all Thou art.

C. WESLEY, 1745.

ALTERNATIVE TUNE, HYMN 526.

Hymn 721. STELLA.—8 8 8 8.8 8.

Easy Hymns for Catholic Schools, 1851.

A - men.

(624)

Holy Communion.

" With great mercies will I gather thee."

mf FATHER, Who dost Thy children feed
With Manna rainèd from above ;
Who dost the saving chalice give,
Fill'd by Thy hand in wondrous love :
f We praise Thee for Thy mercies sent
To us in this great Sacrament.

mp O Word-made-flesh, Whom we adore,
The living Bread sent down from heav'n,
Whose wondrous passion here shown forth
Is the great pledge of sin forgiven ;
f We praise Thee for Thy mercies sent
To us in this great Sacrament.

p O HOLY SPIRIT, Who dost deign
These earthly elements to bless,
Making the bread His flesh to be,
The wine His blood, as we confess ;
f We praise Thee for Thy mercies sent
To us in this great Sacrament.

Ye holy Angels, who, with us,
Around GOD'S altar lowly bow,
Adoring there the Crucified,
Whose precious death is pleaded now,
O praise Him for His mercies sent
To us in this great Sacrament !

Ye blessèd saints, enthroned on high,
Who once the paths of earth did tread,
Who reach'd in safety GOD'S abode,
As strengthen'd by this living bread ;
O praise Him for His mercies sent
To us in this great Sacrament !

mp O Holy FATHER, Holy SON,
And HOLY SPIRIT, Whom we love,
cr Guide, strengthen, save us here below,
And bring us to our home above,
f To praise Thee for Thy mercies sent
To us in this great Sacrament !

G. BODY.

Hymn 722. ST. BASIL THE GREAT.—7 6 7 6. 7 6 7 6.   Sir C. V. STANFORD.

A-men.

[For copyright, see p. lv.]

" Behold, the tabernacle of God is with men."

f WE hail Thee now, O JESU,
Upon Thine Altar-throne,
mf Though sight and touch have fail'd us,
And faith perceives alone !
Thy love has veil'd Thy Godhead
And hid Thy power divine,
In mercy to our weakness,
Beneath an earthly sign.

f We hail Thee now, O JESU ;
p In silence hast Thou come ;
For all the hosts of heaven
With wonderment are dumb ;
So great the condescension,
So marvellous the love,
Which for our sakes, O Saviour,
Have drawn Thee from above.

f We hail Thee now, O JESU ;
For law and type have ceased,
And Thou in each Communion
Art Sacrifice and Priest ;
mf We make this great memorial
In union, LORD, with Thee,
And plead Thy Death and Passion
To cleanse and set us free.

f We hail Thee now, O JESU ;
p For death is drawing near,
cr And in Thy presence only
Its terrors disappear.
Dwell with us, sweetest Saviour,
And guide us through the night,
f Till shadows end in glory,
And faith be lost in sight.

F. G. SCOTT.

ALTERNATIVE TUNE, HYMN 219.

Holy Communion.

Hymn 723. BROCKHAM.—L.M.

J. CLARKE, 1709.

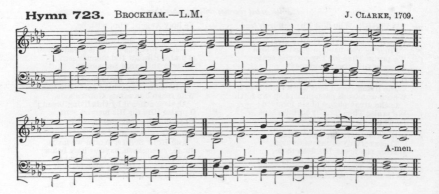

A-men.

"Exceeding abundantly above all we ask or think."

f   H OW glorious is the life above,
        Which in this ordinance we taste ;
     That fulness of celestial love,
       That joy which shall for ever last.

mf That heav'nly life in CHRIST conceal'd
      These earthen vessels could not bear ;
     The part which now we find reveal'd,
      No tongue of Angels can declare.

f   The light of life eternal darts
      Into our souls a dazzling ray ;
    A drop of heav'n o'erflows our hearts,
      And deluges the house of clay.

Sure pledge of ecstasies unknown
     Shall this Divine Communion be ;
  The ray shall rise into a sun,
     The drop shall swell into a sea.

C. WESLEY, 1745.

Hymn 724. HOSANNA IN EXCELSIS.—7 7 4 4 7.7 7 4 4 7. S. H. NICHOLSON.

Holy Communion.

A-men.

" Thanks be unto God for His unspeakable gift."

f H OSANNA in the highest
   To our exalted Saviour,
   Who left behind
   For all mankind
  These tokens of His favour :
mf His bleeding love and mercy,
  His all-redeeming passion,
cr   Who here displays,
   And gives the grace
  Which brings us our salvation.

f Louder than gather'd waters,
  Or bursting peals of thunder,
   We lift our voice
   And speak our joys,
  And shout our loving wonder.

Shout, all our elder brethren,
While we record the story
  Of Him that came
  And suffer'd shame,
To carry us to glory.

mf Angels in fix'd amazement
  Around our altars hover,
   With eager gaze
   Adore the grace
  Of our Eternal Lover :
Himself, and all His fulness,
Who gives to the believer ;
cr   And by this Bread
   Whoe'er are fed
f Shall live with GOD for ever.

C. WESLEY, 1745.

Verses 2 and 3 should begin thus :

Holy Baptism.

Hymn 725. WELLS.—L.M.

W. H. MONK.

A - men.

" Chosen . . . to be a soldier."

mf G RANT to this child the inward grace,
  While we the outward sign impart ;
The Cross we on *his* forehead trace
 Do Thou engrave upon *his* heart.

May it *his* pride and glory be,
 Beneath Thy banner fair unfurl'd,
To march to certain victory
 O'er sin, o'er Satan, o'er the world.

J. MARRIOTT, 1811.

(627)

For the Young.

Hymn 726. GOSHEN.—6 5 6 5. 6 5 6 5. *Bible Class Magazine, 1860.*

A - men.

" Let us hold fast the profession of our faith without wavering."

I WAS made a Christian
    When my name was given,
One of GOD'S dear children,
    And an heir of heaven.
In the name of Christian
    I will glory now,
Evermore remember
    My baptismal vow.

I must, like a Christian,
    Shun all evil ways,
Keep the faith of JESUS,
    Serve Him all my days.

Call'd to be a Christian,
    I will praise the LORD,
Seek for His assistance
    So to keep my word.

All a Christian's blessings
    I will claim for mine :
Holy work and worship,
    Fellowship divine.
FATHER, SON, and SPIRIT,
    Give me grace, that I
Still may live a Christian,
    And a Christian die.

J. S. JONES.

Hymn 727. BEVAN.—6 6 6 6. 8 8. *Sir J. GOSS, 1853.*

A-men.

For the Young.

" Let this mind be in you which was also in Christ Jesus."

mf BEHOLD a little Child,
　　Laid in a manger bed ;
The wintry blasts blow wild
　　Around His infant head.
But Who is this so lowly laid?
'Tis He by Whom the worlds were made.

p Alas ! in what poor state
　　The SON of GOD is seen ;
Why doth the LORD so great
　　Choose out a home so mean ?
That we may learn from pride to flee,
And follow His humility.

mf Where Joseph plies his trade,
　　Lo ! JESUS labours too ;
The hands that all things made

An earthly craft pursue,
That weary men in Him may rest,
And faithful toil through Him be blest.

Among the doctors see
　　The Boy so full of grace ;
Say, wherefore taketh He
　　The scholar's lowly place ?
That Christian boys, with rev'rence meet,
May sit and learn at JESUS' feet.

CHRIST ! once Thyself a Boy,
　　Our boyhood guard and guide ;
Be Thou its light and joy,
　　And still with us abide,
That Thy dear love, so great and free,
May draw us evermore to Thee.

Bishop W. WALSHAM HOW.

Hymn 728. INFANTIUM LAUDES.—7 6 7 6.7 6 7 6.11.　　Sir H. PARRY.

Ho - san - na, Ho - san - na to JE - SUS　　A - men.

" Children crying in the temple, and saying, Hosanna to the Son of David."

f WHEN, His salvation bringing,
　　To Zion JESUS came,
The children all stood singing
　　Hosanna to His Name ;
Nor did their zeal offend Him,
　　But, as He rode along,
He let them still attend Him,
　　And listen'd to their song.
ff　　Hosanna to JESUS they sang.

f And since the LORD retaineth
　　His love for children still,
Though now as King He reigneth
　　On Zion's heav'nly hill :

We'll flock around His banner,
　　Who sits upon the throne,
And cry aloud " Hosanna "
　　To David's royal Son.
ff　　Hosanna to JESUS we'll sing.

f For should we fail proclaiming
　　Our great Redeemer's praise,
The stones, our silence shaming,
　　Would their Hosannas raise.
But shall we only render
　　The tribute of our words?
No ! while our hearts are tender,
　　They, too, shall be the LORD'S.
ff　　Hosanna to JESUS, our King.

J. KING, 1789-1858.

For the Young.

Hymn 729. BEATI IMMACULATI.—C.M.   A. R. REINAGLE, 1799–1877.

A - men.

" There is mercy with Thee, therefore shalt Thou be feared."

p AS now Thy children lowly kneel
     And all for mercy pray,
O FATHER, make us truly feel
    The solemn words we say.

Teach us to hate the power of sin,
    Which parts our souls from Thee ;
Help us to make our life within
    What Thou wilt love to see.

Teach us to trust the LAMB of GOD,
    Who takes our sins away :

Help us to choose the path He trod,
    And so Thy will obey.

Teach us to keep Thy holy laws
    Because we trust Thy love ;
Help us to rise, when JESUS draws
    To better joys above.

O teach us more our sins to fear,
    And more Thy word to love :
Help us on earth the cross to bear,
    And win the crown above.

L. TUTTIETT.

Hymn 730. PASTOR PASTORUM.—6 5 6 5.   F. SILCHER, 1789–1860.

A - men.

" Give ear, O Shepherd of Israel."

mf FAITHFUL Shepherd, feed me
     In the pastures green ;
Faithful Shepherd, lead me
    Where Thy steps are seen.

Hold me fast, and guide me
    In the narrow way ;
So, with Thee beside me,
    I shall never stray.

Daily bring me nearer
    To the heav'nly shore ;

Make my faith grow clearer,
    May I love Thee more.

Hallow every pleasure,
    Every gift and pain ;
Be Thyself my treasure,
    Though none else I gain.

Day by day prepare me
    As Thou seest best,
Then let Angels bear me
    To Thy promised rest.

T. B. POLLOCK.

For the Young.

Hymn 731. WIR PFLÜGEN.—7 6 7 6. 7 6 7 6. 6 6 8 4.

J. A. P. SCHULTZ, 1747–1800.

A-men.

" I went with them to the house of God, with the voice of joy and praise, with a multitude that kept holiday."

SUNDAY.

f
AGAIN the morn of gladness,
    Tho morn of light, is here ;
And earth itself looks fairer,
    And heav'n itself more near.
The bells, like angel voices,
    Speak peace to every breast,
And all the land lies quiet
    To keep the day of rest.
        Glory be to JESUS,
            Let all His children say ;
        He rose again, He rose again,
            On this glad day.

Again, O loving Saviour,
    The children of Thy grace
Prepare themselves to seek Thee
    Within Thy chosen place.
Our song shall rise to greet Thee,
    If Thou our hearts wilt raise ;
If Thou our lips wilt open,
    Our mouth shall show Thy praise.
        Glory be to JESUS, &c.

The shining choir of angels
    That rest not day nor night,
The crown'd and palm-deck'd martyrs,
    The saints array'd in white,

The happy lambs of JESUS
    In pastures fair above,
These all adore and praise Him,
    Whom we, too, praise and love.
        Glory be to JESUS, &c.

The Church on earth rejoices
    To join with these to-day ;
In every tongue and nation
    She calls her sons to pray.
Across the northern snow-fields,
    Beneath the Indian palms,
She makes the same pure offering,
    And sings the same sweet psalms.
        Glory be to JESUS, &c.

Tell out, sweet bells, His praises !
    Sing, children, sing His Name !
Still louder and still further
    His mighty deeds proclaim !
Till all whom He redeemèd
    Shall own Him LORD and King ;
Till every knee shall worship,
    And every tongue shall sing
        Glory be to JESUS, &c.

J. ELLERTON.

For the Young.

Hymn 732. ST. PAUL.—C.M.   CHALMERS, *Collection*, 1749.

A-men.

FOR LITTLE CHILDREN. *"Suffer the little children to come unto Me."*

mf OUR GOD of love, Who reigns above,
　　　　Comes down to us below ;
'Tis sweet to tell He loves so well,
　And 'tis enough to know.

So deep, so high—like air and sky,
　Beyond us, yet around ;
He Whom our mind can never find
　Can in our heart be found.

LORD GOD, so far, past sun and star,
　Yet close to all our ways !

In love so near, be pleased to hear
　Thy little children's praise !

O may that sign that we are Thine—
　Our FATHER, SAVIOUR, FRIEND—
Which seal'd our brow, be on us now,
　And with us to the end.

Through all our way, and every day
　Believed, beloved, adored ;
Be this our grace to see Thy face
　In JESUS CHRIST our LORD.

S. J. STONE.

Confirmation.

Hymn 733. ST. IGNATIUS.—5 5 5 5.6 5 6 5.   J. BEAUMONT, 1801.

A - men.

"Take unto you the whole armour of God."

AFTER THE CONFIRMATION.

f ONCE pledged by the Cross,
　　　As children of GOD.
To tread in the steps
　Your Captain has trod,
Now, seal'd by the SPIRIT
　Of Wisdom and Might,
Go forward, CHRIST'S soldiers,
　Go forward and fight !

Your weapons of war
　Are sent from above,
The SPIRIT'S good sword,
　The breastplate of love ;
Your feet with the Gospel
　Of peace be well shod ;
Put on the whole armour,
　The armour of GOD.

Confirmation.

Full well do ye know
  The foe must be met,
Full well do ye feel
  That Satan has set
His powers of darkness
  In battle array ;
But those who are for you
  Are stronger than they.

mf The fight may be long,
  But triumph is sure,
And rest comes at last
  To those who endure ;

The rest that remaineth,
  The victory won,
And—dearer than all things—
  Your Captain's " Well done."

f Then, on to the fight
  'Gainst sin and the world,
Stand fast in His strength,
  His banner unfurl'd ;
And, seal'd by the SPIRIT
  Of Wisdom and Might,
Go forward, CHRIST'S soldiers,
  Go forward and fight !

ALICE M. BODE.

ALTERNATIVE TUNE, HYMN 431.

Missions.

Hymn 734. RANGOON.—Irregular.

C. WOOD.

A - men.

ORG.

" The ransomed of the Lord shall return, and come with singing unto Zion."

f TRUMPET of GOD, sound high,
  Till the hearts of the heathen shake,
And the souls that in slumber lie
  At the voice of the LORD awake.
Till the fencèd cities fall
  At the blast of the Gospel call,
Trumpet of GOD, sound high !

Hosts of the LORD, go forth :
  Go, strong in the power of His rest,
Till the south be at one with the north,
  And peace upon east and west ;

Till the far-off lands shall thrill
  With the gladness of GOD's " Goodwill,'
Hosts of the LORD, go forth.

Come, as of old, like fire ;
  O Force of the LORD, descend,
Till with love of the world's Desire
  Earth burn to its utmost end ;
Till the ransom'd people sing
  To the glory of CHRIST the King,
Come, as of old, like fire.

A. BROOKS.

Missions.

Hymn 735. BENSON.—Irregular. (*First Tune.*)   Miss M. D. KINGHAM.

[For copyright, see p. lv.]

Hymn 735. STOKE-ON-TERN.—Irregular. (*Second Tune.*)   Sir WALFORD DAVIES.

With dignity.   This Tune may be sung in Unison.

[For copyright, see p. lv.]

Missions.

cres.   *dim.*   A-men.

"The earth shall be filled with the knowledge of the glory of the Lord, as the waters cover the sea."

mf G OD is working His | purpose out as | year succeeds to | year,
  G OD is working His | purpose out and the | time is drawing | near ;
  Nearer and nearer | draws the time, the | time that shall surely | be,
f When the | earth shall be fill'd with the | glory of G OD as the | waters cover the | sea.

mf From | utmost east to | utmost west wher- | e'er man's foot hath | trod,
  By the | mouth of many | messengers goes | forth the voice of | G OD ,
f "Give | ear to Me, ye | continents, ye | isles, give ear to | Me,
  That the | earth may be fill'd with the | glory of G OD as the | waters cover the | sea."

p What can we do to | work G OD 'S work, to | prosper and in- | crease
  The | brotherhood of | all mankind, the | reign of the Prince of | peace?
  What can we do to | hasten the time, the | time that shall surely | be,
cr When the | earth shall be fill'd with the | glory of G OD as the | waters cover the | sea?

f March we forth in the | strength of G OD with the | banner of C HRIST un- | furl'd,
  That the | light of the glorious | Gospel of truth may | shine throughout the | world.
  Fight we the fight with | sorrow and sin, to | set their captives | free,
  That the | earth may be fill'd with the | glory of G OD as the | waters cover the | sea.

p All we can do is | nothing worth un- | less G OD blesses the | deed ;
  Vainly we hope for the | harvest-tide till | G OD gives life to the | seed ;
cr Yet | nearer and nearer | draws the time, the | time that shall surely | be,
f When the | earth shall be fill'd with the | glory of G OD as the | waters cover the | sea.

A. C. A INGER .

Hymn 736. H EAVEN .—7 5 7 5. 7 7.
B. L UARD S ELBY .

A-men.

" He is a great King over all the earth."

f L ET the song go round the earth,
  J ESUS C HRIST is L ORD ;
Sound His praises, tell His worth,
  Be His Name adored ;
Every clime and every tongue
Join the grand, the glorious song.

Let the song go round the earth
  From the eastern sea,
Where the daylight has its birth,
  Glad, and bright, and free ;
China's millions join the strains,
Waft them on to India's plains.

Let the song go round the earth !
  Lands, where Islam's sway
Darkly broods o'er home and hearth,

Cast their bonds away ;
Let His praise from Afric's shore
Rise and swell her wide lands o'er.

Let the song go round the earth,
  Where the summer smiles ;
Let the notes of holy mirth
  Break from distant isles ;
Inland forests, dark and dim,
Snow-bound coasts give back the hymn.

Let the song go round the earth !
  J ESUS C HRIST is K ING !
With the story of His worth
  Let the whole world ring ;
Him creation all adore
Evermore and evermore.

S ARAH G. S TOCK .

(635)

Church Workers.

Hymn 737. HULL NEW.—8 8 8 8.8 8.   IRELAND, *Collection*, 1699.

A-men.

"Who will go for us?"

mf THE Master comes! He calls for thee,—
  Go forth at His Almighty word,
Obedient to His last command,
  And tell to those who never heard,
Who sit in deepest shades of night,
That CHRIST has come to give them light.

The Master calls! Arise and go;
  How blest His messenger to be!
He, Who hath given thee liberty,
  Now bids thee set the captives free;
Proclaim His mighty power to save,
Who for the world His life-blood gave.

The Master calls! Shall not thy heart
  In warm responsive love reply,
"LORD, here am I; send me, send me,—
  Thy willing slave,—to live or die,—
An instrument unfit indeed,
Yet Thou wilt give me what I need"?

And if thou canst not go, yet bring
  An offering of a willing heart;
Then, though thou tarriest at home,
  Thy GOD shall give thee too thy part;
The messengers of peace upbear
In ceaseless and prevailing prayer.

Short is the time for service true,
  For soon shall dawn that glorious Day
When, all the harvest gather'd in,
  Each faithful heart shall hear Him say,—
"My child, well done! your toil is o'er—
Enter My joy for evermore."

                    MRS. CRAWFORD.

ALTERNATIVE TUNE, HYMN 345 (SECOND TUNE).

Church Workers.

Hymn 738.   MENDIP.—4. 10 10. 10 4.   B. JOHNSON.

[*For copyright, see p. lv.*]

" Go work to-day."

mf   COME, labour on !
Who dares stand idle on the harvest plain,
While all around him waves the golden grain ?
And to each servant does the Master say,
     " Go, work to-day ! "

Come, labour on !
Claim the high calling Angels cannot share,
To young and old the Gospel-gladness bear :
Redeem the time : its hours too swiftly fly,
     The night draws nigh.

p   Come, labour on !
The enemy is watching night and day,
To sow the tares, to snatch the seed away ;
While we in sleep our duty have forgot,
     He slumber'd not.

f   Come, labour on !
Away with gloomy doubts and faithless fear !
No arm so weak but may do service here ;
By feeblest agents can our GOD fulfil
     His righteous will.

Come, labour on !
No time for rest, till glows the western sky,
Till the long shadows o'er our pathway lie,
And a glad sound comes with the setting sun—
     " Servants, well done ! "

Come, labour on !
The toil is pleasant, the reward is sure ;
Blessèd are those who to the end endure ;
How full their joy, how deep their rest shall be,
     O LORD, with Thee !

            JANE L. BORTHWICK, 1859.

Church Workers.

Hymn 739. GREENWICH.—C.M.

W. RICHARDSON, 1729.

" The ways of the Lord are right."

mf OH, it is hard to work for GOD,
  To rise and take His part
Upon this battlefield of earth,
  And not sometimes lose heart!

p He hides Himself so wondrously,
  As though there were no GOD;
He is least seen when all the pow'rs
  Of ill are most abroad.

mf Ah, GOD is other than we think,
  His ways are far above,
Far beyond reason's height, and reach'd
  Only by childlike love.

Workman of GOD! O lose not heart,
  But learn what GOD is like,
And in the darkest battlefield
  Thou shalt know where to strike.

Then learn to scorn the praise of men,
  And learn to lose with GOD;
For JESUS won the world through shame,
  And beckons thee His road.

f For right is right, as GOD is GOD,
  And right the day must win;
To doubt would be disloyalty,
  To falter were to sin.

F. W. FABER.

Farewell Service.

Hymn 740. DOMINUS VOBISCUM.—9 8 8 9.

A. SOMERVELL.

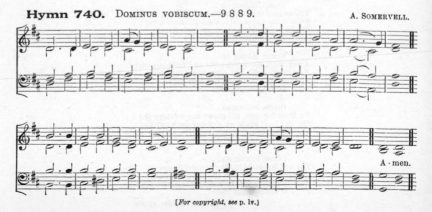

(638)

Farewell Service.

" Certainly I will be with thee."

mf GOD be with you till we meet again ;
    By His counsels guide, uphold you,
With His sheep securely fold you :
GOD be with you till we meet again.

GOD be with you till we meet again ;
    'Neath His wings protecting hide you,
Daily manna still provide you :
GOD be with you till we meet again.

p GOD be with you till we meet again ;
    When life's perils thick confound you,
Put His arm unfailing round you :
GOD be with you till we meet again.

mf GOD be with you till we meet again ;
    Keep love's banner floating o'er you,
Smite death's threat'ning wave before you :
GOD be with you till we meet again.

J. E. RANKIN.

Absent Friends.

Hymn 741. CALVARY.—8 7 8 7.8 7.   S. STANLEY, 1767-1822.

A - men.

" The Lord shall preserve thy going out and thy coming in."

p FOR the dear ones parted from us
    We would raise our hymns of prayer ;
By the tender love which watcheth
Round Thy children everywhere,
    Holy FATHER,
Keep them ever in Thy care.

Through each trial and temptation,
    Dangers faced by night and day,
By the infinite compassion
Pleading for the souls that stray,
    Loving SAVIOUR,
Keep them in the narrow way.

In their hours of doubt and sorrow,
    When their faith is sorely tried,
By the grace divine which strengthens
Souls for whom the Saviour died,
    Gracious SPIRIT,
Be Thou evermore their guide.

In their joys, by friends surrounded,
    In their strife, by foes oppress'd,
May Thy blessing still be with them,
May Thy presence give them rest,
    GOD Almighty,
FATHER, SON, and SPIRIT blest.

ADA R. GREENAWAY.

ALTERNATIVE TUNE, HYMN 287.

Times of Trouble.

Hymn 742. RUSSIAN ANTHEM.—11 10 11 10.

A. LVOV, 1833

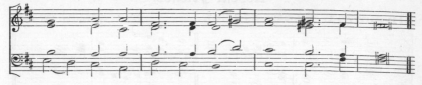

A · men.

" O God, . . . Thou hast been displeased : O turn Thyself to us again."

WAR.

f GOD the All-terrible ! King, Who ordainest
　　Great winds Thy clarions, the lightnings Thy sword,
dim Show forth Thy pity on high where Thou reignest,
　　Grant to us peace, O most merciful LORD.

p GOD the Omnipotent ! Mighty Avenger,
　　Watching invisible, judging unheard,
　　Doom us not now in the day of our danger ;
　　Grant to us peace, O most merciful LORD.

GOD the All-merciful ! earth has forsaken
　　Thy ways of blessedness, slighted Thy word ;
　　Bid not Thy wrath in its terrors awaken ;
　　Grant to us peace, O most merciful LORD.

f So shall Thy children, in thankful devotion,
　　Praise Him Who savèd them from peril and sword ;
　　Singing in chorus from ocean to ocean,
　　Peace to the nations, and praise to the LORD.

H. F. CHORLEY, 1842.

(640)

Times of Trouble.

Hymn 743. MATLOCK.—8 8 8 8. 8 8. M. WISE, 1684.

A-men.

A lower setting of this Tune is given at Hymn 361.

" Thou hast been my defence and refuge in the day of trouble."

WAR.

mf LORD, while afar our brothers fight,
　　Thy Church united lifts her prayer ;
Be Thou their shield by day and night ;
　　Guide, guard, and help them everywhere :
O GOD of battles, hear our cry,
And in their danger be Thou nigh

For those who, wounded in the fray,
　　Are ling'ring still on beds of pain,
Who to their loved ones far away
　　May nevermore return again,
O GOD of pity, hear our cry,
And in their anguish be Thou nigh.

p For wives and mothers sore distress'd,
　　For all who wait in silent fear,
For homes bereaved which gave their best,
　　For hearts now desolate and drear,
mf O GOD of comfort, hear our cry,
And in the darkest hour draw nigh.

p Spare us, good LORD ! If just the strife,
　　Yet still from guilt we are not free ;
Forgive our blind and careless life,
　　Our oft forgetfulness of Thee.
mf O GOD of mercy, hear our cry,
And to our contrite souls draw nigh.

p We bow beneath the chast'ning rod,
　　To us the sin and shame belong :
cr But Thou art righteous, Thou art GOD,
　　And right shall triumph over wrong.
In Thee we trust, to Thee we cry ;
LORD, now and ever be Thou nigh.

S. C. LOWRY.

(641)

Y

Processional.

Hymn 744. ST. AUDREY.—8 7 8 7 8 7.

Verses 1, 4, 6, 9, 11, 14, 15 in Unison.
Slow and majestic.

B. HARWOOD.

The Pedal part well marked.

Verses 2, 3, 5, 7, 8, 10, 12, 13 in Harmony.

A - men.

Processional.

Unison.

f GLORY to the First-begotten,
Risen CHRIST, Incarnate WORD!
Glory to the Faithful Witness,
Over all dominion LORD,
Who hath loved us, Who hath wash'd us
In His precious Blood outpour'd!

Harmony.

*Glory unto Him Who gave us
Heritage of priest and king!
That for ever in His presence
We our Eucharist may sing,
All our crowns cast down before Him,
To His shrine our incense bring.

Harmony.

*Glory to the LORD ALMIGHTY!
Every foe beneath Him cast,
High He reigns in splendour seated,
He the First and He the Last
He both Alpha and Omega,
LORD of future, present, past.

Unison.

Glory unto Him Who holdeth
Mystic stars in His right hand!
Glory unto Him Who walketh
'Midst the lamps that gleaming stand!
Every Church and every pastor
Subject to His dread command.

Harmony.

mf Thou Who knowest how we labour'd,
Fainting not when foemen strove,
Raise once more our fallen courage,
Stir again our early love:
Quench not all the light within us,
Nor our candlestick remove.

Unison.

*From all subtle evil guard us,
False apostles, deeds of ill;
Grant us every lie to conquer,
Every hateful lust to kill:
By the Tree of Life sustain us,
And our hungry spirits fill.

Harmony.

If, wherever Satan dwelleth,
We confess Thee as our LORD,
Bid us fear not Satan's malice,
Tribulation, fire, or sword.
Crown Thy faithful patient servants
With the Martyr's bright reward.

Harmony.

p By Thy HOLY SPIRIT cleanse us,
Pure in heart Thy law to own;
Grant to us the hidden manna,
Grant to us the fair white stone,
And the new name newly written,
Only to Thy servants known.

Unison.

f Thou hast once for our salvation
On the raging Dragon trod,
Keep us steadfast, faithful, loving,
Smite our foes with iron rod,
Scatter all the depths of Satan,
Bright and Morning Star of GOD.

Harmony.

mf Save us from the name of living
While the soul within is dead;
Wash our garments from defilement
In the Blood that Thou hast shed;
cr Then confess us in Thy glory,
Members worthy of their Head.

Unison.

f Thou Who hast the key of David,
Set for us an open door,
Refuge in the Great Temptation
When the testing tempests roar;
Plant us in Thy FATHER'S temple,
Pillars firm for evermore.

Harmony.

p We are wretched, cold, and naked,
Needing all things, poor and blind;
Thou hast raiment, riches, healing,
Meet for body, soul, and mind.
Humbled, shamefast we approach Thee,
All our store in Thee to find.

PART 2.

Harmony.

mf Come, in love rebuke and chasten,
At our hearts' door come and stand;
Knock once more, and bid us open,
Knock with Thine own pierced hand.
We will hear Thee, we will open,
Sup with Thee at Thy command.

Unison.

Grant to us that overcoming
By a virtue not our own,
We may with Thee in Thy glory
Be Thy crownèd brothers shown,
Even as Thou, overcoming,
Sittest on Thy FATHER'S throne.

Unison.

ff Glory unto Him that reigneth
On th' eternal throne on high!
Glory to the LAMB that suffer'd,
Living now no more to die!
Glory to the Blessèd SPIRIT,
One with Both eternally!

AUG. G. DONALDSON.

* These verses may be omitted.

Processional.

Hymn 745. CRUCIFER.—10 10.

S. H. NICHOLSON.

Unison.

f LIFT high the Cross, the love of CHRIST pro - claim

Till all the world ... a - dore ... His Sa - cred Name.

FINE.

Harmony.

D.C.

ORG. A - men.

" Jesus Christ, and Him crucified.'

f LIFT high the Cross, the love of CHRIST
proclaim
Till all the world adore His Sacred Name.

mf Come, brethren, follow where our Captain
trod,
Our King victorious, CHRIST the SON of GOD.
Lift high the Cross, &c.

Led on their way by this triumphant sign,
The hosts of GOD in conquering ranks
combine.
Lift high the Cross, &c.

Each new-born soldier of the Crucified
Bears on his brow the seal of Him Who
died.
Lift high the Cross, &c.

This is the sign which Satan's legions fear,
The mystery which angel hosts revere.
Lift high the Cross, &c.

Saved by this Cross whereon their LORD was
slain,
The sons of Adam their lost home regain.
Lift high the Cross, &c.

f From north and south, from east and west
In growing unison their song of praise.
Lift high the Cross, &c.

p O LORD, once lifted on the glorious Tree,
As Thou hast promised, draw men unto
Thee.
Lift high the Cross, &c.

(644)

Processional.

f Let every race and every language tell
Of Him Who saves our souls from death and
    hell.
       Lift high the Cross, &c.

From farthest regions let them homage bring,
And on His Cross adore their Saviour King.
       Lift high the Cross, &c.

mf Set up Thy Throne, that earth's despair may
    cease
    Beneath the shadow of its healing peace.
       Lift high the Cross, &c.

Unison.
f So shall our song of triumph ever be,
Praise to the Crucified for victory.
       Lift high the Cross, &c.

G. W. KITCHIN and M. R. NEWBOLT

Dedication Festival or other Festivals.

Hymn 746.   DRAPER.—12 11 12 11.   Uettingen MS., 1754.

A · men.

"Their bodies are buried in peace : but their name liveth for evermore."

IN REMEMBRANCE OF PAST WORSHIPPERS.

f   IN our day of thanksgiving one psalm let us offer
      For the Saints who before us have found their reward ;
p   When the shadow of death fell upon them, we sorrow'd,
f   But now we rejoice that they rest in the LORD.

mf In the morning of life, and at noon, and at even,
    He call'd them away from our worship below ;
    But not till His love, at the font and the altar,
    Had girt them with grace for the way they should go.

    These stones that have echo'd their praises are holy,
    And dear is the ground where their feet have once trod ;
    Yet here they confess'd they were strangers and pilgrims,
    And still they were seeking the city of GOD.

f   Sing praise, then, for all who here sought and here found Him,
    Whose journey is ended, whose perils are past ;
    They believed in the Light ; and its glory is round them,
    Where the clouds of earth's sorrow are lifted at last.

W. H. DRAPER.

The Dedication Festival of a Church.

Hymn 747. RAMAULX.—10 10.

B. LUARD SELBY.

The Refrain is first sung by Solo Voices in Unison, then repeated by Chorus in Harmony.

Semi-chorus in Unison sing the Verses.

Ped. ad lib.

Chorus in Unison sing the Refrain.

[*Copyright* 1904 *by the Proprietors of* Hymns Ancient and Modern.]

"This is the day which the Lord hath made."

f HAIL, festal day, for ever sanctified,
When CHRIST is married to the
Church, His Bride.

This is GOD'S Court, the place of peace and
rest ;
The poor with Solomon's own wealth are blest.
Hail, festal day, &c.

The Son of David, GOD and Man, doth come
To knit us to Him in this Mother-home.
Hail, festal day, &c.

Ye are the company of heav'n below,
If ye will keep the faith which makes you so.
Hail, festal day, &c.

Here new Jerusalem descends all bright
In angel raiment from the world of light.
Hail, festal day, &c.

Faith, by the mystic laver, doth possess
This guerdon from the King of righteous-
ness.
Hail, festal day, &c.

Here stands the tower of David ; hither run
And find the pledge of realms beyond the sun.
Hail, festal day, &c.

This is the ark of Noë ; safe within,
Believers ride the flood, and harbour win.
Hail, festal day, &c.

Lo, this is Jacob's ladder ; here 'tis given
By faith and godly life to climb to heaven.
Hail, festal day, &c.

A. J. MASON : from the Latin.

ALTERNATIVE TUNE, HYMN 650.

(646)

Burial of the Dead.

Hymn 748. BARRAGH (Psalm cxii.).—8 8 8 8.8 8.   CHETHAM, *Psalms*, 1718.

A-men.

"It was said unto them, that they should rest yet for a little season."

p   O LORD, to Whom the spirits live
     Of all the faithful pass'd away,
cr   Unto their path that brightness give
     Which shineth to the perfect day.
      p   O LAMB of GOD, Redeemer blest,
       Grant them eternal light and rest.

mf Bless Thou the dead which die in Thee ;
     As Thou hast given them release,
     So quicken them Thy face to see,
     And give them everlasting peace.
      p   O LAMB of GOD, &c.

mf In Thy green, pleasant pastures feed
     The sheep which Thou hast summon'd hence ;
     And by the still, cool waters lead
     Thy flock in loving providence.
      p   O LAMB of GOD, &c.

p   How long, O Holy LORD, how long
     Must we and they expectant wait
cr   To hear the gladsome bridal song,
     To see Thee in Thy royal state ?
      p   O LAMB of GOD, &c.

mf O hearken, Saviour, to their cry,
     O rend the heavens and come down,
     Make up Thy jewels speedily,
     And set them in Thy golden crown.
      p   O LAMB of GOD, &c.

     Direct us with Thine arm of might,
     And bring us, perfected with them,
f   To dwell within Thy city bright,
     The heavenly Jerusalem.
      p   O LAMB of GOD, &c.

             R. F. LITTLEDALE.

ALTERNATIVE TUNE, HYMN 28.

Burial of the Dead.

Hymn 749. SWAHILI.—6 5 6 5. 6 5 6 5.　　　　J. A. P. SCHULTZ, 1785.

A - men.

"The souls of the righteous are in the hand of God."

p THINK, O LORD, in mercy
　　On the souls of those
Who, in faith gone from us,
　　Now in death repose.
Here 'mid stress and conflict
　　Toils can never cease ;
cr 　There, the warfare ended,
p 　　Bid them rest in peace.

Often were they wounded
　　In the deadly strife ;
Heal them, good Physician,
　　With the balm of life.

Every taint of evil,
　　Frailty and decay,
cr Good and gracious Saviour,
p 　Cleanse and purge away.

Rest eternal grant them,
　　After weary fight ;
Shed on them the radiance
　　Of Thy heav'nly light.
cr Lead them onward, upward,
　　To the holy place,
Where Thy Saints made perfect
　　Gaze upon Thy face.

　　　　　　　　　　　　　　E. S. PALMER.

ALTERNATIVE TUNE, HYMN **750.**

Hymn 750. EUDOXIA.—6 5 6 5.　　　　Rev. S. BARING-GOULD

Burial of the Dead.

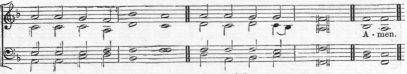

[*For copyright, see p. lv.*]

A higher setting of this Tune is given at Hymn 346.

" Jesus called a little child unto Him."

FOR A CHILD.

p FATHER, Who hast gather'd
 This dear child to rest,
Unto Thee we yield *him*,
 Sure Thou knowest best.

Thou, O LORD, Who gavest,
 Dost Thine own reclaim :
Thou, O LORD, hast taken—
 Blessèd still Thy Name !—

Thine by right creative,
 By redemption Thine,
By regeneration
 And the holy sign.

Thou Who didst endow *him*
 With baptismal grace,
Now in love hast brought *him*
 To behold Thy face.

mf Safe from all earth's sorrow,
 Safe from all its pains,

Now this child of Adam
 Paradise regains :

Safe from all temptation,
 Safe from fear of sin,
Through the Blood of sprinkling
 Holy, bright, and clean.

p Lay we this dear body
 In the earth to sleep,
His sweet soul commending
 Unto Thee to keep ;—

mf Looking for the dawning
 Of that deathless day,
cr When all earthly shadows
 Shall have fled away.

mf Only grant us, FATHER,
 Courage in our strife,
And with *him* a portion
 In unending life.

E. E. DUGMORE.

Saint James the Apostle.

Hymn 751. ST. MAGNUS.—C.M.   J. CLARKE, 1709.

A higher setting of this Tune is given at Hymn 301.

*" Jesus said, Are ye able to drink of the cup that I shall drink of, and to be baptized with the
baptism that I am baptized with ? They say unto Him, We are able."*

mf TWO brothers freely cast their lot
 With David's royal Son ;
The cost of conquest counting not,
 They deem the battle won.

Brothers in heart, they hope to gain
 An undivided joy,
That man may one with man remain,
 As boy was one with boy.

CHRIST heard ; and will'd that James should
 First prey of Satan's rage ; [fall

John linger out his fellows all,
 And die in bloodless age.

Now they join hands once more above
 Before the Conqueror's throne !
Thus GOD grants prayer ; but in His love
 Makes times and ways His own.

f All glory to the FATHER be,
 All glory to the SON,
All glory, HOLY GHOST, to Thee
 While endless ages run.

Cardinal J. H. NEWMAN

Y 2

Michaelmas.

Hymn 752. ST. MICHAEL NEW.—10 10 6 6 10.

S. S WESLEY

A-men.

" When He bringeth in the First-begotten into the world, He saith, And let all the angels of God worship Him."

f   O CAPTAIN of GOD's host, whose dreadful might
        Led forth to war the armèd seraphim,
        And from the starry height,
        Subdued in burning fight,
    Cast down that ancient dragon dark and grim ;

    Thine angels, CHRIST, we laud in solemn lays,
    Our elder brethren of the crystal sky,
        Who 'mid Thy glory's blaze
        The ceaseless anthem raise,
    And gird Thy Throne in faithful ministry.

    We celebrate their love, whose viewless wing
    Hath left for us so oft their mansion high,
        The mercies of their King
        To mortal saints to bring,
    Or guard the couch of slumb'ring infancy.

    But Thee. the First and Last, we glorify,
    Who, when Thy world was sunk in death and sin,
        Not with Thine hierarchy,
        The armies of the sky,
    But didst with Thine own arm the battle win ;

p   Alone didst pass the dark and dismal shore,
    Alone didst tread the winepress, and alone,
        All glorious in Thy gore,
cr   Didst light and life restore
    To us who lay in darkness and undone.

f   Therefore with angels and archangels we
    To Thy dear love our thankful chorus raise,
        And tune our songs to Thee
        Who art, and art to be,
    And, endless as Thy mercies, sound Thy praise.

Bishop HEBER, 1783-1826.

Hymn 753. SPETISBURY.—5 5 5 5. 5 5 5 5.

W. KNAPP, 1738.

Michaelmas.

A - men.

"He shall give His angels charge over thee, to keep thee in all thy ways."

f   ALL praise be to GOD,
  Whom all things obey,
From Angels and men
For ever and aye :
 Who sendeth on earth
The powers of His throne,
His providence good
And love to make known.

His Angels are they
Of countenance fair,
The arm of His strength,
His hand of kind care :
 His message of peace
To us they reveal,
His wisdom most high
They seal or unseal.

mf   By Martyrs of old
They stood in the flame,
And bade them not flinch,
But call on GOD's name.
 Thro' torment, thro' shame,
Thro' darkness of death
They led without fear
The sires of our faith.

f   *They stand with the few,
They fight for the free,
GOD's reign to advance
O'er land and o'er sea :
 And when the brave die
Or fall in the fight,
Their spirits they bear
To rest in GOD's sight.

mf   *For patience and toil
A crown they prepare ;
They found for the meek
A kingdom full fair ;
 No famine nor plague
'Gainst them doth prevail ;
Their bread cannot lack.
Their cruse cannot fail

We pray Thee, Who art
Thy Angels' reward,
Thy flock to defend
Forget not, O LORD :
 But prosper their aid,
cr   That us they may bring
To see the true face
Of JESUS, our King.

R. B. in *Yattendon Hymnal.*

* *These verses may be omitted.*

ALTERNATIVE TUNE, HYMN 431.

Apostles.

Hymn 754.   REX GLORIOSE MARTYRUM.—L.M.   (*First Tune.*)
Catholische Geistliche Gesänge (Andernach, 1608).

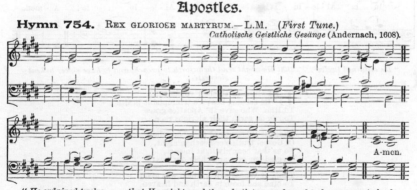

A-men.

"He ordained twelve . . . . that He might send them forth to preach, and to have power to heal sicknesses."

f   LET all on earth their voices raise,
  Re-echoing heav'n's triumphant praise
To Him, Who gave th' Apostles grace
To run on earth their glorious race.

Thou, at Whose word they bore the light
Of Gospel truth o'er heathen night,
To us that heav'nly light impart,
To glad our eyes and cheer our heart.

Thou, at Whose will to them was given
To bind and loose in earth and heaven,

Our chains unbind, our sins undo,
And in our hearts Thy grace renew

Thou, in Whose might they spake the word
Which cured disease and health restored,
To us its healing power prolong,
Support the weak, confirm the strong.

And when the thrones are set on high,
And judgment's awful hour draws nigh,
Then, LORD, with them pronounce us blest,
And take us to Thine endless rest.

Bishop MANT and Compilers ; from the Latin

(651)

Apostles.

Hymn 754. Easter Song.—L.M. with Alleluias. *(Second Tune.)*

Catholische Kirchengesänge (Cologne, 1623).

Al - le - lu - ia! Al - le - lu - ia!

Al - le - lu - ia! Al - le -

- lu - ia! Al - le - lu - ia! Al - le - lu - ia! Al - le - lu - ia! A - men.

" He ordained twelve . . . that He might send them forth to preach, and to have power to heal sicknesses."

f　LET all on earth their voices raise,
　　　Re-echoing heav'n's triumphant praise
　　To Him, Who gave th' Apostles grace
　　To run on earth their glorious race.

　　Thou, at Whose word they bore the light
　　Of Gospel truth o'er heathen night,
　　To us that heav'nly light impart,
　　To glad our eyes and cheer our heart.

　　Thou, at Whose will to them was given
　　To bind and loose in earth and heaven,
　　Our chains unbind, our sins undo,
　　And in our hearts Thy grace renew.

　　Thou, in Whose might they spake the word
　　Which cured disease and health restored,
　　To us its healing power prolong,
　　Support the weak, confirm the strong.

　　And when the thrones are set on high,
　　And judgment's awful hour draws nigh,
　　Then, LORD, with them pronounce us blest,
　　And take us to Thine endless rest.

Bishop Mant and Compilers : from the Latin.

(652)

Evangelists.

Hymn 755. VENICE.—S.M.   W. AMPS.

A-men.

[For copyright, see p. lv.]

" Blessed are your eyes, for they see ; and your ears, for they hear."

mf HOW beauteous are their feet,
    Who stand on Sion's hill ;
Who bring salvation on their tongues
And words of peace instil !

How happy are our ears
    That hear this joyful sound,
Which kings and prophets waited for,
And sought, but never found !

How blessèd are our eyes
    That see this heav'nly light !
Prophets and kings desired it long,
But died without the sight.

f The LORD makes bare His arm
    Through all the earth abroad ;
Let every nation now behold
Their Saviour and their GOD.

I. WATTS, 1707.

Saints' Days.

Hymn 756. BATH.—6 6 6 6. 6 6 8.   *Harmonia Perfecta,* 1700.

A-men.

" Who through faith and patience inherit the promises."

FOR MARTYRS.

f THE triumphs of the Saints,
    The toils they bravely bore,
The love that never faints,
    Their glory evermore,—
For these the Church to-day
Pours forth her joyous lay ;
What victors wear so rich a bay ?

mf This clinging world of ill
    Them and their works abhorr'd ;
Its with'ring flowers still
    They spurn'd with one accord ;
They knew them shortlived all,
How soon they fade and fall,
And follow'd, JESU, at Thy call.

f What tongue may here declare,
    Fancy or thought descry,
The joys Thou dost prepare
    For these Thy Saints on high ?
Empurpled in the flood
Of their victorious blood,
They won the laurel from their GOD.

p O LORD most High, we pray,
    Stretch forth Thy mighty arm
To put our sins away
    And shelter us from harm ;
O give Thy servants peace ;
From guilt and pain release ;

f Our praise to Thee shall never cease.

J. M. NEALE: from the Latin

(653)

Saints' Days.

Hymn 757.   Salus mortalium.—8 8 8.4 8.   *Gesangbuch* (Erfurt, 1663).

f Al - le - lu - ia, .. Al - le - lu - ia.   A - men.

" It is good, being put to death by men, to look for hope from God to be raised again by Him."

FOR MARTYRS.

mf   OUR LORD the path of suff'ring trod,
     And since His Blood for man hath flow'd,
   'Tis meet that man should yield to GOD
       The life he owed.   Alleluia.

No shame to own the Crucified,—
     Nay, 'tis our immortality
That we confess our GOD Who died,
       And for Him die.   Alleluia.

Fill'd with this thought, with patient smile
     All threats the Martyr doth withstand,
Fights, LORD, Thy cause, and leans the while
       Upon Thine hand.   Alleluia.

Beholding his predestined crown,
     Into death's arms he willing goes ;
Dying, he conquers death ; o'erthrown,
       O'erthrows his foes.   Alleluia.

p   LORD, make us Thine own soldiers true,
     Grant us brave faith, a spirit pure,
cr   That for Thy Name, Thy Cross in view,
       We may endure.   Alleluia.

f   Eternal FATHER of the WORD,
     Eternal WORD, we Thee adore,
Eternal SPIRIT, GOD and LORD,
       For evermore.   Alleluia.

         I. WILLIAMS : from the Latin
           of J. B. de Santeuil.

(654)

St. George's Day.

Hymn 758. St. Peter's, Westminster.—8 7 8 7 8 7. J. Turle.

A - men.

" The shout of a king is among them."

f JESUS, LORD of our salvation,
For Thy warrior, bold and true,
Now accept our thankful praises,
And our strength do Thou renew,
That, like George, with courage dauntless
We may all our foes subdue.

Blazon'd on our country's banner,
England bears the true knight's sign :
LORD, our fatherland empower,
That, endued with strength divine,
She may evermore with courage
Bear the standard that is Thine.

Fill her youth with manly spirit,
Patient, self-restrain'd, and pure,
Of Thy cause the ready champions,
Never flinching to endure
Hardness for the Name of JESUS ;
So their triumph shall be sure.

Teach her manhood to confess Thee
As the Master, LORD, and King ;
All their powers consecrated
To Thy service may men bring,
And of loyal speech and action
Make to Thee an offering.

JESUS, LORD, Thou mighty Victor,
Thy all-glorious Name we praise ;
Thou art with us, GOD Almighty ;
'Midst our ranks Thy shout we raise ;
Where Thy kingly war-cry soundeth,
Lead us on through all our days.

F W. Newman.

ALTERNATIVE TUNE, HYMN 232 (SECOND TUNE).

The Transfiguration of our Lord.

Hymn 759. HOLY MOUNT.—S.M.   Rev. W. G. WHINFIELD.

" Lord, it is good for us to be here."

mf   'TIS good, LORD, to be here !
      Thy glory fills the night ;
Thy face and garments, like the sun,
      Shine with unborrow'd light.

'Tis good, LORD, to be here,—
      Thy beauty to behold,
Where Moses and Elijah stand,
      Thy messengers of old.

f   Fulfiller of the past !
      Promise of things to be !
We hail Thy Body glorified,
      And our redemption see.

mf   Before we taste of death,
      We see Thy Kingdom come ;
We fain would hold the vision bright,
      And make this hill our home.

'Tis good, LORD, to be here !
      Yet we may not remain ;
But since Thou bidst us leave the mount
      Come with us to the plain.

J. A. ROBINSON.

ALTERNATIVE TUNE, HYMN 180.

Hymn 760. DORKING.—L.M.   Rev. C. POWELL.

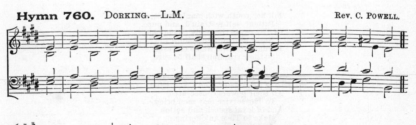

(656)

The Transfiguration of our Lord.

" Jesus was transfigured before them."

f O WONDROUS type, O vision fair
    Of glory that the Church shall share,
Which CHRIST upon the mountain shows,
Where brighter than the sun He glows !

From age to age the tale declare,
How with the three disciples there,
Where Moses and Elias meet,
The LORD holds converse high and sweet.

The Law and Prophets there have place,
The chosen witnesses of grace ;
The FATHER'S voice from out the cloud
Proclaims His Only SON aloud.

With shining face and bright array,
CHRIST deigns to manifest to-day
What glory shall to faith be given
When we enjoy our GOD in heaven.

And Christian hearts are raised on high
By that great vision's mystery,
For which in thankful strains we raise
On this glad day the voice of praise.

mf O FATHER, with th' Eternal SON
And HOLY SPIRIT ever One,
Vouchsafe to bring us by Thy grace
To see Thy glory face to face.

J. M. NEALE and Compilers : from the Latin.

ALTERNATIVE TUNE, HYMN 723.

Retreats.

Hymn 761. ST. AGNES.—10 10 10 10. J. LANGRAN.

A-men.

[For copyright, see p. lv.]

" He said unto them, Come ye yourselves apart into a desert place, and rest awhile."

mp COME ye yourselves apart and rest awhile ;
    Weary, I know it, of the press and throng,
Wipe from your brow the sweat and dust of toil,
And in My quiet strength again be strong.

Come ye aside from all the world holds dear,
    For converse which the world has never known,
Alone with Me and with My FATHER here,
    With Me and with My FATHER not alone.

Come, tell Me all that ye have said and done,
    Your victories and failures, hopes and fears.
I know how hardly souls are woo'd and won :
    My choicest wreaths are always wet with tears.

Come ye and rest : the journey is too great,
    And ye will faint beside the way and sink :
The Bread of Life is here for you to eat,
    And here for you the Wine of Love to drink.

mf Then, fresh from converse with your LORD, return
    And work till daylight softens into even :
The brief hours are not lost in which ye learn
    More of your Master and His rest in heaven.

Bishop E. H. BICKERSTETH.

(657)

Litany for Lent.

Hymn 762. Litany.—11 10 11 7.

To be sung in Unison.

H. A. Branscombe.

A - men.

[For copyright, see p. lv.]

mf FATHER, Whose love we have wrong'd by transgression,
CHRIST, Who wast nail'd for our sins on the Tree,
SPIRIT, Who givest the grace of repentance ;
Hear us, we pray Thee, good LORD.

JESU, adorable Saviour of sinners,
Author of penitence, Hope of our souls,
Plentiful Fountain of grace and compassion ;
Hear us, we pray Thee, good LORD.

PART 1.

Thou Who didst empty Thyself of Thy glory,
Thou Who Thy parents on earth didst obey,
Thou Who for our sake enduredst temptation,
Hear us, we pray Thee, good LORD.

Thou Who hast shown us the love of the Father,
Meeting with mercy the Prodigal Son,
Sonship and home to the lost one restoring,
Hear us, we pray Thee, good LORD.

JESU, Who once by the well to the sinner
Clearly the sins of her heart didst reveal,
Leading her gently to faith and repentance,
Hear us, we pray Thee, good LORD.

Thou Who didst enter the house of Zaccheus,
Blessing his faith and accepting his love,
When for wrong-doing he made restitution ;
Hear us, we pray Thee, good LORD.

PART 2.

CHRIST, with the Twelve the last Passover keeping,
Ere on the Cross the true LAMB should be slain,
Sacrifice offer'd for all and for ever,
Hear us, we pray Thee, good LORD.

JESU, alone with the blood-sweat upon Thee,
JESU, in agony bow'd to the earth,
JESU, Thy will to the FATHER resigning ;
Hear us, we pray Thee, good LORD.

JESU, from Annas to Caiaphas hurried,
Blindfolded, stricken, and falsely accused,
Rudely blasphemed, and declared a blasphemer ;
Hear us, we pray Thee, good LORD.

JESU, denied by Thine eager Apostle,
Whom with a look Thou didst straightway recall,
Moving him straightway to tears and contrition ;
Hear us, we pray Thee, good LORD.

(658)

Litany for Lent.

Thou Who wast wounded to heal our transgressions
Lifted on high to draw all men to Thee,
There on the Cross in Thy majesty reigning,
Hear us, we pray Thee, good LORD.

The following should be sung at the end of either Part ;

That Thou wouldst draw us to heartfelt contrition,
That Thou wouldst help us our sins to confess,
That Thou wouldst grant us the grace of amendment,
Hear us, we pray Thee, good LORD.

That we may bring forth works meet for repentance,
That we give place to the devil no more,
That Thou wouldst lead us to sure perseverance,
Hear us, we pray Thee, good LORD.

V. S. S. COLES.

Litany of Intercession.

Hymn 763.   LITANY.—7 7 7 6.

From H. SCHÜTZ, 1585–1672.

Unison.

Responses in Harmony.

A - men.

GOD the FATHER, GOD the SON,
  GOD the SPIRIT, THREE in ONE,
Hear us from Thy heav'nly throne,
  Spare us, Holy TRINITY.

JESU, evermore ador'd,
As we claim Thy promised word,
Gather'd in Thy Name, O LORD,
  Hear us, we beseech Thee.

For Thy Church so dear to Thee,
That she may for ever be
Kept in peace and unity,
  We beseech Thee, JESU.

For the rulers of our land,
That they may at Thy command
Right promote and wrong withstand,
  We beseech Thee, JESU.

For Thy priests in every place,
That relying on Thy grace
They with patience run their race,
  We beseech Thee, JESU.

All our loved ones we commend,
LORD, to Thee, man's truest Friend,
Guard and guide them to the end,
  We beseech Thee, JESU.

Some on beds of sickness lie,
Some in want and hunger cry ;
LORD, their every need supply,
  We beseech Thee, JESU.

Some are lonely, some are sad,
Some have lost the joy they had ;
With true comfort make them glad,
  We beseech Thee, JESU.

Some have fallen from Thy grace,
Wearied in their heav'nward race ;
May they rise and seek Thy face,
  We beseech Thee, JESU.

Some are sunk in deadly sin
With no spark of love within ;
In their souls Thy work begin,
  We beseech Thee, JESU.

That whoever now doth lie
In his mortal agony,
To the last may feel Thee nigh,
  We beseech Thee, JESU.

That the souls for whom we pray
Of the faithful pass'd away
May find mercy in that Day,
  We beseech Thee, JESU.

V. W. HUTTON and others.

Mission Services.

Hymn 764. JESU JEHOVAH.—6 5 10.6 5 10.6 5 6 4. (*First Tune.*)

Anonymous German, *c.* 1733.

A - men.

Hymn 764. RESCUE —6 5 10.6 5 10.6 5 6 4. (*Second Tune.*) W. H. DOANE.

A - men.

Mission Services.

"The Son of Man is come to seek and to save that which was lost."

mp RESCUE the perishing,
Care for the dying,
Snatch them in pity from sin and the grave ;
Weep o'er the erring one,
Lift up the fallen,
Tell them of JESUS the mighty to save.
Rescue the perishing,
Care for the dying ;
JESUS is merciful,
JESUS will save.

Though they are slighting Him,
Still He is waiting,
Waiting the penitent child to receive ;
Plead with them earnestly,
Plead with them gently ;
He will forgive if they only believe.
Rescue the perishing, &c.

Down in the human heart,
Crush'd by the tempter,
Feelings lie buried that grace can restore ;
Touch'd by a loving heart,
Waken'd by kindness,
Chords that were broken will vibrate once
more.
Rescue the perishing, &c.

Rescue the perishing ;
Duty demands it ;
Strength for thy labour the LORD will pro-
vide :
Back to the narrow way
Patiently win them ;
Tell the poor wand'rer a Saviour has died.
Rescue the perishing, &c.

MRS. VAN ALSTYNE

Hymn 765. MISSIONARY.—7 6 7 6. 7 6 7 6.

L. MASON, 1824.

A-men.

"I have set before thee an open door."

mf TO-DAY Thy mercy calls us
To wash away our sin,
However great our trespass,
Whatever we have been ;
However long from mercy
Our hearts have turn'd away,
f The precious Blood can cleanse us,
And make us white to-day.

To-day Thy gate is open,
And all who enter in
Shall find a FATHER'S welcome,
And pardon for their sin.
The past shall be forgotten,
A present joy be given,
A future grace be promised,
A glorious crown in heaven.

mf To-day our FATHER calls us,
His HOLY SPIRIT waits ;
His blessèd Angels gather
Around the heav'nly gates ;
No question will be ask'd us
How often we have come ;
Although we oft have wander'd,
It is our FATHER'S home !

O all-embracing mercy !
O ever-open door !
What should we do without Thee
When heart and eye run o'er?
When all things seem against us,
To drive us to despair,
f We know one gate is open,
One ear will hear our prayer !

O. ALLEN.

Mission Services.

Hymn 766. BIRMINGHAM.—S.M.
J. STANLEY, 1713–1786.

A-men.

"O Lord, revive Thy work in the midst of the years."

f

REVIVE Thy work, O LORD,
   Thy mighty Arm make bare;
Speak with the Voice that wakes the dead,
   And make Thy people hear.

Revive Thy work, O LORD,
   Disturb this sleep of death;
Quicken the smould'ring embers now
   By Thine Almighty Breath.

Revive Thy work, O LORD,
   Create soul-thirst for Thee:

And hung'ring for the Bread of Life
   Oh may our spirits be.

Revive Thy work, O LORD,
   Exalt Thy precious Name:
And by the HOLY GHOST, our love
   For Thee and Thine inflame.

Revive Thy work, O LORD,
   Give Pentecostal showers;
The glory shall be all Thine Own,
   The blessing, LORD, be ours!

A. MIDLANE.

ALTERNATIVE TUNE, HYMN **339.**

Hymn 767. PORTSEA.—8 7 8 7.
W. BOYCE, 1775.

A-men.

"They shall look upon Me Whom they have pierced."

mf

RIGHTEOUS FATHER, we have wrong'd
   Underfoot Thy laws have cast: [Thee,
Now we fain would serve Thee better,
   O forgive us what is past.

Loving JESUS, we have hurt Thee,
   Yielded to temptation's blast:
Now we long to stand more firmly,
   O forgive us what is past.

HOLY SPIRIT, we have grieved Thee,
   Sin and death have held us fast:
Now we yearn for Life and Freedom,
   O forgive us what is past.

p FATHER, SON, and HOLY SPIRIT,
   GOD eternal, First and Last,
Penitent we kneel before Thee,
   O forgive us all the past.

W. H. DRAPER.

ALTERNATIVE TUNE, HYMN **109.**

Mission Services.

Hymn 768.   KING ALFRED.—7 7 7 7. 7 7.   A. REDHEAD.

A - men.

" He said unto her, Daughter, be of good comfort . . . go in peace."

mf   JESU! speak to me in love,
     Restless, storm-toss'd in my sin ;
With Thy mighty voice, O LORD,
     Thy great calm create within ;
Bid the stormy winds to cease,
Bid, O bid me go in peace.

p   To Thee, JESU, do I fly,
     Waken'd from my soul's dread sleep ;
None but Thou can save me, LORD,
     In this hour of anguish deep ;
Thou alone canst give release,
Bid, O bid me go in peace.

Weeping at Thy feet I fall,
     Wearied, burden'd, lonely, sad ;
Thou dost bid me come, my LORD,
     Thou alone canst make me glad ;
JESU, grant my soul release,
Bid, O bid me go in peace.

mf Boldly at Thy throne of grace,
     LORD, I now forgiveness seek ;
In Thy tender, pitying love
     To my soul Thy pardon speak.
JESU ! make my anguish cease,
Bid, O bid me go in peace.

Prince of Peace ! Who in Thy death
     Didst for me the ransom pay,
Cleanse me in Thy precious blood,
     Give to me Thy peace to-day.
Now, LORD, grant my soul release,
Now, LORD, bid me go in peace.

                           G. BODY.

ALTERNATIVE TUNES, HYMNS 100 AND 184.

Hymn 769. GIBBONS.—7 6 7 6. 7 6 7 6. J. D. SEDDING, 1861.

In free rhythm.

A - men.

" I know that my Redeemer liveth."

mf I LAY my sins on JESUS,
   The spotless Lamb of GOD !
He bears them all, and frees us
   From the accursèd load.
I bring my guilt to JESUS,
   To wash my crimson stains
White in His Blood most precious,
   Till not a spot remains.

I lay my wants on JESUS ;
   All fulness dwells in Him ;
He heals all my diseases,
   He doth my soul redeem.
I lay my griefs on JESUS,
   My burdens and my cares ;
He from them all releases,
   He all my sorrow shares.

p I rest my soul on JESUS,
   This weary soul of mine ;
His Right Hand me embraces,
   I on His Breast recline.
mf I love the Name of JESUS,
   Immanuel, CHRIST, the LORD ;
Like fragrance on the breezes,
   His Name abroad is pour'd.

I long to be like JESUS,
   Meek, loving, lowly, mild ;
I long to be like JESUS,
   The FATHER'S holy Child :
I long to be with JESUS,
   Amid the heav'nly throng ;
f To sing with saints His praises,
   To learn the Angels' song.

H. BONAR.

ALTERNATIVE TUNE, HYMN **186.**

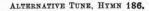

Hymn 770. OLD 120TH.—6 6 6 6. 6 6. *Psalmes,* 1570.

Mission Services.

A-men.

"The Lord is my Shepherd . . . He restoreth my soul."

<table>
<tr><td>p</td><td>

I WANDER'D sore distress'd,
  All weary and forlorn ;
I had no place to rest,
Of all my pleasures shorn—
My thirsting spirit sigh'd,
And in the desert cried.

</td></tr>
</table>

p I WANDER'D sore distress'd,
  All weary and forlorn ;
I had no place to rest,
Of all my pleasures shorn—
My thirsting spirit sigh'd,
And in the desert cried.

mf The Shepherd heard my cry,
  Who came His flock to find,
And drew in mercy nigh,

For He is wondrous kind ;
His winning voice awoke
My spirit as He spoke.

He bade my wandering cease,
And gave my heart a home,
That from the bliss of peace
I might no longer roam ;
cr He gave me hope for fears,
And lasting joy for tears.

J. BROWNLIE.

Hymn 771. NEWBURY.—L.M.
CHETHAM, *Psalms,* 1718.

Slow.

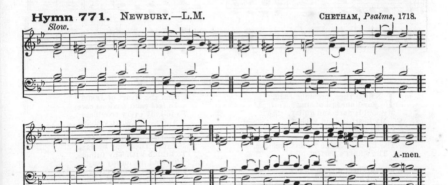

A-men.

" Against Thee, Thee only have I sinned."

p MY GOD ! my GOD ! and can it be
  That I should sin so lightly now,
And think no more of evil thoughts
  Than of the wind that waves the bough ?

I sin, and heav'n and earth go round,
  As if no dreadful deed were done ;
As if Thy Blood had never flow'd
  To hinder sin, or to atone.

I walk the earth with lightsome step,
  Smile at the sunshine, breathe the air,
Do my own will, nor ever heed
  Gethsemane and Thy long prayer.

Shall it be always thus, O LORD ?
  Wilt Thou not work this hour in me

The grace Thy Passion merited,
  Hatred of self, and love of Thee ?

O by the pains of Thy pure love,
  Grant me the gift of holy fear ;
And by Thy woes and bloody sweat
  Wash Thou my guilty conscience clear

Ever when tempted make me see,
  Beneath the olives' moon-pierced shade,
My GOD, alone, outstretch'd, and bruised,
  And bleeding, on the earth He made ;

And make me feel it was my sin,
  As though no other sins were there,
That was to Him Who bears the world
  A load that He could scarcely bear.

F. W. FABER.

This Hymn is suitable for Passion-tide.

ALTERNATIVE TUNE, HYMN 245.

Mission Services.

Hymn 772. St. Anselm.—7 6 7 6. 7 6 7 6.

Sir J. Barnby.

A - men.

"He . . . healed them that had need of healing."

mf   I NEED Thee, precious Jesu,
    For I am full of sin ;
My soul is dark and guilty,
    My heart is dead within.
I need the cleansing Fountain
    Where I can always flee,
The Blood of Christ most precious,
    The sinner's perfect plea.

I need Thee, precious Jesu,
    For I am very poor ;
A stranger and a pilgrim,
    I have no earthly store.
I need the love of Jesus
    To cheer me on my way,
To guide my doubting footsteps,
    To be my strength and stay.

I need Thee, precious Jesu :
    I need a friend like Thee,
A friend to soothe and pity,
    A friend to care for me.

I need the Heart of Jesus
    To feel each anxious care,
To tell my every trouble,
    And all my sorrow share.

I need Thee, precious Jesu ;
    I need Thee, day by day,
To fill me with Thy fulness,
    To lead me on my way ;
I need Thy Holy Spirit
    To teach me what I am,
To show me more of Jesus,
    To point me to the Lamb.

I need Thee, precious Jesu,
cr   And hope to see Thee soon,
Encircled by the rainbow
    And seated on Thy Throne ;
f   There, with Thy Blood-bought children,
    My joy shall ever be,
To sing Thy praises, Jesu,
    To gaze, my Lord, on Thee.

F. Whitfield.

Hymn 773. North Coates.—6 5 6 5.

Rev. T. R. Matthews.

A-men.

[For copyright, see p. lv.]

Mission Services.

p O MY Saviour, lifted
　　　　From the earth for me,
Draw me, in Thy mercy,
　　Nearer unto Thee.

Lift my earth-bound longings,
　Fix them, LORD, above ;
Draw me with the magnet
　Of Thy mighty love.

mf LORD, Thine arms are stretching
　Ever far and wide,

To enfold Thy children
　To Thy loving side.

And I come, O JESUS :—
　Dare I turn away ?
cr No ! Thy love hath conquer'd,
　And I come to-day ;

mf Bringing all my burdens,
　Sorrow, sin, and care,
At Thy feet I lay them,
　And I leave them there.

Bishop W. WALSHAM HOW.

ALTERNATIVE TUNE, HYMN 750.

Hymn 774. WRESTLING JACOB.—8 8 8 8.8 8.　　　　　S. S. WESLEY.

A-men.

" There wrestled a man with him until the breaking of the day."

mf COME, O Thou Traveller unknown,
　　Whom still I hold, but cannot see,
My company before is gone,
　And I am left alone with Thee ;
With Thee all night I mean to stay,
And wrestle till the break of day.

p　I need not tell Thee who I am ;
　　My misery and sin declare ;
Thyself hast call'd me by my name ;
　Look on Thy hands, and read it there !
But Who, I ask Thee, Who art Thou ?
Tell me Thy Name, and tell me now.

mf In vain Thou strugglest to get free,
　I never will unloose my hold ;
Art Thou the Man that died for me ?

The secret of Thy love unfold ;
Wrestling, I will not let Thee go,
Till I Thy Name, Thy Nature know.

Yield to me now, for I am weak,
　But confident in self-despair ;
Speak to my heart, in blessings speak,
　Be conquer'd by my instant prayer !
Speak, or Thou never hence shalt move,
And tell me if Thy Name is Love ?

f　'Tis Love ! 'tis Love ! Thou diedst for me
　I hear Thy whisper in my heart !
The morning breaks, the shadows flee ;
　Pure universal Love Thou art ;
To me, to all, Thy mercies move ;
Thy Nature and Thy Name is Love.

C. WESLEY, 1742.

ALTERNATIVE TUNE, HYMN 777.

Mission Services.

Hymn 775. THEOKTISTUS.—7 6 7 6. 8 8 7 7. Rev. Sir F. A. G. OUSELEY.

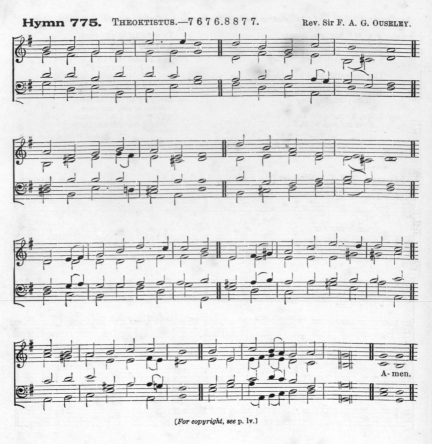

[For copyright, see p. lv.]

" The Name of the Lord is a strong tower: the righteous runneth into it, and is safe."

mf JESU ! Name all names above,
    JESU, best and dearest,
JESU, fount of perfect love,
    Holiest, tenderest, nearest ;
JESU, source of grace completest,
JESU purest, JESU sweetest,
    JESU, well of power divine,
    Make me, keep me, seal me Thine.

JESU, open me the gate,
    That the robber enter'd,
Who in that most lost estate
    Wholly on Thee ventured.
Thou Whose wounds are ever pleading,
And Thy Passion interceding,
    From my misery let me rise
    To a home in Paradise.

p JESU, crown'd with thorns for me,
    Scourged for my transgression,
Witnessing through agony
    That Thy good confession ;
JESU, clad in purple raiment,
For my evil making payment,
    Let not all Thy woe and pain,
    Let not Calvary be in vain.

When I reach death's bitter sea,
    And its waves mount higher,
Earthly help forsaking me
    As the storm draws nigher,
JESU, leave me not to languish
Helpless, hopeless, full of anguish ;
    JESU, let me hear Thee say,
    " Thou shalt be with Me to-day.'

J. M. NEALE: from the Greek
of Theoktistus. c. 890.

Mission Services.

Hymn 776.   Margaret.—Irregular.   Rev. T. R. Matthews.

A - men.

"He came unto His own, and His own received Him not."

mf THOU didst | leave Thy Throne and Thy | kingly Crown,
    When Thou | camest to earth for me ;
  But in | Bethlehem's home was there | found no room
    For Thy | holy Nativity :
      O come to my heart, Lord Jesus ;
      There is room in my heart for Thee.

f Heaven's | arches rang when the | Angels sang,
    Pro- | claiming Thy royal degree ;
  But in | lowly birth didst Thou | come to earth,
    And in | great humility :
      O come to my heart, Lord Jesus ;
      There is room in my heart for Thee.

p The | foxes found rest, and the | bird had its nest
    In the | shade of the cedar tree ;
  But Thy | couch was the sod, O Thou | Son of God,
    In the | desert of Galilee :
      O come to my heart, Lord Jesus ;
      There is room in my heart for Thee.

mf Thou | camest, O Lord, with the | living word
    That should | set Thy people free ;
p But with | mocking scorn and with | crown of thorn
    They | bore Thee to Calvary :
      O come to my heart, Lord Jesus ;
      There is room in my heart for Thee.

f When the | heav'ns shall ring, and the | Angels sing,
    At Thy | coming to victory,
  Let Thy | voice call me home, saying, | "Yet there is room,
    There is | room at My side for thee :"
      O come to my heart, Lord Jesus ;
      There is room in my heart for Thee.

                               Emily E. S. Elliott.

Mission Services.

Hymn 777. BRECKNOCK.—8 8 8 8.8 8.

S. S. WESLEY.

A-men.

" My times are in Thy hand."

mp WHO knows how near my end may be?
Time speeds away, and Death
comes on ;
How swiftly, ah ! how suddenly,
May Death be here, and Life be gone !
My GOD, for JESUS' sake I pray
Thy peace may bless my dying day.

The world that smiled when morn was come
May change for me ere close of eve ;
So long as earth is still my home
In peril of my death I live ;
My GOD, for JESUS' sake I pray
Thy peace may bless my dying day.

p Teach me to ponder oft my end,
And ere the hour of death appears,
To cast my soul on CHRIST her Friend,
Nor spare repentant cries and tears ;
My GOD, for JESUS' sake I pray
Thy peace may bless my dying day.

mf And let me now so order all,
That ever ready I may be
To say with joy, whate'er befall,
LORD, do Thou as Thou wilt with me ,
My GOD, for JESUS' sake I pray
Thy peace may bless my dying day.

p O FATHER, cover all my sins
With JESUS' merits, Who alone
The pardon that I covet wins,
And makes His long-sought rest our own ;
My GOD, for JESUS' sake I pray
Thy peace may bless my dying day.

Then death may come or tarry yet,
I know in CHRIST I perish not ;
He never will His own forget,
He gives me robes without a spot :
My GOD, for JESUS' sake I pray
Thy peace may bless my dying day.

mf And thus I live in GOD at peace,
And die without a thought or fear,
Content to take what GOD decrees,
For through His Son my faith is clear ;
His grace shall be in death my stay,
And peace shall bless my dying day.

CATHERINE WINKWORTH : from the German
of Countess Aemilie von Schwarzburg-
Rudolstadt, 1686.

ALTERNATIVE TUNE, HYMN 644.

Mission Services.

Hymn 778. Hymn of Eve.—9 9 9 8. 8 8 8 8.　　　　　T. A. Arne, 1710–1788.

A - men.

' I will go in the strength of the Lord God.'

f　I WILL go in the strength of the LORD
　　In the path He hath mark'd for my feet :
I will follow the light of His word,
　Nor shrink from the dangers I meet.
His presence my steps shall attend ;
　His fulness my wants shall supply ;
On Him, till my journey shall end,
　My hope shall securely rely.

I will go in the strength of the LORD
　To the work He appoints me to do ;
In the joy which His smile shall afford
　My soul shall her vigour renew.
His wisdom will guard me from harm,
　His pow'r my sufficiency prove ;
I will trust His omnipotent arm,
　I will rest in His covenant love.

I will go in the strength of the LORD
　To each conflict which faith may require ;
His grace, as my shield and reward,
　My courage and zeal shall inspire.
If He issue the word of command
　To meet and encounter the foe,
Though with sling and with stone in my hand,
　In the strength of the LORD I will go.

　　　　　　　　　　　　　　　E. Turney.

(671)

Mission Services.

Hymn 779. GAUDIUM CÆLESTE.—5 5.7 7.7 7.6. Sir H. PARRY.

Slower.

A - men.

" There is joy in the presence of the angels of God over one sinner that repenteth."

f　THERE was joy in heav'n,
　　　There was joy in heav'n,
When this goodly world to frame
The LORD of might and mercy came ;
Shouts of joy were heard on high,
And the stars sang from the sky,
　　Glory to GOD in heav'n.

f　There was joy in heav'n,
　　　There was joy in heav'n,
When the billows heaving dark,
Sank around the stranded ark,
dim And the rainbow's watery span
Spake of mercy, hope to man,
p　　And peace with GOD in heav'n.

f　There was joy in heav'n,
　　　There was joy in heav'n,
p　When of love the midnight beam
Dawn'd on the towers of Bethlehem,
cr　And along the echoing hill
Angels sang "On earth good will,
f　　And glory in the heav'n ! "

f　There is joy in heav'n,
　　　There is joy in heav'n,
mf When the soul that went astray
Turns to CHRIST, the living Way,
And, by grace of heav'n subdued,
Breathes a prayer of gratitude ;
f　　Oh, there is joy in heav'n.

Bishop HEBER, 1827.

(672)